AREAS REFERRED TO IN TEXT

For convenience in assigning geographical distribution, the Central and Eastern states have been arbitrarily divided into nine areas. These are based partly on physiography and partly on distribution pattern as shown by some of the diatoms. The Western and Pacific states are referred to separately.

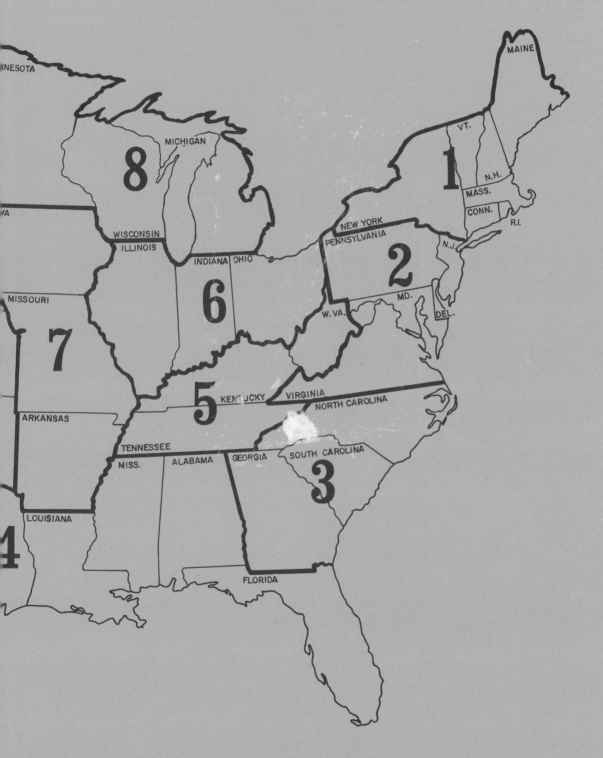

THE DIATOMS
OF THE
UNITED STATES

THE DIATOMS OF

Exclusive of

Alaska and Hawaii

Volume 1

**FRAGILARIACEAE,
EUNOTIACEAE,
ACHNANTHACEAE,
NAVICULACEAE**

THE UNITED STATES

RUTH PATRICK

CHARLES W. REIMER

Department of Limnology
The Academy of Natural Sciences of Philadelphia

MONOGRAPHS of

The Academy of Natural Sciences of Philadelphia

Number 13   *May 10, 1966*

MONOGRAPHIC SERIES of Academy of Natural Sciences
of Philadelphia #13

SECOND PRINTING

This book may be ordered from

The Academy of Natural Sciences of Philadelphia
19th and The Parkway, Philadelphia, Pennsylvania 19103

May 10, 1966
Printed in the United States of America
PRODUCED BY SUTTER HOUSE
LITITZ, PENNSYLVANIA 17543

CONTENTS

FOREWORD

This systematic treatment of the Diatoms of the United States represents the culmination of many years of study and a long period of arduous work by the authors, the artist and various technical assistants. It is written for the use of all those concerned with the multitude of kinds and the fascinating diversity of this very large and important group of algae of our fresh waters.

Observations and experimental work on living organisms must be based on specific kinds to have meaning. We cannot explain or predict phenomena or patterns of behavior without reference to the kinds or groups of organisms involved. Such basic reference works serve this need for the identification of the biota. Philosophically, they are the means of transmitting the specialist's knowledge and judgment to others today and to generations in the future.

This significant contribution to the systematics of diatoms is in the tradition of the work of the Academy of Natural Sciences of Philadelphia. I would express the thanks of the Academy to the National Science Foundation for its long period of support towards the preparation of this volume, and thanks to the George W. Carpenter Fund for support towards its publication. Finally, I would express warm congratulations to the authors on the completion of this first half of their goal and extend best wishes and encouragement towards the completion of the second volume.

H. Radclyffe Roberts, Director
Academy of Natural Sciences
of Philadelphia

Preface

This volume represents the first part of a two part systematic treatment of the fresh-water diatom flora of continental United States exclusive of Alaska. Besides those taxa found in fresh water, a few taxa found in estuaries of rivers and belonging to genera that commonly occur in fresh water are included. No strictly fossil species are included; however, many of the species embraced are found in recent fossil material. Although this book is concerned with the United States, it should be helpful to the students of diatom floras in Mexico, Canada, and other areas.

In this volume are included those taxa belonging to the Fragilariales, Eunotiales, Achnanthales, and the Naviculaceae of the Naviculales. The second volume will include the other families of the Naviculales, the Epithemiales, the Nitzschiales, and the Surirellales. Also included will be a relatively few species belonging to the Eupodiscales, Rhizosoleniales, and Biddulphiales.

To date two comprehensive books have have been written on the diatoms of the United States. In 1890 the Rev. Francis Wolle published *Diatomaceae of North America* which was a collection of illustrations which he copied from other papers on diatoms. References are given for each species as to where descriptions of them may be found. In 1927 Charles Boyer published *Synopsis of North American Diatomaceae*. This book included fresh-water and marine species which were described but not illustrated. Both of these books are out of print.

In this book we have described and illustrated only those taxa which we have been able to verify by specimens in public herbaria. However, at the end of each genus we have included lists of most, if not all, of the taxa which have been reported from the United States. Because it was impossible to be continually inserting new records for the United States, only those records published before 1960 are described, and those after that date are listed only.

In writing the descriptions we have in each case seen the original description of the taxon and have made sure that they include the characteristics of the original diagnosis of the taxon. Insofar as possible we have seen type specimens or authenticated specimens of each taxon. The specimens used for the illustrations have been ringed on the cover glass by means of a diamond marker. Care has been taken to see to it that the specimen illustrated is typical for the taxon described. In many cases lectotypes have been designated. Wherever feasible the specimens illustrated have been chosen from type material, authenticated material, or exsiccatae.

The synonymy for each taxon includes those references necessary to establish the name of the taxon and those synonyms which have been recorded from the United States. Originally we had hoped to work out the complete synonymy for each taxon, but it was soon found that this was a very time consuming task and far beyond the scope of this book.

Keys are given for the various taxonomic categories whenever there are a sufficient number of taxa to make it worth while. The keys to the species usually do not include the varieties unless they are very distinctive from the nominate variety.

The type localities are usually given as originally cited. In some instances the locations have had slight changes made in their citation to make them more understandable.

The geographical distribution in the United States so far as known is given for each species. It is given by regions for the eastern part of the United States (see map) and by states for the western part of the country. Distribution ranges were composited from a) the literature and b) the specimens observed in our herbarium and other herbaria listed elsewhere. Insofar as possible we have verified the ranges, but in some cases where specimens were not available we have accepted range extensions from reports in the literature. The ecological distribution is given only if sufficient data are at hand to allow definite statements.

Besides the systematic treatment, this book contains in the introduction the more current opinions concerning diatom morphology, physiology, reproduction, ecology, and geographic distribution. No attempt has been made to completely treat all the literature on various subjects, but rather to include useful references which may be a guide to further study. Also included is a short section devoted to techniques for collecting, cleaning, and mounting diatoms. In the introduction the names of the taxa are those given by the author of the information used and have not been changed to fit the system of classification used in the systematic section.

Although both authors of this book have been concerned with the describing of most of the taxa, the descriptions for the following genera mainly have been written by Patrick: *Actinella, Amphicampa, Amphipleura, Asterionella, Caloneis, Desmogonium, Diatoma, Diatomella, Diploneis, Eunotia, Fragilaria, Frickia, Frustulia, Hannaea, Meridion, Navicula, Opephora, Peronia, Pinnularia, Semiorbis, Synedra, Tabellaria, Tetracyclus.* Reimer has written mainly the descriptions of: *Achnanthes, Anomoeoneis, Capartogramma, Cocconeis, Gyrosigma, Mastogloia, Neidium, Pleurosigma, Rhoicosphenia, Scoliopleura, Stauroneis.*

Any comprehensive book such as this one is the result of the efforts of many institutions and individuals. The authors are particularly indebted to the National Science Foundation without whose financial support this book would not have been possible. They are also indebted to the Carpenter Publication Fund of the Academy of Natural Sciences of Philadelphia and to Miss Anne Rowland, Mr. Walter R. Coley and other personal friends who have contributed to the publication cost of this book.

Many institutions have been most kind in allowing us to consult specimens and in loaning specimens. We wish to particularly thank the Agardh Herbarium, Lund; Botanisches Museum, Regensburg; Botanisk Museum, Copenhagen; the British Museum; the California Academy of Sciences; the Chicago Museum of Natural History; Conservatoire et Jardin Botaniques, Geneva; Eidgenössische Technische Hochschule, Zürich; the Farlow Herbarium, Cambridge, Mass.; Museum der Humboldt-Universität, East Berlin; Muséum National d'Histoire Naturelle, Paris; Naturkunde Museum, Kassel; Naturhistorisches Museum, Wien; the New York Botanical Garden; Rijksmuseum, Stockholm; the Shortridge High School, Indianapolis, Indiana; the Smithsonian Institution, Washington; the University of California; and the Van Heurck Herbarium in Antwerp.

We are particularly indebted to Mr. Robert Ross of the British Museum; Dr. H. R. Roberts, Director of the Academy of Natural Sciences of Philadelphia, and Dr. G. E. Hutchinson for their helpful advice and criticism during the writing of this book. We are also indebted to Dr. Friedrick Hustedt, Dr. G. Dallas Hanna, Dr. Astrid Cleve-Euler, Mr. J. Ingram Hendey, Dr. Francis Drouet, Dr. Hermann Jaeger, Dr. Kurt Diebel, Dr. Fredrick Ehrendorfer, Dr. Harald Riedl, and Dr. William Randolph Taylor for their help in the acquiring of information for the writing of this book.

Many have helped with the preparation of this book for publication. Mrs. Helen Loos and Miss Noma Ann Roberts, with the help of the two authors, have prepared the illustrations for this work. Miss Evelyn Wells, Miss Margaret LeMesurier, Miss Leona Townsend, Mrs. Phyllis Pivar, Miss Roberts, Mrs. Naomi Smith, Mr. C. W. Hart, and Mr. Maurice Phillips have carried out the editing of this book, and to them we are deeply grateful.

Assistance of various types has been offered by the following, and to them we wish to express our thanks: Mr. Yun Yong, Mrs. Mary Anne Schumacher, Mr. Robert R. Grant, Jr., Mr. Raymond J. Cummins, Miss Noma Ann Roberts, Mrs. Anne Reilly, Miss Marjorie E. Shipley, Mrs. Mary E. Lavin, Mrs. Marcia Zanger, Miss M. E. Humphreys, Mrs. A. Weiland, Dr. Eugene F. Stoermer, Dr. Joan Hellerman, Dr. M. H. Hohn, Dr. L. G. Livingston.

For continual help and assistance the authors are particularly indebted to Mrs. Reba Reimer and Dr. Charles Hodge, IV.

The senior author wishes to acknowledge her gratitude to her father, Frank Patrick, who originally inspired her to pursue this field of science and who with Dr. Ivey F. Lewis of the University of Virginia was largely responsible for her training in diatoms.

THE DIATOMS

OF THE

UNITED STATES

Introduction

Diatoms are unicellular plants with cell walls of silica, which belong to the Bacillariophyta. They are found in fresh and salt water of all types where light is sufficient to support photosynthesis. They live in intertidal zones and on damp soil, rocks, or plants where the spray from waves or falling water reaches them. Some species have been recorded from various types of soil.

The oldest known diatoms for which we have specimens are Cretaceous; these were all marine species. No fresh-water diatoms are definitely known before the Miocene. Hanna (personal communication) reports that *Melosira granulata*, a fresh-water diatom, has been found from what may be the Oligocene. Diatom deposits have been found in all continents. These are summarized by Cummins and Mulryan (1937). The composition of diatom floras has been useful in indicating oil containing horizons (Hanna, 1928), and in the indicating of fresh-water bearing strata (Woolman, 1891, 1892). Various workers have used diatoms to trace the advance and retreat of glaciers (Cleve, 1899; Cleve-Euler, 1944; Mölder, 1944; Hyyppa, 1955; Hanna, 1933; Patrick, 1946). Diatom floras have been useful in tracing the prehistoric conditions of lakes (Ross, 1950; Patrick, 1936, 1943, 1954; Hutchinson, *et al.*, 1956).

I. MORPHOLOGY
Structure of the Cell Wall

GENERAL STRUCTURE

The basic structure of the cell wall or frustule of a diatom is two valves, each of which is connected to a circular piece of silica known as a girdle. Early workers believed this girdle to be a rigid band of silica, but more recent works of Palmer and Keeley (1900), Hendey (1959), and others have shown it to be open at one end, or at least expandable. One valve with its girdle fits over the other girdle with its valve. The outer one is often referred to as the epitheca and the inner one as the hypotheca.

The valve in most fresh-water diatoms is the larger surface; and, therefore, most diatoms in cleaned preparation are seen in this view. However, a portion of the valve is bent at more or less of a 90 degree angle to join half of the girdle. This part of the valve is referred to as the valve mantle. The parts of the girdle are firmly united to the valve mantles, but often separate when the diatoms are cleaned. The clean diatoms, therefore, are often found as separated valves, and the girdles may be found as bands of silica in the mounts.

1

Because of the structure of the diatom frustule the valve surface is the view most often seen, and it is on the pattern and structure of the valve that the systematics of most taxa of diatoms are largely based. All of the structures seen in diatoms are the result of holes or chambers in the siliceous wall or various kinds of thickened or thin areas in the wall. The color sometimes seen is a result of refracted light, and is not due to the presence of pigments.

Most of the diatoms which are considered in this book have the valve markings arranged so that they are symmetrical to either the apical or the transverse axis, or to both. A few, such as members of the Coscinodiscaceae, are radially symmetrical. Only in a few genera is the symmetry otherwise arranged. Hustedt (1930), Fritsch (1935), and Hendey (1959) have given excellent accounts of the structure of the diatom wall, and much of the information given in this account was obtained from these sources. In this book we will briefly describe the symmetry and structure of the cell wall.

DIATOM SYMMETRY

The symmetry of diatoms is usually related to their axes and their related planes. The pervalvar axis, fig. 1(a-a) is the one which joins the center points of the two valves. The apical axis (sometimes called the sagittal axis) is the one which connects the two ends of a valve such as in *Navicula*, fig. 1(b-b). The transverse axis lies perpendicular to the apical axis on the valve of the diatom, fig. 1(c-c).

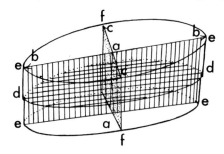

FIGURE 1.
Diagrammatic sketch of the structure of a pennate diatom (after Fritsch). a-a, per-valvar axis; b-b, apical axis; c-c, transverse axis; d-d, valvar plane; e-e, apical plane; f-f, transapical plane.

The valvar plane is the plane of cell division. It cuts through the center of the pervalvar axis and lies parallel to the valve, fig. 1(d-d). The apical plane is the one which runs through the pervalvar and apical axes, fig. 1(e-e). The transapical plane is the one which runs through the transverse and pervalvar axes, fig. 1(f-f).

The symmetry of the various genera of diatoms to these three axes is variable. The main types of symmetry of the species treated in this book are illustrated in figs. 2, 3 and 4. *Pinnularia* is symmetrical to all three axes, fig. 2. In *Cymbella* and *Amphora*, the two valves do not lie in planes which

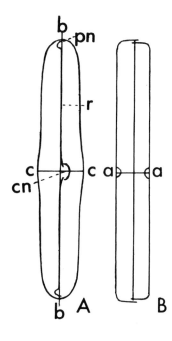

FIGURE 2.
A—Valve view of *Pinnularia*. b-b, apical axis;
c-c, transverse axis; r, raphe; cn, central
nodule; pn, polar nodule. B—Girdle view of
Pinnularia. a-a, pervalvar axis.

are parallel to each other, figs. 3A[1],A[2]. The shape of the valve is asymmetrical to the apical axis but symmetrical to the transverse, figs. 3A[2],A[3]. In *Amphora* the valve surface is typically convex or gable-shaped, and the valve mantle is strongly developed, fig. 3A[2]. Due to this structure the genus *Amphora* is often seen in girdle view and many intercalary bands are present.

The shape of the valve in the genus *Gomphonema* is usually flat or slightly convex and symmetrical to the apical but not to the transverse axis, figs. 3B[1], B[3]. However, the sculpture of the valve surface, particularly in the central area, may not be symmetrical to the apical axis. The frustule in girdle view is wedge-shaped, fig 3B[1]. The valve of the genus *Rhopalodia*, figs. 3C[1], C[2], is strongly convexed and asymmetrically gabled, much as in the genus *Amphora*. However, in *Rhopalodia* the raphe is found in the crest of the gable in a canal, fig. 3C[2]. The genus *Achnanthes* is not symmetrical to the pervalvar axes as the markings on the two valves are dissimilar. The shape of the valve is usually symmetrical to the transverse and apical axis. The sculpturing of the valve surface is sometimes asymmetrical. The symmetry of the genus *Amphiprora* can best be understood by a study of figs. 3D[1], D[2], D[3]. In this genus the valve is strongly convex and projected into a wing-like structure which is well developed over most of the valve except at the pervalvar axis, fig. 3D[1]. This wing-like structure is sigmoid in shape, fig. 3D[3]. Because of this complex structure the frustule is most often

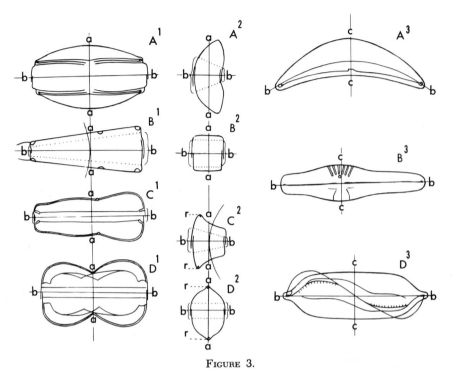

FIGURE 3.

A¹, A², A³—Girdle, cross section, and valve view of *Amphora*. B¹, B², B³—Girdle, cross section, and valve view of *Gomphonema*. C¹, C²—Girdle and cross section of *Rhopalodia*. D¹, D², D²—Girdle, cross section, and valve view of *Amphiphora*. a-a, pervalvar axis; b-b, apical axis: c-c, transverse axis; g, girdle; r, raphe. (After Fritsch.)

seen in girdle view. In the genera *Gyrosigma* and *Pleurosigma* the valve, axial area, and raphe are sigmoid in shape.

In *Nitzschia, Hantzschia,* and *Bacillaria* a keel is present on the surface of the valve and the raphe in *Nitzschia* and *Bacillaria,* figs. 4A, B, lies in the summit of the keel subtended by a porous silica layer (Kolbe, 1951).

When one observes a frustule of *Nitzschia* in cross section, the keels of the two valves are more or less diagonally placed to each other, fig. 4B. In *Hantzschia* in cross section the two keels appear to be on top of each other. In *Bacillaria* they appear to be almost opposite each other. This is also true for a few species of *Nitzschia.* Thus in *Nitzschia* the so-called "keel puncta" do not appear opposite to each other, whereas in *Hantzschia* they do.

The structure of the diatom frustule as illustrated by *Surirella* is quite different from that found in other diatoms, fig. 4C. In girdle view the frustule is sometimes wedge-shaped, fig. 4D. The valve is symmetrical in outline to the apical but not always to the transverse axis, fig. 4E. This is also generally true for the sculpturing on the valve surface.

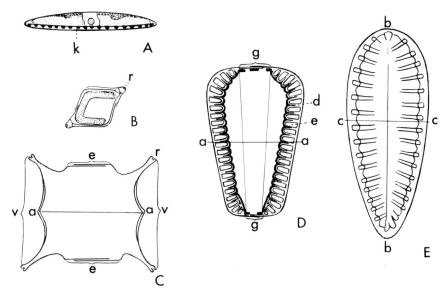

FIGURE 4.

A—Valve view of *Nitzschia*. B—Cross section of *Nitzschia*. C—Cross section of *Surirella*. D—Longitudinal section of *Surirella*. E—Valve view of *Surirella*. a-a, pervalvar axis; b-b, apical axis; c-c, transverse axis; d, canal through which protoplasm and chloroplast project; e, siliceous membrane between canals; g, girdle; v, valve; r, raphe; k, keel.

The valve surface is complex with a wing-like structure on each side of the valve which arises at varying distances from the apical axis, figs. 4D-4E. A series of thickened siliceous ribs is a part of the structure of the wings. Between the ribs is a series of canals by which the protoplasm of the cell proper communicates with the protoplasm in the raphe, fig. 4D. The raphe is on the margin of the valve in the tip of the wing, fig. 4E. Some frustules of diatoms are twisted. Examples are found in *Surirella spiralis* and the genus *Cylindrotheca*.

INTERCALARY BAND

In many diatoms intercalary bands are present between the valve mantle and the girdle. These are sometimes hard to see and they may be more common than the literature would indicate. They may be in the form of bands of silica or in the form of scales as in the genus *Rhizosolenia*. In some species the number of intercalary bands in young cells is less than in old cells, but in other species the intercalary bands may be fairly constant regardless of age.

Often the intercalary band grows inwardly to form a plate-like structure known as a septum. The septa may be flat as in *Diatomella* or undulate as

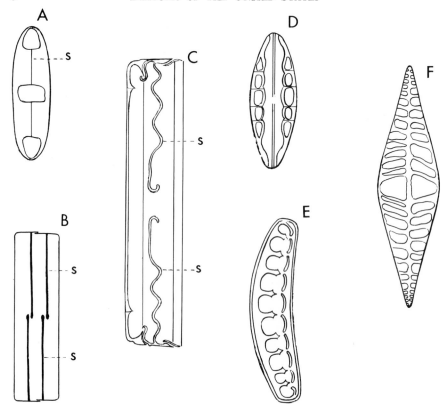

FIGURE 5.

A—Internal septum of *Diatomella*, valve view. B—Internal septum of *Tabellaria*, girdle view. C—Internal septum of *Grammatophora*, girdle view. D—Internal septum of *Mastogloia*, valve view. E—Craticular plate of *Epithemia*, valve view. F—Craticular plate of *Navicula cuspidata* var. *major*. s, septum.

in *Grammatophora*, figs. 5A, C. One or many such septa may be present in a frustule. These septa may appear to develop only from the intercalary bands at the poles of the valve and be relatively small or they may develop from the sides of the bands as well as from the ends and extend entirely across the valve. In some instances in which they are only developed in about one half of the valve as in *Tabellaria*, fig. 5B, they develop alternately from each pole and in girdle view give the appearance of thickened lines extending in an alternating manner from each end of the frustule. Sometimes the septum is a sheet of silica extending across the valve and perforated with large holes as in *Diatomella balfouriana*, fig. 5A. The septum may be attached to the valve by means of thickened siliceous ribs which together form a chambered structure between the valve and the septum. These chambers are marginal in *Mastogloia*, fig. 5D, or they may extend entirely across the valve as in *Epithemia* and *Denticula*, fig. 5E.

The intercalary bands seem to be connected to the valve mantle and the girdle by a series of folds, horn-like processes, or knife-like edges. They are often separated from the valve and the girdle in the cleaning of diatoms.

Besides septa, diatoms sometimes contain internal plates which are called craticular plates. These are often seen in *Navicula cuspidata* var. *major*, fig. 5F. They have the outline of the valve and consist of a strongly siliceous median rib and less strongly silicified transverse ribs. Such internal plates have also been found in *Meridion circulare* and *Eunotia soleirolii*. In some of these diatoms the internal plate does not lie parallel to the valve but is somewhat curved or bent. In *Eunotia serpentina* as many as eight internal plates have been observed.

The internal plates such as those found in *E. serpentina* have irregular sculpturing. Payne (1922) believes that the diatoms described as belonging to the genus *Liostephania* are actually the internal plates of other diatoms, particularly the genus *Asterolampra*. These internal plates seem to be formed most often under ecological conditions unfavorable for the species.

STRUCTURE OF THE VALVE SURFACE

The valve surface usually consists of pores, poroids, or alveoli; hyaline areas; and in some cases thickened ribs arranged in a fairly definite pattern for a given taxon. Other structures which may be present are various processes and a raphe.

STRIAE, PORES, POROIDS, AND ALVEOLI. The pores, poroids, or alveoli usually lie close to each other and form lines or striae. In some cases the pores or poroids are very small and cannot be distinguished under the light microscope. In these cases the striae appear as lines and their granular structure cannot be seen.

The pores are actually fine openings in the cell wall. The poroids are pores which are not open but covered with a thin membrane. The alveoli are cavities or depressed chambers in the cell wall which have perpendicular sides and resemble a honeycomb in structure. The alveoli are often covered with a layer of silica with very fine puncta. The pattern of the striae of the valve is usually fairly constant for a species or variety. Voigt (1943) has found that if irregularities in the striae occur they follow a definite rule and are not haphazardly placed.

The types of pore, poroid, or alveolar structures of the diatom wall which one may encounter are as follows:

a. Cell wall a single layer of silica.

The cell wall is traversed by simple pores or pore canals, and alveoli or chambers are absent. The pore canals may be simple as in *Melosira* or complex as in *Triceratium plano-concavum* which has wart-like structures on the surface of the valve that are punctured by three pore canals which join together to form a main canal. The pore canals reach their best development in thick siliceous walls.

Superimposed on these simple pore-like structures or larger openings may be various types of silica layers which extend across the aperture of the opening. As Hendey (1959) summarizes they may be of the following types:

1. The sieve membrane may be multiperforated and the pores of the "membrane" in rows as in *Synedra ulna.*

2. The "membrane" may be reticulate as in *Achnanthes longipes.*

3. The "membrane" may be incised and compound as in *Cocconeis stauroneiformis.*

4. The "membrane" may consist of plate-like marginal outgrowths as in *Rhaphoneis amphiceros.*

5. The "membrane" may consist of dendriform marginal outgrowths as in *Didymosphenia geminata.*

b. Cell wall with chambers or alveoli.

1. Cell wall with very small cavities or chambers with inner and outer openings. Good examples of this type of structure are found in the genera *Pleurosigma* and *Gyrosigma.* The minute chambers are opened to the exterior by one or two slit-like pores and to the interior by minute pore canals giving the wall the appearance of a minute sieve. It is the arrangement of these alveoli which produces the three directional lines in *Pleurosigma* and the longitudinal and transverse striae in *Gyrosigma* when viewed with the light microscope.

2. The cell wall has chambers which are closed on the outside by a porous "membrane" (Hendey 1959) and have an elliptical opening on the inside of the wall. This is the structure of the costae-like stria in *Pinnularia* which is a cavity with an upper and lower wall through most of its length. However, midway between the axial area and the margin of the valve or somewhat nearer the margin, the lower layer of silica is absent and the cavity opens by a more or less large space to the interior of the valve. It is the edges of those openings which give the appearance of a band crossing the striae in many species of *Pinnularia.*

3. The cavities are covered on the outside by a porous or poroid "membrane" and opened to the inside by a broad opening. A good example of this structure can be found in *Coscinodiscus concinnus,* wherein the cell wall is covered by a polygonal-shaped network, the ridges being the boundaries of the alveoli. These cavities are covered on the outside by a porous or poroid "membrane." The cavities open to the inside of the cell by a large rounded hole, and inside the juncture of the ridges that bound the alveoli are often found what Müller called "process pore canals " which

extend from the outside of the valve to the protoplast. In *Craspedodiscus* the structure is similar but not so definitely developed.

In *Isthmia nervosa* the alveoli appear to be flatter cavities in a coarse network. The ridges enclosing the alveoli which extend inwardly are rather short and have at their inward end an inverted T formation. They may enclose a few to many alveoli. The "membrane" covering these chambers consists of dendriform marginal outgrowths (Hendey, 1959), and near the margins delicate, radially disposed ridges. Occasionally pore canals traverse these ridges.

In *Biddulphia titiana* (Hendey, 1959) the sieve "membrane" may be formed by plate-like marginal outgrowths.

In *Epithemia* the cavities are internal and open widely into the cell. The "membrane" covering the alveoli have at their margin a number of fine pores which by pore canals extend from the outside of the cell wall to the protoplasm.

4. The cavities are opened to the outside and closed to the inside by a porous or poroid "membrane." An example is *Triceratium favus* which has a network of external ridges enclosing polygonal chambers. The chambers open to the outside by a large, rounded opening. The internal wall of the cavity is poroid and seems to contain some true pores. On the margins of the valve the ridges are produced into wing-like structures which are traversed by long pore canals. In *Eupodiscus argus* the cavities are on the outside of the wall and completely opened to the outside and somewhat narrowed toward their base. The base of the cavity is traversed by three to seven pore canals. In *Navicula crucigera* (Hendey, 1959) the "membrane" in the base of the alveoli has a slit incision.

SPINES AND VARIOUS TYPES OF PROCESSES. The valve surface often has various types of extensions which are referred to as processes (Hendey, 1959). These processes aid in attaching a cell to its neighboring cell in the formation of various types of filaments or colonies. These processes may be short and horn-like arising from the apices or angles of the valve as in *Biddulphia* and *Triceratium*. Sometimes these processes appear as knobs in the angles of the valves as in *Triceratium arcticum*. Processes which are smaller, more slender, and open at the ends are referred to as apiculi; examples of these are found in *Skeletonema costatum* and some species of *Biddulphia* and *Coscinodiscus*. If these are very small and probably closed at the ends they are called thorns, spines, or spinulae. They are found in *Stephanodiscus* and some species of *Melosira*. In *Chaetoceras* spp. there are long thin lateral processes which are referred to as setae or awni. They are open at the ends in some species (Iyengar and Subrahmanyan, 1944).

JELLY PORES. Besides the pores described in connection with the structure of striae and chambers, there are other pores which seem to have to do with the excretion of jelly. Their general position is a characteristic of the genus and their exact location a characteristic of species. In *Diatoma* the pore is located on one side of the apical axis near the pole. In the next cell it is usually located near the opposite pole, thus producing a diagonal symmetry in a filament. However, occasionally they do occur in adjacent valves at the same end. In *Tabellaria fenestrata* a small pore is located at the pole where the valve and the valve mantle join; a small spine is often seen in girdle view in this position. A number of pores may be present and they may be at one or both poles. In *T. fenestrata* and *T. flocculosa* another pore is present near the center of the valve. It seems to function in the excreting of the thinner jelly that covers the valve surfaces. In *Grammatophora* each valve possesses two pores at some distance from the poles. There is also a pore near a small spine at the end of the valve. Müller (1898-1901) believes this small spine is the accumulation point for the jelly pad that is the means of attachment. The thick jelly is secreted by this pore near the spine and the other two pores secrete the thinner jelly that covers the valve surface.

Axial and Central Areas. In those diatoms with bilateral symmetry there is usually present in the apical axis a hyaline area which is known as the axial area. The raphe traverses this area. Although this area is usually hyaline it may at times have irregular markings in it. It also may have a single row of puncta on one or both sides of the raphe. Siliceous ribs which are found on each side of the raphe or a single rib in which the raphe may be embedded are present in this area. The area may be very narrow or broad and variously shaped. The shape of this area is usually constant for a given taxon at the specific or intraspecific level.

The central area is a hyaline area about and including the central nodule which is between the median ends of the raphe. This area is formed by the shortening or absence of striae. It may contain isolated puncta or various types of markings. When the thickened central nodule extends throughout this area, it is referred to as a stauros. The shape of the central area is various and may be large or small, symmetrical or asymmetrical. As with the axial area usually the shape does not vary greatly in a given taxon at the specific or subspecific level.

Other Hyaline Areas. Besides those areas referred to as central and axial, other hyaline areas may be present. They may appear to be extensions of the central area as in *Navicula lyra*. In some genera such as *Neidium,* these hyaline areas may be thickened and appear as longitudinal lines near the margins of the valve.

The Raphe. The structure of the raphe which seems to be the best developed and most often used as an example of a raphe is the one found in *Pinnularia.* It is found in the apical axis of the valve.

The raphe is a > shaped slit. A membrane in the apex of the > is believed to divide the slit into an outer and inner channel through which the protoplasm flows. Whether or not the raphe appears as a thread or broad filament, twisted or straight is dependent on the shape of the slit. At the terminal nodule which is an enlarged hollow hyaline area are developed the terminal fissures of the raphe. The outer one is twisted and curved, often into the shape of a hook. The inner fissure is funnel-shaped and extends inwardly into the protoplasm. At one end of a frustule the terminal fissures are usually turned in opposite directions so that a diagonal asymmetry develops. However, on one valve the terminal fissures in the two apices are usually turned in the same direction.

At the central nodule which is a thickening of the cell wall, the end of the external raphe and that of the internal raphe may join by the formation of a transverse canal. The median ends of the raphe branches are joined by a canal. The ends of the raphe at the central nodules are referred to as the central pores or median pores. They usually lie on one side of the apical axis. Sometimes one median pore, as in *Neidium*, is turned to one side and the other to the opposite side.

Hustedt (1930) thinks that the most primitive type of raphe is that found in *Peronia* in which the terminal fissures and the central canals are absent. Kolbe (1956) believes that the most primitive raphe is to be found in *Amphicampa eruca. Semiorbis hemicyclus* seems to have a raphe which is a little more developed. In *Eunotia* there are two raphe systems on each valve. They are not joined as in many of the Naviculaceae. The raphe slit is usually seen in the terminal nodules and extends for a variable but short distance into the valve mantle. The ends of the raphe which might be regarded as primitive terminal fissures, branch at angles into the protoplasm. No true central nodule is present.

In many of the Naviculales we find modifications of the *Pinnularia* raphe and associated structures. The terminal nodule in some species seems to be solid rather than hollow. The raphe branches may be short as in the genus *Amphipleura*. Also the terminal nodules may be elongated, and the terminal fissures may not be well developed as in *Amphipleura* and *Frustulia*. The shapes of the terminal nodules in these two genera are very characteristic. The raphe may lie between two siliceous ribs, as in *Frustulia* and *Frickia;* it may lie near the apical axis, as in *Navicula, Mastogloia, Pinnularia,* etc.; or it may be eccentrically placed, as in *Amphora* and *Cymbella.*

A different line of development of the raphe is seen in its enclosure in a canal or keel. In the Epithemiales the raphe is enclosed in a cylindrical canal which extends longitudinally through the cell wall, and communicates to the exterior by a narrow fissure. This canal raphe may be on the valve surface as in *Epithemia* or may be slightly raised as in *Denticula.* In both *Epithemia* and *Denticula* the valve is slightly convex or almost flat. In *Rhopalodia* the valve is strongly asymmetrically gabled, and the canal raphe occupies the extreme edge of the valve in girdle view and is often not very distinct in valve view. Although there may be a structure resembling a central area, and central pores of the raphe are present, the two branches of the raphe are separate. In some species the so-called central area is not recognizable. In other species a type of central area is formed by the fusing together of two of the openings in the silica membrane that subtends the raphe. In the canal raphe the silica layer forming the bottom of the canal is perforated by a series of holes through which the protoplasm comes into contact with the raphe.

The structure of the raphe in the Nitzschiales is similar to that of the Epithemiales except that it is in or closely associated with a keel. It consists of a fissure subtended by a perforated silica layer. In *Nitzschia* and *Bacillaria* the raphe is located in the keel. The "keel puncta" or "carinal dots" usually have been shown to be the apertures in the subtending silica layer; however, sometimes they refer to the silica between the apertures. A central nodule is present in some species between the two central apertures. The terminal nodules are not distinct. The two branches of the raphe do not seem to be connected if a central nodule is present. In those species without a central nodule the central pores of the raphe are absent.

In the Surirellales a canal raphe is present in the top of the wing-like structure on the margin of the valve. The raphe is sometimes interrupted at one or both poles of the valve, but in other cases it seems to run across one pole of the valve. The pole at which the two ends of the raphe terminate in such cases is thought of as the terminal nodule.

In *Surirella baldjickii* a central nodule and the central pores of the raphe appear to be on one side of the valve and terminal pores on the other.

POLYMORPHISM

Polymorphism has been found in several species of diatoms. Oswald (Gran, 1912) found that in regions where the temperature was quite variable, species often have summer and winter forms. For example, *Rhizosolenia hebetata* and *R. semispina* have been found to be two forms of the same species rather than distinct species. *Rhizosolenia hebetata* is the arctic form with a thick wall and attenuated ends while *R. semispina* is the Atlantic form with thin walls and hair-like ends. Wimpenny (1936) found that *R. styliformis* and *R. alata* increased their diameter with increase of temperature. His results show that this effect is positively correlated with temperature.

Literature Cited

CLEVE, P. T. 1899 Postglaciala bildningarnas klassifikation på grund af deras fossila diatomaceer. *In* N. O. Holst, Bidrag till kännedomen om Östersjöns och Bottniska Vikens postglaciala geologi. *Sveriges geologiska undersökning*, Series C, N:o 180, pp. 59-61.

CLEVE-EULER, A.   1944   Die Diatomeen als quartärgeologische Indikatoren. *Geologiska Föreningens i Stockholm Förhandlingar*, 66(3):383-410.

CUMMINS, A. B. AND H. MULRYAN   1937   Diatomite. Industrial minerals and rocks. Published by the American Institute of Mining and Metallurgical Engineers, pp. 243-260.

FRITSCH, F. E.   1935   The structure and reproduction of the algae. Vol. I. London and New York, Cambridge University Press, xvii + 791 pp.

GRAN, H. H.   1912   Pelagic plant life. *In* Depths of the Ocean, J. Murray and J. Hjort. London, Macmillan and Co., Chapter 6, pp. 307-386.

HANNA, G. D.   1928   The Monterey shale of California at its type locality with a summary of its fauna and flora. *Bulletin of the American Association of Petroleum Geologists*, 12(10):969-983.

————   1933   Diatoms of the Florida peat deposits. *Florida State Geological Survey. Twenty-third—twenty-fourth Annual Report.* 1930-1932, pp. 57-96 + 11 pls.

HENDEY, N. I.   1959   The structure of the diatom cell wall as revealed by the electron microscope. *Journal of the Quekett Microscopical Club*, Series 4, 5(6):147-175.

HUSTEDT, F.   1930   Die Kieselalgen Deutschlands, Österreichs und der Schweiz mit Berücksichtigung der übrigen Länder Europas sowie der angrenzenden Meeresgebiete. *In* Dr. L. Rabenhorst's *Kryptogamen-Flora von Deutschland, Österreich und der Schweiz.* Volume 7, part 1, numbers 1-2, pp. 12-216. Akademische Verlagsgesellschaft, Leipzig.

HUTCHINSON, G. E., R. PATRICK, AND E. S. DEEVEY   1956   Sediments of Lake Patzcuaro, Michocoan, Mexico. *Bulletin of the Geological Society of America*, 67:1491-1504.

HYYPPA, E.   1955   On the Pleistocene geology of Southeastern New England. *Geologinen Tutkimuslaitos. Bulletin de la Commission géologique de Finlande*, N:o 167, pp. 155-225.

IYENGAR, M. O. P. AND R. SUBRAHMANYAN   1944   On the structure and development of the spines or setae of some centric diatoms. *Proceedings of the National Academy of Sciences.* India, 14(3):114-124.

KOLBE, R. W.   1951   Elektronenmikroskopische Untersuchungen von Diatomeenmembranen. II. *Svensk Botanisk Tidskrift*, 45(4):636-647.

————   1956   Zur Phylogenie des Raphe-Organs der Diatomeen: *Eunotia (Amphicampa) eruca* Ehr. *Botaniska Notiser*, 109(1):91-97.

MÖLDER, K.   1944   Die Postglaziale Klimaentwicklung im Lichte der fossilen Diatomeenfunde in Südfinnland. *Geologinen Tutkimuslaitos. Bulletin de la Commission géologique de Finlande*, N:o 132, pp. 16-54.

MÜLLER, O.   1898-1901   Kammern und Poren in der Zellwand der Bacillarien. I-IV. *Berichte der Deutschen Botanischen Gesellschaft*, 16:386-402; 17:423-452; 18:480-497; 19:195-210.

PALMER, T. C. AND KEELEY, F. J.   1900   Structure of the diatom girdle. *Proceedings of the Academy of Natural Sciences of Philadelphia*, 52:465-479.

PATRICK, R.   1936   Some diatoms of Great Salt Lake. *Bulletin of the Torrey Botanical Club*, 63(3):157-166.

————   1943   The diatoms of Linsley Pond, Connecticut. *Proceedings of the Academy of Natural Sciences of Philadelphia*, 95:53-110.

————   1946   Diatoms from Patschke Bog, Texas. *Notulae Naturae of the Academy of Natural Sciences of Philadelphia*, No. 170, 7 pp.

————   1954   The diatom flora of Bethany Bog. *Journal of Protozoology*, 1:34-37.

PAYNE, F. W.   1922   Diatomaceae. Liostephania and its allies. London, Wheldon and Wesley, Ltd., 30 pp. + 4 pls.

ROSS, R.   1950   Appendix. *In* A. P. Conolly, H. Godwin, and E. M. Megaw, Studies in the Post-Glacial history of British vegetation. XI. Late-Glacial deposits in Cornwall. *Philosophical Transactions of the Royal Society of London*, Series B, Biological Sciences, 234(615):461-464.

Voigt, M. 1943 Sur certaines irrégularités dans la structure des diatomées. *Notes de Botanique Chinoise*, Musée Heude, No. 4, 50 pp. + 2 pls.

Wimpenny, R. S. 1936 The size of diatoms. I. The diameter variation of *Rhizosolenia styliformis* Brightw. and *R. alata* Brightw. in particular and of pelagic marine diatoms in general. *Journal of the Marine Biological Association*. United Kingdom, 21:29-60.

Woolman, L. 1891 Geology of artesian wells at Atlantic City, New Jersey. *Proceedings of the Academy of Natural Sciences of Philadelphia*, 42:132-147, 444.

———— 1892 A review of artesian-well horizons in southern New Jersey. With notes of new wells in New Jersey, Delaware and South Carolina and also in Philadelphia, Pa. *Geological Survey of New Jersey*, Annual Report of the State Geologist for the year, 1891, pp. 223-232.

Protoplast

The typical diatom cell consists of a single nucleus, usually located in the pervalvar axis of the frustule; cytosome; and the bounding membranes. The cytoplasm usually extends into the cavities and openings in the siliceous wall. It is through these openings that osmotic exchange or active transport takes place.

In the diatoms with a raphe or pseudoraphe the nucleus is usually in the center of the cell, whereas in some of the centric diatoms it may be nearer one of the valves. The resting nucleus contains many minute chromatin granules and one to several nucleoli. The nucleus is variable in size depending on the species of diatom, and is usually either round or oval or reniform. Centrosomes lying near the nucleus have been seen in many species of diatoms.

When the nucleus starts to divide a spindle is formed. Early workers believed the formation of the spindle to be extra-nuclear. However, later workers such as Cholnoky have doubted the extra-nuclear origin of the spindle. The chromatin granules become arranged in moniliform threads, and later the spiremes break up into chromosomes.

A large central vacuole is present. In the diatoms with a raphe or pseudoraphe it is usually divided into two portions by the protoplasmic bridge in the pervalvar axis of the cell. However, in many centric diatoms in which the nucleus lies near one of the valves this is not the case. In such cases thin, cytoplasmic strands traverse the vacuole.

Within the cytosome are found the chloroplasts, mitochondria, and storage bodies. Contractile vacuoles have been reported in some species such as *Rhizosolenia longiseta*, *Attheya zachariasi*, and perhaps in *Nitzschia hantzschiana* (Pascher, 1932).

Chadefaud (1939) has found in the genus *Fragilaria* what he calls active and inactive mitochondria. The active mitochondria are near the nucleus, and the inactive mitochondria are found between the plastids.

The chloroplasts are variously shaped, varying from very small granules or discs to large plate-like structures of many shapes. If they are small, they are numerous; whereas a single large choroplast may be found in some species. The small disc-shaped chloroplasts are most commonly found in the centric diatoms although they do occur in some of the species with a pseudoraphe. Most of the diatoms with a raphe have large plate-like chloroplasts which may be variously incised. In the Achnanthaceae a single large chloroplast is usually present, whereas in the Naviculaceae in the genera *Navicula* and *Pinnularia* two large chloroplasts appressed to the girdle are usually present. In *Gomphonema parvulum* var. *micropus* one large, deeply incised chloroplast is present. Many of the species of *Nitzschia* have one chloroplast lying next to one side of the girdle or stretched out, diagonally from keel to keel. In *Surirella* there are usually two deeply lobed chloroplasts, the lobes of which often penetrate into the canals connected with the raphe. In many of the marine Tabellariaceae there are elaborately incised chloroplasts. Pfitzer (1871, 1882) developed a classification of diatoms based on the structure of the chloroplasts. However, it often happens that within the same genus there are several different types of chloroplasts. In some species of *Chaetoceros* the chloroplasts or chromatophores are seen embedded in the cytoplasm in the spines (Iyengar and Subrahmanyan, 1944).

The structure of the chloroplast of *Nitzschia palea* has been described by Drum (1962, 1963). It is laminated, and resembles the structure of other algal chloroplasts. The chloroplast is surrounded by a membrane. Oil droplets occur between the laminae. The location of the oil bodies is predetermined by the location of special areas of the cytoplasmic strands which become inflated with food reserve during active periods of photosynthesis. The oil droplets in the chloroplasts appear to have the same density as the oil bodies. The greatest number appear in the vicinity of the pyrenoid. A single discoid pyrenoid is in each chloroplast. The pyrenoid matrix is granular and homogeneous except for four small tubules. The membrane about the pyrenoid is 7 mμ thick (Drum, 1963).

Drum (1963) describes columnar vesicles which occur in groups near the nucleus. These he calls dictyosomes. They resemble golgi bodies found in most plant and animal cells. These dictyosomes may be the "double rods" observed by Lauterborn (1896) with the light microscope.

Besides oil, leucosin also is a storage product in diatom cells. It seems to be a carbohydrate. Pringsheim (1952) called it chrysose. Meeuse (1962) found that autolysis of leucosin produced glucose. It seems to be closely related to lamenarin which is found in the brown alga, *Lamenaria*. Low (1955) and others have studied the amino acids in diatoms. Low (1955) lists the following amino acids which have been found in diatoms: glycine, alanine, serine, threonine, valine, leucine, isoleucine, phenylalanine, tyrosine, cystine (as cysteic acid), methionine, tryptophan, proline, hydroxyproline, aspartic acid, glutamic acid, histidine, arginine, lysine. The sterols, chondrillasterol and fucosterol, have been reported from diatoms (Low 1955; Heilbron, 1942).

All diatoms seem to be covered by a thin mucilaginous substance external to the silica wall. It is because of such mucilaginous substances that diatoms have the ability to adhere to substrates. In many species it is so thin that it is difficult to see unless special staining techniques are used. In some species of diatoms this mucilaginous covering is quite thick. The thickness of this covering may also vary with the physiological condition of the diatom.

Besides this covering over the surface of the diatom, various types of mucilaginous hold-fasts often develop. In some species the hold-fast is a small thickened pad of jelly located at one end of the frustule. Other species such as some members of the genus *Navicula* (*Schizonema*) typically develop gelatinous tubes. Other diatoms, such as *Gomphonema* and *Cymbella*, are attached to the substrate by gelatinous stalks.

Some diatoms such as many of the Fragilariales and some of the Eunotiales have a jelly pore which can be distinguished on the surface of the valve. It is believed that mucilaginous material is excreted through this pore. The diatoms with these specially developed mucilaginous structures often occur in water with a fair amount of current. They are also often attached to aquatic plants and floating substrates.

This mucilaginous substance was for many years considered to be pectin. However, Lewin (1962) has shown in several diatoms that when this substance is treated with dilute alkali it yields glucuronic acid. The mucilage tubes of *Amphipleura rutilans*, a marine diatom, consist mainly of xylose and mannose units (Lewin, R. A., 1958).

Literature Cited

CHADEFAUD, M. 1939 Éléments mitochondriaux actifs et inactifs chez les Diatomées du genre *Fragilaria*. *Comptes Rendus Académie des Sciences*, 208:1422-1424.

DRUM, R. W. 1962 The non-siliceous fine structure of a diatom. *In* Fifth International Congress for Electron Microscopy. New York, Academic Press, p. UU-14.

———— 1963 The cytoplasmic fine structure of the diatom *Nitzschia palea*. *The Journal of Cell Biology*, 18(2):429-440.

HEILBRON, I. M. 1942 Some aspects of algal chemistry. *Journal of the Chemical Society*, London, for Feb., 1942:79-89.

IYENGAR, M. O. P. AND R. SUBRAHMANYAN 1944 On the structure and development of the spines or setae of some centric diatoms. *Proceedings of the National Academy of Sciences*. India, 14(3):114-124.

LAUTERBORN, R. 1896 Untersuchungen über Bau, Kernteilung, und Bewegung der Diatomeen. Leipzig, W. Engelmann, 165 pp. + 10 pls. + 2 figs.

LEWIN, J. C. 1962 Silification. *In* Physiology and Biochemistry of Algae, edited by R. A. Lewin. New York, Academic Press, Chapter 27, pp. 445-455.

LEWIN, R. A. 1958 The mucilage tubes of *Amphipleura rutilans*. *Limnology and Oceanography*, 3:111-113.

Low, E. M.   1955   Studies on some chemical constituents of diatoms. *Journal of Marine Research,* 14(2):199-204.

Meeuse, B. J. D.   1962   Storage products. *In* Physiology and Biochemistry of Algae, edited by R. A. Lewin. New York, Academic Press, Chapter 18, pp. 289-313.

Pascher, A.   1932   Über das Vorkommen von kontraktilen Vakuolen bei pennaten Diatomeen. *Beihefte zum Botanischen Centralblatt,* 49(3):703-709.

Pfitzer, E.   1871   Untersuchungen über Bau und Entwicklung der Bacillariaceen (Diatomaceen). *In* Hanstein, *Botanische Abhandlungen aus dem Gebiet der Morphologie und Physiologie.* Bonn, 1(2):vi+189 pp. + 6 pls.

———   1882   Die Bacillariaceen (Diatomaceen). *In* Schenk, *Handbuch der Botanik.* Breslau, 2:403-445 + 16 figs.

Pringsheim, E. G.   1952   On the nutrition of *Ochromonas. Quarterly Journal of Microscopical Science,* 93:71-96.

II. PHYSIOLOGY

The knowledge of diatom physiology has largely developed during the twentieth century. Much of the information in this account has been obtained from *Physiology and Biochemistry of the Algae,* edited by R. A. Lewin (1962). However, other references have been consulted and the more recent literature has been added.

The results of these studies indicate that diatoms vary considerably in their physiological processes. Because a relatively few species have been studied, one should be cautious in making generalizations as to the physiological behavior of diatoms.

Nutrition

Diatoms were originally believed to be autotrophic organisms. However, more recent literature (Fritsch, 1935; Provasoli, 1958; Lewin and Lewin, 1960) has shown that at least some of them may also live heterotrophically. Lewin (1953) screened 42 cultures of fresh-water and soil diatoms representing at least 7 species: of these only 13 were capable of heterotrophic growth on the substrates tested. *Navicula pelliculosa* was tested on some 60 compounds, but only glucose supported growth. Lactate, pyruvate, acetate, citrate, and succinate stimulated respiration. Glycerol and fructose permitted growth in light in a CO_2 free medium. Later Lewin and Lewin (1960) tested 44 cultures of marine diatoms for their ability to grow in the dark on glucose, lactate, and acetate. Of these 16 grew only on glucose, 8 on glucose or lactate, 1 on glucose or acetate, 1 on glucose, lactate, or acetate, and 2 only on lactate. Certain diatoms such as *Nitzschia putrida* have only heterotrophic nutrition.

VITAMINS AND ORGANIC SUBSTANCES

Vitamins have been found to be necessary for certain diatoms. In some species various clones require different vitamins. Clones of species requiring thiamine were *Amphora coffeaeformis, A. paludosa* var. *duplex,* and

Nitzschia closterium (Lewin and Lewin, 1960). Clones of species requiring vitamin B_{12} were *Amphora coffeaeformis, A. lineolata, Nitzschia frustulum, N. ovalis, Opephora* sp., and *Cyclotella* sp. Some clones were found to require both thiamine and B_{12}. They belonged to the following species: *Amphipleura rutilans, Amphora coffeaeformis,* and *Nitzschia closterium.* Guillard and Cassie (1963) have found that for the marine diatoms *Cyclotella nana, Thalassiosira fluviatilis, Skeletonema costatum, Fragilaria* sp., *Chaetoceros* sp., and *Skeletonema* sp., the number of molecules per cell of B_{12} required by these diatoms varied from 5-18.4, which is about the same as in other organisms. The shell of *Skeletonema costatum* became abnormal in the absence of B_{12}. *Cyclotella meneghiniana* has also been found to require B_{12} (McLachlan, 1959). Droop (1955) has shown that the growth of *Skeletonema costatum* was stimulated by cobalamin.

The need of diatoms for organic substances has been indicated for many species, but the exact nature of these organic substances often has not been determined. Harvey (1939) showed that *Ditylum brightwellii* required for vigorous growth two organic substances that acted in a complementary manner. One of these contained a compound that has a S-$CH_2CH(NH_2)COOH$ group. The importance of soil extract and extracts from algae and natural sea water for improving the growth of many diatoms has been shown, but just what the characteristics of these substances are that induce better growth is not completely understood.

Droop (1955, 1957, 1958) has found that the growth of *Skeletonema costatum* is stimulated by Tris (hydroxymethyl) aminomethane, glycylglycine, and various mixtures of amino acids. Patrick and Wallace (1953) found that the growth of *Nitzschia linearis* was stimulated by extract of agar which according to Lewin (1955) may in part be due to the silica content of the extract. Various reduced sulphur compounds seem to stimulate diatom division (Harvey, 1939; Matsudaira, 1942). This may be due to their role in the uptake of silicon (Lewin, 1954). Under most conditions diatoms need some silica in order to divide. Bentley (1958) found that 1-10 mg. per liter of 3-indolacetic acid increased the filament lengths and doubled the number of cells in *Skeletonema.*

MINERAL NUTRIENT REQUIREMENTS

The mineral requirements of diatoms are similar to those of most plants. The major chemicals are phosphates, nitrogen (usually in the form of ammonium or nitrates), sulphates, calcium, magnesium, potassium, iron, manganese, and silicon. Chlorides are needed by some but not by all diatoms. Chu (1942) has set forth a variety of mixtures of these chemicals which are suitable for diatom growth. Besides these there are a number of chemicals, often referred to as "trace elements," which seem to be beneficial in very small amounts and are included in nutrient solutions.

However, diatoms vary in their requirement, and the nutrition of diatoms to date is not thoroughly understood.

Chu (1942, 1943) gives the optimum ranges of the major chemicals for the diatoms he studied. Nitrates are generally the best form of nitrogen for diatoms, but some species can use ammonium and various organic sources. Kain and Fogg (1958) found that the nitrogen requirement per cell for *Asterionella japonica* was 0.25 micromilligram atoms.

The phosphorus content in *Asterionella japonica* (Goldberg *et al.*, 1951) and *A. formosa* (Mackereth, 1953) seems to be dependent on the concentration in the medium. In *A. formosa* the greatest uptake occurred in the range of pH 6-7. Lund (1950) found that in *A. formosa* the concentration of phosphorus per cell ranged from 6×10^{-8} to 4×10^{-6} μg. Goldberg *et al.* (1951) found the minimum for *A. japonica* to be 5×10^{-8} μg. of phosphorus per cell.

Calcium seems to be one of the more important elements in diatom nutrition, but just what is its most important role is not known. It is part of the buffering system which controls pH. It also acts as an antagonizer and counteracts the toxic effect of excesses of various ions. It may control the amount of H_2SO_4 in the water, which may be produced as a result of bacterial action and might otherwise be toxic. Calcium and magnesium can be utilized by diatoms in various ratios (Provasoli *et al.*, 1954). *Fragilaria capucina* had its best growth where the calcium-magnesium ratios were between 3:1 and 24:1.

Harvey (1933, 1937) and Gran (1931) found that diatoms were very dependent on iron for rapid growth, and that lack of iron checked growth. They determined that iron as ferric citrate or tartrate is utilizable by some diatoms. However, the marine diatom *Asterionella japonica* can utilize only colloidal ferric hydroxide or particulate iron (Goldberg, 1952).

Lund (1950) found that when the concentration of silica in the medium is less than 0.5 mg. per liter, *Asterionella formosa* cannot multiply to any extent. The mean silica content of *Asterionella* cells is 140 μg. per million cells.

Manganese is necessary for nitrate reduction. It can be utilized in the form of hydrated oxides. Von Stosch (Lewin, 1962) has found that manganese is necessary for the formation of new silica walls in *Achnanthes longipes*.

Absorption

Absorption in diatoms may be accomplished by osmosis, active transport, or a combination of both. Gross and Zeuthen (1948) have found evidence that diatoms may exert a measure of control over their specific gravity by preferential accumulation of lighter materials such as univalent rather than divalent ions.

The permeability of diatom membranes to nonelectrolytes is usually higher than that of most plant cells, and the range of permeability constants may not be as great (Stadelmann, 1962). Certain diatoms seem to be highly permeable to sugar which usually penetrates other kinds of cells slowly. However, Höfler (Höfler et al., 1956; Höfler, 1960) have shown that *Cymbella aspera* and *Caloneis obtusa* are almost impermeable to sugar. The permeability of halophylic diatoms to salt is relatively high (Cholnoky, 1928; Höfler et al., 1956). Calcium chloride was able to penetrate into the vacuole of diatom cells whereas this was not true for all the other plant cells tested. This property together with active transport probably is largely the cause of the high osmoregulatory ability of diatoms.

Growth of Diatoms

Diatom growth is largely manifested by cell division and the two terms are generally used interchangeably. The division rate seems to be determined by the conditions of the environment such as the temperature, amount of light, nutrients, and the genetic makeup of the species.

Richter (1911) has shown that the optimum growth temperature for *Nitzschia putrida* is 24°-25° C. Growth also occurred at 10° and at 30° C., but was not as rapid. A temperature of −10° to −11° C. could be withstood for 24 hours without harm. Schreiber (1927) found that *Biddulphia sinensis* grew more rapidly at 16° C. than *B. aurita*. Barker (1935) found that the maximum photosynthesis rate for *Nitzschia palea* was at 27° C.; at 30° C. the rate was irreversibly lowered and at 37° C. photosynthesis did not occur.

Talling (1955) has found that under the same environmental conditions *Tabellaria flocculosa* var. *asterionelloides* had a much slower growth rate than *Asterionella formosa* and *Fragilaria crotonensis*. Temperature seemed to influence growth rate, this being considerably slower at 5.5° C. than at 18.5° C. Wallace (1955) studied the effect of high temperature on *Nitzschia filiformis* and *Gomphonema parvulum* and of both high and low temperature on *Nitzschia linearis*. In *Nitzschia filiformis* from 22°-30° C. the cell division rates were quite similar after ten days, but at 34° C. growth had stopped after seven days. In *Gomphonema parvulum* the cell division rates after ten days were quite similar at temperatures between 22° and 30° C., and at 34° C., although the cell division was less, it was still continuing at ten days. In *Nitzschia linearis* growth was stopped at 4° C., but when the cells were subsequently placed in suitable temperatures the expected division rate occurred. Division rate increased with increase in temperature and the optimum temperature was between 20° and 24° C. at ten days. Above this temperature growth decreased, and was inhibited at 32° C.

Kain and Fogg (1958) found that 20°-25° C. was the optimum temperature for growth of *Asterionella japonica*. Ukeles (1961) has given the ranges in temperature in which good growth occurs for the following diatoms: *Actinocyclus*, 18°-25° C.; *Amphiprora*, 8°-30° C.; *Nitzschia laevis*, 15°-24° C.; *Melosira* sp., 15°-24° C.; and for *Amphora* sp., 8°-30° C. No growth occurred for *N. laevis* at 30° C.; for *Melosira* sp. between 27°-30° C. Ryther and Guillard (1962) found that *Cyclotella nana*, a warm water form, did not grow below 15° C. *Thalassiosira fluviatilis* did not grow at 5° C. but grew between 10°-25° C. *Rhizosolenia setigera* which is a cold water species did not grow at 25° C. *Skeletonema costatum* took more than two weeks to acclimate at 5° C.; however, once it was acclimated, it grew well. Respiration seemed to increase fairly regularly with increase in temperature for the eurythermal diatoms, *C. nana* and *S. costatum*. The stenothermal species, *Detonula confervacea* and *C. nana* (strain 13-1) in general had a low rate of respiration and were relatively insensitive to temperature as compared with the eurythermal species. Hustedt (1956) gives a system for classifying diatoms according to the temperature they prefer. His four major groupings are eu-stenothermal forms (lowest temperature about 5° C.); meso-stenothermal forms (lowest temperature about 10° C.); meso-eurythermal forms (lowest temperature about 15° C.); and eu-eurythermal forms (lowest temperature 20° C. or more). Lewin and Guillard (1963) cite various data which indicate that light intensity may influence the temperature at which the rate of growth is fastest.

The rate of division seems to differ greatly from species to species and perhaps in various clones of the same species. The author (Patrick) has maintained individual cells of *Pinnularia major* in apparently healthy condition for a period of six weeks without cell division, whereas some species such as *Nitzschia closterium* and *Gomphonema* may divide several times a day. Talling (1955) records division rate of about two divisions per day for *Asterionella formosa*. The maximum rate of *Skeletonema costatum* may be eight divisions per day (Lewin and Guillard, 1963—Morozova-Vodyanitskaya and Lanskaya).

Various workers (Lefèvre *et al.*, 1952; Rice, 1954) have reported that certain species of diatoms may excrete substances which inhibit their growth or the growth of other species. Talling (1957) finds no evidence for the production of such substances by *Asterionella formosa* and *Fragilaria crotonensis*. Pringsheim (1951; Fogg, 1962) found that *Nitzschia putrida* could liquefy gelatin and, therefore, may excrete a proteolytic enzyme. Steemann Nielsen (1955) found that *Thalassiosira nana* produced antibodies that reduced the oxygen consumption of bacteria.

Photosynthesis

The pigments which are directly or indirectly associated with photosynthesis in diatoms are chlorophyll a and c; carotin α, β, ϵ; diadinoxanthin; diatoxanthin; fucoxanthin; neofucoxanthin A, and neofucoxanthin B. Dutton and Manning (1941) found in *Nitzschia closterium* that the light absorbed by some if not all of the carotinoid pigments was utilized in photosynthesis. Tanada (1951) working with *Navicula minima* var. *atomoides* found that the light absorbed by fucoxanthin could be utilized in photosynthesis with about the same efficiency as light absorbed by chlorophyll. He concluded that the light absorbed by the other carotinoid pigments in this species were not useful in photosynthesis.

Hendey (1964) has listed the wave lengths in which the maximum absorption of light occurs for the various diatom pigments. In acetone they are as follows: chlorophyll a, 430 mμ and 663-665 mμ; chlorophyll c, 445 and 630 mμ; β carotin, 452-456 mμ; diatoxanthin, 450-452 mμ; diadinoxanthin, 444-446 mμ; fucoxanthin, 449 mμ; neofucoxanthin A, 448-450 mμ; neofucoxanthin B, 448 mμ.

The amount and duration of light for optimum photosynthesis seems to vary greatly with the species. This is evidenced by the various depths in lakes and in the oceans at which various species live. It is also shown by the difference in species living in tropical and arctic areas. Photosynthesis in diatoms increases with increased light intensity, reaching a maximum value at about 10 kilolux, (Lewin and Guillard, 1963).

The carbon fixed in photosynthesis in *Navicula pelliculosa* is rapidly incorporated in substantial amounts into fatty substances as well as into sugars and insoluble cell constituents (Fogg, 1956). The photosynthetic carbon assimilation is intermeshed with other metabolic processes. The detailed mechanism of fat and protein synthesis from the primary products of photosynthesis is not well understood (Fogg, 1956). The amount of fat in the cell seems to increase with age. The drying of diatom cells also brings about an increase in fat content (Miller, 1962). The storage products in diatoms seem to be mostly fats.

Movement

In diatoms both internal and external movement takes place. Examples of internal movement are: 1) the shift of the nucleus in auxospore germination as occurs in *Cocconeis* (Haupt, 1962), and 2) the change in shape of the chloroplasts of *Nitzschia palea* which have been seen to round up in the dark and expand in the light (von Denffer *in* Haupt, 1962).

The cause of active external movement in diatoms seems to be the rotation of the cytoplasm in the raphe. Thus, only those diatoms with a raphe can move. The path of the diatom seems to be dependent on the shape of the raphe (Nultsch, 1956). The *Navicula* type of raphe has straight movement; the *Amphora* type, curved movement; and the *Nitzschia* type, curved with two different radii. Nultsch (1956) differentiates between swaying movement, rotating movement, and movement pivoting about a central point. Many diatoms exhibit a to-and-fro movement alternating at intervals of about a minute (Heidingsfeld, 1943; *in* Haupt, 1962).

The most complicated diatom movement is that shown by *Bacillaria paradoxa* in which the cells of the colony line up and then slide out in a straight line in accordance with a rather definite rhythm. Usually the lining up takes about 80 seconds at 20° C. and the sliding out of the cells into a straight line is at the rate of 10μ per second. The rhythm is usually synchronous, but in very large colonies may not be. The rate of movement may be altered by the change in osmotic pressure of the medium or by the presence of narcotics (von Denffer, 1949).

Most diatoms seem to show positive tropotaxis to white light (Halldal, 1962). However, Heidingsfeld (*in* Halldal, 1962) recorded that *Navicula radiosa* showed only negative topotaxis. Nultsch (1956) found *Navicula radiosa* responded negatively to blue light and positively to red light.

It has been postulated that movement of the protoplasm is accomplished by protein fibrils in the protoplasm which form a dynamic system of oscillation like a polyrhythmic system. The transverse waves in these fibrils cause the diatom to glide in the opposite direction. Such waves would be able to shift a great deal of protoplasm if the fibrils were fixed to the cell wall (Haupt, 1962). The carinal fibrils seen by Drum and Pankratz (1963) may be these protein fibrils.

Formation of the Cell Wall

The cell wall of living diatoms is considered by many to be mainly composed of hydrated amorphous silica with a small amount of Al_2O_3 or Fe_2O_3. However, Desikachary (1962) states the chemical nature of the silica is not thoroughly understood. The specific gravity of living diatom silica is 2.07 (Einsele and Grim, 1938). The specific gravity of fossil diatom silica is 2.00, and there is evidence to believe its chemical composition is α-quartz.

Although the silica may be supplied to the medium as Ca, Na, or K salts, it is probably in the form of orthosilicic acid when absorbed by the diatom. It is probably deposited at various levels in an organic matrix which has been called pectin, but may not be true pectin (Lewin, 1962). The thin areas of the cell walls which seem to have a spongy substructure appear to be a highly porous silica gel. The absorption of Si seems to take place more rapidly at 20° C. than at 25° C. (Jørgensen, 1952).

The thickness of the diatom silica wall is quite variable and in tropical plankton or in rapidly dividing cells may be very thin. In the formation of the cell walls silica cannot be replaced by other elements similar to it in chemical or physical properties or in atomic radius (Lewin, 1962).

Literature Cited

BARKER, H. A. 1935 Photosynthesis in diatoms. *Archiv für Mikrogeologie*, 6:141-156.
BENTLEY, J. A. 1958 Role of plant hormones in algal metabolism and ecology. *Nature*, 181(4622):1499-1502.

Cholnoky, B. J. 1928 Über die Wirking von hyper- und hypotonischen Lösungen auf einige Diatomeen. *Internationale Revue der Gesamten Hydrobiologie und Hydrographie.* Leipzig, 19:452-500.

Chu, S. P. 1942 The influence of the mineral composition of the medium on the growth of planktonic algae. Part I. Methods and culture media. *Journal of Ecology,* 30:284-325.

———— 1943 The influence of the mineral composition of the medium on the growth of planktonic algae. II. The influence of the concentration of inorganic nitrogen and phosphate phosphorus. *Journal of Ecology,* 31:109-148.

Desikachary, T. V. 1962 The diatoms. *Current Science,* 31(2):43-45.

Droop, M. R. 1955 A pelagic marine diatom requiring cobalamin. *Journal of the Marine Biological Association.* United Kingdom, 34:229-231.

———— 1957 Auxotrophy and organic compounds in the nutrition of marine phytoplankton. *Journal of General Microbiology,* 16:286-293.

———— 1958 Requirement for thiamine among some marine and supralittoral protists. *Journal of the Marine Biological Association.* United Kingdom, 37:323-329.

Drum, R. and H. S. Pankratz 1963 Fine structure of a diatom centrosome. *Science,* 142(3588):61-63.

Dutton, H. J. and W. M. Manning 1941 Evidence for carotenoid-sensitized photosynthesis in the diatom *Nitzschia closterium. American Journal of Botany,* 28:516-526.

Einsele, W. and J. Grim 1938 Über den Kieselsäuregehalt planktischer Diatomeen und dessen Bedeutung für einige Fragen ihrer Ökologie. *Zeitschrift für Botanik.* Jena, 32:545-590.

Fogg, G. E. 1956 Photosynthesis and formation of fats in a diatom. *Annals of Botany,* New Series, 20(78):265-286.

———— 1962 Extracellular products. *In* Physiology and Biochemistry of Algae, edited by R. A. Lewin. New York, Academic Press, Chapter 30, pp. 475-489.

Fritsch, F. E. 1935 The structure and reproduction of the algae. Vol. I. London and New York, Cambridge University Press, xvii + 791 pp.

Goldberg, E. D. 1952 Iron assimilation by marine diatoms. *Biological Bulletin,* 102:243-248.

————, T. J. Walker, and A. Whisenand 1951 Phosphate utilization by diatoms. *Biological Bulletin,* 101:274-284.

Gran, H. H. 1931 On the conditions for production of plankton in the sea. *Conseil Permanent International pour l'Exploration de la mer, Rapports et procès-verbaux des réunions,* 75:37-46.

Gross, F. and E. Zeuthen 1948 The buoyancy of plankton diatoms: a problem of cell physiology. *Proceedings of the Royal Society of London,* Series B, 135:382-389.

Guillard, R. R. L. and V. Cassie. 1963 Minimum cyanocobalamin requirements of some marine centric diatoms. *Limnology and Oceanography,* 8(2):161-165.

Halldal, P. 1962 Taxes. *In* Physiology and Biochemistry of Algae, edited by R. A. Lewin. New York, Academic Press, Chapter 37, pp. 583-593.

Harvey, H. W. 1933 On the rate of diatom growth. *Journal of the Marine Biological Association.* United Kingdom, 19:253-276.

———— 1937 The supply of iron to diatoms. *Journal of the Marine Biological Association.* United Kingdom, 22:205-219.

———— 1939 Substances controlling the growth of a diatom. *Journal of the Marine Biological Association.* United Kingdom, 23:499-520.

Haupt, W. 1962 Intracellular movements. *In* Physiology and Biochemistry of Algae, edited by R. A. Lewin. New York, Academic Press, Chapter 35, pp. 567-572.

Heidingsfeld, I. 1943 Phototaktische Untersuchungen an *Navicula radiosa.* University of Breslau, Germany. Unpublished thesis, cited *in* Nultsch, 1956.

Hendey, N. I. 1964 An introductory account of the smaller algae of British Coastal Waters. Part V. Bacillariophyceae (Diatoms). Ministry of Agriculture, Fisheries and Food, Fisheries Investigations, Series IV, pp. 1-317.

HÖFLER, K. 1960 Über die Permeabilität der Diatomee *Caloneis obtusa*. *Protoplasma*, 52(1):5-25.

————, W. URI, AND A. DISKUS 1956 Zellphysiologische Versuche und Beobachtungen an Algen der Lagune von Venedig. *Bollettino Museo Civico Storia Naturale*. Venezia, 9:63-94.

HUSTEDT, F. 1956 Kieselalgen (Diatomeen). Stuttgart, Fränckh'sche Verlagshandlung, W. Keller and Co., 70 pp., 35 figs., + 4 pls.

JØRGENSEN, E. G. 1952 Effects of different silicon concentrations on the growth of diatoms. *Physiologia Plantarum*, 5:161-170.

KAIN, J. M. AND G. E. FOGG 1958 Studies on the growth of marine phytoplankton. I. *Asterionella japonica* Gran. *Journal of the Marine Biological Association*. United Kingdom, 37:397-413.

LEFÈVRE, M., H. JAKOB, AND M. NISBET 1952 Auto- et heteroantagonisme chez les algues d'eau douce in vitro et dans les collections d'eau naturelles. *Annales Station Centrale d'Hydrobiologique Appliquée*. Paris, 4:5-198.

LEWIN, J. C. 1953 Heterotrophy in diatoms. *Journal of General Microbiology*, 9:305-313.

———— 1954 Silicon metabolism in diatoms. I. Evidence for the role of reduced sulfur compounds in Si utilization. *Journal of General Physiology*, 37:589-599.

———— 1955 Silicon metabolism in diatoms. II. Sources of silicon for growth of *Navicula pelliculosa*. *Plant Physiology*, 30(2):129-134.

———— 1962 Silicification. *In* Physiology and Biochemistry of Algae, edited by R. A. Lewin. New York, Academic Press, Chapter 27, pp. 445-455.

———— AND R. A. LEWIN 1960 Auxotrophy and heterotrophy in marine littoral diatoms. *Canadian Journal of Microbiology*, 6:127-134.

LEWIN, J. C. AND R. R. L. GUILLARD 1963 Diatoms. *Annual Review of Microbiology*, 17:373-414.

LUND, J. W. G. 1950 Studies on *Asterionella formosa* Hass. II. Nutrient depletion and the spring maximum. Parts I.-II. *Journal of Ecology*, 38(1):1-35.

MACKERETH, F. J. 1953 Phosphorus utilization by *Asterionella formosa* Hass. *Journal of Experimental Botany*, 4:296-313.

MATSUDAIRA, T. 1942 On inorganic sulphides as growth-promoting ingredient for diatoms. *Proceedings of the Imperial Academy of Tokyo*, 18:107-116.

McLACHLAN, J. 1959 The growth of unicellular algae in artificial and enriched sea water media. *Canadian Journal of Microbiology*, 5:9-15.

MILLER, J. D. A. 1962 Fats and steroids. *In* Physiology and Biochemistry of Algae, edited by R. A. Lewin. New York, Academic Press, Chapter 21, pp. 357-370.

NULTSCH, W. 1956 Studien über die Phototaxis der Diatomeen. *Archiv für Protistenkunde*. Jena, 101:1-68.

PATRICK, R. AND N. M. WALLACE 1953 The effect of agar on the growth of *Nitzschia linearis*. *American Journal of Botany*, 40(8):600-602.

PRINGSHEIM, E. G. 1951 Über farblose Diatomeen. *Archiv für Mikrobiologie*, 16:18-27.

PROVASOLI, L. 1958 Nutrition and ecology of protozoa and algae. *Annual Revue of Microbiology*, 12:297-308.

PROVASOLI, L., J. J. A. McLAUGHLIN, AND I. J. PINTNER 1954 Relative and limiting concentrations of major mineral constituents for the growth of algal flagellates. *Transactions of the New York Academy of Sciences*, 16:412-417.

RICE, T. R. 1954 Biotic influences affecting population growth of planktonic algae. United States Department of Interior. *Fishery Bulletin* 87, volume 54:227-245.

RICHTER, O. 1911 Die Ernährung der Algen. *Monographien und Abhandlungen zur Internationalen Revue der gesamten Hydrobiologie und Hydrographie*, 2:1-192.

RYTHER, J. H. AND R. R. L. GUILLARD 1962 Studies of marine phytoplankton. III. Some effects of temperature on the respiration of five species. *Canadian Journal of Microbiology*, 8(4):447-453.

Schreiber, E. 1927 Die Reinkultur von marinem Phytoplankton und deren Bedeutung für die Erforschung der Produktions-fähigkeit des Meerwassers. *Wissenschaftliche Meeresuntersuchungen.* Abteilung Helgoland, Neue Folge, 16(10):1-34.

Stadelmann, E. J. 1962 Permeability. *In* Physiology and Biochemistry of Algae, edited by R. A. Lewin. New York, Academic Press, Chapter 31, pp. 493-528.

Steemann Nielsen, E. 1955 An effect of antibiotics produced by plankton algae. *Nature,* 176(4481):553.

Talling, J. F. 1955 The relative growth rates of three plankton diatoms in relation to underwater radiation and temperature. *Annals of Botany,* New Series, 19(75): 329-341.

———— 1957 The growth of two plankton diatoms in mixed cultures. *Physiologia Plantarum,* 10:215-223.

Tanada, T. 1951 The photosynthetic efficiency of carotenoid pigments in *Navicula minima. American Journal of Botany,* 38:276-283.

Ukeles, R. 1961 The effect of temperature on the growth and survival of several marine algal species. *Biological Bulletin,* 120:255-264.

Von Denffer, D. 1949 Die planktische Massenkultur pennater Grunddiatomeen. *Archiv für Mikrobiologie,* 14:159-202.

Wallace, N. M. 1955 The effect of temperature on the growth of some freshwater diatoms. *Notulae Naturae of the Academy of Natural Sciences of Philadelphia,* No. 280, 11 pp.

III. REPRODUCTION*

Vegetative Division

The most common type of reproduction of diatoms is accomplished by vegetative reproduction in which mitosis occurs. The mitotic spindle lies in the pervalvar axis of the cell. A distinct centrosome is present near each pole of the spindle in many species of diatoms. The chromosomes are small and numerous in the various species of diatoms where cell division has been observed. The details of division are therefore difficult to follow.

Chromatophore division takes place during mitosis. If many small chloroplasts are present, they usually separate into equal numbers in each of the two new cells. The division of these chloroplasts occurs later. Where only one chloroplast is present it divides longitudinally. If two chloroplasts are present they may divide longitudinally or transversely. The pyrenoids increase in number by division.

The new cell membranes are formed from the outer edges of the protoplast and extend inward parallel to the valve. After the cell membranes are formed a vesicle is formed and the siliceous wall is developed within it. Thus each valve with its girdle of the parent cell becomes one of the valves of the daughter cell. If there was no way in which the new cell could expand, the cells of the populations would gradually get smaller in accord-

---

*A large portion of this section is taken from "Sexual reproduction in diatoms," by Ruth Patrick, *Sex in Microorganisms.* Editorial Committee: D. H. Wenrich, Ivey F. Lewis, and John R. Raper, American Association for the Advancement of Science, pp. 82-99, 1954.

ance with a theory set forth by Pfitzer (1871). However, later workers have shown that such regular diminution in size does not always take place. This has been most conclusively demonstrated by Wiedling (1948). He showed that in certain unialgal diatom cultures lasting over several years no diminution in size of the species occurred. This, however, does not necessarily seem to be a species characteristic because in different clones of the same species various patterns of behavior were observed, some decreasing much more markedly and in a different pattern than that of others.

Mitosis or vegetative division usually takes place in the early morning hours. What appear to be oil globules usually accumulate in the cell as the time for cell division approaches. If the cell divides, most of these globules, if not all of them, disappear. However, if for some reason the cell does not divide they often coalesce and form very large globules. These cells appear in mass culture to be very light brown in color, and not golden brown or the brown of strong tea which color is usually characteristic of actively dividing cultures.

Microspore Formation

Microspores are produced in many centric diatoms, but as yet it has not been proved that they are reproductive cells. They are formed by the division of the protoplast. Each microspore has two flagella.

Auxospore Formation

Of much less frequent occurrence than mitosis is reproduction by auxospore formation. An auxospore is a resting cell which usually develops from a zygote. This process has been observed occasionally in many of the genera of diatoms, but in only a comparatively few species.

To date there seems to be little correlation between the type of auxospore formation and the taxonomic relationship of the species. Indeed, several different types of auxospore formation have been observed in different varieties and forms of the same species.

Often auxospore formation seems to be the result of sexual processes. However, in many cases, as Sonneborn (Calkins and Summers, 1941) has said, perhaps we should "abandon the concepts of male and female in unicellular organisms and view sexual union as brought about by copulation-conditioning factors."

The cause of auxospore formation seems to be a combination of cell size and external environmental conditions. All species of diatoms are known to vary in length. According to Geitler (1932, 1935), auxospore formation occurs only when the cells of a taxon are of a certain length, characteristic for each taxon. Often this range in length is fairly wide or again it may be very narrow depending on the taxon. This range is very constant for each taxon. If auxospore formation does not occur when the cells are of the correct size, it never occurs. The cells often become smaller and morphologically quite changed, especially in culture.

Auxospore formation in diatoms has been a frequent subject of research during the nineteenth and twentieth centuries. Although the complete process has been observed in only a relatively few species, it is partially known in a great many more. Because many species are very small and their chromosomes are numerous, detailed cytological studies are difficult. The best summaries of this work have been made by Geitler (1932, 1957) and Fritsch (1935).

Little is known concerning the nuclear reorganization which takes place in auxospore formation in diatoms. The vegetative stage in many species of diatoms without raphe or pseudoraphe has been considered to be haploid, but the work of Schmidt (1927), von Stosch (1950), and Geitler (1952e) would indicate that the vegetative stage of several members of this group are diploid. The vegetative stage of diatoms with a raphe or pseudoraphe so far as is known is diploid.

Von Stosch (1959) indicates the close relationship of diatoms to the brown algae by the similarity of the structure of the spermium in *Chaetoceros eibeni* and *Actinoptychus undulatus* to the spermatozoids of *Fucus*. He also points out that the disaccharide in the hydrolyzed state in diatom leucosin is not distinguishable from labinaribose.

Von Stosch (1958) believes that the findings of oögamy in *Rhabdonema adriaticum*, a member of the *Fragilariales*, may indicate that it is a connecting link between the diatoms without a raphe and those with a raphe.

AUXOSPORE FORMATION IN DIATOMS WITHOUT RAPHE OR PSEUDORAPHE

The simplest type of auxospore formation is that which has been reported in the genus *Melosira*. The two halves of the wall of the cell are pushed apart by the protoplast. Over the protoplast is secreted a slightly silicified membrane called the perizonium. After a lapse of time new valves and connecting bands are formed inside the perizonium, and a new individual results. In *Melosira nummuloides* the auxospore lies outside the theca of the parent. Reduction division takes place and autogametes are formed (Erben, 1959). There is considerable difference of opinion about the nuclear phenomena that accompany auxospore formation in this genus (Karsten, 1897; Geitler, 1932; Erben, 1959).

In *Biddulphia mobiliensis* (Bergon, 1907) cell division immediately precedes auxospore formation. The two daughter protoplasts escape from the parent cell and form a pair of spores. Little is known about the nuclear behavior during this process.

In *Chaetoceras cochlea* (Fritsch, 1935) the auxospores arise laterally on the parent cell by budding. A similar lateral formation of auxospores also takes place in some species of *Rhizosolenia* (Schütt, 1893).

Iyengar and Subrahmanyan (1944) observed in *Cyclotella meneghiniana* zygote formation and subsequent auxospore formation. They considered this the result of autogamy and automixis.

Von Stosch (1950) has reported oögamy in *Melosira varians.* He has observed the filaments to be of two types, narrow male filaments and broader female filaments. In about nine per cent of the cases where the size of the filaments overlap they are found to be monoecious.

The antheridial cells undergo reduction division. Two spermatozoid mother cells bud off the main cytoplasm in the second metaphase and then divide to form four sperms. Flagella have not been seen, but it is presumed that the sperms are flagellated.

The young oögonia resemble vegetative cells in shape, yet their plastids and chromatophores are larger. Meiosis takes place in the usual manner. In the first telophase one of the daughter nuclei gradually aborts. In the second telophase one of the nuclei becomes pycnotic. The two "polar bodies" thus formed are gradually absorbed.

The oögonium swells, and a strip of naked protoplasm is exposed between the margins of the epitheca and hypotheca. The spermium may enter the oögonium as early as anaphase I or as late as the maturation of the egg nucleus. Later the zygote is released and swells to form a subglobose auxospore.

Geitler (1952e) has observed in *Cyclotella* sp. sexual reproduction similar to that described in *Melosira varians.* There seems to be no morphological difference in the filaments that form the eggs and sperms. In spermatogenesis there occurs a first and a second meiotic division which result in the formation of four sperms. The sperm enters the oögonium by the time diakinesis takes place. As a result of first and second meiotic divisions of the nucleus, one egg nucleus and two pycnotic nuclei are produced. The sperm nucleus migrates during interkinesis from the peripheral region of the egg to the center, where fusion with the egg nucleus takes place after the second division is complete. A metagamic mitosis occurs between the formation of the first and second shells of the cell formed in the germination of the auxospore. Although metagamic mitosis has been observed many times in diatoms with a raphe or pseudoraphe, this is the first time it has been observed in this group.

Oögamy has been observed in *Biddulphia rhombus, B. granulata* and *Cerataulus* by von Stosch (1956). In spermatogenesis each mother cell produces two to four diploid spermatogonia in *B. rhombus,* four to eight in *B. granulata,* and four in *Cerataulus smithii.* Each spermatogonium produces four uniciliate spermia which have no plastids. The number of eggs produced per oögonium varied with the species. In *B. granulata,* two eggs were produced per oögonium. In *B. rhombus* and *Cerataulus smithii* only one egg was produced per oögonium. After fertilization the fertilization membrane which becomes the perizonium was formed. With the formation of the first theca a metagamic mitosis takes place. The formation of sperms has been observed in *Melosira moniliformis* (von Stosch, 1958).

AUXOSPORE FORMATION IN DIATOMS WITH TRUE RAPHE OR PSEUDORAPHE

MOVEMENT OF CELLS. Auxospore formation is usually initiated by the coming together of the mother cells. Of course, in cases of apomixis and automixis, this may not occur. These cells are diplonts and are usually considered not to be sexually differentiated. However, in *Navicula halophila* (Subrahmanyan, 1946), *Synedra ulna* (Geitler, 1939), and *Synedra rumpens* var. *fragilarioides* (Geitler, 1952f), it has been reported that one cell produces two passive gametes, and one produces two active gametes. This might indicate that the two mother cells are sexually differentiated.

These cells may be about the same size as in *Rhoicosphenia curvata* (Geitler, 1952a), or may be very unequal in length as in *Eunotia arcus* (Geitler, 1951b). Sometimes more than two cells come together for auxospore formation, as in *Gomphonema parvulum* var. *micropus, Achnanthes lanceolata,* and *Navicula seminulum* (Geitler, 1932). In *Anomoeoneis exilis* (Geitler, 1949), *Navicula radiosa* (Geitler, 1952d), and *Synedra ulna* (Geitler, 1939), several cells often come together. Usually these cells are not sister cells, but in *Navicula seminulum* they may be (Geitler, 1932).

In most cases both cells are active and approach each other. In *Gomphonema parvulum* var. *micropus* one cell is attached by a gelatinous stalk and only one is mobile (Geitler, 1932). These cells assume various positions on contacting each other. The most common position is for them to lie opposite and parallel with their girdle faces in juxtaposition. The cells of *Gomphonema parvulum* var. *micropus* orient themselves so that the apical pole of one cell is opposite the basal pole of the other. Owing to the curvature of the frustule of *Rhoicosphenia curvata,* the cells may be in various positions (Geitler, 1952a).

Jelly is produced by both cells in varying quantities. Liebisch (1929) considered this jelly part of the hydrated pectin membrane of the cell. Other research indicates that it has a different origin. It is evident that more work needs to be done on this point.

This jelly is usually homogeneous and varies in thickness according to the kind of diatom. In *Achnanthes longipes, Navicula didyma,* and *Pleurosigma nubecula* it is fairly soft, whereas in *Frustulia rhomboides* var.

saxonica and *Achnanthes lanceolata* it is relatively stiff. Geitler (1932) thinks that tensions which develop in this jelly as a result of its viscosity determine to some extent the movement of the gametes and the position of the developing zygote and auxospore.

In many species a large quantity of jelly is produced and the copulating cells are embedded in it. However, in other species the jelly is only represented by the formation of a copulation tube or tubes. In *Eunotia arcus* and *Eunotia flexuosa* (Geitler, 1951c) the copulation tube is formed by papillae which are formed by each of the two copulating cells.

The number and shape of the tube or tubes may vary. Usually only one tube is formed; however, in *Frustulia rhomboides* var. *saxonica* (Geitler, 1949) two tubes are present. The tube may be long and narrow as in *Eunotia arcus* (Geitler, 1951b) or short and narrow as in *Nitzschia subtilis* and *Amphipleura pellucida* (Geitler, 1932, 1952c). Usually the tube is formed at or near the middle of the longitudinal axis. In *Frustulia rhomboides* var. *saxonica* (Geitler, 1949) one tube is found near each of the apices of the cell. In *Eunotia arcus* and *Eunotia flexuosa* (Geitler, 1951a,b) a tube may be formed at either end of the cell or on the girdle face of the dorsal or ventral side of the valve.

GAMETOGENESIS. So far as is known, gametes are formed by two nuclear divisions. The spindle lies in the pervalvar axis of the cell. Sometimes it it tipped slightly to one side as in *Amphipleura pellucida* (Geitler, 1952c). The prophase of the first meiotic division appears to be normal, but owing to the high numbers of chromosomes and the small size of the nucleus in diatoms, it is difficult to make out all the stages. The two nuclei resulting from the first meiotic division are usually normal. However, in Cocconeis one of the nuclei forms a polar body. It is believed to be an aborted gamete. In *Navicula seminulum* (Geitler, 1932), one nucleus becomes pycnotic and is ejected, whereas in *Navicula cryptocephala* var. *veneta* one nucleus is reabsorbed (Geitler, 1952f).

Cytokinesis usually follows the first meiotic division. Previous to this the chloroplasts usually have divided. The cell membrane is developed in a plane parallel to the valves of the cell.

The second division usually follows cytokinesis. One of the two nuclei formed in this division usually degenerates. Sometimes it is reabsorbed in the protoplasm as in *Gomphonema parvulum* var. *micropus* (Geitler, 1932). In other instances it becomes pycnotic and remains in the gamete as in *Eunotia arcus* and *Eunotia flexuosa* (Geitler, 1951a,b) or is cut off as in *Amphipleura pellucida*. However, in *Navicula radiosa* (Geitler, 1952d) and *Navicula cryptocephala* var. *veneta* (Geitler, 1952f) both nuclei remain functional, so that each gamete has two functional nuclei.

One or two functional gametes may develop in each cell. If two gametes develop, they usually change position. Instead of lying parallel to the valves in the position in which they are formed, they come to lie one above the other when viewed from the apex of the cell. In *Navicula radiosa* (Geitler, 1952d) this change of position of the gametes does not occur.

One notable exception to this type of gamete formation is that found in *Eunotia arcus* and *Eunotia flexuosa* (Geitler, 1951a,b,c). In these species there is a transverse differentiation of protoplasts. In *Eunotia arcus* one chloroplast becomes very large, while in *Eunotia flexuosa* they both move to the same side of the cell. The spindle of the first meiotic division is formed so that one pole is close to the epitheca. A very unequal cell division takes place. The larger cell develops into a gamete. The smaller cell forms what Geitler calls a "remaining cell." Geitler thinks that this remaining cell, by affecting the osmotic pressure of the cell, brings about the movement of the gamete. After cytokinesis occurs, the second division follows in both the gamete and the "remaining cell." One nucleus in each degenerates.

Another exception is, for example, in *Cymbella ventricosa* var. (Geitler, 1932) where parthenogenesis occurs. In such cases reductional division does not take place.

Sometimes it happens, as in *Eunotia arcus* (Geitler, 1951b), that the cells resulting from meiosis develop shells and become vegetative cells rather than gametes. This phenomenon has been observed several times in diatoms.

The sex differentiation of gametes, if it occurs, takes place during meiosis. Geitler (1932) thinks that the anisogamy recognized by the difference in size and movement is more apparent than real. He states that movement is due to tensions which develop in the cell. This is well described for *Amphipleura pellucida* (Geitler, 1952c). The first gamete to mature is the one that starts the movement. Carefully controlled experiments are necessary to determine the true condition.

Fusion of Gametes. The fusion of gametes in diatoms is of three types. Isogamous fusion is the result of equal movement of the gametes or of copulation of the gametes *in situ*. Anisogamous fusion is the result of unequal movement of the gametes. Autogamous fusion is the result of the fusion of two gametes in the same mother cell.

Isogamous fusion may be of various types. In one type, as in *Amphora* and *Denticula* (Geitler, 1932), the two gametes from each cell move into the jelly mass between the cells. In *Rhopalodia gibba* (Klebahn, 1896) the jelly is restricted and appears as a bridge between the two cells. Two zygotes are formed in this bridge. This is believed to be the most primitive type of auxospore formation.

Isogamous fusion may also take place within a copulation tube. In this type the zygote is formed within the tube. This type of fusion occurs in *Eunotia arcus* and *Eunotia flexuosa* (Geitler, 1951a,b). In *Navicula radiosa* each half of each mother cell rotates through an arc of 90 degrees and the two gametes copulate (Geitler, 1952d).

Anisogamous fusion occurs if one gamete is active and the other is passive. As in isogamous fusion this may occur with or without a copulation tube. In *Gomphonema parvulum* var. *micropus* usually four gametes are involved. One gamete migrates into the other mother cell and fuses with the passive gamete. This stimulates the other gamete to move out and into the first mother cell. As a result two auxospores are formed. Of less frequent occurrence in *Gomphonema parvulum* var. *micropus* is the production of only one zygote. Of rare occurrence is the production of one zygote from three gametes (Geitler, 1932).

Of common occurrence in anisogamous fusion is the production of a copulation tube. Depending on the species of diatom, one or two tubes may be produced.

Usually one tube is produced, as in many species of *Nitzschia* in which the gametes pass in succession through the tube. If two tubes are present, as in *Frustulia rhomboides* var. *saxonica,* the two fusions may take place at the same time (Geitler, 1949).

An unusual type of anisogamous fusion is that reported for *Navicula halophila* (Subrahmanyan, 1946), *Synedra ulna* (Geitler, 1935), and *Synedra rumpens* var. *fragilarioides* (Geitler, 1952f). In these species two active gametes are formed in one mother cell and two passive gametes in the other mother cell. The resulting fusion produces two auxospores in the same mother cell. No copulation tube is formed.

Automixis is not common in diatoms. Several cases which need further investigation indicate that this is a means of reproduction. In no case is the nuclear behavior thoroughly understood. What seems to be a true case of automixis is described for *Amphora normanii* (Geitler, 1935), in which one auxospore is formed from a single cell. The protoplast contracts, and two nuclei, two nucleoli, and two chromatophores are formed. The valves of the cell are spread apart, and the protoplast is transformed into an auxospore. Later there is found only a single nucleus with a nucleolus.

Autogamy occurs in *Achnanthes subsessilis* and *Gomphonema constrictum* var. *capitatum* (Karsten, 1897; Geitler, 1952b). Within a single cell two gametes are formed which later fuse to form a single protoplast which is transformed into an auxospore.

Parthenogenesis is a method of auxospore formation in *Cocconeis placentula* var. *lineata* (Geitler, 1932). The nucleus of the parent cell goes through two divisions, which correspond to the two divisions in meiosis except that reduction in chromosome number does not occur. Polar bodies are formed. The protoplast then becomes transformed into an auxospore.

Parthenogenesis is also known to occur in one of the varieties of *Cymbella ventricosa*.

Asexual auxospore formation has been reported for *Synedra affinis* (Karsten, 1897) and *Rhabdonema arcuatum*. In these species the mother cell divides by mitosis to form two daughter cells. These protoplasts, instead of developing normal vegetative walls, become auxospores. Further cytological investigation is needed to make sure that this is truly asexual formation of auxospores (Fritsch, 1935).

Sometimes two types of auxospore formation occur within a single mass of copulating cells. For instance, in *Gomphonema parvulum* var. *micropus* three cells come together. One cell forms an auxospore by automixis and the other two produce auxospores by heteromixis (Geitler, 1932).

The time interval for the fusion of gametes varies greatly. In *Navicula seminulum* the fusion of gametes takes two to three minutes, whereas in *Amphipleura pellucida* the process takes an hour (Geitler, 1932, 1952b).

DEVELOPMENT OF ZYGOTE AND AUXOSPORE FORMATION. On fusion of the gametes the zygote starts to develop. The fusion of the nuclei is often delayed until the auxospore is developed. In *Navicula radiosa* (Geitler, 1952d), and *Navicula cryptocephala* var. *veneta* (Geitler, 1952f) there are two pairs or four functional nuclei. During auxospore development one pair fuses and the other pair degenerates.

The zygote may be found in various positions. As a result of isogamy it is formed between the mother cells. The polar axis of the zygote is at right angles to that of the mother cells. As a result of anisogamous fusion the zygote is first formed in the mother cell. When two zygotes are formed, one is usually produced in each mother cell. However, in *Navicula halophila* (Subrahmanyan, 1946), *Synedra ulna* (Geitler, 1939), and *Synedra rumpens* var. *fragilarioides* (Geitler, 1952f) the two zygotes are produced in the same mother cell. Likewise in automixis and parthenogenesis the zygote is first formed in the mother cell. Later it migrates out of the mother cell. Usually in anisogamous fusion the long axis of the auxospore is parallel to that of the mother cell, whereas in isogamous reproduction the long axis of the auxospore is perpendicular to the long axis of the mother cells. However, if the jelly surrounding the copulating cells is relatively thick the auxospores may vary somewhat in position. Geitler (1932) believes that this interesting correlation of the position of the auxospore with type of reproduction is a result of tensions developed within the jelly rather than a result of the type of gametes.

The zygote elongates in the formation of the auxospore. In this process the zygote membrane often breaks and appears as caps on the ends of the auxospore, as in *Frustulia rhomboides* var. *saxonica* (Geitler, 1949). In *Anomoeoneis exilis* the zygote membrane persists as laminations over the poles of the auxospore (Geitler, 1949). In *Nitzschia fonticola* (Geitler, 1932) the zygote membrane is elastic and does not break.

The perizonium, which is the auxospore cell wall, develops under the membrane of the zygote. It becomes weakly silicified. The silicification starts at the center of the auxospore membrane and develops out toward the poles. The perizonium may develop a distinctive pattern of markings or be smooth.

When the auxospore is mature, a nuclear division (metagamic division) occurs. One of the resulting nuclei is pycnotic. This phenomenon has been observed in various genera.

After a period of time the auxospore develops the cell wall typical of the vegetative cell. The first wall to develop is the epitheca. It is irregular in that it does not have a girdle band. Therefore, the edges of the valve bend over and the valve has a curved appearance. The hypotheca, however, is normal in that it possesses a girdle band. Thus the first vegetative cell is not symmetrical in appearance; and, therefore, it differs from subsequent vegetative cells.

SUMMARY OF TYPES OF AUXOSPORE FORMATION

Various authors have made classifications of the different types of auxospore formations. The classification given below is taken from Geitler (1932) but modified to include the results of more recent research.

NORMAL TYPE A. Two mother cells each produce two gametes, which copulate in pairs to produce two auxospores.

a. The gametes are isogamous; the apical axes of the auxospores are perpendicular to the apical axes of the mother cells. *Amphiprora alata* (?), *Amphora coffeaeformis, A. cymbelloides, A. ovalis, A. ovalis* var. *pediculus, A. pusio, A. veneta, Auricula hyalina, Denticula vanheurckii, Epithemia argus* (?), *E. sorex, E. turgida, E. zebra, E. zebra* var. *saxonica, Navicula radiosa, Rhopalodia gibba, R. gibba* var. *ventricosa, Surirella ovata* (Geitler, 1963).

b. Each mother cell produces a wandering and a resting gamete. The apical axes of the auxospores are parallel to those of the mother cells. *Achnanthes lanceolata, A. minutissima, Amphipleura pellucida, A. rutilans* (?), *Amphiprora alata* (?), *Anomoeoneis sculpta, A. serians, Brebissonia boeckii, Cymbella affinis, C. caespitosa* var. *pediculus, C. cistula, C. cymbiformis* (?), *C. gastroides, C. helvetica, C. lacustris, C. lanceolata,* **C.** *parva* (?), *C. prostrata, C. sumatrensis, C. ventricosa, C. ventricosa* vars. I and II, *Frustulia rhomboides* var. *saxonica, Gomphonema constrictum,* **G.** *constrictum* var. *capitatum, G. geminatum, G. intricatum* (?), *G. intricatum* var. *dichotomum* (?), *G. longipes* (?), *G. olivaceum, G. parvulum* var. *micropus,*

G. tenellum (?), *Libellus constrictus* (?), *Navicula crucigera, N. cuspidata* var. *ambigua, N. directa, N. firma* (?), *N. pygmaea, N. ramosissima, N. scopulorum, N. subtilis, N. viridula, Neidium affine* var. *amphirhynchus* (?), *Nitzschia hybrida, N. longissima, N. sigmoidea, N. subtilis, Pinnularia gibba, P. hemiptera, P. stauroptera* (?), *P. viridis, Rhoicosphenia curvata, Schizonema lacustre, Stauroneis phoenicenteron* (?).

c. One mother cell produces two wandering gametes, and one mother cell produces two passive gametes. The apical axes of the auxospores are parallel to those of the mother cells. *Navicula halophila, Synedra ulna, S. rumpens* var. *fragilarioides.*

d. The gametes behave according to no rule; the auxospore position varies. *Achnanthes brevipes, A. lanceolata, A. longiceps, Denticula tenuis, Navicula didyma, N. fonticola, N. hybrida, Nitzschia longissima, Pleurosigma nubecula.*

NORMAL TYPE B. Spermatozoa and an egg cell are formed.

a. An antheridial cell buds off two spermatozoid mother cells, each of which produces two spermatozoids. One oögonium produces one egg cell. A spermatozoid enters the egg and a zygote is formed, *e.g., Melosira varians.*

b. Four spermia are produced from a spermatogonia cell. One oögonium produces one egg cell. A spermium enters the egg and a zygote is formed. *Cyclotella* sp., *Biddulphia rhombus, Cerataulus smithii, Rhabdonema adriaticum.* In *Biddulphia granulata* two eggs per oögonium are formed.

REDUCED TYPE A. Two mother cells each build one gamete; these fuse to form a single auxospore.

a. The gametes behave isogamously. *Cocconeis pediculus, C. placentula, C. placentula* var. *klinoraphis, C. placentula* var. *tenuistriata, Cymatopleura solea, Eunotia arcus, E. flexuosa, E. formica, E. pectinalis, Navicula cryptocephala* var. *veneta, Rhoicosphenia curvata, Surirella capronii, S. splendida, S. striatula, S. calcarata.*

b. The gametes behave anisogamously. *Navicula seminulum, Cocconeis pediculus, C. placentula, C. placentula* var. *pseudolineata.*

REDUCED TYPE B. One mother cell develops an auxospore through automixis.

a. Two gametes of one mother cell copulate with each other. *Achnanthes subsessilis; Cyclotella meneghiniana; Melosira nummuloides* (?); *Gomphonema constrictum* var. *capitatum;* Form I, *Gomphonema angustatum.*

b. The sexual nuclei of a mother cell copulate. *Amphora normanii, Bacillaria paradoxa* (?), *Chaetoceras borealis, C. densus, Grammatophora marina, Libellus constrictus* (?), *Navicula constricta* (?), *Nitzschia palea.*

REDUCED TYPE C.   The auxospore formation is apomictic.

a. From one mother cell there develop through vegetative division two auxospores. *Achnanthes longipes* (?), *Bacillaria paradoxa* (?), *Cocconeis pediculus, Cymbella* spp., *Libellus constrictus, Navicula constricta* (?), *Rhabdonema arcuatum, Synedra affinis, Tabellaria* sp.

b. From one mother cell (the mother cells may pair) there develops one auxospore.

1. Parthenogenetically. *Bacillaria paradoxa* (?), *Cocconeis pediculus, C. placentula, C. placentula* var. *klinoraphis, C. placentula* var. *lineata, C. placentula* var. *euglypta, Cymatopleura elliptica, C. solea, Cymbella cistula* (?), *C. sumatrensis* (?), *C. ventricosa* var. I, *Grammatophora marina* (?), *Meridion circulare, Navicula grevillei, Nitzschia palea* (?), *Surirella gemma.*

2. Purely vegetatively. *Bacillaria paradoxa* (?) and *Melosira.*

Literature Cited or Used

BERGON, P. 1907 Biologie des diatomées.—Les processus de division, de rajeunissement de la cellule et de sporulation chez le *Biddulphia mobiliensis* Baily. *Bulletin de la Société Botanique de France,* 54:327-358.

CALKINS, G. N. AND F. M. SUMMERS, eds. 1941 Protozoa in biological research. New York, Columbia University Press, xli + 1148 pp.

ERBEN, K. K. 1959 Untersuchungen über Auxosporenentwicklung und Meioseauslösung an *Melosira nummuloides* (Dillw.) C. A. Agardh. *Archiv für Protistenkunde.* Jena, 104(1):165-210.

FRITSCH, F. E. 1935 The structure and reproduction of the algae. Vol. I. London and New York, Cambridge University Press, xvii + 791 pp.

GEITLER, L. 1932 Der Formwechsel der pennaten Diatomeen. *Archiv für Protistenkunde.* Jena, 78(1):1-226.

——— 1935 Reproduction and life history in diatoms. *The Botanical Review.* New York, 1(5):149-161.

——— 1939 Gameten- und Auxosporenbildung von *Synedra ulna* im Vergleich mit anderen pennaten Diatomeen. *Planta; Archiv für wissenschaftliche Botanik.* Berlin, 30(3):551-567.

——— 1949 Beiträge zur Kenntnis der Auxosporenbildung pennater Diatomeen. *Österreichischen Botanischen Zeitschrift.* Wien, 96(3/4):467-472.

——— 1951a Prägame Plasmadifferenzierung und Kopulation von *Eunotia flexuosa* (Diatomee). *Österreichischen Botanischen Zeitschrift.* Wien, 98(4):398-403.

——— 1951b Kopulation und Formwechsel von *Eunotia arcus. Österreichischen Botanischen Zeitschrift.* Wien, 98(3):292-337.

——— 1951c Zelldifferenzierung bei der Gametenbildung und Ablauf der Kopulation von *Eunotia* (Diatomee). *Biologischen Zentralblatt.* Leipzig, 70(9/10): 385-398.

——— 1952a Die Auxosporenbildung von *Rhoicosphenia curvata. Österreichischen Botanischen Zeitschrift.* Wien, 99(1):78-89.

——— 1952b Untersuchungen über Kopulation und Auxosporenbildung pennater Diatomeen. I. Automixis bei *Gomphonema constrictum* var. *capitata. Österreichischen Botanischen Zeitschrift.* Wien, 99(2/3):376-384.

GEITLER, L.   1952c   Untersuchungen über Kopulation und Auxosporenbildung pennater Diatomeen. II. Wander- und Ruhegameten bei *Amphipleura pellucida*. *Österreichischen Botanischen Zeitschrift*. Wien, 99(2/3):385-395.

———   1952d   Untersuchungen über Kopulation und Auxosporenbildung pennater Diatomeen. III. Gleichartigkeit der Gonenkerne und Verhalten des Heterochromatins bei *Navicula radiosa*. *Österreichischen Botanischen Zeitschrift*. Wien, 99(4):469-482.

———   1952e   Oogamie, Mitose, Meiose und metagame Teilung bei der zentrischen Diatomee *Cyclotella*. *Österreichischen Botanischen Zeitschrift*. Wien, 99(4):506-520.

———   1952f   Untersuchungen über Kopulation und Auxosporenbildung pennater Diatomeen. IV. Vierkernige Zygoten bei *Navicula cryptocephala* var. *veneta*. V. Allogamie bei *Synedra rumpens* var. *fragilarioides*. *Österreichischen Botanischen Zeitschrift*. Wien, 99:598-605.

———   1957   Die sexuelle Fortpflanzung der pennaten Diatomeen. *The Biological Review*. Cambridge, 32(3):261-295.

———   1963   Auxosporenbildung von *Surirella ovata* und die Lagebeziehungen von Mutterzellen und Erstlingszellen bei Diatomeen. *Österreichischen Botanischen Zeitschrift*. Wien, 110(1):44-52.

IYENGAR, M. O. P. AND R. SUBRAHMANYAN   1944   On reduction division and auxospore-formation in *Cyclotella meneghiniana* Kütz. *Journal of the Indian Botanical Society*, 23(4):125-153.

KARSTEN, G.   1897   Untersuchungen über Diatomeen. III. *Flora oder Allgemeine Botanische Zeitung*. Marburg, 83(2):203-221.

KLEBAHN, H.   1896   Beiträge zur Kenntniss der Auxosporenbildung. 1. *Rhopalodia gibba* (Ehr.) O. Müller. *Jahrbücher für Wissenschaftliche Botanik*. Leipzig, 29:595-654.

LIEBISCH, W.   1929   Experimentelle und kritische Untersuchungen über die Pektinmembran der Diatomeen unter besonderer Berücksichtigung der Auxosporenbildung und der Kratikularzustände. *Zeitschrift der naturwissenschaftlichen Abteilung*. Botanik, 22:1-65.

PFITZER, E.   1871   Untersuchungen über Bau und Entwicklung der Bacillariaceen (Diatomaceen). *In* Hanstein, *Botanische Abhandlungen aus dem Gebiet der Morphologie und Physiologie*. Bonn, 1(2):vi+189 pp. + 6 pls.

———   1882   Die Bacillariaceen (Diatomaceen). *In* Schenck, *Handbuch der Botanik*. Breslau, 2:403-445 + 16 figs.

SCHMIDT, P.   1927   Weiteres uber die Fortpflanzung der Diatomee *Bidulphia sinensis*. *Internationale Revue der Gesamten Hydrobiologie und Hydrographie*, 18:400-415.

SCHÜTT, F.   1893   Wechselbeziehungen zwischen Morphologie, Biologie, Entwicklungsgeschichte und Systematik der Diatomeen. *Berichte der Deutschen Botanischen Gesellschaft*, 11:563-571.

SUBRAHMANYAN, R.   1946   On somatic division, reduction division, auxospore formation and sex differentiation in *Navicula halophila* (Grun.) Cl. *Journal of the Indian Botanical Society*, 25:239-266.

VON STOSCH, H. A.   1950   Oögamy in a centric diatom. *Nature*, 165(4196):531-532.

———   1956   Entwicklungsgeschichtliche Untersuchungen an zentrischen Diatomeen. II. Geschlechtszellenreifung, Befruchtung und Auxosporenbildung einiger grundbewohnender Biddulphiaceen der Nordsee. *Archiv für Mikrobiologie*, 23:327-365.

———   1958   Entwicklungsgeschichtliche Untersuchungen an zentrischen Diatomeen. III. Die spermatogenese von *Melosira moniliformis* Agardh. *Archiv für Mikrobiologie*, 31:274-282.

———   1959   Zum Chromosomenformwechsel der Dinophyten sowie zur Mechanik und Terminologie von Schrauben. *Archiv für Protistenkunde*. Jena, 103(1/2):229-240.

WIEDLING, S.   1948   Beiträge zur Kenntnis der vegetativen Vermehrung der Diatomeen. *Botaniska Notiser*, for 1948 (3):322-354.

IV. DISTRIBUTION*

Diatoms occur in all types of water—and in some moist and dry habitats where the light, temperature, and chemical conditions are suitable for their growth. They also occur in all latitudes and longitudes of the world.

The literature containing information on factors affecting diatom distribution is very large, as more papers have been written on this aspect of diatom biology than on any other. Perhaps the most important summary papers are Kolbe (1932) and Patrick (1948). This present account is largely based on Patrick's previous publications, but has been brought up to date by more recent findings.

When one thinks of diatoms, one almost automatically divides them into marine and fresh-water species. This, in general, is a very good division to use in the consideration of diatom distribution, for the factors which act as barriers to distribution are very different in the two groups. It is under these headings and the subheadings of ecological and geographic factors that the distribution of diatoms will be considered here.

Fresh and Brackish-water Diatoms

ECOLOGICAL FACTORS

TYPE OF HABITAT. Before considering the more specific geographical and ecological conditions which affect fresh-water diatom growth, it might be well to consider the more general habitats afforded fresh and brackish-water diatoms and how they are adapted for such habitats.

Water Habitats

Plankton. True plankton diatoms, such as those found in the sea (which spend all their life afloat, including their sexual reproductive stages), do not seem to occur in fresh water. The "plankton" diatoms found in fresh water are commonly benthic neritic species which spend the vegetative part of their life cycle afloat. Many diatoms found in the plankton of fresh water also occur in littoral habitats. Plankton diatoms vary a great deal in size and might roughly be divided into small forms or nannoplankton, and large forms or net plankton. The nannoplankton consist, among others, of *Stephanodiscus hantzschii, Cyclotella glomerata, C. meneghiniana, C. kutzingiana* and *C. comta.* The net plankton owe their size to colony formation or to the size of the individual. To this group belong *Rhizosolenia, Synedra, Asterionella, Melosira, Fragilaria,* etc. Although plankton diatoms are usually in

*The author wishes to acknowledge permission given by Dr. William Steere, Director of the New York Botanical Garden, for use of the article "Factors effecting the distribution of diatoms," *The Botanical Review* 14:473-525, 1948.

some way particularly adapted for this mode of life, there are some genera, e.g. *Nitzschia, Surirella,* and *Cymatopleura,* which are found in plankton or littoral condition.

Bottom Forms. The bottom diatoms are those which live on the substrata. Most of them possess raphes and are able to move about. They may live in shallow or deep water, depending on the light penetration and the amount of O_2, H_2S, CH_4, and CO_2 present. Temperature also limits their distribution. In shallow water in very cold weather the benthic flora is greatly reduced. This flora is often well developed in lakes and ponds, and in streams and rivers in places where the current is not too swift. To this flora belong many genera such as *Navicula, Suirirella, Nitzschia, Pleurosigma,* and *Campylodiscus.*

Epiphytic Forms. The epiphytic forms are those which attach themselves by a secretion of jelly to the substratum. This jelly may form a cushion; a tube in which the diatoms live; or stalk-like structures, as are found in *Cymbella* and *Gomphonema.* In other cases by the secretion of jelly the whole valve may be attached to the substratum, as in the genera *Achnanthes* and *Cocconeis.*

Diatoms may live epiphytically on a great many different types of substrata. The commonest are rocks and rooted vegetation. However, Kolbe (1932) reports that *Gomphonema olivaceum* has been found abundantly on the fungus *Sphaerotilus.* He also states that *Nitzschia* has been noted living endophytically in *Sphagnum* leaves. It is also true that certain species of *Frustulia* and *Eunotia* often live in the tops of *Sphagnum* plants.

In considering the distribution of fresh-water diatoms, the type of water mass, whether it be lake, pond, moor, river, stream, or spring, is important in determining the type of diatom flora in it.

A lake is differentiated from a pond mainly by conditions associated with its depth. In both, the diatom flora consists of benthic, epiphytic, and planktonic species. The degree of development of these various types depends on the physical conditions present. If a broad littoral zone is present, the lower part of which is occupied by rooted vegetation, then a well-developed epiphytic and benthic flora may be present. The plankton species find their best development where there are large expanses of open water. In fairly deep waters which have spring and fall overturns we sometimes find great masses of plankton diatoms which are often referred to as spring and fall blooms. Just what factors are involved in initiating a bloom seem to vary depending on the lake. In Lake Michigan (Eddy, 1927a) and Lake Erie (Chandler, 1944) turbidity of the water seems to greatly influence the amount and duration of diatom bloom. In Lake Erie (Chandler, 1944) wind, precipitation, and solar and sky radiation are also very important. According to Pearsall (1930, 1932) and the Wests (1912) nitrogen and phosphorus do not seem to act as limiting factors. Some studies on English lakes seem to emphasize the importance of some dissolved salts in relation to diatom productivity. Pearsall (1930) states that most diatoms must have a calcium carbonate hardness above 3 mg. per liter, and Lund (1950) has found that silica above 0.5 mg. per liter is necessary for some diatoms to occur in abundance. Thus it would seem that any one of several factors may limit diatom production.

As a rule the spring diatom bloom is much larger than the fall bloom, though some exceptions may occur (Petersen, 1943; Chandler, 1940, 1942; Gottschall and Jennings, 1933; Budde and Burkholder, 1929; Damann, 1945; Eddy, 1927b). Though some diatoms may exhibit both a spring and a fall pulse, usually the dominant species are different. As noted by Chandler (1940), those genera which are usually dominant in the spring bloom—*Asterionella*, *Synedra*, and *Fragilaria*—belong to the Pennales, while those which are dominant in the fall pulse—*Melosira*, *Cyclotella*, and *Stephanodiscus*—belong to the Centrales. Of course, all genera may occur at any time, but their time of dominance varies. For instance, many workers have noted that *Asterionella* usually occurs earliest in the spring, and is then succeeded by other species. Pearsall (1932) believes this succession is due to the fact that *Asterionella* has a higher nutritive requirement than the succeeding species. Akehurst (1931), however, believes that this succession is due to the fact that one group produces substances which are toxic to itself but stimulating to another group. For example, *Asterionella* would produce a substance toxic to itself but which would stimulate *Synedra*. Thus a *Synedra* pulse would follow an *Asterionella* one. Talling (1957) working with *Asterionella formosa* and *Fragilaria crotonensis* found no evidence that either species produced an extracellular substance that appreciably modified the growth of the other.

The kinds of species detected in these various habitats are dependent upon whether the water is eutrophic, oligotrophic, or dystrophic (Thienemann, 1920; Naumann, 1921). The eutrophic water, rich in dissolved nutrients, is often characterized by plankton species such as *Stephanodiscus binderanus*, *Cyclotella dubia*, and *Asterionella formosa* and by littoral forms such as various species of the genera *Cymbella*, *Epithemia*, *Gomphonema*, *Navicula,* and *Nitzschia* (Krieger, 1927). Oligotrophic water, low in dissolved nutrients, is typical of mountainous streams and glacier lakes, but may be found under any condition which produces a low level of dissolved nutrients. The plankton is usually poorly developed (Schroeder, 1939). *Cyclotella comta, C. kutzingiana,* and *Tabellaria fenestrata* may be gathered under these conditions.

A similar classification of lakes is that of Pearsall (1924) in which he divides them into rocky and silted lakes. The rocky lakes, corresponding to the oligotrophic group, are poorer in Ca, Si, CO₃, and organic water. The diatom flora is not so well developed as that of other algae. In one such lake *Surirella robusta* var. *splendida* was a constant species. Silted lakes are richer in Ca, Si, CO₃, and organic matter, and thus correspond to the eutrophic group. They have a richer diatom flora.

Sometimes it so happens that oligotrophic conditions develop in a eutrophic lake. This is particularly true after the diatom bloom of a species with fairly high nutritive requirements. Thus *Melosira granulata* is often considered eutrophic, because it occurs in eutrophic lakes. Actually it is oligotrophic because it occurs after a *Synedra* bloom (Hustedt, 1939).

Nygaard (1949) and Foged (1954) describe a method for determining the trophic level of a lake by the ratio of Centrales to Pennales and the kinds of species which are dominant. The larger the ratio the more eutrophic the lake is.

Dystrophic water is that which is high in humates and low in dissolved nutrients and oxygen. The water of bogs and swamps is usually of this type. In the beginning of the formation of the bog the water is often eutrophic, being rich in dissolved nutrients and circumneutral in reaction. As it progresses in formation the oxygen and dissolved nutrients become poorer and the humates richer. A low pH develops. A rather specialized flora can live under these conditions. Some of the species have been found to be aerophilous and live in the tops of *Sphagnum* and other moss. Under such conditions various species of the genus *Eunotia* together with certain species of *Pinnularia, Frustulia,* and *Stenopterobia* are found (Patrick, 1945; Krieger, 1929; Kolbe, 1932).

In contrast to these more or less quiescent types of water are those which are flowing. The amount of current greatly influences the kinds of diatoms which may be present. Allen (1920) points out that water current above a very modest speed is distinctly inimical to plankton development. Likewise, slime forms are not able to develop where the current is rapid. Indeed, in fast flowing streams only those forms which can attach themselves by gelatinous mass or stalks can survive. These species are often called rheophils. Thus the typical genera of such habitats are *Achnanthes, Cocconeis, Cymbella,* and *Gomphonema. Ceratoneis arcus* is also considered a typical stream species (Godward, 1937).

The amount of current has been found also to affect the shapes of diatoms. *Desmogonium* in fast flowing water is long with scarcely capitate ends, while in standing water it is short with broad, capitate ends (Hustedt, 1939).

Plankton development is usually scarce except in places where the current is reduced. Often along the edges and on the stream bed, or in little pools where the current is not very great, a benthic flora will develop.

Not only does the current affect the availability of diatom habitats, but also the amount of dissolved nutrients, temperature, oxygen, and turbidity of the water. Thus, in muddy rivers a very poor diatom flora is present, whereas in a clear river or stream excellent conditions may develop for diatom growth. A mountainous stream with high oxygen, and low temperature and mineral content will support a very different diatom flora from a stream in an open plain where the current and dissolved oxygen are often less and the temperature and dissolved mineral content higher (Krieger, 1929; Budde, 1928; Kolbe, 1932). Due also to erosion and spotty pollution a great variation may exist in many streams as to the dissolved nutrients available for growth.

Large rivers and smaller streams usually are characterized by having masses of constantly moving water which is thoroughly mixed and usually not stratified as in lakes. The rate of movement of the water greatly influences the temperature, dissolved nutrients, and gases. Rivers are usually larger and have regions of slower water movement particularly in the estuary so that plankton often develops better than in streams. Reservoirs and flood plain ponds which are natural areas for plankton development are often part of a river system. Indeed, the Volga, the Thames, the Illinois, and the San Joaquin have been shown to have well-developed plankton floras (Rice, 1938; Kofoid, 1908; Allen, 1920; Behning, 1928). The main genera are *Asterionella, Cyclotella, Diatoma, Fragilaria, Melosira, Nitzschia, Synedra,* and *Stephanodiscus.* Williams and Scott (1962) have listed the most common plankton diatoms found in rivers of the United States. *Melosira, Cyclotella, Stephanodiscus, Fragilaria, Tabellaria,* and *Synedra* are the most common genera.

Many of the species found in plankton are often the same as those found in the littoral zone and are derived from this source. Just when certain species reach their maxima seems to be more closely correlated with the temperature of the water and the dissolved nutrients and gases than with the calendar month of the year. At any given time, due to varying ecological factors, blooms may develop in some stretches of a river and not in others (Claus and Reimer, 1961). Allen (1920) found that *Bacillaria paradoxa* was the foremost plankton species during the flood season. The source of the species which make up the plankton of a river seem to vary, but in most instances it is the benthic or epiphytic communities of the river. In some cases the species seem to be derived from the head waters (Krieger, 1927; Kofoid, 1908). A special type of plankton formation, which has been called a "neuston" (Kolbe, 1932), is often found near where waste water enters a stream or river. The diatoms form a thin film over the surface of the water. Schroeder (1939) found in the Mulde River that *Nitzschia palea* was the main inhabitant of this film, but concluded that almost any slime diatom which is not too heavy might live in the neuston.

Besides the plankton flora of a river, a well-developed benthic and epiphytic flora may exist if littoral conditions are suitable. These are composed of many species representing a wide variety of genera. Along the edges of the river, in the so-called spray zone, there may be many aerial forms which are often the same species as those in similar habitats on the edges of lakes and ponds.

The typically rheophilic diatoms sometimes contain the most characteristic or the endemic species of a region. Hustedt found in his studies of the diatoms of the Dutch East Indies that of the 222 endemic species or varieties, 131 were rheophils (Hustedt, 1939).

Another type of flowing water habitat is that of springs. The pool spring is a much better diatom habitat than the spring which forms a waterfall. Especially suited to such habitats is *Odontidium hiemale* var. *mesodon* (Kolbe, 1932). The flora of hot springs, contrary to what might be expected, consists of eurythermal species of the flora of the region (Petersen, 1928, 1943; Elenkin, 1914; Kolbe, 1932; Krasske, 1929; Hustedt, 1939). In the Dutch East Indies the flora of hot springs was found to be the same as that in running water of 45° C.

Aerial Habitats. A third general habitat of fresh-water diatoms is that in which the diatoms are more or less exposed to the air. Such aerial habitats are in moss, on trunks of trees, on damp stones and leaves, and in the soil. Species which can live in such habitats must be able to endure much more rigorous environmental changes than those which live in water. They must be able to withstand flooding as well as extreme drought and sudden changes in temperature. Thus, as would be expected, the diatoms which can survive such changes represent a small and specialized group. For the most part they are small forms; very few large diatoms are found under dry conditions. Several different classifications of aerial habitats for diatoms have been proposed (Beger, 1927; Kolbe, 1932; Petersen, 1935, 1943). Perhaps the most convenient division is between those which live in moist aerial conditions, and those which are subject to truly dry conditions.

Under the group of moist aerial habitats are included wet rocks and moss; caves; snow and ice; and the spray or surf zones of lakes, rivers, and oceans. In such habitats are located typically aerophilous forms which can live in water or out of it.

On rocks or moss kept wet by seeping springs are often located *Pinnularia borealis, Melosira roeseana, Navicula fragilarioides,* and *N. confervacea;* also certain species of *Cymbella, Gomphonema, Synedra, Achnanthes,* and *Cystopleura.* In very wet moss, such as the tops of *Sphagnum,* species of the genera *Eunotia* and *Frustulia* are abundant.

Caves also furnish a suitable habitat for diatoms if light is not too limiting a factor. The very moist atmosphere permits a great variety of diatoms to flourish, including *Fragilaria construens* var. *venter, Melosira dickiei, M. roseana, Navicula kotschyi, N. perpusilla,* and *Pinnularia borealis* (Schröder, 1916; Hustedt, 1922; Kolbe, 1932).

Another interesting habitat for diatoms is the spray zone of lakes, rivers, etc. Though the species in this zone are often found in other habitats, they all belong to genera which produce a well-developed jelly sheath. Close to the water's edge are *Achnanthes, Cymbella, Gomphonema, Epithemia,* and *Denticula.* Hustedt found the genus *Gomphonema* sometimes high above the water's edge, where only spray produced by the strongest wave action could wet it. This genus seems to be better able to resist drying out than *Cymbella.* Perhaps this is due to the greater amount of jelly in the dendritic colonies than in the linear ones.

Soil and Rock Habitats. The diatoms which live in a truly dry atmosphere are those that live in the soil, those that live on only slightly damp rocks or moss, and those that live on leaves. Our knowledge of diatoms which live in the soil is still quite limited, and no doubt many new species will be found in this specialized habitat. For the most part they are small, belonging to the Pennales. It is believed that because they have a raphe and are able to move to deeper regions when the soil dries out, they are able to live in this more or less unfavorable habitat. Diatoms are less often encountered in woods soil than in field or garden soil, and are most plentiful in the top cm. *Hantzschia amphioxys, Navicula atomus, N. nitrophila, N. mutica, N. contenta* f. *biceps, Pinnularia balfouriana, P. brebissonii,* and *P. borealis* (Bristol, 1920; Petersen, 1928; Hedlund, 1913; Moore and Carter, 1926; Francé, 1912; Hayek and Hulbary, 1956) are the more common soil species.

As for diatoms that can live on dry rocks, Krasske (1929) has reported *Eunotia fallax* var. *gracillima, Melosira dickiei, Navicula contenta, N. krasskei,* and *N. sohrensis* living among *Protococcus.* The species which can live in such habitats are rather limited in number.

The extent to which diatoms will occur on dry moss seems to be limited for the most part by the drying of the moss, the amount of light, and the temperature of the substrata. Cool, damp, humus-rich moss of kaolinic rock will have more species than warm, dry, humus-poor moss on limestone rocks (Beger, 1927; Kolbe, 1932). Diatoms which can live in such habitats must be able to withstand extreme variation in moisture conditions and, thus, great variation in salt concentration. Usually the smaller varieties of species are found in dry moss. For example, *Navicula contenta* var. *parallela* and var. *elliptica* instead of *N. contenta; N. mutica* var. *cohnii* instead of *N. mutica;* smaller forms of *N. fragilarioides* and *Pinnularia borealis;*

also the smaller forms of *Melosira roeseana* rather than its long filamentous varieties, *spiralis* and *epidendron* (Krasske, 1936).

Some aerophils have been found to store a large amount of oil. Often diatoms living in such habitats build inner plates, as found most commonly in *Melosira dickiei* and *M. roeseana*. Kolbe (1932) believes this adaptation to be more closely correlated with drying out, while Hustedt (1938) associates it with increased salt concentration. The reduction in size, increase in oil storage, and the building of inner plates may well be special adaptations of these species to withstand drying out and increased salt concentrations (Kolbe, 1932; Hustedt, 1938). The diatoms occurring in such habitats are for the most part geographically widely distributed species, though a few endemics have been found.

Other Habitats.   Whether or not moist leaves furnish a separate habitat for diatoms is still uncertain. Indeed, various species have been reported from moist leaves and on trees in tropical forests (West and West, 1899; van Oye, 1927; Hustedt, 1938) or on leaves sprayed by mist from a water fall. The species were mostly stream or lake forms (Kolbe, 1932; Hustedt, 1938). The one truly atmospheric species was *Navicula contenta* var. *biceps*.

Chemical and Physical Factors.   *Salinity.*   Sodium chloride was the first salt that was recognized as important in determining diatom distribution; and water was classified as marine, brackish, or fresh. With more investigation a more refined system was needed and several were suggested. The most satisfactory system is that developed by Kolbe (1927, 1932). Various authors have tried to classify species according to this system (Budde, 1930, 1932; Petersen, 1943; Foged, 1947; and Krasske, 1932). Hustedt (1938, 1953) has criticized and made suggested modifications of the system.

Kolbe divides diatoms into four groups—"polyhalobiens," "euhalobiens," "mesohalobiens," "oligohalobiens." The polyhalobiens are species which can stand a salt concentration greater than that of the sea. To this group belongs *Navicula longirostris*. The euhalobien species develop best in water with total salt concentration of 3-4% (NaCl 1.7-2%). To this group belong the marine and brine-water species. The mesohalobien species have their optimum in a total salt concentration of .5-2% (NaCl .2-1.5%). To this group belong such brackish-water species as *Achnanthes brevipes* var. *intermedia*, *Amphora coffeaeformis*, *Nitzschia hungarica*, *Stauroneis salina* var. *latior*, *Navicula salinarum*, *N. integra*, *N. pygmaea*, and *Diponeis interrupta*. The oligohalobien species have their optimum condition in water with a very low salt concentration. This group is subdivided into three subgroups. First, those species which have their best development in water with a small amount of salt, such as *Navicula cincta*, *Anomoeoneis sphaerophora*, *Caloneis amphisbaena*, *Cyclotella meneghiniana*, *Diatoma elongatum*, and

Navicula hungarica. These are known as halophilic species. Second, those fresh-water species, such as *Diploneis elliptica, Cymbella lacustris, Gyrosigma attenuatum, Melosira arenaria,* and *Hantzschia elongata* which are not sensitive to a little salt are known as indifferent species. Third, those which live in very pure water and dislike salt, are halophobs. To this group belong most species of *Eunotia, Actinella, Stenopterobia, Tabellaria flocculosa,* and *Asterionella ralfsii* and some of the species of *Pinnularia* and *Frustulia.* These species are often referred to as sphagnophils, because they are in waters which are usually rich in humic material. It is hard to be sure whether the lack of salt or the accumulation of humic materials or other unknown factors determine their preference for this type of habitat.

Sodium chloride is certainly one of the most important salts which limits the distribution of diatom species. Indeed diatoms may be generally classified into those which are specific for certain salt conditions and those which are euryhaline or indifferent. Richter (1906) has noted that with *Nitzschia putrida* it is the sodium which causes the influence of the salt on diatom development. In other diatoms it would seem that it is the chloride which is the important atom. Petersen (1943) found in his study of the lakes and bogs of Denmark that the threshold of the effect of the chloride factor was at about 100 mg. Cl per liter. Where the chloride content was below this amount, indifferent species formed 80-95% of the flora. Above 100 mg. Cl per liter these species dropped off to 56-70% of the flora and halophilic and mesohalobic species increased correspondingly. If the chloride content was between 16-42 mg. per liter it was of no significance, since other factors were more important.

The so-called brackish-water habitats are mainly of three types: those which are formed by the mixing of fresh and salt water; inland salt lakes; and waste water of various industries. The first type formed by the mixing of fresh and salt water contains mainly euhalobien and oligohalobien species. The littoral flora, frequently very rich, is composed of many characteristic species which are often fairly restricted geographically. The inland salt lakes, if old, contain many mesohalobiens. If new, there are fewer species. The brine or waste waters contain very few species. A salt content of 10% (Krasske, 1932) was found to support large populations of *Amphora coffeaeformis, A. delicatissima, Nitzschia closterium, N. frustulum, Navicula cincta,* and *N. salinarum.*

Calcium. The amount of calcium in solution is somewhat dependent on the type of water, as for example whether oligotrophic or eutrophic conditions exist. The soluble calcium bicarbonate is often changed to the insoluble calcium carbonate in the epilimnion. As such it settles to the bottom and out of solution in oligotrophic lakes. However, in eutrophic lakes the bacterial activity changes it back to the soluble bicarbonate form, and thus a higher calcium content is maintained (Kolbe, 1932). That many diatoms definitely like calcium-rich waters is evidenced by the fact that diatom phytoplankton predominates when the $\frac{Na + K}{Ca + Mg}$ is < 1.5. However, it may be due to the effect which calcium has on the availability of other elements. When the $\frac{Na + K}{Ca + Mg}$ ratio is low, water is usually rich in nitrates, carbonates, and silicates (Pearsall, 1922). Pearsall (1924) goes even further and states that in calcium-poor waters carbohydrate-producing organisms dominate, while in calcium-rich water fat-producing species dominate.

Some species of diatoms seem definitely to prefer calcium. Most species of *Synedra* seem to like some calcium, but it seems especially important for the development of *Synedra acus* and its varieties. *Achnanthes minutissima, Gomphonema olivaceum,* and certain species of *Cymbella, Diploneis,* and *Navicula* have been-found living in close association with deposits of calcium carbonate (Wisłouch, 1924; Kolbe, 1932). The calcium-iron ratio seems to be important to some diatoms. *Tabellaria flocculosa* seems to demand a very definite calcium-iron ratio. Other species seem to dislike calcium and are referred to as "calciophobes." Many species of the genera *Eunotia, Stenopterobia,* and *Actinella* and certain species of *Pinnularia, Frustulia,* and *Fragilaria* are of this type.

The effects of calcium seem to be very closely linked to those of pH. Indeed, in many inland lakes the buffering system is that of calcium bicarbonate and carbonic acid. This is particularly true of oligotrophic and eutrophic lakes. In dystrophic lakes the pH is largely controlled by the amount of humic acid present. In the epilimnion, where the phytoplankton activity is great and the carbon dioxide is used up, the alkalinity is higher than in the hypolimnion where the carbon dioxide and carbonic acid accumulate.

Hydrogen-ion Concentration. The species which make up a flora seem to be greatly influenced by the pH of the water, and waters of different pH have very different floras. Very few species can live in a water with a pH below 3.5; though the flora may be rich quantitatively, it is poor qualitatively. Species found in such acid waters are *Tabellaria flocculosa, Eunotia trinacria, E. exigua,* and *Navicula subtilissima* (Schroeder, 1939). In a pH of 3.5 to 6 are many species of *Eunotia* and some of *Frustulia, Stenopterobia,* and *Pinnularia* (Schroeder, 1939; Hustedt, 1939; Patrick, 1945). In the circumneutral range is the greatest diversity of species (Kolbe, 1932; Patrick, 1945). The more alkaline waters, those with a pH above 8, also often show a more or less restricted flora. Patrick (1945) found in her Pocono studies that two lakes with the same pH but different calcium contents might support very different floras.

In considering the effect of pH, one should think not only of its direct effect upon the organisms, but, what is even more important is its indirect influence on the solubility of various substances. Very acid lakes often support much less life than circumneutral ones, and, thus, the supply of oxygen and carbon dioxide may be much more limited.

Iron. Iron is much more soluble in acid than in circumneutral waters. Uspenski (1927) believed it to be as selective a factor in diatom growth as NaCl. Typical inhabitants of iron-rich water are many species of *Eunotia*, some large forms of *Pinnularia, Stauroneis phoenicenteron, Anomoeoneis serians* var. *brachysira, Navicula subtilissima, Pinnularia subcapitata* var. *hilseana, Stenopterobia intermedia, Surirella linearis, Gomphonema acuminatum, Pinnularia microstauron* (Schroeder, 1939; Kolbe, 1932).

Silicon. There seems to be a correlation between the calcium and silica content of the water. The more alkaline waters often have a high silica content, and the dead shells of diatoms in such waters are often found to be badly corroded (Kolbe, 1932). It has been pointed out that there is a decrease in dissolved silica in the water following a diatom bloom (Meloche *et al.,* 1938).

Nitrogen. In oligotrophic water the nitrogen is often so low that it is hard to detect by analytical methods, while in eutrophic waters it may be relatively high. Some diatoms, such as *Diatoma vulgare, Gomphonema parvulum, Navicula viridula, Nitzschia palea,* and *Surirella ovata* seem to grow best when the nitrate concentration is relatively high. Other diatoms, such as *Melosira granulata,* though growing in an eutrophic lake, actually prefer a low nitrate-phosphate ratio, for they occur after the nutrients have been exhausted by other diatoms (Hustedt, 1939). Many diatoms also seem to be able to use ammonia as a source of nitrogen.

Sulphur. Sulphur is found most commonly as hydrogen sulfide or in the sulphate form. The hydrogen sulfide, which is largely due to bacterial activity, is often in relatively high concentration in the ground slime or in stagnant water. *Cyclotella meneghiniana, Caloneis amphisbaena,* and many species of *Nitzschia, Campylodiscus,* and *Surirella* are often found under such conditions (Kolbe, 1932). In habitats where the hydrogen sulfide was 3.9 p.p.m., *Achnanthes affinis, Cymbella ventricosa, Hantzschia amphioxys,* and *Nitzschia palea* were abundant. In hydrogen sulfide concentrations of 1.5-3.7 p.p.m., *Cyclotella meneghiniana, Neidium bisulcatum, Navicula minima, Nitzschia ignorata, N. tryblionella* var. *debilis,* and *Surirella ovata* var. *salina* occurred (Schroeder, 1939).

In the Mulde River sulphate seemed to have an effect on the diatom flora similar to that of chloride. In a concentration up to 200 p.p.m. no effect on the diatom flora was noted. In waste water with a sulphate concentration of 6,000 p.p.m. and a chlorine content of 45 p.p.m., mesohalobe and halophil species such as *Caloneis amphisbaena, Navicula halophila, N. peregrina, N. radiosa,* and *Nitzschia frustulum* var. *subsalina* were found.

Copper. Copper, which is usually poisonous to many algae, may be tolerated by diatoms in small amounts. In concentration of 1.5 mg. per liter *Fragilaria virescens, Synedra ulna, Achnanthes affinis, Neidium bisulcatum, Navicula viridula, Cymbella naviculiformis, Cymbella ventricosa, Gomphonema parvulum,* and *Nitzschia palea* were found living. In a concentration of 2.1 mg. of copper per liter only *Achnanthes affinis, Cymbella ventricosa,* and *Nitzschia palea* were able to live (Schroeder, 1939). Corbella *et al.* (1958) found *Achnanthes nodosa* was very tolerant to copper and ammonia.

Chromium. Blum (1957) has reported *Nitzschia palea, Nitzschia linearis, Navicula atomus,* and *Navicula cuspidata* resistant to chromium and other pollutants.

Titanium. Griel and Robinson (1952) found that diatoms can concentrate titanium. It is deposited in the cell wall.

Humates. The role of humates in diatom nutrition, though recognized, is not clearly understood. It is true that dystrophic waters, which have a high humic acid content, support a very characteristic diatom flora. However, the fact that such waters are usually low in certain inorganic salts commonly found in other waters and have a low pH may be the determining factors (Kolbe, 1932). Petersen (1943) found that certain lakes and bogs which had similar chlorine, hardness, and pH range supported very different diatom floras. The most obvious difference was in the amounts of humic substances present. The importance of these substances may lie in their role as chelating agents.

Light. Besides the above chemical factors, there are certain physical factors which seem to be very important in determining diatom growth. Just as in higher plants, there are some species which prefer abundant light while others live in regions of low light intensity. Those diatoms which prefer abundant light are usually found in the plankton or in the shallow littoral zones (Schroeder, 1939). Sunshine seems to favor the development of *Cyclotella meneghiniana, Fragilaria capucina,* and *Navicula cryptocephala* (Rice, 1938). Diatoms which seem to tolerate low light conditions are those which live in caves, such as *Melosira roeseana,* and those which can live in ground slime in deep water, such as species of *Campylodiscus* and *Surirella,* and *Synedra acus* (Koorders, 1901). The fact that in winter, diatoms seem to grow in shallower water than in summer may be due to the smaller amount of light penetration (Godward, 1937).

Temperature. The effect of temperature on diatom growth seems to be both direct and indirect. The direct effect is seen in the fact that certain diatoms are stenotherms and are found only in cold or warm water. Such species are characteristic of the Arctic or Tropic regions. Other species seem to be eu-eurytherms and are tolerant of a wide temperature range. Hustedt (1956) gives groupings for diatoms according to their temperature tolerances. Also diatoms vary as to the season of the year when they are most abundant, thus perhaps reflecting the effect of change of temperature. The indirect effects of temperature are equally, if not more important, for the temperature of the water affects the solubility of the salts and also the bacterial activity. It is also temperature which determines the spring and fall overturn in a lake and, thus, the supply of nutrients. The melting of snow and ice, which also affects the nutrient supply of water is determined by temperature. It has been stated that temperature is the most important factor affecting diatom growth, even more than nutrients, and that phytoplankton abundance varies directly with it (Kofoid, 1908; Roach, 1932; Coffing, 1937; Hustedt, 1939; Allen, 1920). However, Pearsall (1922) and Daily (1938) do not seem to think that temperature is of such primary importance.

The optimum temperature for diatom development is dependent on the type of flora present (Budde, 1928; Hustedt, 1939). It is the similarity of temperatures of the water of the two regions rather than the latitude or altitude which is often the important factor in determining the type of flora present. Some species such as *Anomoeoneis serians* var. *brachysira*, *Pinnularia streptoraphe*, and *Cymbella gracilis* prefer cold water. Others such as *Cyclotella meneghiniana*, *Melosira granulata*, and *Melosira varians* have their maximum development in warm water (Schroeder, 1939; Rice, 1938; Budde, 1928; Kolbe, 1932). Bursa (1961) found that the pennate diatoms were dominant in the brackish-water plankton in the Arctic during low light and temperature conditions, and that the plankton was characterized by centric diatoms during the warmer temperature and longer and larger light intensities of the summer. Whitford and Schumacher (1963) found in their study of warm temperate rivers that diatoms grew best at lower temperatures and medium to good light intensity.

Turbulence. The turbulence produced by wind action may affect in several ways the abundance of plankton diatoms. It may produce turbidity and thus prevent sufficient light penetration to make diatom growth possible. It may, if the water carries a considerable suspended solid load, produce a scouring effect which will eliminate diatom growth. Lund (1955) believed that turbulence is largely responsible for the change in density of populations of *Melosira italica* var. *subarctica* in two lakes he studied.

In general, fresh-water diatom distribution seems to be more closely correlated with the chemistry of the water, rate of flow, and temperature than with altitude. However, Hustedt found in the Dutch East Indies that at 1,500 meters altitude standing water had a tropical flora, while at 2,000 meters the flora was more temperate in relationship, though a few tropical forms were still plentiful. In flowing water the tropical character remained to 1,900-2,000 meters but above 2,500 meters it had practically disappeared. This was true of thermal as well as of water of ambient temperatures. Altitude has been reported to affect diatom structure in that at higher altitudes the striation of diatoms becomes finer (Héribaud, 1894; Schumann, 1867).

GEOGRAPHICAL FACTORS

It is very difficult, if not impossible, to separate geographical from ecological barriers, for the two overlap and it is hard to tell whether one or both are affecting distribution. Certainly the geographical barriers do not seem to be so confining as in higher plants, for we do not have so much endemism.

As Kolbe states, so little is known about the diatoms in certain regions of the world that it is difficult to draw any general conclusions concerning the geographical distribution of diatoms. Also, in many cases, identification of diatoms has been made by people unfamiliar with the literature. Thus new species have been misidentified or overlooked (Kolbe, 1932). These facts would tend perhaps to make diatoms appear to have less endemism than they really do.

Though the statement is sometimes made that diatom species are cosmopolitan in their geographical distribution, it is not supported by the work of diatomists. Cleve (1894, 1895) states, "Many diatoms are cosmopolitan, occurring in all parts of the world, but there are on the other hand many species, genera and more inclusive taxa which occur in only certain seas and climates." Boyer found that the diatoms of eastern and western North America are quite distinct and that the Mississippi Valley region is more or less intermediate.

SOUTH AMERICA. In South America the degree of endemism seems to vary according to the region investigated; in South Chile 10-11% were endemic (Krasske, 1939), in the Rio de La Plata 20% were endemic (Frenguelli, 1941). In Lake Titicaca, of the 118 diatoms which were found, 38 were determined as endemic and 4 were new (Frenguelli, 1939). Frenguelli has written numerous papers on the fresh-water diatoms in South America, but much more work needs to be done before any general conclusions can be reached as to patterns of distribution.

ASIA. In Asia the amount of endemism seems to be somewhat greater. In Siberia in Hanka Lake, Primorsk Government, 43% of the diatoms were endemic, while in Baikal Lake various species listed have shown endemism to be between 33% and 60% (Skvortzow, 1929a, 1937). In North Manchuria in a stream in Khingan, 19% were new (Skvortzow, 1928a). In the river Imengol near Hailar in northeastern Mongolia, 9% were new (Skvortzow,

1928b). In Pin-Chiang-Sheng, Manchoukuo, the subaerial diatoms were found to have a large number of species in common with Europe (Skvortzow, 1938a). However, of the 59 species listed in this flora, 32% were new. In the Argun River, only 5% were new (Skvortzow, 1938b). In ponds from Tientsin, North China, 30% were new; while in ponds from Peking, 11% were new (Skvortzow, 1927, 1932). In Japan there is quite a variation in amount of endemism; in Ikeda Lake, Satsuma Province, Kiusiu Island, 14% (Skvortzow, 1937); in a lake at Suriori near Seoul, Korea, 15% (Skvortzow, 1929c); in Biwa Lake, Honshu Island, 25% (Skvortzow, 1936b); and in Kizaki Lake, Honshu Island, 31% (Skvortzow, 1936a). In Fukien Province, South China (Skvorzow, 1930a), at Kuliang in an Alpine stream, 20% were endemic (Skvortzow, 1930a), while at Amoy, 12% were new (Skvortzow, 1929b). Patrick, in her studies of Siam and the Federated Malay States, found that 22% of the species were confined to eastern Asia and the Tibet region (Patrick, 1936). Further study showed that of the species considered, only 33% are found in all continents, but that 60% are well distributed in the Northern Hemisphere. Seventy per cent of the species have been found in Eastern United States, while only 28% have been located in Western United States. These figures are no doubt exaggerated, since more work has been done in Eastern than in Western United States.

No very thorough study has yet been made concerning the distribution of diatoms in India. Of 56 species and varieties from Calcutta identified by Skvortzow, 46% were new. In Assam the diatom flora of Loktak Lake, Manipur, was found to be Malayan in character (Biswas, 1936).

At Ceylon (Skvortzow, 1930b) the diatom flora is tropical in character and very similar to that of India, Sumatra, Java, and the Malayan region. However, very little study has been made of this region.

In the Sundai Islands, 35% of the flora studied by Hustedt (1938, 1939) was endemic. Of these, about 60% characteristically live in running water, while 37% are typical of quiet water. From this Hustedt concluded that the most endemic flora is that characteristic of running water. Of the 645 species considered, 56% were cosmopolitan in distribution. No doubt further studies in tropical regions may extend the range of some of the endemic species. Hustedt (1942) found a fairly large number of endemic species in the Hawaiian Islands, particularly in the genera *Surirella* and *Denticula*.

EUROPE. Europe is perhaps the best known region in the world with respect to diatom flora. Though most of the species found in Europe are also found elsewhere, there are many alpine and northern species which so far have not been found in other geographical regions. As might be expected the flora of western Europe is most similar to that of Eastern United States.

NORTH AMERICA.   As for North America there seems to be considerable
difference between the diatom floras of Eastern and Western United States.
Boyer (1927) states that the Mississippi Valley region is intermediate as to
its flora, between that of Eastern and Western United States. Patrick (1936)
has shown that there is a greater similarity between the diatom flora of
Eastern United States and eastern Asia than between Western United States
and eastern Asia. As stated above, there is a great similarity between the
floras of eastern North America and western Europe.

To date much more thorough work has been done on the distribution
of marine diatoms than on the distribution of fresh-water and aerophil
forms. No doubt further studies will extend some distributions and reveal
other endemic species.

Marine Diatoms

ECOLOGICAL FACTORS

In considering the ecological distribution of marine diatoms, one thinks
at first of littoral species which grow attached to or closely associated with
the bottom, and of planktonic species which spend all or at least the
vegetative part of their lives afloat. The zonation of littoral diatoms has
been mainly studied by Castenholz (1963) in the United States. The
European studies have been summarized by Hendey (1964).

The truly oceanic planktonic species not only spend their vegetative
life afloat, but also reproduce in the open sea. The neritic planktonic species,
however, are afloat during their vegetative stage, but their spores fall to
the bottom and rest there during unfavorable conditions. Thus it is evident
that the ability to float is essential for the existence of planktonic species
which are so prevalent in the oceans. There are various ways in which the
structure of the diatoms has been modified for this function.

Many of them have various types of processes to produce more surface
area. Gran (1912) classifies them into the following types: the bladder
type, e.g. *Coscinodiscus,* in which the cell is large and the protoplasm
occupies a thin layer around the outside, while the center is filled with a
thin fluid of about the same specific gravity as water; the ribbon type, e.g.
Fragilaria, in which the diatom is flattened and thus has a broad surface in
one plane; and the hair type, e.g. *Rhizosolenia,* in which the cells are greatly
prolonged in one direction. Cells of this last type produce a great deal of
friction when horizontal but sink rather rapidly when perpendicular. In
the branching appendage type, e.g. *Chaetoceros,* the cell surface is enlarged
by various types of hair-shaped or lamelliform outgrowths.

Ostwald (Gran, 1912) found that species in regions where the temperature is quite variable often have summer and winter forms, the summer
forms having more surface area to aid them in keeping afloat. This is necessary because the viscosity of the water is less. For example, the two forms

of *Rhizosolenia, hebetata* and *semispina*, were originally thought to be two distinct species. *Rhizosolenia hebetata*, the Arctic form, has thick walls and attenuated ends, while *R. semispina*, the Atlantic form, has thin walls and hair-like ends.

Allen (1941) finds that the cells of diatoms which spend their life afloat have thinner walls than those of sedimentary forms, and many of the former exhibit various types of protuberances which delay sinking.

Riley (1943) has found that under unfavorable conditions of light or nutrients diatoms may keep afloat by passing into a state of senescence. When in this condition the organic content and, thus, the weight of the cell is decreased, and the ends of the cells often become curved. In this state they seem to remain viable for years.

Production of oil and gas within the cell also helps to keep it afloat (Hendey, 1937; Allen, 1941). Riley (1941) found that *Coscinodiscus* sank faster in April than in March. This was due to the fact that the diatom was using up the stored oil as photosynthesis slowed down. Steele and Yentsch (1960) found that healthy cells of *Skeletonema costatum* did not sink as fast as nutrient deficient cells.

CHEMICAL AND PHYSICAL FACTORS

Viscosity, Salinity, and Temperature. Another important factor in determining the flotation of diatoms is the viscosity of the water in which they live (Braarud, 1935; Fish, 1925). Temperature is the main factor which influences the viscosity of sea water. Ostwald has found that àt 25° C. sea water offers only one-half the resistance to the sinking of diatoms as at freezing. Perhaps one of the reasons why diatoms seem to have their best development at certain specific depths is that at that depth the viscosity is sufficient to keep them afloat (Allen, 1928a). The tendency of warm waters to exhibit better development of diatoms at lower levels than cold waters may be due in part to the difference in viscosity of warm and cold water (Riley, 1939).

The fact that diatom species are specific as to their salt requirements has long been recognized. The early division of species into fresh, brackish, and salt water forms was based on this fact. Thus, the association of certain species into a flora and the delimiting of that flora to a certain region is often, in part, due to a difference in salinity. For example, Hjort and Gran (1899) believe that the difference of diatom flora in Lemfjord (Norway) and the North Sea is largely due to a difference in salinity between Lemfjord and the North Sea. The characteristic floras of ocean currents at a given time seem to be, at least in part, due to different salinity requirements. Gran (1929) noted at Romsdalsfjord that a definite diatom succession occurs. In the latter part of March *Skeletonema costatum* and *Chaetoceros socialis* developed, but soon *C. debile* became dominant. *Chaetoceros debile* is replaced in turn by *C. constrictus* and *C. compressus*. In July *Rhizosolenia alata* became the dominant species. Such a succession of dominants is probably due to the special requirements of each species for temperature and salinity, but the abundance of the plankton is dependent on the nutrients present. Braarud (1935) also states that salinity, pH, and other factors affect the kind of species that may be abundant more than the total amount of plankton.

Temperature and salinity may also affect the extent of an ocean current and, thus, indirectly the distribution of diatoms. Nathansohn (1906) states that temperature and salinity of the water are important factors in determining the extent of the Atlantic and polar waters. The Atlantic water is saltier than the polar water. In summer when the Atlantic waters become very warm they become lighter than the polar waters and thus spread farther north, whereas in winter when the Atlantic waters become cool, the polar waters, having less salinity, are lighter and spread farther south.

Temperature, in addition to affecting the viscosity of sea water, has many other effects, both direct and indirect, on diatoms. It seems to influence both the kind and abundance of species. Brandt (1899) was the first to show the effect of temperature on the nutrient content of the water. In cold water nitrates are allowed to accumulate due to the fact that the low temperature hinders the activity of denitrifying bacteria. The abundance of diatoms in the polar seas is partially due to this effect. Conversely the low nitrate content of warm water is due to the great activity of denitrifying bacteria. Thus the surface waters are not rich enough to support an abundant flora. However, as pointed out by Riley (1939) and Allen (1941), there may be an accumulation of diatoms at lower depths where the water is cooler. Mann (1937) believes that the abundant growth of diatoms at each of the poles is in part due to the large amount of carbonic acid held there in solution which is made possible by the low temperature of the water.

Temperature seems to affect the germination of spores. Gran (1902) believes that one of the reasons for the abundance of diatoms in cold water is that the temperature favorable to their germination is lower than that necessary to stimulate bacterial activity. One reason why diatom blooms usually occur earlier in the spring in coastal waters than in the ocean is that the Arctic or northern neritic species start to develop at a lower temperature than the Atlantic oceanic forms. Again (Braarud, 1935) the occurrence of a rich diatom flora at the edge of melting ice is partially due to the fact that the melting ice contributes spores of species which can germinate at a low temperature.

Temperature is also one of the main factors which causes different species to occur at different latitudes and in the various currents. The reason that a current at a given time of year can be characterized by a specific diatom flora is that it has a given salinity, dissolved gas content, and temperature which are favorable for its development. For instance, Schreiber (1927) has found that *Biddulphia aurita* has a lower temperature optimum than *B. sinensis*. Thus, in the North Sea *B. aurita* is abundant in winter and *B. sinensis* is abundant in summer. Allen (1928b) notes that *Skeletonema costatum* prefers cool waters and is found either at northern stations or in the cool part of the year. On the other hand, *Chaetoceros curvisetum* requires a temperature of 18°-20° C. for best development (Gran, 1929). Many other examples of this sort could be given.

The plankton of the tropical Atlantic shows a greater diversity of species than that of polar regions, though the abundance of individuals is not so great. Allen (1927b) finds support for the statement that the higher the latitude the greater the amount of the plankton, though, of course, exceptions do exist and there is no definite evidence that high latitudes are more productive year by year per thousand square miles than low ones (Allen, personal communication).

Light. The effects of heat cannot be divorced from those of light; and, therefore, these two factors which affect diatom development and growth are somewhat integrated. Germination of diatom spores seems to be affected by light (Gran, 1902). Kreps and Verjbinskaya (1930), in their studies of the productivity of diatoms in the Barents Sea, noted that at the time of spring flowering of diatoms in the coastal water and in water near the Arctic ice, there was a meager diatom flora in branches of the North Cape Current of the Atlantic waters, though it was rich in nutritive materials. They believed that perhaps this was due to the fact that though light conditions were ideal for development of spores of Arctic species, they were not right for the development of spores of species carried by the Atlantic Current.

As light is necessary for photosynthesis, it follows that for best growth, diatoms must remain in the photosynthetic zone. This zone varies not only with geographic latitude and season, but also with the transparency of the surface layers and the density of the plankton (Gran, 1931). As with other plants too much or too little light may be harmful to this process. Not only the intensity but also the duration of light is important. The meagerness of diatom growth has in some cases been attributed to lack of sufficient light which may be due to turbulence of the water or lack of solar radiation. Riley (1941) found that at George's Bank in the Gulf of Maine vertical turbulence and solar radiation were the chief limiting factors on plankton growth throughout the late autumn, winter, and early spring. Gran and Braarud (1935) attributed the small diatom growth in the Bay of Fundy and along the New Brunswick coast to lack of sufficient light due to turbulence. They state that in order for a diatom to survive, it must be exposed to light at least one-fifth of the time. The idea held by some that the intensity of radiation during winter in the north temperate zone is not sufficient for abundant diatom growth is somewhat refuted by the results of research (Marshall and Orr, 1928; Riley, 1941), wherein it was noted that not only is there sufficient light for diatom growth in mid-winter, but that on some days it may be strong enough to inhibit growth.

The depth at which diatoms will grow is, in part, due to the amount of radiation which they can receive. Marshall and Orr (1928) suggest that at the deeper levels day length is an important consideration. Allen (1928b) noted that certain species of diatoms reach their best development at various specific depths. For example, at the surface, where there is the greatest amount of radiation and substances derived from the atmosphere, *Chaetoceros* sp. reached its best development. *Hemiaulus hauckii* was most abundant in the upper ten meters. *Chaetoceros compressus* was richest at 20 meters. *Chaetoceros scolopendra* and *Thalassiothrix nitzschioides* were found only below 20 meters. In southern California waters the greatest abundance of diatoms occurs between 20 and 35 meters (Dorman, 1927). Karsten (1905-07) found the best development of diatoms in the Antarctic between 20 and 80 meters while in the Indian Ocean the best development was between 80 and 100 meters. Riley also states that in the northern Atlantic the greatest diatom development was between the surface and a depth of 100 meters. In tropical areas the greatest abundance was between 100 and 400 meters. Riley (1939) found the optimum light penetration in northern water 5 meters, in the Sargasso Sea 80 meters. Though light undoubtedly is an important factor in determining the depth at which diatoms may live, it must be remembered that nutrients, viscosity of water, etc., also influence their ability to grow at various depths.

For the best development of diatoms Nathansohn (1906) reports that both light and nutrients must be correct. The beginning of spring flowering is considered by some to be conditioned by light. Marshall and Orr (1928) believe that the critical cause of the beginning of the spring maximum is the total amount of light which in turn is dependent on day length and brightness. Atkins (1928) observed at Plymouth that the spring diatom outbursts occurred before the vernal equinox, when the day length was 10 to 12 hours and about 3 hours of sunshine were present. The variation of the time of outbreak seemed to be brought about by variation in sunshine. Riley (1942) reached the conclusion that a balance between the effects of vertical turbulence and the increase of vernal radiation determines the beginning of spring diatom flowering. According to several authors (Harvey *et al.*, 1935), the duration of the autumn outburst is controlled by the amount of light available. Davidson and Huntsman (1926) state that the reason for the negligible amount of diatom growth in winter is the small amount of light and low temperature. The abundant growth of diatoms in the polar regions is due in part to the abundance of continuous light during a long portion of the year (Mann, 1937).

Nutrients. Since the time of Brandt (1899) the importance of the nutrient content of the water to diatom growth has been recognized. He was the first one to suggest that Leibig's law for land plants might apply to diatoms. The law states that any nutritional requirement if not present in sufficient amounts may act as a limiting factor of the assimilation of other nutrient substances. He and Hensen (1887) pointed out that plankton production is closely correlated with the amount of nitrates present. A deficiency of nitrogen may act as a limiting factor. Cooper (1937) states that the most important source of nitrogen for diatom growth is the nitrate form. Gran (1930), Schreiber (1927), and others have suggested that one of the important factors which makes possible the spring bloom of diatoms is the abundance of nitrates in the water. During winter when the temperature of the water is too low for much bacterial activity, nitrates are allowed to accumulate.

Phosphorus also seems to be a very important element for diatom growth (Gran, 1902). Hentschel (1928) found on the west coast of Africa that the regions of diatom and phosphorus abundance are very similar. Likewise, Gunther (1936) found on the western coast of South America that in waters rich in phosphorus the diatoms are particularly well developed. Phosphorus may also be a limiting factor in diatom growth. Marshall and Orr (1928) noted that when the PO_4 was used up the diatom maximum disappeared. Phosphorus, as nitrogen, may be responsible for diatom succession (Gran and Braarud, 1935). Lillick (1937b), from her study of diatoms in the Woods Hole region, concluded that NO_3 is more critical for phytoplankton production than PO_4. One of the causes for a succession of different species in a flora seems to be the various requirements for these mineral substances. Gran and Braarud (1935) found in the Gulf of Maine that when the water was rich in nutrients a *Thalassiosira* plankton was dominant. As the NO_3 and PO_4 were used up, species, including *Rhizosolenia alata*, which can live on less nutrients came in. Thus, depending on the nutrient supply, the species of a flora may vary.

The importance of other mineral elements in diatom growth has also been recorded. Braarud (1935) states that the calcium content, as well as the pH and salinity, affect the kind of species present rather than the abundance. Hendey (1937) believes that one of the reasons for the thin walls of diatoms in tropical waters is the low silica content of the water.

From the above studies it is clear that the kind and abundance of nutrient salts are very important to diatom growth in the sea. Nutrients in the sea are received by drainage from land or are brought to the surface from deep water. Thus, the regions of most abundant diatom growth are in the coastal waters where drainage from land occurs or where upwelling is taking place (Dorman, 1927; Gran, 1929; Hentschel, 1928; Gunther, 1936). It is also true that rich diatom production occurs just in front of melting ice. Formerly it was supposed that it was some component or components of the melting ice water that stimulated growth. Braarud (1935) states that the reason why phytoplankton is often abundant at the edge of melting ice is that the turbulence in the water caused by the melting ice brings up nutrients from the lower layer. The melting ice contributes spores, but is not rich in nutrients.

The supply of nutrients is so closely correlated with diatom abundance that the periodicity of diatom blooms or richness can be forecast from the type of nutrient supply. Gran concludes that in northern Europe the plankton development may be any one of three types. When the nutrients are continually augmented by a supply from land or vertical currents, a diatom flora may continue throughout the year, unless light is a limiting factor in winter. If the nutrient supply is intermittent, the diatom maximum and minimum will alternate. In some cases there is little or no supply of nutrients derived from land, and vertical circulation is possible only early in the spring. Such conditions produce only one diatom "bloom," and that early in the spring.

Miscellaneous factors.   One other factor of importance which may limit diatom abundance is the feeding of plankton animals (Gran, 1902; Harvey *et al.,* 1935). As diatoms increase by geometric progression, intensive feeding when the diatoms are just beginning to increase may greatly limit the bloom.

Other factors affecting successful growth of diatoms include excessive turbulence. Such a factor may hinder the ability of diatoms to float or may cause the water to become so muddy that insufficient light is available for photosynthesis. Still other factors, singly or in combination, such as exhaustion of nutrients, intolerable accumulation of wastes, epidemics of disease, or attacks of predatory organisms may also limit diatom growth (Allen, 1927a).

GEOGRAPHICAL FACTORS

NORTHERN EUROPE.   The first seas to be studied intensively with respect to geographical distribution of diatoms were those around northern Europe. Workers were then led to a consideration of the North Atlantic and the Arctic Sea. Cleve (1873) found that many forms which occurred frequently in the Arctic Sea were not in the Tropics and that some of the species which are nearly always in the middle and southern Atlantic were absent. Cleve, in his studies of the diatoms of Franz Josef Land, found that 55% were in Spitsbergen and only 26% in Lapland. No species of the genera

Gyrosigma, Pleurosigma, Cocconeis, Epithemia, Cymatopleura, Surirella, and *Campylodiscus*, which are so common on the continent of Europe, were on Franz Josef Land. The diatoms of Franz Josef Land (Grunow, 1884) were in part more similar to the fossil diatoms in the polar state of Simbirsk and in the "cementstein" and "moleren" of Jutland than to those of the Arctic Sea.

The current pattern is often elucidated by the diatom flora. Cleve found that the diatoms on the underside of the ice blocks on the west coast of Novaya Zemlya were the same as those described by Cleve from northern Siberia, but some of the more characteristic forms of Siberia were missing (1873, 1884). A study of diatoms gathered on the mud on an ice floe 48 miles south of Bell Isle (Cleve, 1898) showed that the mud probably was derived from the Kara Sea, though some of the marine species were the same as those on drifting ice at Cape Wankarema.

A similarity seems to exist between the floras of Cape Wankarema and the east side of Greenland (Cleve, 1892; Gran, 1900). The latter is characteristic of floating ice. Therefore, there must exist a communication between the Sea of Siberia and the sea off the coast of Greenland. Likewise in the study of dust from drift ice north of Jan Mayen Land, Cleve (1900a) found that the marine diatoms were the same as those at Cape Wankarema. The fresh-water forms were of more local origin, probably blown in by wind from land.

Similar conclusions were reached by Gran (1900) from his studies of collections at Cape Wankarema, east coast of Greenland, Cape Eglinton, and some of the collections of Hansen from the Arctic Ocean. He also noted the difference between the diatoms of these collections and those of collections from Novaya Zemlya, Karajak Fjord, and the Barents Sea. These findings seemed to indicate that there is a west to east polar current across the Arctic Ocean which extends down the east coast of Greenland.

The influence of the polar sea is also seen in the plankton of Baffin Bay and Davis Strait, the latter of which is derived in part from the North Atlantic (Cleve, 1896). Cleve found in this plankton an abundance of *Thalassiosira nordenskioldii* which characterizes the polar sea. He also found in the Laborador Current many species which had been noted on ice at Cape Wankarema, on ice flakes between Novaya Zemlya and Franz Josef Land, and on ice flakes that drift along the east coast of Greenland. The Atlantic influence was apparent by the presence of *Chaetoceros atlanticus* and *Thalassiothrix longissima* which were abundant in the North Atlantic. Cleve believed that these findings indicated that the ice flakes drifted from the Bering Straits to the north of Greenland where they divided, part going to the east coast of Greenland and part to the Labrador Current. Gran's (1897) findings seem to support this theory.

As a result of his various studies Cleve came to the conclusion that each ocean current is characterized by a specific diatom flora. Thus the diatoms in a current would indicate the source of the water in that current. In 1899 he published the following list of the various plankton types of the North Atlantic Ocean:

The desmo-plankton is characteristic of the warmest part of the Atlantic where the temperature of the water is 20°-28° C. Many of the species in this plankton are found in the Indian Ocean. Some of the characteristic ones are *Chaetoceros coarctatus, C. tetrastichon,* and *Climacodium biconcavum.*

The styli-plankton surrounds the desmo-plankton, in a temperature varying from 10°-20° C. and a salinity of 35 p.p.t. It extends from the Caribbean Sea to Bermuda. The current bearing this plankton broadens out at about 40° N. Lat., and curves toward Europe and Africa: a part of it swings south to the Canary Islands and Cape Verde; a second part goes north, approaching in summer the Faeroes Channel and in autumn Spitsbergen. The second part sends off two branches, one through the English Channel into the German Ocean (didymus-plankton), the other around Scotland into the North Sea (tripos-plankton). The temperature favorable to the development of didymus-plankton is 8°-17° C. and the salinity 32-33 p.p.t. The tripos-plankton prefers a temperature of 5°-14° C. and a salinity of 34 p.p.t. The styli-plankton is composed of a large variety of species, some being brought in from the north and some from the south. Some species are found only in certain regions.

The chaeto-plankton is confined to the northern and western Atlantic only in the spring. From March to June it may be traced from latitude 40° N., longitude 70° W., to the Newfoundland Banks and to the south of Iceland across to the Faeroes Channel and into the North Sea where it replaces the tripos-plankton. It disappears from the North Sea in summer, being replaced by the styli-plankton. In July and August the chaeto-plankton is found around Spitsbergen. When the current bearing the chaeto-plankton touches a coast, that of Iceland, for example, it sweeps away neritic plankton and spreads it along the coasts of Scotland and Scandinavia where it enters the fjords. Thus many species of northern origin may remain imprisoned during the summer in the fjords, especially in the deeper water. The chaeto-plankton is found in a temperature of 5°-9° C. and in a salinity of 35 p.p.t. Some of the important diatoms which characterize this plankton are *Chaetoceros decipiens, C. constrictus, C. borealis, C. criophilus.*

The tricho-plankton is confined in summer to the western and arctic Atlantic, in a temperature of 6°-12° C. and a salinity of 34 p.p.t. In winter it may spread to Scandinavia. Some of the species characteristic of this plankton were gathered from the Bering Sea on the Vega Expedition (Cleve,

1884). Cleve questioned whether these species spread from the North Pacific to the North Atlantic or vice versa. In the winter of 1897-1898 some of the characteristic species of this plankton were found south of the Azores. Cleve believed that they were picked up from the Labrador Current by the Gulf Stream and thus conveyed southward. Some of the more characteristic species of this plankton are *Chaetoceros atlanticus, Coscinodiscus oculus-iridis, Rhizosolenia semispina, Thalassiosira gravida, Thalassiothrix longissima,* and *Rhizosolenia obtusa.*

The northern neritic plankton is found in winter along the coast of Iceland, in the Skagerack, and in the fjords of Norway and Sweden. In summer it is slowly replaced by the tricho-plankton. The northern neritic plankton invades the coasts of Scotland and Scandinavia twice a year, in the spring with the chaeto-plankton and in the autumn with the tricho-plankton. The temperature at which this plankton grows is 4°-7° C. and the salinity 32-33 p.p.t. The characteristic species are *Asterionella spathulifera, Biddulphia aurita, Chaetoceros debilis, C. diadema, C. scolopendra, C. teres, Coscinodiscus polychordus, Leptocylindrus danicus, Skeletonema costata, Thalassiosira gelatinosa, Thalassiothrix frauenfeldii.*

The sira-plankton has been found on the coast of Greenland, in Baffin Bay, and in the Arctic Ocean. It is the plankton of water with melting ice drift. As it touches the tricho-plankton it becomes mixed with it, so it is sometimes hard to tell the two apart. The water of the sira-plankton has a lower temperature and less salinity than that of the tricho-plankton. The characteristic species are *Thalassiosira nordenskioldii, Fragilaria oceanica, Lauderia fragilis, Chaetoceros furcellatus,* and *C. socialis.*

The arctic neritic plankton is composed of a mixture of sira-plankton and neritic forms found along the coast of Greenland. Some of the more characteristic species are *Amphiprora hyperborea, Achnanthes taeniata, Chaetoceros septentrionalis, Coscinodiscus bioculatus, C. hyalinus, Eucampia groenlandica, Fragilaria cylindrus, Navicula septentrionalis, Nitzschia frigida,* and *Pleurosigma stuxbergii.*

These studies led Cleve to believe that in summer the southern currents with their characteristic plankton extend farther north, while in winter the northern currents extend farther south. These and subsequent investigations of the North Atlantic and seas about northern Europe caused him (Cleve, 1900b) to be of the opinion that the shifting of plankton in a given region is due to a shifting of the various currents to which the respective plankton floras belong.

Though this theory was accepted by many, Hjort and Gran (1899) believe that the idea supported by Cleve, Aurivillius, Petersen, Ekman, and others to the effect that the origin of a current can be determined by the type of plankton in it is not correct. They point out that diatoms are very sensitive to changes in hydrographic conditions, such as temperature, salinity, etc., and that an ocean current changes in these respects according to the season of the year and the direction of its flow. Therefore, it would be impossible for the same diatom to dominate the plankton over a long distance. It is more probable that certain specific diatoms dominate the plankton of a given current at certain places and times of year. At any one time the various currents could be recognized by the plankton they support, for different currents would not have the same hydrographic conditions at the same time, and thus they would support different flora. Furthermore, the change of dominant species at a given locality is due to a change in the hydrographic conditions which make the environment more favorable for the development of species which hitherto, under less favorable conditions, have existed as resting spores. Hjort and Gran, thus, contradict the theory of Cleve that such changes are due to shifts in currents. They believe that species of diatoms can be used to tell the origin or direction of a current only when hydrographic conditions remain constant within relatively short distances, and that the abundance of a certain species indicates similarity of ecological conditions rather than a common origin of the water which contains them.

Gran (1902) recognizes various plankton types such as Cleve did, but would classify them according to the type of condition in which they are found. He recognizes an arctic plankton, a boreal plankton, and a temperate plankton and subdivides each into oceanic and neritic forms. Cleve (1905) states that his styli-plankton corresponds to Gran's temperate Atlantic oceanic plankton, his didymus-plankton to Gran's temperate Atlantic plankton, his tricho-plankton to Gran's boreal oceanic plankton, and his sira-plankton to Gran's boreal neritic plankton.

Gran (1902) further points out that currents are characterized by certain forms occurring in great abundance at specific times of the year. It is these blooms at definite times that characterize a current. At a given time the limits of a stream in a certain region can be determined by the dominance of characteristic species. In a region where there is a mixture of water currents one can tell something as to their origin by determining their plankton, but one cannot state that just because an arctic diatom is present in a stream, there has been a mixture of arctic water.

Cleve (1903) criticises Gran's theory that a diatom may persist in a given locality during unfavorable conditions by the formation of resting spores which drop to the bottom and become embedded in the mud. His chief objections are three in number. First, no one as yet has germinated diatoms from bottom mud. Second, spores might drop to the bottom in a sheltered bay, but this would not be possible in rough water. Third, it is true that spores which have been found have been mostly of neritic species, but it is equally true there are many neritic species whose spores have never been found.

He (Cleve, 1903) points out that Gran admits that certain species drift with currents. As an example he states that in February the usual littoral species *Paralia sulcata* was scattered over the whole of the North Sea. The very compact *Aulacodiscus argus* was found midway between Portugal and the Azores, seven degrees from the coast. The neritic forms *Stephanopyxis turris* and *Eucampia zodiacus* were midway between the Azores, the European coastal bank, and Newfoundland.

In 1903 Cleve again stated that each current carries its own indigenous flora. There are in each current some species which are able to adapt themselves to changing conditions. Thus, when two currents meet and their waters become mixed, such species will spread. For example, *Coscinodiscus oculus-iridis* which belongs to the Arctic Current in the western Atlantic will establish itself in the eastern Atlantic west of Norway when in winter and early spring the current expands eastward and mixes with the water of the temperate Atlantic.

The opinion held today by many diatom students is that diatom floras are characteristic of various currents because of differences in hydrographic conditions. At a given time probably no two currents would have the same hydrographic conditions and, therefore, their diatom floras would be different. Thus, at any one time the currents may be recognized by their floras. The theories that various currents invade a given region at various times of the year and, thus, produce a succession of floras and that the origins of the water of a current can be determined by the species of diatoms present need further verification. Nathansohn (1906) has, however, pointed out that the extent of the northern and southern currents depends on the season of the year. In winter the northern water, being less saline, tends to extend farther south than in summer, for in summer the southern water, though saltier, because of rise in temperature, becomes lighter than the northern water, and thus the southern currents at that season extend farther north than in winter.

NORTHWESTERN ATLANTIC. In the western Atlantic the main studies of diatoms have been made in the Gulf of Maine and its vicinity (Bigelow, 1926; Gran and Braarud, 1935; Lillick, 1937a; Sears, 1941), and the Chaleur Bay (Brunel, 1962). The various types of plankton which may be found in this region during a year are arctic neritic, boreal oceanic, boreal neritic, temperate oceanic, and temperate neritic.

The spring bloom starts from March to late April, depending on the locality. The type of species which dominates seems to vary somewhat over a period of years. Bigelow (1926) found in March that in open waters *Coscinodiscus asteromphalus* was dominant, with the oceanic species *Chaeto-*

ceros decipiens, C. atlanticum, and *C. criophilum* universally distributed in the Gulf, while in the coastal waters, species of the genera *Thalassiosira* and *Chaetoceros* were the most characteristic members of the diatom flora. Likewise, in 1935 (Gran and Braarud, 1935) the more common neritic species were found to belong to these two last named genera: *Thalassiosira nordenskioldii, Chaetoceros debilis, C. compressus,* and *C. diadema.* In addition, *Podosira glacialis* was also common. In 1941 Sears found at George's Bank that the dominant species were *Chaetoceros debilis, C. decipiens,* and *Thalassiosira nordenskioldii.*

The summer flora is divided into three parts: early, middle, and late. The early flora has as its dominant members *Leptocylindrus minimus* and a small form of *Thalassiosira* at George's Bank, *Chaetoceros debilis* in Passamaquoddy Bay, and *Chaetoceros* sp., *Corethron hystrix, Guinardia flaccida, Leptocylindrus danicus,* and *Nitzschia seriata* at Woods Hole.

In mid-summer there was a flowering of *Guinardia, Thalassiothrix,* and *Rhizosolenia* on George's Bank (Sears, 1941). Elsewhere in the Gulf of Maine and in the Bay of Fundy *Asterionella japonica, Chaetoceros constrictus,* and *Skeletonema costatum* were the main species.

In the late summer in the Woods Hole region (Lillick, 1937b) a temperate flora consisting mainly of *Rhizosolenia calcar-avis, R. alata, R. setigera,* and *Thalassionema nitzschioides* was found. At Martha's Vineyard *Rhizosolenia* was the main genus. The late summer flora in Passamaquoddy Bay consisted of *Chaetoceros diadema, C. compressus, C. constrictus,* and *C. socialis.*

In October in the Woods Hole region the main species were a mixture of temperate and boreal forms: *Rhizosolenia alata, Skeletonema costatum, Leptocylindrus danicus, Chaetoceros decipiens,* and *Rhizosolenia setigera.* The winter flora of this region consisted mainly of boreal species: *Rhizosolenia hebata* var. *semispina, Thalassiosira nordenskioldii, Rhizosolenia fragillissima, Nitzschia seriata, Thalassiosira decipiens,* and *Thalassionema nitzschioides* (Lillick, 1937b).

SOUTHWESTERN ATLANTIC. In the southwest Atlantic and the Bellingshausen Sea, Hart (1935) found that there are four main types of water which can be distinguished by the diatom flora they support. The eastern Weddell Sea is dominated by *Chaetoceros criophilum, Rhizosolenia styliformis,* and *Corethron valdiviae.* Also present in considerable numbers are *Nitzschia seriata* and *Thalassiosira antarctica.* This flora is moderately rich in species and very rich in quantity. The western Weddell Sea is dominated by *Chaetoceros socialis, Thalassiosira antarctica,* and *Chaetoceros neglectus. Fragilaria antarctica* and *Nitzschia seriata* are also very common. This flora is very rich in species with minute forms dominant.

The Bellingshausen Sea water is characterized by an abundance of

Corethron valdiviae, Thalassiothrix antarctica, Nitzschia seriata, Fragilaria antarctica, Chaetoceros neglectus, and *Rhizosolenia alata* f. *gracillima.* The water of Bransfield Strait, which is a branch of the Bellingshausen Sea, is dominated by *Corethron valdiviae.*

SOUTHERN SEAS. Hendey (1937), in his study of diatoms of the Southern Seas, recognized three floras: a warm water flora, a cold water flora, and an antarctic convergence flora which is abundant in species and genera and is formed by the association of cold water and warm water. Owing to the cold Antarctic Drift which sweeps across the South Atlantic from Cape Horn past South Africa to the south Indian Ocean in almost circumpolar fashion, very few species from warm water ever reach the far south and become established. Although cold water species sometimes associate with warm water floras, very seldom, if ever, does a warm water species become established in a flora which is subject to polar or subpolar conditions.

It is more important to consider floras in relation to ocean currents which support them than in relation to actual degrees of latitude through which they spread. For example, the warm Brazil Current running southward along the eastern seaboard of South America enables a large warm-water flora to be supported to 50° S. lat. On the other hand, in the eastern Atlantic and eastern Pacific Oceans cold upwellings of the waters of the Benguela and Peruvian Currents enable these seas to support floras with distinctly colder facies. The disposition of land masses in the Southern Hemisphere and the currents which operate around them have marked effect on the geographical range of various species. Also the layering and zoning of surface water exerts a considerable effect on certain species.

In general three types of plankton, as defined by Lebour (1930), are recognized: holo-plankton, composed of true plankton forms; tychopelagic forms, bottom species which form chains that may break off and float but never reproduce in the plankton; mero-plankton forms, dependent on the coast but sometimes found under oceanic conditions. However, all true oceanic species are holoplanktonic. The neritic flora may consist of holoplanktonic, meroplanktonic, and tychopelagic species.

In warm water floras the oceanic or holoplanktonic flora is not well developed. The solenoid forms are poorly represented and the discoid forms predominate. The genera *Chaetoceros* and *Bacteriastrum* are scarce, while the genera *Hemidiscus* and *Asterolampra* are very common. Several neritic species, such as *Fragilaria striatula, Melosira sulcata,* and *Planktoniella sol,* have been observed in the oceanic flora. The holoplanktonic species of the neritic flora are sometimes very characteristic of a given geographical area such as the east coast of Africa which supports a flora that is largely endemic. The meroplanktonic species seem to be common to all coasts enjoying a temperate climate.

The oceanic holoplanktonic flora of cold water is characterized mainly by such genera as *Corethron, Chaetoceros, Fragilariopsis,* and *Nitzschia.* The normal habit of the discoid forms is solitary rather than colonial. In the oceanic plankton, besides the holoplanktonic forms, we also find parasitic and adventitious species. The parasitic diatom flora is that which inhabits the skin of whales and consists of true constituents, *e.g. Licmophora lyngbyei,* species of *Cocconeis* and *Climacosphenia,* and fortuitous ones, such as some neritic species. Hart (1935) believes that after more study the diatoms in the skin film of whales may be used to indicate their movements, but now our knowledge of them simply indicates that some whales spend at least one month in the Antarctic.

The adventitious forms of the oceanic flora are those obtained from melting ice. The predominant species are truly neritic diatoms, and there is no evidence of any fresh-water species from the mainland. The principal species are *Fragilaria curta* and *F. linearis.* Small numbers of *Navicula corymbosa* and *Amphiprora oestrupii* which were mentioned by Grunow as being in the Arctic are also present.

The neritic holoplanktonic forms of cold water are mostly solenoid species. Some discoids, *e.g. Coscinodiscus bouvet* which is a characteristic Antarctic species, are found. There are also present some species of *Coscinodiscus* which are well known in northern waters. The genera *Nitzschia* and *Chaetoceros* are abundant, but by far the most common genus is *Corethron.*

ANTARCTIC. Hoshiai and Kato (1961) found in the sea water in Antarctica ten types of diatom communities: (1) *Corethron-Chaetoceros* sp. 2, (2) *Chaetoceros* sp. 2-*Corethron,* (3) *Corethron-Rhizosolenia* sp. 2, (4) *Corethron-Fragilaria,* (5) *Chaetoceros* sp. 2-*Fragilaria-Corethron,* (6) *Chaetoceros* sp. 2-*Fragilaria,* (7) *Fragilaria-Chaetoceros* sp. 2, (8) *Fragilaria-Corethron,* (9) *Fragilaria-Nitzschia* sp. 1, (10) *Nitzschia* sp. 1-*Fragilaria.*

Mann (1937), in his studies of diatoms from the Antarctic, found that the species were large, elegant forms of which no small proportion seems to be of subtropical rather than of temperate or frigid origin. Indeed, many of the species were known previously only from the tropical or subtropical regions or as fossils from subtropical conditions. Many of them are known from Miocene deposits in various parts of the earth. He also noted the similarity of the Antarctic flora to that of the ornate floras of the Philippines and the East Indies.

ARCTIC. In contrast to that of the Antarctic, the Arctic flora consists of species which are simple in construction as to both shape and elaborateness or ornamentation, and they are very different from the tropical or subtropical species. Perhaps the reason for this is that the Arctic Ocean is practically cut off from tropical currents, while the Antarctic is easily accessible to the waters of warm currents, since the continents in the Southern Hemisphere become much narrower toward the Antarctic.

NORTHEASTERN PACIFIC. In the northeastern part of the Pacific, Scotch Cape, Alaska, Cupp (1937) found that the diatom flora consisted of pelagic species of arctic and temperate oceanic and neritic species. However, the temperate neritic species which are characteristic of more northerly temperate regions predominated. *Biddulphia aurita* reaches its maximum in April. It is followed by *Thalassiosira nordenskioldii* and *Chaetoceros socialis* in April and May with *Chaetoceros debilis* becoming dominant in June or July. *Leptocylindrus danicus* reaches its greatest maximum in July. *Asterionella japonica*, a southerly temperate neritic species, predominates in the warmest months, September and October. The seasonal succession at Scotch Cape most closely resembles that in the Passamaquoddy region, New Brunswick, and the Gulf of Maine, except for the abundance of *Asterionella japonica* in September and October.

EASTERN PACIFIC. In the eastern part of the Pacific the greatest amount of study has been in the waters adjacent to California. The flora here seems to be a mixture of northern and southern forms. The common occurrence in the subsurface plankton of such boreal-arctic oceanic forms as *Rhizosolenia semispina*, *Chaetoceros criophilum*, and *Thalassiothrix longissima* is due to the upwelling of deep water which occurs in this region (Sleggs, 1927). Also strays from the north, *e.g. Asterionella kariana* and *Thalassiosira nordenskioldii*, occasionally appear in this region. *Thalassiosira* is the characteristic genus of the flora of Alaskan waters and serves to distinguish it from other floras (Allen, 1927b). Typical southern species are *Eucampia zodiacus* which is characteristic of the southern stations of this region and *Guinardia flaccida* which is sometimes encountered as a stray from the south (Allen, 1927a).

Allen (1945) noted in his study of marine diatoms in the waters off the coast of southern California that the setose genera *Chaetoceros*, for example, were dominant in the spring, and in the summer the filiform genera, *e.g. Rhizosolenia*, *Thalassionema*, and *Thalassiothrix*, were common.

The flora of the Gulf of California may be divided more or less into three parts: the southern section of the outer gulf, which is an oceanic flora; the middle section, which is a neritic flora characterized by *Coscinodiscus wailesii*; and a northern section in which *Asterionella japonica*, *Chaetoceros radians*, *C. compressus*, *C. debilis*, and *Skeletonema costatum* are common forms.

In the Gulf of Panama, Allen (1939) found some striking similarities both quantitatively and qualitatively with the diatoms of northern waters. The abundance of *Chaetoceros debilis* and the common occurrence of *Nitzschia seriata* were notable. These two species have been found to be of common occurrence in northern Pacific waters. The abundance of a planktonic flora of diatoms which is often associated with waters of northern latitudes was noted here. Though this region differs in many ecological factors from northern seas, it is similar in one major way, that is, in the inundation of the coast line. The coast line of the Gulf of Panama is much more inundated than that of most tropical seas. Thus more nutrients are provided by run-off. Other interesting coastal floras are the occurrence of certain species and endemic varieties in the Philippine Islands and Campeche Bay in the Gulf of Mexico. It is difficult to explain how they arrived at their present distribution, for they are not found in intervening regions (Mann, 1925).

WESTERN PACIFIC. As for the western Pacific, Aikawa (1936) came to the conclusion that the various sea areas about Japan might be divided into neritic and oceanic groups according to their plankton. He recognizes five oceanic communities: the Kurosio group, the Tusima Current group, the Oyasio group, the Liman group, and the Yellow Sea group.

The Kurosio group may consist of desmo-plankton, styli-plankton, tripos-plankton, or disco-plankton. One or two of the following species are generally always present: *Climacodium biconcavum, C. frauenfeldianum, Dactyliosolen tenuis, Gossleriella tropica, Guinardia flaccida, Hemiaulus heibergii, H. hauckii, Planktoniella sol, Streptotheca indica, Ditylium sol.* There are also several species of *Rhizosolenia.* The relative abundance of *Rhizosolenia* usually corresponds to the purity of the Kurosio group.

The Kurosio group is found in the tropical regions around the Marianne and Western Caroline Islands, in the seas off the Philippines, and off Formosa as far as around the Bonin chain.

Tusima Current group. Aikawa applies the name Tusima Current group to the Kurosio group which was found along the west coast of Kyûsyû in the Japan Sea after passing through the Tusima Straits. Though modified several times by neritic groups, the flora of this current always retains its Kurosio character. In the southern Japan Sea the Tusima Current covers a wide expanse a little distance off shore. North of the Noto Peninsula or of Sadoga Sima, it is usually restricted to a narrow strip in the neritic part of the Japan Sea. Considerable influence is exhibited by the Tusima Current group over the plankton off Seisin or even off Vladivostok in summer, while this influence diminishes in the vicinity of Uturyô Tô in winter.

The Oyasio group contains *Corethron hystrix, Thalassiothrix longissima, Thalassiosira nordenskioldii, Thalassiosira decipiens, Denticula* sp., *Coscinodiscus* sp., and *Biddulphia aurita.* In summer some southern forms are intermixed. The group was found in summer in the Okhotsk Sea and around the western Aleutian Islands. In December it was off Hokkaido, and in January it was around Rasyôwa Tô.

The Liman group is located in the northern part of the Japan Sea and has a marked influence over the area near the Tugaru Straits. In winter it is along the east coast of Tyosen as far as Uturyô Tô while in summer it recedes to the area off Vladivostok. It is characterized by *Corethron hystrix, Thalassiosira longissima,* and *Coscinodiscus* sp. In summer such southern forms as *Rhizosolenia hebetata* are also present.

The Yellow Sea group is greatly influenced by the Kurosio group. The flora is poor as to species and consists of neritic species together with some southern forms.

In the neritic communities the geographical influences play an important role in determining the numbers and kinds of diatoms present. The diatoms are rich in both numbers and species. The genus *Chaetoceros* is always a leading group. These facts are generally true regardless of the influence of either the Kurosio or Oyasio group. Simple floras consisting of *Chaetoceros, Thalassiothrix, Nitzschia seriata, Skeletonema costata,* and other neritic forms often make up the neritic floras on the northern Pacific Coast and on the shores of the Sea of Japan, but seldom occur in the southern Pacific. Seasonal succession is very marked in the neritic communities of the Japan Sea and the Tohoku region where plankton groups of different origin influence the neritic community throughout the year. However, the neritic communities of the southwest Pacific, which are influenced only by the Kurosio group, remain remarkably stable throughout the year.

THE OCCURRENCE OF OCEANIC DIATOM BLOOMS

As a rule, oceanic communities are not so diverse in species or as rich in specimens as neritic ones. Thus we may have a diatom community of low density and few species spreading out over a wide area in oceanic communities, while the variable neritic communities are much more limited in area. The diatom production in cold waters is usually very abundant quantitatively while that of warm water is richer in species number.

It is interesting to note the similarities and differences in times of diatom maxima or blooms throughout the world. There is great similarity in the times of diatom maxima in the waters of the eastern and western North Atlantic. In both cases there is a distinct spring maximum and a smaller fall maximum. In the southwest Pacific at Great Barrier Reef the amount of microplankton is remarkably stable except for an increase in August (Marshall, 1933). In the coastal waters of New South Wales the spring maximum begins in August. The autumn maximum does not start till January and reaches its peak in February. In Aomori Bay, Japan, the greatest abundance of diatoms occurred on September 1, 1929 and from October 16 to November 1, 1930 (Kokubo, 1932).

At Scotch Cape Light, Alaska, the diatom maxima were similar to those of temperate and northerly regions, that is, there was a strong spring and a lesser fall maxima. At Friday Harbor, Washington, there was an almost continuous maximum from May till September which is similar to conditions at Karajakford, Greenland (Phifer, 1933). In southern California waters the greatest maximum occurs in the first third of the year (Cupp, 1937).

As brought out in the consideration of the ecological factors affecting distribution, it is the type of nutrient supply which largely determines the kind and extent of diatom dominance. Also it must be remembered that no latitude should be considered the most productive for diatom growth, for though northern latitudes are generally considered more productive, very large catches have been reported from the Gulf of Panama and along the coast of Central America. Likewise the diatom population at La Jolla and Point Hueneme in southern California waters and Friday Harbor in Washington have been found to be larger than those in Scotch Cape, Alaska.

Summary. From the above review of the literature it is evident that both geographical and ecological factors together, or either of them, may serve as isolating mechanisms in the distribution of marine diatoms. It is the combination of these factors which enables geographical regions and ocean currents to have at a given time characteristic floras. It is not only the kind of species, but their relative abundance which gives a flora its individuality. Through the study of these floras much has been learned about ocean currents. As a rule, the neritic species are more often endemic to certain geographical areas than the oceanic species. However, only a very few oceanic species have been found to be bipolar.

Literature Cited

AIKAWA, H. 1936 On the diatom communities in the waters surrounding Japan. *Records of Oceanographic Works in Japan,* 8:1-160.

AKEHURST, S. C. 1931 Observations on pond life with special reference to the possible causation of swarming of phytoplankton. *Journal of the Royal Microscopical Society.* London, Series 3, 51:237-265.

ALLEN, W. E. 1920 A quantitative and statistical study of the plankton of the San Joaquin River and its tributaries in and near Stockton, California, in 1913. *University of California Publications in Zoology,* 22:1-292.

———— 1927a Quantitative studies on inshore marine diatoms and dinoflagellates of southern California in 1921 and in 1922. *Bulletin of the Scripps Institute of Oceanography,* Technical Series, 1:19-29, 31-38.

———— 1927b Surface catches of marine diatoms and dinoflagellates made by U.S.S. "Pioneer" in Alaskan waters in 1923. *Bulletin of the Scripps Institute of Oceanography,* Technical Series, 1:39-48.

———— 1928a Catches of marine diatoms and dinoflagellates taken by boat in southern California waters in 1926. *Bulletin of the Scripps Institute of Oceanography,* Technical Series, 1:201-246.

———— 1928b Review of five years of study on phytoplankton at southern California piers, 1920-1924, inclusive. *Bulletin of the Scripps Institute of Oceanography,* Technical Series, 1:357-401.

———— 1939 Surface distribution of marine plankton diatoms in the Panama region. *Bulletin of the Scripps Institute of Oceanography,* Technical Series, 4:181-196.

ALLEN, W. E. 1941 Depth relationships of plankton diatoms in sea water. *Journal of Marine Research*, 4:107-112.

———— 1945 Seasonal occurrence of marine plankton diatoms off southern California in 1938. *Bulletin of the Scripps Institute of Oceanography*, Technical Series, 5:293-334.

ATKINS, W. R. G. 1928 Seasonal variation in phosphate and silicate content of sea water during 1926 and 1927 in relation to the phytoplankton crop. *Journal of the Marine Biological Association*. United Kingdom, 15:191-205.

BEGER, H. 1927 Beiträge zur Ökologie und Soziologie der luftlebigen (atmosphytischen) Kieselalgen. *Berichte der Deutschen Botanischen Gesellschaft*, 45(6): 385-407.

BEHNING, A. 1928 Das Leben der Wolga. *Die Binnengewässer*, 5:1-162.

BIGELOW, H. B. 1926 Plankton of the offshore waters of the Gulf of Maine. United States Bureau of Fisheries. *Fisheries Bulletin*, 40, part 2:1-509.

BISWAS, K. 1936 Common diatoms of the Loktak Lake, Manipur, Assam. *Journal of the Royal Asiatic Society of Bengal*. Calcutta, 2:171-175.

BLUM, J. L. 1957 An ecological study of the algae of the Saline River, Michigan. *Hydrobiologia*, 9(4):361-407.

BOYER, C. S. 1927 Synopsis of North American Diatomaceae. *Proceedings of the Academy of Natural Sciences of Philadelphia*, volume 78 (1) Supplement:1-228; volume 79(2) Supplement:229-583.

BRAARUD, T. 1935 The Öst expedition to the Denmark Strait 1929. II. The phytoplankton and its condition of growth. *Norske videnskaps-akademi i Oslo. Hvalrådets Skrifter*, 10:5-144.

BRANDT, K. 1899 Über den Stoffwechsels im Meer. *Wissenchaftliche Meeresuntersuchungen*. Abteilung Kiel, Neue Folge, 4:213-230.

BRISTOL, B. M. 1920 On the alga-flora of some desiccated English soil: an important factor in soil biology. *Annals of Botany*, 34:35-80.

BRUNEL, JULES 1962 Le Phytoplancton de la Baie des Chaleurs. *Contributions du Ministère de la Chasse et de Pêcheries* No. 91. Montreal, Canada, 365 pp.

BUDDE, H. 1928 Die Algenflora des sauerländischen Gebirgsbaches. *Archiv für Hydrobiologie*, 19:433-520.

———— 1930 Die mesohaloben und halophilen Diatomeen der Lippe in Westfalen. *Berichte der Deutschen Botanischen Gesellschaft*, 48:415-419.

———— 1932 Die Algenflora Westfälischer Salinen und Salzgewässer. Part I. *Archiv für Hydrobiologie*, 23:462-490.

———— AND P. R. BURKHOLDER 1929 Microplankton studies of Lake Erie. *Bulletin of the Buffalo Society of Natural Sciences*, 14:73-93.

BURSA, A. S. 1961 The annual oceanographic cycle at Igloolik in the Canadian Arctic. II. The phytoplankton. *Journal of the Fisheries Research Board of Canada*, 18(4):563-615.

CASTENHOLZ, R. W. 1963 An experimental study of the vertical distribution of littoral marine diatoms. *Limnology and Oceanography*, 8(4):450-463.

CHANDLER, D. C. 1940 Limnological studies of western Lake Erie. I. Plankton and certain physical-chemical data of the Bass Islands region, from September, 1938, to November, 1939. *Ohio Journal of Science*, 40:291-336.

———— 1942 Limnological studies of western Lake Erie. III. Phytoplankton and physical-chemical data from November, 1939, to November, 1940. *Ohio Journal of Science*, 42:24-44.

———— 1944 Limnological studies of western Lake Erie. IV. Relation of limnological and climatic factors to the phytoplankton of 1941. *Transactions of the American Microscopical Society*, 63:203-236.

CLAUS, G. AND C. W. REIMER 1961 A quantitative and qualitative study of the phytoplankton of the Danube River at Vienna. *Revista de Biologia*, 2(3/4):261-275.

CLEVE, P. T. 1873 On diatoms from the Arctic Sea. *Bihang till Kongliga Svenska Vetenskaps-Akademiens Handlingar*, 1(13):1-29.

CLEVE, P. T.   1883, 1884   Diatoms collected during the expedition of the Vega. *Vega-Expeditionens Vetenskapliga Jakttagelser,* 3:455-517; *Botanisches Centralblatt,* 18:132-133.

———— 1892   Note sur les diatomées trouvées dans la poussière glaciale de la côte orientale du Groënland. *Le Diatomiste,* 1(8):78.

———— 1894, 1895   Synopsis of the Naviculoid diatoms. I-II. *Kongliga Svenska Vetenskaps-Akademiens Handlingar,* Ny Följd, 26(2):1-194; 27(3):1-219.[*]

———— 1896   Diatoms from Baffins Bay and Davis Strait collected by M. E. Nilsson. *Bihang till Kongliga Svenska Vetenskaps-Akademiens Handlingar,* 22(4):1-22.

———— 1898   Diatoms from Franz Josef Land collected by the Harmsworth-Jackson Expedition. *Bihang till Kongliga Svenska Vetenskaps-Akademiens Handlingar,* 24(2):3-26.

———— 1899   Plankton collected by the Swedish expedition to Spitzbergen in 1898. *Kongliga Svenska Vetenskaps-Akademiens Handlingar,* Ny Följd, 32(3):1-48.

———— 1900a   Microscopical examination of dust from drift ice north of Jan Mayen. *Öfversigt af Kongliga (Svenska) Vetenskaps-Akademiens Förhandlingar.* Stockholm, 57:393-397.

———— 1900b   Report on the plankton collected by the Swedish expedition to Greenland in 1899. *Kongliga Svenska Vetenskaps-Akademiens Handlingar,* Ny Följd, 34(3):1-21.

———— 1903   Plankton-researches in 1901 and 1902. *Kongliga Svenska Vetenskaps-Akademiens Handlingar,* Ny Följd, 36(8):1-53.

———— 1905.   On the plankton from the Swedish coast stations, Moesesker and Vaderobod, collected during August 1902 to July 1903, and on the seasonal variation of the plankton of the Baltic Current. *Svenska Hydrografisk Biologiska Kommissionens Skrifter,* 2:1-9.

COFFING, C.   1937   A quantitative study of the phytoplankton of the White River Canal, Indianapolis, Indiana. *Butler University Botanical Studies,* 4:13-31.

COOPER, L. H. N.   1937   On the ratio of nitrogen to phosphorus in the sea. *Journal of the Marine Biological Association.* United Kingdom, 22:177-183.

CORBELLA, C., V. TONOLLI, AND L. TONOLLI   1958   I sedimenti del lago d'Orta, testimoni di una diastrosa polluzione euprc-ammoniacale. *Memorie Istituto italiano di idrobiologia "Dottor Marco de Marchi."* Pallanza, 10:9-50.

CUPP, E. E.   1937   Seasonal distribution and occurrence of marine diatoms and dinoflagellates at Scotch Cape, Alaska. *Bulletin of the Scripps Institute of Oceanography,* Technical Series, 4:71-100.

DAILY, W. A.   1938   A quantitative study of the phytoplankton of Lake Michigan collected in the vicinity of Evanston, Illinois. *Butler University Botanical Studies,* 4:65-83.

DAMANN, K. E.   1945   Plankton studies of Lake Michigan. *The American Midland Naturalist,* 34:769-797.

DAVIDSON, V. M. AND A. G. HUNTSMAN   1926   The causation of diatom maxima. *Transactions of the Royal Society of Canada,* Series 3, 20:119-125.

DORMAN, H. P.   1927   Studies on marine diatoms and dinoflagellates caught with the Kofoid bucket in 1923. *Bulletin of the Scripps Institute of Oceanography,* Technical Series, 1:49-61.

EDDY, S.   1927a   The plankton of Lake Michigan. *Illinois State Natural History Survey Bulletin,* 17:203-232.

———— 1927b   Growth of diatoms in relation to dissolved gases. *Transactions of the Illinois State Academy of Sciences,* 20:63-66.

ELENKIN, A. A.   1914   Die Süsswasseralgen Kamtschatka's. Expédition à Kamtchatka, organisée par Th. P. Riabouchinsky. Livre 2, Plantes cryptogames de Kamtchatka. Moscou, pp. 3-402 + 1 pl. + 14 figs.

---

[*]Kongliga Svenska Vetenskaps-Akademiens Handlingar, Ny Följd, vol. 27 was received by the British Museum of Natural History and the Academy of Natural Science in Philadelphia in 1896.

FISH, C. J. 1925 Seasonal distribution of plankton of the Woods Hole region. United States Bureau of Fisheries, *Fishery Bulletin* 975, volume 61:91-179.

FOGED, N. 1947 Diatoms in the water courses in Funen. *Dansk Botanisk Archiv*, 12(5):1-40.

———— 1954 Diatom flora of some Funen Lakes. *Folia Limnologica Scandinavica*, No. 6, 75 pp. + 3 pls.

FRANCÉ, R. H. 1912 Studien über edaphische Organismen. *Centralblatt für Bakteriologie, Parasitenkunde, und Infektionskrankheiten.* Jena, 32(2):1-7.

FRENGUELLI, J. 1939 Diatomeas del Lago Titicaca. *Notas Museo La Plata*, Botánica, 4:175-196.

———— 1941 Diatomeas del río de La Plata. *Revista del Museo de La Plata.* Sección Botánica, 3:213-334.

GODWARD, M. 1937 An ecological and taxonomic investigation of the littoral algal flora of Lake Windermere. *Journal of Ecology*, 25:496-568.

GOTTSCHALL, R. Y. AND O. E. JENNINGS 1933 Limnological studies at Erie, Pennsylvania. *Transactions of the American Microscopical Society*, 52:181-191.

GRAN, H. H. 1897 Bemerkungen über das Plankton des Arktischen Meeres. *Berichte der Deutschen Botanischen Gesellschaft*, 15:132-136.

———— 1900 Diatomaceae from the ice-floes and plankton of the Arctic Ocean. *Norwegian North Polar Expedition 1893-1896.* Scientific results edited by F. Nansen, 3(11):1-74.

———— 1902 Das Plankton des Norwegischen Nordmeeres von biologischen und hydrographischen Gesichtspunkten behandelt. *Report on Norwegian Fishery and Marine Investigations*, 2(5):1-222.

———— 1912 Pelagic plant life. *In* Depths of the Ocean, J. Murray and J. Hjort. London, Macmillan and Co., Chapter 6, pp. 307-386.

———— 1929 Investigation of the production of plankton outside the Romsdalsfjord 1926-1927. *Conseil Permanent International pour l'Exploration de la mer*, Rapports et procès-verbaux des réunions, 56(6):1-112.

———— 1930 The spring growth of the plankton at Møre in 1928-29 and at Lofoten in 1929 in relation to its limiting factors. *Skrifter Norske Videnskaps-Akademi i Oslo*, Matematisk-naturvidenskapelig Klasse, 1930(5):1-77.

———— 1931 On the conditions for production of plankton in the sea. *Conseil Permanent International pour l'Exploration de la mer*, Rapports et procès-verbaux des réunions, 75:37-46.

———— AND T. BRAARUD 1935 A quantitative study of the phytoplankton in the Bay of Fundy and the Gulf of Maine. *Journal of the Biological Board of Canada*, 1:279-467.

GRIEL, J. V. AND R. J. ROBINSON 1952 Titanium in sea water. *Journal of Marine Research*, 11(2):173-179.

GRUNOW, A. 1884 Die Diatomeen von Franz Josefs Land. *Denkschriften der Kaiserlichen Akademie der Wissenschaften*, Mathematisch-Naturwissenschaftliche Classe. Wien, 48:53-112 + 5 pls.

GUNTHER, E. R. 1936 A report on the oceanographical investigations in the Peru coastal current. *Discovery Reports*, 13:107-276.

HART, T. J. 1935 On the diatoms of the skin film of whales and their possible bearing on problems of whale movement. *Discovery Reports*, 10:247-282.

HARVEY, H. W. *et al.* 1935 Plankton production and its control. *Journal of the Marine Biological Association.* United Kingdom, 20:407-441.

HAYEK, J. M. AND R. L. HULBARY 1956 A survey of soil diatoms. *Proceedings of the Iowa Academy of Sciences*, 63:327-338.

HEDLUND, T. 1913 Till frågan om växternas frosthärdighet. I-II. *Botaniska Notiser*, for 1913:65-78, 153-174.

HENDEY, N. I. 1937 The plankton diatoms of the Southern Seas. *Discovery Reports*, 16:151-364.

HENDEY, N. I. 1964 An introductory account of the smaller algae of British Coastal Waters. Part V. Bacillariophyceae (Diatoms). Ministry of Agriculture, Fisheries and Food, Fisheries Investigations, Series IV.

HENSEN, V. 1887 Über die Bestimmung des Plankton's oder des im Meere treibenden Materials an Pflanzen und Thieren. *Wissenschaftliche Meeresuntersuchungen* (Fünfter Bericht), XII bis XVI Jahrgang:1-108.

HENTSCHEL, E. 1928 Die Grundzüge der Planktonverteilung im Südatlantischen Ozean. *Internationale Revue der Gesamten Hydrobiologie und Hydrographie,* 21:1-6.

HÉRIBAUD, J. 1894 De l'nfluence de la lumière et de l'altitude sur la striation des valves diatomées. *Comptes Rendus Académie des Sciences,* 118:82-84.

HJORT, J. AND H. H. GRAN 1899 Currents and pelagic life in the northern ocean. Bergens Museum Report on the Norwegian Marine Investigations 1895-97, by Dr. J. Hjort, O. Nordgaard, and H. H. Gran. Bergen, J. Grieg, 24 pp. + 28 tables + 7 pls.

HOSHIAI, T. AND M. KATO 1961 Ecological notes on the diatom community of the sea ice of Antarctica. *Bulletin of 'the Marine Biological Station,* Asamushi, Tohoku University. Japan, 10(4):221-230.

HUSTEDT, F. 1922 Bacillariales aus Schlesien. I. *Beriche der Deutschen Botanischen Gesellschaft,* 40:98-103.

———— 1938 Systematische und ökologische Untersuchungen über die Diatomeenflora von Java, Bali und Sumatra. II. Die Diatomeenflora der untersuchten Gewässertypen. *Archiv für Hydrobiologie Supplement,* 16:1-155.

———— 1939 Systematische und ökologische Untersuchungen über die Diatomeenflora von Java, Bali und Sumatra nach dem Material der Deutschen Limnologischen Sunda-Expedition. III. Die ökologischen Faktoren und ihr Einfluss auf die Diatomeenflora. *Archiv für Hydrobiologie Supplement,* 16:274-394.

———— 1942 Süsswasser Diatomeen des indomalayischen Archipels und der Hawaii-Iseln. *Internationale Revue der Gesamten Hydrobiologie und Hydrographie,* 42:1-252.

———— 1953 Die systematisk der diatomeen in ihren Beziehungen zur Geologie und Ökologie nebst einer Revision des Halobien-Systems. *Svensk Botanisk Tidskrift,* 47(4):509-519.

———— 1956 Kieselalgen (Diatomeen). Stuttgart, Fränckh'sche Verlagshandlung, W. Keller and Co., 70 pp., 35 figs., + 4 pls.

KARSTEN, G. 1905-1907 Das Phytoplankton des Antarktischen Meeres nach dem Material der Deutschen Tiefsee Expedition 1898-1899. *Deutsche Tiefsee-Expedition auf dem Dampfer "Valdivia" 1898-1899,* 2:1-136, 137-219, 223-544.

KOFOID, C. A. 1908 The plankton of the Illinois River 1894-1899. Part II. Constituent organisms and their seasonal distribution. *Bulletin of the Illinois State Laboratory of Natural History,* 8:1-360.

KOKUBO, S. 1932 Quantitative studies on microplankton in Aomoie Bay during 1929-1930. *Records of Oceanographic Works in Japan,* 4:171-244.

KOLBE, R. W. 1927 Zur Ökologie, Morphologie und Systematik der Brackwasser-Diatomeen. *Pflanzenforschung,* 7:1-146.

———— 1932 Grundlinien einer algemeinen Ökologie der Diatomeen. *Ergebnisse der Biologie.* Berlin, 8:221-348.

KOORDERS, S. H. 1901 Notiz über die dysphotische Flora eines Süsswassersees in Java. *Natuurkundig Tijdschrift voor Nederlandsch-Indië,* 41:119-126.

KRASSKE, G. 1929 Beiträge zur Kenntnis der Diatomeenflora Sachsens. *Botanisches Archiv.* Leipzig, 27:348-380.

———— 1932 Diatomeen deutscher Solquellen und Gradierwerke. II. Die Diatomeen von Bad Nauheim, Wisselsheim und Bad Salzungen a. d. Werra. *Hedwigia,* 72(4/5):135-143.

———— 1936 Die Diatomeenflora der Moosrasen des Wilhelmshöher Parkes. Festschrift des Vereins für Naturkunde zu Kassel zur Feier seines hundertjährigen Bestehens, pp. 151-164.

———— 1939 Zur Kieselalgenflora Südchiles. *Archiv für Hydrobiologie,* 35:349-468.

KREPS, E. AND N. VERJBINSKAYA 1930 Seasonal changes in the phosphate and nitrate content and in hydrogen ion concentration in the Barent Sea. *Journal du Conseil Permanent International pour l'Exploration de la Mer,* 5:329-346.

KRIEGER, W. 1927 Zur Biologie des Flussplanktons. Untersuchungen über das Potamoplankton des Havelgebietes. *Pflanzenforschung,* 10:1-66.

———— 1929 Algologisch-monographische Untersuchungen über das Hochmoor am Diebelsee. *In* Vegetations-studien am Plötzendiebel bei Joachimsthal (Uckermark). *Beiträge zur Naturdenkmalpflege.* Berlin, 13(2):231-300 + 3 pls.

LEBOUR, M. V. 1930 The planktonic diatoms of northern seas. London, Ray Society, ix + 244 pp.

LILLICK, L. C. 1937a Preliminary report of the phytoplankton of the Gulf of Maine. *The American Midland Naturalist,* 20:624-640.

———— 1937b Seasonal studies of the phytoplankton of Woods Hole, Massachusetts. *Biological Bulletin,* 73:488-503.

LUND, J. W. G. 1950 Studies on *Asterionella formosa* Hass. II. Nutrient depletion and the spring maximum. Parts I-II. *Journal of Ecology,* 38(1):1-35.

———— 1955 Further observations on the seasonal cycle of *Melosira italica* (Ehr.) Kütz. subsp. *subarctica* O. Müll. *Journal of Ecology,* 43(1):90-102 + 1 fig.

MANN, A. 1925 Marine diatoms of the Philippine Islands. *Smithsonian Institution, United States National Museum Bulletin,* No. 100, volume 6, part 1, 182 pp. + 39 pls.

———— 1937 Report of the diatoms collected by the Australian Antarctic Expedition. *Australian Antarctic Expedition 1911-1914,* Science Report, Series C, 1:5-82.

MARSHALL, S. M. 1933 The production of microplankton in the Great Barrier Reef region. *British Museum of Natural History, Great Barrier Reef Expedition 1928-1929, Science Report,* 2:111-157.

———— AND A. P. ORR 1928 The photosynthesis of diatom cultures in the sea. *Journal of the Marine Biological Association.* United Kingdom, 15(1):321-360.

MELOCHE, V. W. *et al.* 1938 The silica and diatom content of Lake Mendota water. *Transactions of the Wisconsin Academy of Sciences, Arts, and Letters,* 31:363-376.

MOORE, G. T. AND N. CARTER 1926 Further studies on the subterranean algal flora of the Missouri Botanical Garden. *Annals of the Missouri Botanical Garden,* 13:101-140.

NATHANSOHN, A. 1906 Über die Bedeutung vertikaler Wasserbewegungen für die Produktion des Planktons im Meere. *Abhandlungen der Könglichen Sächsischen Gesellschaft der Wissenschaften,* Mathematisch-Physischen Klasse, 29(5):355-441 + 1 map.

NAUMANN, E. 1921 Die Bodenablagerungen des Süsswassers. *Archiv für Hydrobiologie,* 13:97-169.

NYGAARD, G. 1949 Hydrobiological studies on some Danish ponds and lakes. II. The quotient hypothesis and some new or little known phytoplankton organisms. *Det Kongelige Danske Videnskabernes Selskab Biologiske Skrifter,* 7(1):1-293.

PATRICK, R. 1936 A taxonomic and distributional study of some diatoms from Siam and the Federated Malay States. *Proceedings of the Academy of Natural Sciences of Philadelphia,* 88:367-470.

———— 1945 A taxonomic and ecological study of some diatoms from the Pocono plateau and adjacent regions. *Farlowia,* 2(2):143-214.

———— 1948 Factors effecting the distribution of diatoms. *The Botanical Review,* 14(8):473-524.

PEARSALL, W. H. 1922 A suggestion as to factors influencing the distribution of free-floating vegetation. *Journal of Ecology,* 9(2):241-253.

———— 1924 Phytoplankton and environment in the English Lake District. *Revue Algologique,* 1:53-67.

———— 1930 Phytoplankton in the English Lakes. I. The proportions in the water of some dissolved substances of biological importance. *Journal of Ecology,* 18(2):306-320.

Pearsall, W. H.   1932   Phytoplankton in the English Lakes. II. The composition of the phytoplankton in relation to dissolved substances. *Journal of Ecology,* 20(2):241-262.

Petersen, J. B.   1928   The aërial algae of Iceland. *The Botany of Iceland,* volume 2, part 2(8):325-447.

———   1935   Studies on the biology and taxonomy of soil algae. *Dansk Botanisk Arkiv,* 8:1-180.

———   1943   Some halobion spectra (Diatoms). *Det Kongelige Danske Videnskabernes Selskab Biologiske Meddelelser.* Copenhagen, 17(9):3-95.

Phifer, L. D.   1933   Seasonal distribution and occurrence of planktonic diatoms at Friday Harbor, Washington. *University of Washington Publications in Oceanography,* 1(2):39-81.

Rice, C. H.   1938   Studies in the phytoplankton of the River Thames (1928-1932). I and II. *Annals of Botany,* New Series, 2(7):539-557, 559-581.

Richter, O.   1906   Zur Physiologie der Diatomeen. *Sitzungsberichte der Mathematish-Naturwissenschaftlichen Klass der Kaiserlichen Akademie der Wissenschaften.* Wien, 115(1):27-119.

Riley, G. A.   1939   Plankton studies. II. The western North Atlantic, May-June, 1939. *Journal of Marine Research,* 2(2):145-162.

———   1941   Plankton studies. IV. Georges Bank. *Bulletin of the Bingham Oceanographic Collection,* 7(4):1-73.

———   1942   The relationship of vertical turbulence and spring diatom flowering. *Journal of Marine Research,* 5(1):67-87.

———   1943   Physiological aspects of spring diatom flowerings. *Bulletin of the Bingham Oceanographic Collection,* 8(4):1-53.

Roach, L. S.   1932   An ecological study of the plankton of the Hocking River. *Bulletin of the Ohio State University Biological Survey,* 5:253-279.

Schreiber, E.   1927   Die Reinkultur von marinem Phytoplankton und deren Bedeutung für die Erforschung der Produktionsfähigkeit des Meerwassers. *Wissenschaftliche Meeresuntersuchungen.* Abteilung Helgoland, Neue Folge, 16(10):1-34.

Schröder, B.   1916   *Melosira Roeseana* Rabenh., eine "leuchtende" Bacillariacee. *Berichte der Deutschen Botanischen Gesellschaft,* 34(9):796-800.

Schroeder, H.   1939   Die Algenflora der Mulde. *Pflanzenforschung,* 21:1-88.

Schumann, J.   1867   Die Diatomeen der hohen Tatra. *Verhandlungen der Zoologisch-Botanischen Gesellschaft in Wien,* Supplement, 17:1-102.

Sears, M.   1941   Notes on the phytoplankton on Georges Bank. *Journal of Marine Research,* 4(3):247-256.

Skvortzow, B. W.   1927   Diatoms from Tientsin, North China. *The Journal of Botany,* 65:102-109.

———   1928a   Diatoms from Khingan, North Manchuria, China. *Philippine Journal of Science,* 35(1):39-51.

———   1928b   Diatoms of northeast Mongolia. *Hedwigia,* 68:311-314.

———   1929a   A contribution to the algae, Primorsk District of Far East, USSR. Diatoms of Hanka Lake. *Memoirs of the Southern Ussuri Branch of the State Russian Geographical Society,* 3:1-66.

———   1929b   Freshwater diatoms from Amoy, South China. *The China Journal,* 11(1):40-44.

———   1929c   Fresh-water diatoms from Korea, Japan. *Philippine Journal of Science,* 38(3):283-291.

———   1930a   Alpine diatoms from Fukien Province, South China. *Philippine Journal of Science,* 41(1):39-49.

———   1930b   Notes on Ceylon diatoms. I. *Annals of the Royal Botanical Gardens.* Peradeniya, 11:251-260.

———   1932   Diatoms from ponds of Peking. *Peking Society of Natural History Bulletin,* 1928-29, 3:43-48.

———   1936a   Diatoms from Kizaki Lake, Honshu Island. *Philippine Journal of Science,* 61(1):9-73.

SKVORTZOW, B. W. 1936b Diatoms from Biwa Lake, Honshu Island, Nippon. *Philippine Journal of Science*, 61(2):253-296.

———— 1937 Diatoms from Ikeda Lake, Satsuma Province, Kiusiu Island, Nippon. *Philippine Journal of Science*, 62(2):191-218.

———— 1938a Subaërial diatoms from Pin-Chiang-Sheng Province, Manchoukuo. *Philippine Journal of Science*, 65(3):263-283.

———— 1938b Diatoms from Argun River, Hsing-An-Pei Province, Manchoukuo. *Philippine Journal of Science*, 66(1):43-74.

SLEGGS, G. T. 1927 Marine phytoplankton in the region of La Jolla, California, during the summer of 1924. *Bulletin of the Scripps Institute of Oceanography*, Technical Series, 1:93-117.

STEELE, J. H. AND YENTSCH, C. S. 1960 The vertical distribution of chlorophyll. *Journal of the Marine Biological Association*. United Kingdom, 39:217-26.

TALLING, J. E. 1957 The growth of two plankton diatoms in mixed culture. *Physiologia Plantarum* 10:215-223.

THIENEMANN, A. 1920 Biologische Seetypen usw. *Archiv für Hydrobiologie*, 13:347-370.

USPENSKI, E. E. 1927 Eisen als Faktor für die Verbreitung niederer Wasserorganismen. *Pflanzenforschung*, 9:1-104.

VAN OYE, P. 1927 Over de Wierflora van Belgisch-Kongo. *Botanisch Jaarboek*, 20:19-144.

WEST, W. AND G. S. WEST 1899 A further contribution to the freshwater algae of the West Indies. *The Journal of the Linnean Society of London*. Botany, 34:279-295.

———— 1912 On the periodicity of the phytoplankton of some British lakes. *The Journal of the Linnean Society of London*. Botany, 40:393-432.

WHITFORD, L. A. AND G. J. SCHUMACHER 1963 Communities of algae in North Carolina streams and their seasonal relations. *Hydrobiologia*, 22(1/2):133-196.

WILLIAMS, L. G. AND C. SCOTT 1962 Principal diatoms of major waterways of the United States. *Limnology and Oceanography*, 7(3):365-379.

WISLOUCH, S. 1924 Przyczynek do biologji solnisk i genezy szlamów leczniczych na Krymie. (Beiträge zur Biologie und Entstehung von Heilschlamm der Salinen der Krim.) *Acta Societatis Botanicorum Poloniae*, 2(2):99-129.

V. STRUCTURE OF DIATOM COMMUNITIES

The kinds and relative abundance of diatom species composing the diatom community have been of interest to diatom workers since the latter part of the nineteenth century. The composition of such associations has been used to trace the sequences of the advance and retreat of glaciers. Associations of species have also been used to trace the history of development of lakes. They have been used to classify lakes and streams as to whether they are oligotrophic, mesotrophic, eutrophic, or dystrophic. Likewise they have been used to categorize bodies of water as hard or soft or fresh; acid, neutral or alkaline; brackish or marine. Thienemann (1939) was the first to give names to species in accordance with their relative occurrence in different kinds of environments. Those species which were characteristic of a single kind of environment (biotope) were called "coenobionte." "Coenophile" were those species which had their best development in a given biotope although the species might be found in other biotopes. "Coenoxene" species were those which did not seem to be characteristic of the environment in which they are found. They are found in small numbers.

As seen by an examination of the literature, diatom floras are usually composed of many species. Patrick (1949, 1963) has shown that natural river communities of diatoms are characterized by a large number of species most of which are represented by a small number of specimens. The sample of the community which one studies can be best represented by a truncated normal curve (Patrick, Hohn, and Wallace, 1954; fig. 6). Any environmental condition which reduces the number of species that can live in an area but does not reduce the nutrient level results in certain species being more common, some rarer, and σ^2 becoming larger. This is true whether the environmental condition is a natural one such as in certain somewhat acid streams, fig. 7, or due to the effect of man-made pollution, fig. 8 (Patrick, Hohn, and Wallace, 1954; Patrick, 1963). It has been found that the structure of the natural community does not change significantly from season to season or from year to year so long as there is no great change in the environment (Patrick, 1949, 1964). However, the kinds of species and the sizes of the populations of individual species may vary greatly (Patrick, 1961, 1964). There is evidence from studies in a natural spring that if the environment remains nearly constant there is also a reduction in the number of species which may occupy an area (Patrick, 1962). Thus, it would appear that a somewhat variable but stable environment is necessary if a high diversity of species is to be maintained.

Patrick and Strawbridge (1963a, 1963b) have determined the 99% and 95% confidence intervals for the height of the mode and σ^2 in natural meso-

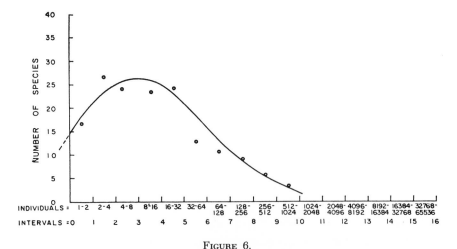

FIGURE 6.

Sample of a diatom community from a natural stream expressed as a truncated normal curve.

trophic to eutrophic streams in Eastern and Southeastern United States. There is evidence from some oligotrophic streams which we have examined that the structure of the diatom community may be similar to those of eutrophic streams, but more work needs to be done.

Patrick and Hohn (1956) have shown that the structure of the diatom communities in a brackish to salt water estuary is very similar to that in a river. However, the numbers of the species composing the community

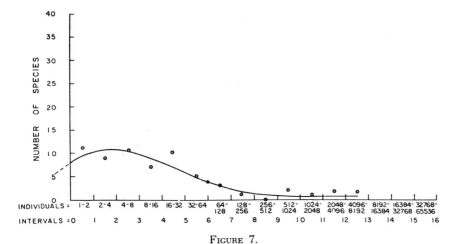

FIGURE 7.

Sample of a diatom community from a dystrophic stream expressed as a truncated normal curve.

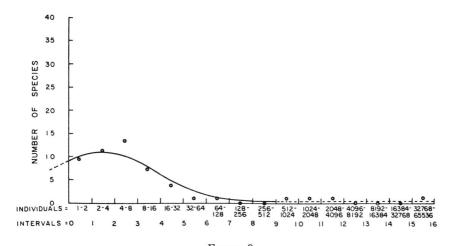

FIGURE 8.

Sample of a diatom community from a polluted stream expressed as a truncated normal curve.

seem to be a little less. Patrick and Strawbridge (*loc. cit.*) have shown the 99% and 95% confidence intervals for the height of the mode and σ^2 for estuary communities in South and Southeastern United States.

Margalef (1957) has developed methods for studying the diversity of plankton based on the information theory. This method uses total number of individuals in the sample as well as the individuals per species and the number of species. Margalef (1961) has also used the diversity of pigments as an index of the diversity of species in a plankton community.

Hohn (1961a) has described a shorter method than that described by Patrick, Hohn, and Wallace (1954) for arriving at the structure of the diatom community. Yount (1956) developed a method for determining the relationship of species to individuals based on the count of diatoms growing on glass slides seen in ten microscopic fields. He measured the amount of productivity by the amount of chlorophyll a. Hohn (1961b), using Yount's material, has shown that his method for studying species-to-individuals relationship does not produce a reliable representation of the structure of the diatom community, and that the structure of the diatom communities as to species diversity in low and high productivity areas are quite similar.

There does seem to be a tendency for the community on glass slides to decrease in species diversity on the slides in both high and low productive areas if they are exposed from 148 to 335 days. One would expect a glass slide not to be equally suitable for all species in the diatom community and that with a great increase in individuals on the slide the species less suited to the habitat would be eliminated. This effect would probably be more noticeable if new species were not continually invading the slide.

The study of the structure of diatom communities under the influence of man-made pollution has largely developed in the twentieth century. Kolkwitz and Marsson (1908) classified some species of diatoms according to the amount of organic pollution they could withstand. This system was followed and to some extent modified by such workers as Hentschell (1925), Naumann (1925), Butcher (1947), and Liebmann (1951). Depending on the classification of the dominant species of diatoms, a given environment was characterized as having been degraded to a given condition such as oligosaprobic, beta-mesosaprobic, alpha-mesosaprobic, polysaprobic. Fjerdingstad (1950, 1960) in referring to aquatic communities classified diatom species according to their ability to withstand varying amounts of pollution and then described the community in terms of dominant and associated species.

Patrick, Hohn, and Wallace (1954), Patrick and Hohn (1956), Patrick (1963, 1964), and Hohn (1959) have shown that depending upon the amount of pollution present, there is a shift from the structure of the natural community of diatoms. A very small amount of pollution causes certain species to become much more common and a reduction in the sizes of populations of other species. As a result σ^2 of the truncated normal curve is increased and the curve covers more intervals. A further increase in the organic pollution and/or the presence of a small amount of toxic pollution cause a reduction in the number of species, an increase in σ^2, and a much further extension of the curve due to the very large numbers of a few species, fig. 8. Heavy toxic or organic pollution intensifies this decrease in species, and, of course, if severe enough may result in the elimination of all species.

In measuring the effect of pollution on a diatom population it is interesting to note that if the pollution load remains the same and does not change significantly in composition, the percent of dominant species remains similar although the kinds of species may vary (Patrick, 1964). Williams and Scott (1962) have used the percent of the diatom population composed of dominant species and the kinds of species as a means of judging the pollution load of the various rivers in the United States' Basic Data Program.

Cholnoky (1958) has developed a method of determining the change in the amount of pollution present or the recovery of a river from a given type of pollution by a shift in the numbers of individuals in the species of diatoms which were dominant. Patrick (1964 and in press) has not found this method feasible for indicating amounts of pollution present in rivers in the United States.

Literature Cited

BUTCHER, R. W. 1947 Studies in the ecology of rivers. VII. The algae of organically enriched waters. *Journal of Ecology*, 35(1/2):186-191.

CHOLNOKY, B. J. 1958 Beitrag zu den Diatomeenassoziationen des Sumpfes Olifants-vlei südwestlich Johannesburg. *Berichte der Deutschen Botanischen Gesellschaft*, 71(4):177-187.

FJERDINGSTAD, E. 1950 The microfauna of the river Mølleaa; with special reference to the relation of the benthal algae to pollution. *Folia Limnologica Scandinavica*, No. 5, 123 pp.

——— 1960 Forurening af vandløb biologisk bedømt. *Nordisk Hygienisk Tidskrift*, 41:149-196.

HENTSCHELL, E. 1925 Abwasserbiologie. Abderhanden's *Handbuch der Biologischen Arbeitsmethoden*, Abt. 9, Teil 2, 1 Häfte, pp. 233-280.

HOHN, M. H. 1959 The use of diatom populations as a measure of water quality in selected areas of Galveston and Chocolate Bay, Texas. *Publications of the Institute of Marine Science*, 6:206-212.

——— 1961a Determining the pattern of the diatom flora. *Journal of the Water Pollution Control Federation*, 33(1):48-53.

——— 1961b The relationship between species diversity and population density in diatom populations from Silver Springs, Florida. *Transactions of the American Microscopical Society*, 80(2):140-165.

KOLKWITZ, R. AND M. MARSSON 1908 Ökologie der pflanzlichen Saprobien. Festschrift zur Feier des 25 Jährigen Bestehens der Deutschen Botanischen Gesellschaft, *Berichte der Deutschen Botanischen Gesellschaft*, 26A:505-519.

LIEBMANN, H. 1951 Handbuch der Frischwasser- und Abwasserbiologie. Band 1. München, Verlag von R. Oldenbourg, 539 pp.

MARGALEF, R. 1957 La teoria de la informacion en ecologia. *Memorias de la Real Academia de Ciencias y Artes de Barcelona*, 32(13):373-449.

———— 1961 Correlations entre certains caractères synthétiques des populations de phytoplancton. *Hydrobiologia*, 18(1/2):155-164.

NAUMANN, E. 1925 Die Arbeitsmethoden der regionalen Limnologie. Abderhanden's *Handbuch der Biologischen Arbeitsmethoden*. Susswasserbiologie. 1.

PATRICK, R. 1949 A proposed biological measure of stream conditions based on a survey of Conestoga Basin, Lancaster County, Pennsylvania. *Proceedings of the Academy of Natural Sciences of Philadelphia*, 101:277-341.

———— 1961 A study of the numbers and kinds of species found in rivers in eastern United States. *Proceedings of the Academy of Natural Sciences of Philadelphia*, 113(10):215-258.

———— 1962 Effects of river physical and chemical characteristics on aquatic life. *Journal of the American Water Works Association*, 54(5):544-550.

———— 1963 The structure of diatom communities under varying ecological conditions. Conference on the problems of environmental control on the morphology of fossil and recent protobionta. *Annals of the New York Academy of Sciences*, 108(2):359-365.

———— 1964 A discussion of natural and abnormal diatom communities. *In* Algae and Man, edited by D. F. Jackson, New York, Plenum Press, pp. 185-204.

———— AND M. H. HOHN 1956 The diatometer—a method for indicating the conditions of aquatic life. *Proceedings American Petroleum Institute*, Section 3, Refining, Addresses and Reports, 36(3):332-339.

————, M. H. HOHN, AND J. H. WALLACE 1954 A new method for determining the pattern of the diatom flora. *Notulae Naturae of the Academy of Natural Sciences of Philadelphia*, No. 259, 12 pp.

———— AND D. R. STRAWBRIDGE 1963a Methods of studying diatom populations. *Journal of the Water Pollution Control Federation*, 35(2):151-161.

———— 1963b Variation in the structure of natural diatom populations. *The American Naturalist*, 97(892):51-57.

THIENEMANN, A. 1939 Grundzüge einer allgemeinen Ökologie. *Archiv für Hydrobiologie*, 35(2):267-285.

WILLIAMS, L. G. AND C. SCOTT 1962 Principal diatoms of major waterways of the United States. *Limnology and Oceanography*, 7(3):365-379.

YOUNT, J. L. 1956 Factors that control species numbers in Silver Springs, Florida. *Limnology and Oceanography*, 1(4):286-295.

VI. CLASSIFICATION OF DIATOMS

The first systems of classification of diatoms, particularly in the higher categories, were largely based on the manner of growth and the general shape and characteristics of the frustules. This, no doubt, was largely due to the lack of suitable optics which could critically examine the frustules. This general classification was followed by such workers as Agardh, Ehrenberg, Kützing, and William Smith. Ralfs in 1861 (*in* Pritch., Hist. Infusoria, 4th ed.) added the characteristics of the median longitudinal line and the nodules in defining the higher categories of diatoms. At about the same time (1860-61) Grunow, likewise, developed a classification which included the characteristics of the raphe in the classifications of diatoms.

In 1871 Pfitzer developed a classification of diatoms in which the major divisions were based on the characteristics of chromatophores, which was as follows:

I. Coccochromaticae—cells with numerous granular or disc-shaped chromatophores.
   a. Valves with centric structure. A mother cell forming an asexual auxospore.
   b. Valves with bilateral symmetry. Auxospore forming from one or two mother cells.
II. Placochromaticae—cells with one or two large plate-like chromatophores.

Schütt in 1896 divided the Family Bacillariaceae into two main divisions and several subdivisions as follows:

A. Centricae
   I. Discoideae
   II. Solenioideae
   III. Biddulphioideae
   IV. Rutilarioideae

B. Pennatae
   V. Fragilarioideae
   VI. Achnanthoideae
   VII. Naviculoideae
   VIII. Surirelloideae

The genus *Eunotia* was included in the Fragilarioideae and the genera *Epithemia and Rhopalodia* in the Naviculoideae.

Østrup (1910) followed Schütt in recognizing two main subdivisions, the Centricae and the Pennatae. He recognized no major subdivisions under the Centricae, but the following divisions were recognized under the Pennatae.

A. Raphideae

   I. Euraphideae
      1. Diraphideae—*Navicula, Pinnularia*, etc.
      2. Monoraphideae—*Achnanthes, Cocconeis*, etc.

   II. Kalyptoraphideae
      1. Brachyraphideae—*Eunotia*
      2. Gonyraphideae—*Epithemia*
      3. Tropidoraphideae—*Rhopalodia, Nitzschia, Hantzschia*
      4. Eschatoraphideae—*Cymatopleura, Surirella, Campylodiscus*

B. Arraphideae

In 1872 H. L. Smith set forth a classification based on the shape of the valve and the presence or absence of the raphe. He considered all diatoms as belonging to a single order—Diatomaceae—and divided this order into three tribes:

I. Raphidieae—diatoms with a true raphe, usually bacillar in shape, sometimes broadly oval.

II. Pseudoraphidieae—diatoms with a pseudoraphe (simple line or blank space); valve usually bacillar, sometimes broadly oval or sub-orbicular in shape.

III. Cryptoraphidieae—diatoms never having a raphe or pseudoraphe; usually circular, subcircular or angular, rarely elliptical or bacillar.

Petit (1877) further developed the system of Pfitzer which is based on the chromatophores. Van Heurck (1880-85) expanded the system of H. L. Smith based on the shape and structure of the cell wall and the presence or absence of a raphe or pseudoraphe. This was particularly true in the lower categories.

Although the basis of classification of Pfitzer and Petit on the chromatophores and H. L. Smith and Van Heurck on the raphe and the structure and shape of the cell wall were very different, the resulting groupings were similar. Group Ia of Pfitzer corresponded to Group III of Smith; Group Ib of Pfitzer to II of Smith; and Group II of Pfitzer to Group I of Smith. However, Mereschkowsky (1903) developed a system of classification mainly based on the type of auxospores. His main divisions were:

Mobiles
   Raphideae
   Carinatae
   Archaideae

Immobiles
   Anaraphideae
   Bacilloideae

Karsten (1928) considered the Bacillariophyta as a major group and recognized two subgroups of diatoms which he designated as Centrales and Pennales. It is not clear whether he considered these groups as orders even though the ending designating orders in botanical nomenclature is used. He subdivided these groups as follows:

Centrales
  Eucyclicae
    Discaceae
    Soleniaceae
  Hemicyclicae
    Biddulphiaceae
    Rutilariaceae

Pennales
  Araphideae
    Fragilariaceae
  Raphidioideae
    Eunotiaceae
  Monoraphideae
    Achnanthaceae
  Biraphideae
    Naviculaceae
    Epithemiaceae
    Nitzschiiaceae

Heiden and Kolbe (1928) called the two main divisions Radiales and Bilaterales rather than Centrales and Pennales as set forth by Karsten.

Hustedt (1930) followed the general system of Karsten but made some alterations in it.

  Bacillariophyta
  Class Diatomatae
  Order Centrales
  Suborder Discineae
  Suborder Solenionae
  Suborder Biddulphineae
  Order Pennales
  Suborders as given by Karsten (1928)

Hendey (1937) considered diatoms as a class of algae and that they were contained in a single order Bacillariales. He then recognized the following suborders:

  Order Bacillariales
    Suborder Discineae
    Suborder Aulacodiscineae
    Suborder Aulisceneae
    Suborder Biddulphiineae
    Suborder Soleneneae
    Suborder Araphidineae

Suborder Raphidioidineae
Suborder Monoraphidineae
Suborder Biraphidineae
Suborder Surirellineae

Cleve-Euler's classification (1952) is the same as Østrup's except that she places the Brachyraphideae as a group of equal rank to the Euraphideae and Kalyptoraphideae.

Silva (1962) proposes the following classification of diatoms. The names of many of the subordinate groups have been made to conform with the present *International Rules of Botanical Nomenclature*.

Division Bacillariophyta
  Class Centrobacillariophyceae
    Order Eupodiscales
    Order Rhizosoleniales
    Order Biddulphiales
  Class Pennatibacillariophyceae
    Order Fragilariales
    Order Eunotiales
    Order Achnanthales
    Order Naviculales
    Order Phaeodactylales
    Order Bacillariales
    Order Surirellales

Hendey (1964) proposes the following classification:

Division Chrysophyta
  Class Bacillariophyceae
    Order Bacillariales
      Suborder Coscinodiscineae
        Family Coscinodiscaceae
        Family Hemidiscaceae
        Family Actinodiscaceae
      Suborder Aulacodiscineae
        Family Eupodiscaceae
      Suborder Auliscineae
        Family Auliscaceae
      Suborder Biddulphineae
        Family Biddulphiaceae
        Family Anaulaceae
        Family Chaetoceraceae

Suborder Rhizosoleniineae
    Family Bacteriastraceae
    Family Leptocylindraceae
    Family Corethronaceae
    Family Rhizosoleniaceae
Suborder Fragilariineae
    Family Fragilariaceae
Suborder Eunotiineae
    Family Eunotiaceae
Suborder Achnanthineae
    Family Achnanthaceae
Suborder Naviculineae
    Family Naviculaceae
    Family Auriculaceae
    Family Gomphonemaceae
    Family Cymbellaceae
    Family Epithemiaceae
    Family Bacillariaceae
Suborder Surirellineae
    Family Surirellaceae

The classification used in this treatise will reflect both the thinking of Hendey (1964) and Silva (1962). The diatoms should be considered as a Division of Plants. There does not seem to be any logical reason to subdivide them into classes as Silva has done. Originally they were placed in two major groups (Centrales and Pennales) on the basis of symmetry of the markings on the cell wall, the lack of raphe or pseudoraphe, and the belief that the Centrales were haploid in their vegetative state. The recent works of Schmidt (1927), von Stosch (1950), and Geitler (1952) show that some members of this group are diploid in their vegetative stage. Certainly many of them do not have symmetrical structure of the valve or of the markings on the valves; however, the markings are usually oriented about one or more loci, whereas the other group of species (Pennales) has these markings in a bilateral symmetry about the apical axis. Until further study is made, it seems best to consider all the diatoms as we now know them to belong to one class, the Bacillariophyceae.

Recently Hendey and Lewin have described the structure of *Phaeodactylum* which does not have the typical structure of the diatom frustule— that is, it does not have two well-developed valves and a girdle. It does have a partial siliceous valve structure which seems to vary in development according to the form which the species has. Lewin's illustrations indicate that it has in the oval form a raphe and a valve structure that is similar to some *Cymbella* species. Ross and Hendey (personal communications) consider it a degenerate *Cymbella* type. However, it differs from all other diatoms in that it has polymorphic non-siliceous forms in the vegetative state. The siliceous frustule when present is different in form from that of known diatoms.

The systematic classification of the diatoms considered in this work is as follows:

Division Bacillariophyta
  Class Bacillariophyceae
    Order Fragilariales
    Order Eunotiales
    Order Achnanthales
    Order Naviculales
    Order Bacillariales
    Order Surirellales
    Order Eupodiscales
    Order Rhizosoleniales
    Order Biddulphiales

In the first volume the following orders and families will be considered:

Order Fragilariales
  Family Fragilariaceae
Order Eunotiales
  Family Eunotiaceae
Order Achnanthales
  Family Achnanthaceae
Order Naviculales
  Family Naviculaceae

Literature Cited

CLEVE-EULER, A. 1952 Die diatomeen von Schweden und Finnland. *Kongliga Svenska Vetenskaps-Akademiens Handlinger*, Fjärde Serien, 3(3):1-153.

GEITLER, L. 1952 Oogamie, Mitose, Meiose und metagame Teilung bei der zentrischen Diatomee *Cyclotella*. *Österreichischen Botanischen Zeitschrift*. Wien, 99(4):506-520.

GRUNOW, A. 1860 Ueber neue oder ungenügend gekannte Algen. *Verhandlungen der Zoologisch-Botanischen Gesellschaft in Wien*, 10:503-582.

HEIDEN, H. AND A. W. KOLBE 1928 Die Marinen Diatomeen der Deutschen Südpolar-Expedition, 1901-1903. *Deutsche Südpolar Expedition*, Band 8, Heft 5, pp. 450-714.

HENDEY, N. I. 1937 The plankton diatoms of the Southern Seas. *Discovery Reports*, 16:151-364.

———— 1964 An introductory account of the smaller algae of British Coastal Waters. Part V. Bacillariophyceae (Diatoms). Ministry of Agriculture, Fisheries and Food, Fisheries Investigations, Series IV. London, 317 pp. + 45 pls.

HUSTEDT, F.   1930   Bacillariophyta. *In* A. Pascher's *Die Susswasser-Flora Mitteleuropas.* Volume 10, pp. 1-466. Jena.

KARSTEN, G.   1928   Bacillariophyta (Diatomeae). *In* Engler & Prantl, Die Natürlichen Pflanzenfamilien: Peridineae, Diatomae, Myxomycetes, 2nd edition, volume 2. Leipzig, pp. 105-303.

MERESCHKOWSKY, C.   1903   Les Types des Auxospores chez Les Diatomées et leur Evolution. *Ann. Sc. Nat. Bot.*, 17(15):225-262.

ØSTRUP, E.   1910   Diatoms from North-East Greenland collected by the Danmark-Expedition. *Kommisionen for Videnskabelige Undersøgelser i Grønland.* Kjøbenhavn, 13/14:193-256.

PETIT, P.   1877   Liste des Diatomées et des Desmidiées observées dans les environs de Paris. *Bulletin de la Société Botanique de France*, 23/24:30 pp.

PFITZER, E.   1871   Untersuchungen über Bau und Entwicklung der Bacillariaceen (Diatomaceen). *In* Hanstein, *Botanische Abhandlungen aus dem Gebiet der Morphologie und Physiologie.* Bonn, 1(2):vi+189 pp. + 6 pls.

RALFS, J.   1861   Diatomaceae. *In* A history of Infusoria including the Desmidiaceae and Diatomaceae, British and foreign, by A. Pritchard. London, Whittaker and Co., 968 pp. + 40 pls.

SCHMIDT, P.   1927   Weiteres über die Fortpflanzung der Diatomee Biddulphia sinensis. *Internationale Revue der Gesamten Hydrobiologie und Hydrographie*, 18(5/6): 400-414.

SCHÜTT, F.   1896   Bacillariales (Diatomaceae). *In* Engler and Prantl, Die Natürlichen Pflanzenfamilien, volume 1, part 1b. Leipzig, pp. 31-150.

SILVA, P. C.   1962   Classification of Algae. *In* Physiology and Biochemistry of Algae, edited by R. A. Lewin. New York, Academic Press, Appendix A.

SMITH, H. L.   1872   Conspectus of the families and genera of the Diatomaceae. *The Lens*, 1:1-19.

VAN HEURCK, H. F.   1880-1885   Synopsis des Diatomées de Belgique, Atlas et texte. Anvers, L'auteur, 235 pp. + 132 pls.

VON STOSCH, H. A.   1950   Oögamy in a centric diatom. *Nature*, 165(4196):531-532.

VII. METHODS AND TECHNIQUES

Collection of Diatoms

The method of collection is largely determined by the manner of growth of the diatoms.

Plankton diatoms may be taken by a net provided the net is of fine mesh. It should not allow particles of 10μ to pass through it. Often a #20 (about 75μ mesh) silk bolting cloth net is used. However, a net of this fineness does allow the very small forms to pass through. Nannoplankton nets (28μ mesh) for some types of plankton are useful. If a rough estimate of the amount of plankton present is desired, water may be poured through a net and the amount of water passed through measured. A net may be towed but it is often very difficult to determine just how much water has actually passed through the net. Such a method is suitable for qualitative sampling.

Whole water samples are often collected and the sample immediately passed through a millipore filter. This method insures the collection of all diatoms in the sample. The diatoms can be removed, but if soluble filters are used they can be dissolved and the diatoms can be separated from the solution by decanting. In this way all specimens are retained for study. Another method is to treat the whole water sample with Lugol's solution and allow it to settle. The supernatant is decanted and the sediments retained for study.

If it is desirable to study plankton which may be at various depths, particularly in the ocean, such samples may be secured by pumping water from a known water level to a container on shipboard. It is sometimes desirable to use one of the various types of water samplers which actually take a core of water from a given level. In either case such samples may be filtered or concentrated by one of the methods described above.

Benthic diatoms may live either near or on but not attached to the substrate. Such diatoms are best collected by an aspirator bottle, the tube of which is held a short distance above the substrate so that one can suck up the surface layer. Such diatoms may also be collected by means of a spoon in which one can skim off the surface layer without removing much of the substrate. Where the diatoms are attached to the substrate they can best be removed by a spoon which has been filed on one margin so as to present a smooth, fairly sharp edge, or by a knife.

Epiphytic diatoms are those which grow attached to plants. Usually the best way to collect them is by squeezing fairly large samples of the plants to which they are attached. Sometimes scraping the surfaces of plants is advisable particularly when the diatoms are attached to the stems or under sides of leaves of various higher plants. Occasionally it is advisable to collect small portions of the plant on which the diatoms are growing and subsequently destroy the plant substrate by the cleaning process.

Diatoms living in soil are collected by obtaining small samples of the soil. They are separated from the soil in cleaning process.

Fossil diatoms are also collected by preserving a portion of the matrix in which they are embedded. They are subsequently separated from the matrix.

Diatoms living on moist rocks or other aerial substrates are best collected by scraping the substrate. Care should be taken to remove as little of the substrate as possible.

Diatometer. When it is desirable to collect diatoms in order to compare one section of a body of water with another section or two separate bodies of water, the Catherwood diatometer is a very satisfactory means for obtaining the samples, fig. 9. This method was developed by Patrick *et al.* (1954). Both benthic and plankton forms are collected. The glass

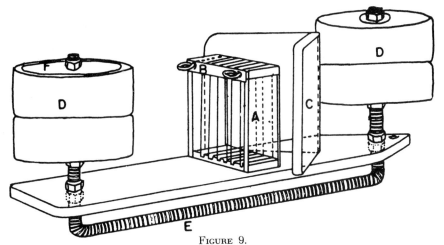

FIGURE 9.

The diatometer. A, slide holder; B, retaining bar; C, deflector; D, cork floats or styrofoam; E, threaded iron rod; F, identification tag.

slides are usually exposed for a period of two weeks or until the surface is fairly well covered with diatoms. The slides are then removed and placed in a dry place. In this condition they will last indefinitely. When it is desirable to study the diatoms, the slides are soaked in distilled water and the diatoms are removed from the slide by lightly scraping or rubbing them off. They are then cleaned and mounted on slides as described below.

Preservation

Following collection the method of preservation depends on the type of study one wishes to make. For cytological studies the methods of fixation have been well described by Hustedt (1927). Since at the present time taxonomic studies are based mainly on the structure of the siliceous wall, no special care need to be taken for preservation for this purpose. However, for wet samples it is usually advisable to add 4% neutral formalin in order to preserve them in solution. If preferred, they may be preserved in 70% ethanol. The most important consideration is to place them in a container or packet so that contamination will not occur. Because diatoms are microscopic, one is often not aware that contamination is taking place. Therefore, those methods used for maintaining sterile cultures should be employed in handling diatoms.

Cleaning of Diatoms

For most diatoms it is advisable to clean them in order to remove the organic matter within them and/or the substrate with which they are associated. However, tropical marine plankton of species which are lightly silicified will be destroyed by cleaning. In such cases they should be carefully washed to remove the salt solution in which they were collected or the particulate matter associated with them. They should be mounted onto slides as soon as possible.

The type of cleaning varies with the condition of the diatoms. Van Heurck (1896), Boyer (1916), and Hustedt (1927) describe various methods. The following methods have been used by the authors.

If the diatom collections are not intermixed with other algae and do not contain bits of the substrate, they may be cleaned by incineration. This is done by placing the cover slips on which the diatoms are to be mounted on a piece of metal which is fitted over the top of an electric hot plate. A small amount of the diatom material is placed on the cover slip and heated until it turns an ash gray or brown color. The cover slip is then inverted on the mounting medium which has been placed in the center of a slide.

This method can only be used when sediments are absent and the material is primarily diatoms. The advantage of this method of preparation is that it often preserves the manner of growth of the diatoms.

If the diatoms are associated with other algae or organic sediments, a very satisfactory way is to place the sample in a small beaker (100 cc.) and decant most of the water. Then add a little sulphuric acid. This solution will usually become very hot due to the interaction of the acid and water. Additional heat is usually applied and the solution cooked for twenty minutes. The sample should be stirred so as to keep the sediments from accumulating on the bottom of the flask. When the oxidation of the organic matter seems to be almost complete, a very small amount of potassium dichromate is slowly added until the solution becomes a brown color. The solution is then removed from the stove and allowed to cool. Next, the solution is decanted and distilled water added. This is repeated until the pH is 7. Great care should be taken to keep all of the diatoms, which will form a sediment, in the beaker. Alcohol is added after the final washing and after most of the water has been decanted. It is often desirable to add a crystal of thymol to prevent fungi from forming in preserved material. The fungi usually will not grow if the material has been thoroughly cleaned. Often the cleaned material is preserved dry on small pieces of plastic or mica. If this is done, the material should be sealed in cellophane or carefully protected so that contamination will not occur.

If one does not wish to heat the acid solution, cleaning can be accomplished by simply allowing the acid mixture to stand until most of the organic matter is removed. The subsequent procedures are the same as those given above.

Fossil diatoms should be cleaned according to the matrix in which they are embedded. If the diatoms are embedded in limestone, they should be cleaned with hydrochloric acid. If organic matter is present, this treatment should be followed by treatment with nitric acid. However, if cellulose is present, treatment with sulphuric acid may be required. The method of treatment is similar regardless of what acid is used. If only hydrochloric acid treatment is required, the addition of potassium dichromate is not necessary. If diatoms are embedded in clay, they should be cleaned in 30% hydrogen peroxide. This will usually break up the clay into a more or less homogeneous mixture.

Separation of Diatoms

The separation of diatoms is usually accomplished by magnifying the effect of the difference of specific gravity between the diatoms and the material you wish to separate them from. To do this, diatoms may be suspended in solutions of varying specific gravity. The choice is whether one wishes the diatoms to float and the matrix to settle or the matrix to float and the diatoms to settle. Once this is decided the sample is placed in a burette so that as the sediments settle they can be drawn off.

Mounting of Diatoms

Strewn mounts or mounts containing a mixture of diatoms are those most commonly made. If the diatoms are very poorly silicified such as some tropical plankton species, they should have the salt removed by washing and then be mounted directly into Pleurax. Pleurax is a synthetic medium made by Hanna (1949). Diatoms which have been cleaned according to one of the procedures given above should be mounted in Hyrax (Hanna, 1930). Until this medium for mounting diatoms was described by Hanna, most diatoms were mounted in Styrax which is a natural gum. The important consideration is to have an easy to handle medium with a high refractive index. In using Styrax or Hyrax the diatoms first should be thoroughly dried on the cover glass. A small amount of the mounting medium is placed on the slide and the cover glass inverted on it. The cover glass should be carefully pressed down on the medium in order to make as thin and even a mount as possible. The mount should then be heated over an alcohol flame or a slow heat in order to evaporate all the solvent. It is only in this way that a hard permanent mount can be made.

Sometimes it is desirable to make a mount of one or a few diatom specimens. To do this the sample from which the diatom is to be selected should be very thoroughly washed with distilled water after cleaning. A small amount of the material should be spread out on a clean glass slide. The specimen to be mounted should be located. This may be transferred to a prepared cover glass by a bristle or a fine glass thread. A mechanical manipulator is very useful; however, this procedure can be done by hand. The cover glass on which the diatom is to be placed should be coated by a very thin layer of gelatin prepared in the following way:

Glacial acetic acid	12 parts
Gelatin	2 parts
Alcohol	1 part

Add the acid to the gelatin and heat in a water bath. Then add the alcohol. Filter while warm. Spread a small amount in a very thin layer over the cover glass and allow the thin layer to dry.

After the diatom has been transferred to the dry, coated cover glass, gently breathe on the cover glass. This will melt the gelatin sufficiently to hold the diatom in place. Then invert the cover glass on the mounting medium and gently press, but not enough to disarrange the diatom. In order to make a hard mount, the slide should be heated. This should be done very slowly so that bubbles will not form that might dislodge the diatom.

The slides and cover slips to be used in making strewn or single mounts should be carefully cleaned. The following mixture is a satisfactory one in which slides and cover slips may be soaked for cleaning:

2 parts potassium dichromate
3 parts sulphuric acid (conc.)
25 parts water

Preparation for Electron Microscope Study

The specimens should be thoroughly cleaned by acid treatment. The mounting of the specimens for electron microscope study calls for special techniques. Those have been described by Hendey (1959) as follows: " . . . the specimens have to be mounted on a supporting film sufficiently thin to offer little opacity or scattering power to the electron beam. For a 50kV beam, films of a thickness of the order of 100Å should be aimed at, and these are supported on metal grids. These grids are about 3 mm. in diameter, having 200 meshes to the inch. The square apertures in this grid are about 60-70μ on each side and are separated by wires of approximately the same width. The supporting films may be made either of nitro-cellulose, ethyl cellulose or polyvinyl formal (formvar).

"The simplest method of making a film is by allowing a drop of nitro-cellulose, 3% in amyl acetate, to fall upon the surface of clean distilled water in a dish about 20 cm. in diameter. The drop should spread out radially and evenly and will halt at a distance of approximately 2 cm. from the edge of the dish. Irregular spreading of the film indicates that the surface of the water is not clean and such films should be gently swept off. This usually cleans the water surface and enables a more perfect film to be cast. When a satisfactory film has been obtained six or eight metal grids are laid on it at rougly equal intervals at a distance of about 2-3 cm. from the edge. By means of a special ring tool plunged beneath the water surface, the film, with the grid immediately above it, is lifted slightly above the general level. The film is then cut around the grid and from the stem of the ring tool by a mounted needle, and is lifted up. The ring is then inverted over a cylindrical peg which is mounted on a special stand. The film is now lying on the upper surface of the grid and the cut margin is hanging skirt-wise around the peg. The ring tool is now withdrawn from below the peg and any residual drop of water on the film may be removed by the edge of a piece of filter paper. Several such pegs with grids and films are prepared and placed in a desiccator until required . . .

"By means of a pipette one drop of the cleaned diatom material, sufficiently diluted, is allowed to fall on to the prepared film which is then returned to the desiccator until dry. The dried film, without further treatment, is now ready to be placed in the electron microscope. With some large specimens the making of supporting films is unnecessary as the specimens may be selected on a bristle and placed by hand directly on the surface of the grid."

R. Patrick

Literature Cited

Boyer, C. S. 1916 The Diatomaceae of Philadelphia and vicinity. Philadelphia, J. B. Lippincott Co., 143 pp. + 40 pls.

Hanna, G. D. 1930 Hyrax, a new mounting medium for diatoms. *Journal of the Royal Microscopical Society.* London, Series 3, 50(4):424-426.

———— 1949 A synthetic resin which has unusual properties. *Journal of the Royal Microscopical Society.* London, Series 3, 69(1):25-28.

Hendey, N. I. 1959 The structure of the diatom cell wall as revealed by the electron microscope. *Journal of the Quekett Microscopical Club,* Series 4, 5(6):147-175.

Hustedt, F. 1927 Die Kieselalgen Deutschlands, Österreichs und der Schweiz mit Berücksichtigung der übrigen Länder Europas sowie der angrenzenden Meeresgebiete. *In* Dr. L. Rabenhorst's *Kryptogamen-Flora von Deutschland, Österreich und der Schweiz.* Volume 7, part 1, number 1, pp. 12-216. Akademische Verlagsgesellschaft, Leipzig.

Patrick, R., M. H. Hohn, and J. H. Wallace 1954 A new method for determining the pattern of the diatom flora. *Notulae Naturae of the Academy of Natural Sciences of Philadelphia,* No. 259, 12 pp.

Van Heurck, H. F. 1896 A treatise on the Diatomaceae, containing introductory remarks on the structure, life history, collection, cultivation and preparation of diatoms, and a description and figure of every species found in the North Sea and countries bordering it, including Great Britain, Belgium, etc. Translated by W. E. Baxter. London, William Wesley and Son, xx + 558 pp. + 35 pls.

Systematic Section

Division **BACILLARIOPHYTA**

The Bacillariophyta (diatoms) are considered by some to be a class in the Chrysophyta. In the *International Rules of Botanical Nomenclature*, Hustedt (1931), and Silva (1962), they are regarded as a division of the Plant Kingdom as are the other main groups of algae.

They are characterized by being unicellular plants which in their vegetative state are surrounded by a wall of silica. This wall of silica is known as the frustule and consists of two halves. Each half is composed of a valve and a girdle. As in the Chrysophyta their storage products are not carbohydrates. Both groups are rich in carotenoid pigments. They propagate mainly by asexual reproduction, although sexual reproduction is now known in many genera.

The diatoms considered in this book belong to the class Bacillariophyceae. Whether another class should be recognized depends on whether one considers *Phaeodactylum coronutus* sufficiently different from all other diatoms to place it in a separate class.

KEY TO THE ORDERS OF BACILLARIOPHYCEAE

1. Valve of frustules with raphe or pseudoraphe 4
1. Valve of frustules without raphe or pseudoraphe 2
    2. Valve radially symmetrical, without well-developed horns, long spines, or large knobs or protuberances . . . . Eupodiscales
    2. Valve not radially symmetrical 3
3. Frustules cylindrical in shape, with many intercalary bands which are apparent in girdle view, the side of the frustule usually apparent . . . . Rhizosoleniales
3. Frustules not cylindrical in shape, valve bipolar or multipolar, symmetry emphasized by the angular shape or by knobs or horns or long spines . . . . . . Biddulphiales
    4. Both valves of the frustule with pseudoraphe . . . . Fragilariales
    4. Valves with a true raphe on one or both valves 5
5. Valves with a short raphe on one or both valves . . . . Eunotiales
5. Valve with a raphe extending the full length of the valve on one or both valves 6
    6. One valve with a well-developed raphe, the other with a pseudoraphe
                                                                     Achnanthales
    6. Both valves with well-developed raphes 7
7. Raphe not enclosed in a keel or a canal . . . . Naviculales
7. Raphe enclosed in a keel or a canal 8

8. Raphe enclosed in a keel which is on the edge of a raised "wing-like" structure
Surirellales
8. Raphe otherwise placed.. 9
9. Raphe enclosed in a keel, "wing-like" structures absent ....Nitzschiales
9. Raphe enclosed in a canal, costae present, between which are rows of striae
Epithemiales

This book is concerned mainly with species living in fresh water. For this reason the orders which include most of the fresh-water species will be considered first.

Order FRAGILARIALES

Silva *in* Lewin, Physiol. & Biochem. Algae, p. 835. 1962.

The diatoms belonging to this order are characterized by having a pseudoraphe present on both valves. No easily definable raphe is present. Kolbe (1956) describes what he calls a rudimentary raphe in *Amphicampa* and a "true" raphe in *Pseudoeunotia hemicyclus* (referred to in this book as *Semiorbis hemicyclus*). However, until these structures are verified for certain as being true raphe, I prefer to place these genera in this order.

Family FRAGILARIACEAE

Hust. *in* Pasch., Süssw.-Fl. Mitteleuropas, Heft 10, Aufl. 2, p. 56. 1930.

The Fragilariales are represented by a single family Fragilariaceae in the species considered in this book. The species of the Fragilariaceae may live singly, in filaments, or in more or less star-shaped colonies. A pseudoraphe is present on both valves. The chloroplasts are usually small plates, but are occasionally large plates. The apical axis of the valve is usually straight and the valve is usually isopolar.

Some of the species are planktonic while others are benthic, being either free-living or epiphytic.

Three subfamilies are considered in this book.

The type genus of this family is *Fragilaria* Lyngb.

KEY TO THE SUBFAMILIES OF FRAGILARIACEAE

1. Septa present ....Tabellarioideae (p. 100) 1
1. Septa absent 2
   2. Costae and striae present on the valve surface ....Diatomoideae (p. 105) 2
   2. Striae present and costae absent on the valve surface
Fragilarioideae (p. 114) 3

Subfamily TABELLARIOIDEAE

Hust. *in* Pasch., Süssw.-Fl. Mitteleuropas, Heft 10, Aufl. 2, p. 120. 1930.

This subfamily is characterized by the presence of septa.

Genus **Tetracyclus** Ralfs

Ralfs, Ann. Mag. Nat. Hist., 12:105. 1843.

Frustules occurring in filaments; in girdle view rectangular with numerous intercalary bands and short septa. The septa are well developed at one end of the valve, but as only a narrow band throughout the rest of the valve. Valve varying in shape, with costae and striae present. The costae are usually curved and of irregular length, some extending across the valve. Striae between the costae numerous and finely punctate. Pseudoraphe narrow, usually indistinct. Chloroplasts numerous small discs.

The species of this genus are usually found in shallow water and seem to prefer cold water.

Type species. — *Tetracyclus lacustris* Ralfs.

1. **Tetracyclus elliptica** (Ehr.) Grun. var. **elliptica**   PL. 1, FIG. 7

Biblarium ellipticum Ehr., Ber. Akad. Wiss. Berlin, for 1845:74.   1845.
Tetracyclus ellipticus (Ehr.) Grun., Verh. Zool.-Bot. Ges. Wien, 12:411.   1862.
Tetracyclus rhombus var. *maxima* Temp. & Perag., Diat. Monde Entier, 2nd ed., p. 195.   1910.

Frustules in girdle view rectangular, with intercalary bands and septa. Valve elliptical to elliptical-lanceolate. Pseudoraphe narrow, often indistinct. Costae varying in length, some extending across the valve, others marginal. Fine punctate striae between the costae. Costae, 2-4 in 10μ. Striae, 20-24 in 10μ. Length, 30-50μ. Breadth, 16-32μ.

This taxon is distinguished by the shape of the valve. It is known from only one locality in the United States.

Type locality. — Blaue Eisenerde, vivianit von Bargusinsk, Siberia.

U. S. distribution. — GEOGRAPHICAL: Oregon.

2. **Tetracyclus emarginatus** (Ehr.) W. Sm. var. **emarginatus**

PL. 1, FIG. 8

Biblarium emarginatum Ehr., Ber. Akad. Wiss. Berlin, for 1845:74.   1845.
Tetracyclus emarginatus (Ehr.) W. Sm., Syn. British Diat., vol. 2, p. 38.   1856.

Frustules in girdle view quadrate, with intercalary bands and septa evident. Valve cruciform in shape with rostrate to somewhat capitate ends. Transverse expanded portion of the valve incised. Pseudoraphe narrow, distinct. Costae irregular in length, some extending entirely across the valve; usually curved. Striae distinctly but finely punctate. Costae, 2-4 in 10μ. Striae, 20-25 in 10μ. Length, 28-55μ. Breadth of the valve at widest point, 22-28μ.

This taxon is distinguished from *Tetracyclus lacustris* by the emarginate valves. Perhaps it should be considered a variety of *T. lacustris*. The *Mikro-*

geologie is often given as the reference for the original description of this species.

Type locality. — Infusorien-Lager von Bargusina im Gouvernement Irkutzk in Siberia.

U. S. distribution. — GEOGRAPHICAL: New Jersey, Oregon. ECOLOGICAL: Seems to prefer cool water in lakes or ponds.

3. **Tetracyclus lacustris** Ralfs var. **lacustris**   PL. 1, FIG. 9

> *Tetracyclus lacustris* Ralfs, Ann. Mag. Nat. Hist., 12:105, pl. 2, fig. 2. 1843.
> *Tetracyclus stella* (Ehr.) Hérib., Diat. Foss. Auvergne, vol. 1, p. 17, pl. 8, fig. 9. 1902.

Frustules in girdle view almost as broad as long with numerous intercalary bands and septa. Valve strongly swollen in the middle portion with rostrate, somewhat capitate or wedge-shaped ends. Pseudoraphe distinct, narrow. Costae irregular in length, usually somewhat curved. Striae distinctly and finely punctate. Costae, 3-4 in 10μ. Striae, about 24 in 10μ. Length, about one and one-half times the breadth of the valve. Length, 30-80μ. Breadth, 15-35μ.

This taxon is most easily distinguished by the shape of the valve.

Type locality. — Llyn Prefeddyr near Barmouth, the Rev. T. Salwey.

U. S. distribution. — GEOGRAPHICAL: Tennessee, Nebraska, Utah, Oregon. ECOLOGICAL: Seems to prefer cool water with little or no current.

Genus **Tabellaria** Ehr.

Ehr., Ber. Akad. Wiss. Berlin, for 1840:217. 1840.

Frustules forming zigzag or straight filaments; in girdle view rectangular. Intercalary bands and septa present. In girdle view the septa appear as short thickened lines. In valve view the septa extend at varying lengths under the surface of the valve. Valve finely striated, costae absent.

Most of the species of this genus occur in fresh water.

Type species —*Tabellaria trinodis* Ehr. which is the same as *Tabellaria fenestrata* (Lyngb.) Kütz.

KEY TO THE SPECIES OF TABELLARIA

1. Valve constricted in the middle ....[1] *T. binalis*
1. Valve swollen in the middle... 2
   2. Rudimentary septa absent, jelly pore near the center of the median inflation
                                                             [2] *T. fenestrata*
   2. Rudimentary septa present.. 3
3. Septa four or less, jelly pore near one end of the inflation in the middle of the valve
                                                          [4] *T. quadrisepta*
3. Septa numerous ....[3] *T. flocculosa*

1. Tabellaria binalis (Ehr.?) Grun. var. binalis   PL. 1, FIG. 6

Fragilaria? binalis Ehr., Mikrogeol., pl. 1(3), fig. 9; pl. 14, fig. 52. 1854.
Tabellaria binalis Grun. *in* V. H., Syn. Diat. Belgique, pl. 44, fig. 23. 1881.

Colonies with usually straight filaments of frustules. In girdle view many intercalary bands with numerous, very short septa which are usually not perpendicular to the transverse axis. In valve view swollen, somewhat wedge-shaped apices; constricted in the middle portion of the valve. Pseudoraphe distinct. Striae parallel in the middle portion of the valve, radiate toward the ends. Striae, 15-18 in 10μ. Length, $8\text{-}22\mu$. Breadth at the center of the valve, $3\text{-}5\mu$.

This taxon is distinguished in girdle view by the straight filaments and frustules with very short septa; in valve view it is distinguished by its shape.

One cannot be certain from Ehrenberg's plates that his taxon was the same as ours.

Type locality. — Kieselguhr (Vulkanische Asche) von Isle de France der Mascarenen-Inseln.

U. S. distribution. — GEOGRAPHICAL: New Hampshire, North Carolina. ECOLOGICAL: In water of very low mineral content (oliogotrophic).

2. Tabellaria fenestrata (Lyngb.) Kütz. var. fenestrata   PL. 1, FIGS. 1-2

Diatoma fenestratum Lyngb., Tent. Hydropht. Danicae, p. 180, pl. 61, fig. E, 3. 1819.
Tabellaria trinodis Ehr., Ber. Akad. Wiss. Berlin, for 1840:217, 1840.
Tabellaria fenestrata (Lyngb.) Kütz., Bacill., p. 127, pl. 18, fig. 2. 1844. (pl. 17, fig. 22; pl. 30, fig. 73; questionable.)
Striatella fenestrata [Lyngb.] (Kütz.) Kuntze, Revisio Gen. Plant., vol. 3, pt. 2, p. 432. 1898.

Colonies forming a more or less straight filament—not zigzag. Girdle view with four or less septa which are bent away from the valve for a short distance below the point of insertion. Knudson (1952) has very rarely observed five septa. No rudimentary septa present. In valve view linear; swollen at the center of the valve and at the distinctly capitate apices. The width of the valve in the middle portion and at the apices is about the same. The jelly pore is located near the center of the median inflation. Pseudoraphe distinct, sometimes somewhat wider at the center of the valve forming a small central area of variable shape. Striae parallel, 14-18 in 10μ. Length, $25\text{-}116\mu$, usually $40\text{-}75\mu$. Breadth in the middle portion, usually $5\text{-}10\mu$, but occasionally less.

This species is distinguished by the shape of the septa in girdle view, the lack of rudimentary septa, the position of the jelly pore, and the kinds of filaments formed by the frustules.

Knudson (1952, pp. 433-435) has given a fine account of this species.

Type locality. — Habitat in rivulo leniter fluente ad Naes Norvegiae.

U. S. distribution. — GEOGRAPHICAL: The distribution of this species has been confused due to misidentification. We are including only the American distribution we have verified. New England States, Middle Atlantic States, Southeastern States, Gulf Coast States, South Central States, East Central States, Lakes States; Montana, Wyoming, Utah, Washington, Oregon, California. ECOLOGICAL: Seems to prefer lakes or ponds which are mesotrophic to eutrophic; seems to prefer circumneutral water; usually in shallow water, often attached to substrate.

3. **Tabellaria flocculosa** (Roth) Kütz. var. **flocculosa**   PL. 1, FIGS. 4-5

> *Conferva flocculosa* Roth, Catalecta Bot., Fasc. 1, p. 192, pl. 4, fig. 4; pl. 5, fig. 6. 1797.
> *Tabellaria flocculosa* (Roth) Kütz., Bacill., p. 127, pl. 17, fig. 21. 1844.
> *Tabellaria flocculosa* var. *ventricosa* (Kütz.) Grun., Verh. Zool.-Bot. Ges. Wien, 12:410. 1862.
> *Tabellaria fenestrata* var. *intermedia* Grun. *in* V. H., Syn. Diat. Belgique, pl. 52, figs. 6-8. 1881.
> *Striatella flocculosa* (Roth) Kuntze, Revisio Gen. Plant., vol. 3, pt. 2, p. 432. 1898.

Colonies composed of zigzag filaments of frustules. In the girdle view the septa are usually more than four, usually not straight. Rudimentary septa usually present. The number of septa seems to increase with decrease in the length of the valve. The length-to-breadth ratio of the frustule in girdle view is usually less than 4:1. However, in those specimens often referred to as "*T. fenestrata* var. *intermedia*" the ratio may be as great as 6:1. Valve with swollen central area often wider than the swollen apices which are quite variable in shape. Valve slightly asymmetrical to either the transverse or apical axis, sometimes slightly asymmetrical to both. Pseudoraphe narrow. The position of the mucilage pore is variable. Striae, 14-18 in 10μ. Length of the valve usually less than 80μ, but may be as great as 130μ.

This taxon is distinguished in girdle view by its usually numerous septa, which are generally not straight, and the zigzag shape of the colonies.

In valve view this taxon is distinguished by the median swelling usually being greater than the apical ones and the variously placed mucilage pore. The valve often has an asymmetrical appearance.

Knudson (1952, pp. 428-433) has given a very fine account of the variability of this species.

Type locality. — Uncertain.

U. S. distribution. — GEOGRAPHICAL: New England States, Middle Atlantic States, Southeastern States, Gulf Coast States, South Central States, East Central States, West Central States, Lakes States, Plains States; Montana, Wyoming, Utah, Oregon and California. ECOLOGICAL: This taxon has a wide tolerance for different types of water. The specimens with shorter frustules are more often found in acid water of bogs and ponds, whereas those with longer frustules seem to be more often found in oligotrophic to mesotrophic water.

4. **Tabellaria quadrisepta** Knuds. var. **quadrisepta**   PL. 1, FIG. 3

Tabellaria quadrisepta Knuds., Ann. Bot., N.S., 16(63):436, figs. 1d-j, 6i-n. 1952.

Colonies of zigzag filaments of frustules. Frustules with usually four but sometimes less septa. Septa straight. Rudimentary septa may be present or absent. Valve with median and apical inflations which are approximately the same width. Apical inflations not distinctly capitate as in *Tabellaria fenestrata*. Pseudoraphe narrow. Mucilage pore near the periphery of the median inflation. Striae, 14-18 in 10μ. Length, $23-129\mu$. Breadth of the valve at broadest portion, about $6-9\mu$. Short marginal spines are sometimes present, as shown in the illustrated specimen.

This taxon is distinguished in girdle view by the straight septa, usually four, and the usual presence of rudimentary septa. In valve view it can usually be distinguished by the shape of the valve and the position of the jelly pore.

Type locality. — Tarn-at-Leaves, Cumberland, England. (*Holotype*—B.M. 36263, Knudson, 1952.)

U. S. distribution. — GEOGRAPHICAL: New Jersey, Minnesota, Nevada, California. ECOLOGICAL: Prefers acid bogs or pond water (dystrophic) or water of very low mineral content (oligotrophic).

Names of Taxa recorded from the U. S. (fresh water) which could not be verified by a specimen from a public herbarium.

Tabellaria fenestrata var. *asterionelloides* (recorded by Sister M. Maloney).
Tabellaria fenestrata var. *gracilis* Meist. (recorded by G. M. Smith).
Tabellaria venter Ehr. (recorded by Ehrenberg).
Tabellaria vulgaris Ehr. (recorded by Ehrenberg).

Taxa Recorded Since 1961

Tabellaria teilingii (recorded by Thomasson, 1962).

Subfamily **DIATOMOIDEAE**

Hust. *in* Pasch., Süssw.-Fl. Mitteleuropas, Heft 10, Aufl. 2, p. 125. 1930.

This subfamily is characterized by the presence of costae as well as striae on the valve and the absence of internal septa.

Genus **Diatoma** Bory nom. cons. non Loureiro 1790

Bory, Dict. Class. Hist. Nat., 5:461. 1824.
Odontidium Kütz. *emend* Bessey, Trans. American Micr. Soc., 21:76. 1899.

Frustules forming zigzag or linear filaments. Frustules in girdle view rectangular; intercalary bands sometimes present. Septa absent. Frustules in valve view linear to elliptical. Valve traversed by costae between which there are striae which are usually indistinctly punctate. Pseudoraphe very narrow or obscure. Jelly pore often distinct.

In the *Flora Française*, vol. 2, by Lamarck et De Candolle (1805, p. 48), the genus *Diatoma* is first described, but the species included in the genus are not those assigned to this genus today.

Type species. — *Diatoma vulgare* ("*vulgares*") Bory.

KEY TO THE SPECIES OF DIATOMA

1. Costae on the valve, usually less than 5 in 10μ; frustules forming straight fila-
   mentous colonies 2
1. Costae on the valve, usually more than 7 in 10μ; frustules forming zigzag bands . . 3
   2. Valve linear with distinctly formed apices which are capitate or attenuated,
      rostrate . . . . [1] *D. anceps*
   2. Valve lanceolate to elliptical-lanceolate, with rounded or only slightly attenu-
      ated apices . . . . [2] *D. hiemale*
3. Valve narrow, linear or linear-lanceolate, length-to-breadth ratio large; in girdle
   view narrowly rectangular . . . . [3] *D. tenue*
3. Valve linear to elliptical-lanceolate, in girdle view broadly rectangular, valve
   having a fairly broad appearance . . . . [4] *D. vulgare*

1. **Diatoma anceps** (Ehr.) Kirchn. var. **anceps**   PL. 2, FIGS. 1-3

> *Fragilaria* ? *anceps* Ehr., Phys. Abh. Akad. Wiss. Berlin, for 1841:415. 1843.
> *Odontidium anomalum* W. Sm., Ann. Mag. Nat. Hist., Ser. 2, 15:7, pl. 1, fig. 8.
>   1855.
> *Odontidium anceps* (Ehr.) Ralfs *in* Pritch., Hist. Infusoria, 4th ed., p. 776. 1861.
> *Diatoma anceps* (Ehr.) Kirchn. *in* Cohn, Kryptog.-Fl. Schlesien, Band 2(1), p. 204.
>   1878.
> *Diatoma anceps* var. *capitata* M. Perag. *in* Temp. & Perag., Diat. Monde Entier, 2nd
>   ed., p. 56. 1908.
> *Diatoma anceps* var. *constricta* Temp. & Perag., Diat. Monde Entier., 2nd ed., p. 349.
>   1912.

Frustules rectangular in girdle view, sometimes with intercalary bands, forming straight filamentous colonies. Valve linear or somewhat constricted, with slightly capitate to distinctly capitate ends. Pseudoraphe somewhat variable in width, sometimes indistinct. Costae, 3-6 in 10μ. Striae, 17-22 in 10μ. Length, usually 12-50μ; Hustedt (1931, p. 104) says they may be 100μ in length. Breadth, 4-8μ.

This species is distinguished by the shape of the valve and the fineness of the striae.

Type locality. — U. S. A., Pelham, Massachusetts.

U. S. distribution. — GEOGRAPHICAL: New England States, Middle Atlantic States, South Central States, East Central States, West Central States, Lakes States; Wyoming, Colorado, Utah, Oregon, California. ECOLOGICAL: Seems to prefer cool water of low mineral content, often found in mountainous regions.

1. **Diatoma anceps** var. **linearis** M. Perag.   PL. 2, FIG. 4

> *Diatoma anceps* var. *linearis* M. Perag. *in* Temp. & Perag., Diat. Monde Entier, 2nd ed., p. 56. 1908.

Valve linear with attenuated, rounded apices. Pseudoraphe very narrow. Costae, 3-4 in 10μ. Striae, 16-19 in 10μ. Length, about 45μ. Breadth, about 5μ.

This taxon is distinguished from the nominate variety by the shape of the apices of the valve.

Type locality. — U. S. A., Connecticut, Hartford County, Bristol, Fall Mountain (*Lectotype*—A-T.&P. 104, 2nd ed., Patrick.)

U. S. distribution. — GEOGRAPHICAL: Known only from the type locality.

2. **Diatoma hiemale** (Roth) Heib. var. **hiemale**   PL. 2, FIG. 7

> *Conferva hyemalis* Roth, Tent. Fl. Germanicae, vol. 3, pt. 1, no. 22, p. 506.   1800.
> *Odontidium hyemale* (Roth) Kütz., Bacill., p. 44, pl. 17(4), figs. 1-4.   1844.
> *Diatoma hyemale* (Roth) Heib., Consp. Crit. Diat. Danicarum, p. 58.   1863.

Frustules, forming straight filamentous colonies, rectangular in girdle view; intercalary bands present in girdle view. Valve linear-lanceolate to linear; narrowed toward the somewhat attenuated, rostrate apices. Pseudoraphe fairly broad in the middle portion of the valve, narrowing toward the apices. Costae, 2-4 in 10μ. Striae, 18-20 in 10μ. Length, $30\text{-}100\mu$. Breadth, $7\text{-}13\mu$.

This taxon is distinguished by the shape of the valve and the coarseness of the costae.

Both Kützing and Heiberg give Lyngbye as the authority for this specific name. Lyngbye cites Roth as the authority.

Type locality. — In piscinis prope Schoenebeck non procul vegesack primo observavi, postea passim in fossis.

U. S. distribution. — GEOGRAPHICAL: New England States, Middle Atlantic States, Gulf Coast States, South Central States, East Central States, West Central States, Lakes States, Plains States; Colorado, Utah, Washington. ECOLOGICAL: Seems to prefer cool, fresh water.

2. **Diatoma hiemale** var. **mesodon** (Ehr.) Grun.   PL. 2, FIG. 8

Fragilaria mesodon Ehr., Phys. Abh. Akad. Wiss. Berlin, for 1838:57, pl. 2(1), fig. 9. 1839.

Odontidium hiemale var. *mesodon* (Ehr.) Grun., Verh. Zool.-Bot. Ges. Wien, 12: 357. 1862.

Diatoma hiemale var. *mesodon* (Ehr.) Grun. *in* V. H., Syn. Diat. Belgique, pl. 51, figs. 3-4. 1881.

Frustules usually in zigzag filaments. Valve elliptical to elliptical-lanceolate, sometimes rhombic in shape. Pseudoraphe linear, narrow. Costae very few, usually 2-4 in 10µ. Striae, 18-24 in 10µ. Length, 12-40µ. Breadth, 6-15µ.

This taxon is distinguished by its shape and the low number of costae.

Type locality. — Schwarzenberg bei Sachsen.

U. S. distribution. — GEOGRAPHICAL: New England States, Middle Atlantic States, Southeastern States, South Central States, West Central States; Montana, Wyoming, Colorado, Utah, Oregon, California. ECOLOGICAL: Seems to prefer flowing water with fairly high nutrient content (mesotrophic).

3. **Diatoma tenue** Ag. var. **tenue**   PL. 2, FIG. 5

Diatoma tenue Ag., Sv. Bot., vol. 7, pl. 491, figs. 4-5. 1812.

Diatoma elongatum var. *tenue* (Ag.) V. H., Syn. Diat. Belgique, p. 160, 1885.

Odontidium elongatum var. *tenue* (Ag.) Patr., Not. Nat. Acad. Nat. Sci. Philadelphia, No. 28, p. 5. 1939.

Frustules in girdle view linear, rectangular with costae and striae evident. Valve linear to linear-lanceolate, with apices which are not clearly differentiated from the main body of the valve. Apices acute in the linear-lanceolate form; rounded, occasionally slightly swollen in the linear form. Pseudoraphe indist nct. Costae, 6-10 in 10µ. Striae, 16-20 in 10µ; usually 4 or less striae between 2 costae. Length, 20-55µ. Breadth, 3-5µ.

This taxon is distinguished by the shape of the valve and the costae which are closer together than in most species of *Diatoma*.

The correct species name for this taxon is *D. tenue* Ag., because it is the oldest valid name.

Type locality. — In aquis dulcibus Scandinaviae.

U. S. distribution. — GEOGRAPHICAL: New England States, East Central States; Kansas. ECOLOGICAL: In lakes or standing water; often found in water with relatively high conductivity or slightly salty.

3. **Diatoma tenue** var. **elongatum** Lyngb. PL. 2, FIG. 6

Diatoma tenue var. *elongatum* Lyngb., Tent. Hydrophyt. Danicae, p. 179, pl. 61, figs. E 1-2. 1819.
Diatoma elongatum (Lyngb.) Ag., Syst. Alg., p. 4. 1824.
Odontidium elongatum (Lyngb.) Elm., Univ. Nebraska Stud., 21(1/4):50, pl. 2, figs. 57-61. 1922.

Valve linear with definitely swollen, capitate apices. Pseudoraphe indistinct. Costae, 6-10 in 10μ. Striae, 16-18 in 10μ; usually 4 or less striae between the costae. Length, 40-120μ. Breadth, 2-4μ.

This taxon is distinguished by the linear shape of the valve and its swollen, capitate ends.

Hustedt (1931, p. 99) apparently did not know that Agardh had first published the name *Diatoma tenue* in 1812.

I have examined specimens of W. Smith's *D. tenue* (no. 228) which agree with these of Van Heurck. *D. Ehrenbergii* Kütz. is probably a synonym of this taxon. See discussion under *D. vulgare* var. *grande*.

Type locality. — In stagnosis Körup Fioniae.

U. S. distribution. — GEOGRAPHICAL: New England States, Middle Atlantic States, South Central States, East Central States, Lakes States, Plains States; Montana, Oregon, California. ECOLOGICAL: In fresh or slightly brackish water.

4. **Diatoma vulgare** Bory var. **vulgare** PL. 2, FIG. 9

Diatoma vulgare Bory, Dict. Class. Hist. Nat., 5:461. 1824. Dict. Sci. Nat., Planch.
  Bot.: Vég. Acot. 10 (Arthrodiées—4th pl.) fig. 1. 1816-1829.
Bacillaria vulgaris (Bory) Ehr., Ber. Akad. Wiss. Berlin, for 1836:53, 56. 1836.
Diatoma vulgare var. *productum* Grun., Verh. Zool.-Bot. Ges. Wien, 12:363. 1862.
Odontidium vulgare (Bory) Pfitz., Bot. Abh. Geb. Morph. Physiol., 1(2):121, pl. 6, fig. 20. 1871.

Frustules forming zigzag filaments. In girdle view frustules rectangular with intercalary bands. Valves linear-lanceolate to elliptical-lanceolate with somewhat attenuated, rostrate apices. Pseudoraphe very narrow. Jelly pore evident near one of the apices of the valve. Costae, 6-8 in 10μ. Striae, about 16 in 10μ. Length, 30-60μ. Breadth, 8-13μ.

This taxon is distinguished by its size, shape, and the number of costae in 10μ.

Many authors have considered *Diatoma vulgare* var. *productum* as distinct from the nominate variety. However, we have seen specimens which indicate these two taxa intergrade.

Kützing (1844, p. 47) seems to have confused this taxon with *Conferva flocculosa* Roth (*Tabellaria flocculosa*), probably because both taxa form zigzag filaments.

Type locality. — Uncertain, France.

U. S. distribution. — GEOGRAPHICAL: New England States, Middle Atlantic States, Southeastern States, South Central States, East Central States, West Central States, Lakes States, Plains States; Montana, Wyoming, Colorado, New Mexico, Idaho, Arizona, Nevada, Washington, California. ECOLOGICAL: Seems to prefer cool, flowing water; often found in water with fairly high nutrient content.

4. **Diatoma vulgare** var. **breve** Grun.   PL. 2, FIGS. 10-11

Diatoma vulgare var. *breve* Grun., Verh. Zool.-Bot. Ges. Wien, 12:363. 1862.
Odontidium vulgare var. *brevis* (Grun.) Patr., Not. Nat. Acad. Nat. Sci. Philadelphia, No. 28, p. 7. 1939.

Valve elliptical-lanceolate with rounded apices. Pseudoraphe indistinct. Jelly pore present, but often not as distinct as in the nominate variety. Costae, 6-8 in 10μ. Striae, about 16 in 10μ. Length, 24-50μ. Breadth, 11-13μ.

This taxon is distinguished from the nominate variety by the shape of the valve.

Type locality. — Uncertain.

U. S. distribution. — GEOGRAPHICAL: New England States, Middle Atlantic States, Southeastern States, West Central States, Plains States; Utah. ECOLOGICAL: Seems to prefer cool water.

4. **Diatoma vulgare** var. **grande** (W. Sm.) Grun.   PL. 2, FIGS. 13-14

Diatoma grande W. Sm., Syn. British Diat., vol. 2, p. 39, pl. 40, fig. 310. 1856.
Diatoma vulgare var. *grande* (W. Sm.) Grun., Verh. Zool.-Bot. Ges. Wien, 12:364. 1862.
Odontidium vulgare var. *grande* (W. Sm.) Patr., Not. Nat. Acad. Nat. Sci. Philadelphia, No. 28, p. 8. 1939.

Valve linear to slightly linear-lanceolate with distinctly capitate ends. Pseudoraphe narrow, often indistinct. Striae as in the nominate variety. Costae, 7-10 in 10μ. Length, 32-120μ. Breadth, 6-8μ.

This taxon is distinguished by its large size and shape.

This taxon has been confused with *Diatoma ehrenbergii* Kütz. Kützing states that his taxon is the same as *Bacillaria elongata* Ehr. which is based on *Diatoma elongata* (Lyngb.) Ag. W. Smith (1856) states that he has seen authenticated specimens of *D. ehrenbergii* Kütz. and that they undoubtedly belong to *D. elongata.* Likewise Van Heurck, who had part of Kützing's collection, considered *D. ehrenbergii* as a variety of *D. elongata.* Grunow (1862) considered *D. ehrenbergii* a variety of *D. vulgare,* but states that it is incomprehensible to him why one should consider it the same as *D. grande* W. Sm. Hustedt (1932) considered *D. grande* of W. Smith as synonymous with *D. ehrenbergii* Kütz. I have examined specimens of W. Smith's *D. grande* from material on which his original illustrations were based and have drawn one of them. This taxon is undoubtedly a variety of *D. vulgare*.

Type locality. — Uncertain.

U. S. distribution. — GEOGRAPHICAL: Pennsylvania, South Carolina, Florida.

4. **Diatoma vulgare** var. **linearis** V. H. PL. 2, FIG. 12

Diatoma vulgare var. *linearis* V. H., Syn. Diat. Belgique, pl. 50, figs. 7-8. 1881. (text, p. 160. 1885.)

Odontidium vulgare var. *linearis* (V. H.) Patr., Not. Nat. Acad. Nat. Sci. Philadelphia, No. 28, p. 8. 1939.

Valve linear with rounded apices. Pseudoraphe indistinct. Jelly pore evident near one of the apices of the valve. Costae irregularly placed, 5-8 in 10μ. Striae, about 16 in 10μ. Length, 44-75μ. Breadth, 7-10μ.

This taxon differs from the other varieties in the shape of the valve and the usually more irregularly placed costae.

Van Heurck states that his taxon is the same as *Diatoma vulgare* var. β of William Smith.

Type locality. — Uncertain.

U. S. distribution. — GEOGRAPHICAL: New York, Pennsylvania, Missouri, Minnesota, New Mexico. ECOLOGICAL: Seems to prefer cool, flowing water.

Names of Taxa reported from the U. S. (fresh water) which could not be verified by a specimen from a public herbarium.

Diatoma stellaris (recorded by Bailey).

Diatoma stellata (recorded by Bailey).

Names of Taxa which were misidentified or for which the original description cannot be found.

Diatoma vulgare var. *capitulatum* Grun. *in* V. H. (recorded by Boyer).

Diatoma hyemale f. *curta* (recorded *in* Temp. & Perag., 2nd ed., p. 56, with no description).

Genus **Meridion** Ag.

Ag., Syst. Alg., p. xiv. 1824.

Frustules in girdle view wedge-shaped; forming semicircular filaments. Intercalary bands present; septa absent. Valve linear-clavate. Costae present; some extend only partially across the valve, whereas others extend across the valve surface. Between the costae, striae are present. Pseudo-raphe of variable distinctness. Valve, except for length and placement of the costae, symmetrical to the apical axis; asymmetrical to the transverse axis; symmetrical to the pervalvar axis.

Agardh (*loc. cit.*) says that the type of this genus is *Meridion vernale* which is questionably *Echinella olivacea* Lyngb. (1819, pl. 70(C), figs. 2 and 3). In Agardh (*op. cit.*, pp. 2-3), he lists the following species as belong-ing to this genus: *M. vernale, M. ovatum,* and *M. radians.*

Leiblein (1830, pp. 308-313) states that his taxon is the same as Agardh's, but that Agardh's taxon probably is not the same as Lyngbye's.

Agardh (1824) described the genus *Meridion* (p. xiv) and three species —*M. vernale, M. ovatum,* and *M. radians* (pp. 2, 3). In his description he stated that the type is *M. vernale* and may be that illustrated by Lyngbye in pl. 70, figs. 2, 3. In the description of *M. vernale* (pp. 2, 3) he questions the synonymy of *Ulva olivacea* as described by Lyngbye and of *Echinella olivacea* Lyngb. (Pl. 70).

Through the courtesy of Dr. Hansen of Copenhagen, I have examined Lyngbye's specimens which Dr. Francis Drouet has designated as types for *Ulva olivacea* Hornemann and *Echinella cuneata* Lyngb. Both of these are mainly composed of *Gomphonema olivaceum* which fit the illustrations of Lyngbye (Pl. 70, C, F). They also contain specimens of *Diatoma elongatum.* However the circular filaments described by Agardh as charac-teristic of *Meridion* were not found. Therefore, based on these specimens it is doubtful that what Agardh was describing is the same taxon as what Lyngbye had previously described. Examinations of other specimens from Lyngbye's herbarium did not reveal the presence of the genus *Meridion,* although *Diatoma* was frequently found, and *Gomphonema olivaceum* was always present.

I have also, through the courtesy of Dr. Sven Snogerup, examined speci-mens of *M. vernale* and *M. ovatum* from the Agardh Herbarium.

M. vernale was studied from two sets of specimens. One, #4088, " . . . bro on stones at the water mill," (according to Dr. Snogerup) has a short diagnosis on the paper. Dr. Snogerup thinks this may be the type. However, the locality is not the same as that given in the type description of the spe-cies. In the portion of the specimen examined by me I could find no *Meridion.* This is a mixed collection and *G. olivaceum* is common. No circular filaments were found.

Another collection from Agardh's Herbarium, No. 4104, "Uppsala in rivulo fridiose, 23-5. 1833," is a later collection. It was examined and named by Agardh as he refers to his earlier description in the *Systema Algarum* of this species. This collection does contain specimens of *Meridion vernale* which is recognized today as *Meridion circulare.*

I have also examined the type of *Meridion ovata* (No. 4109). The species is described and illustrated on the label accompanying the species. It is the type collection of this taxon. There are specimens of *Meridion* present which we today would call *M. circulare*. Why Agardh (1830) considered this a species inquirenda I do not know. He certainly described it as a definite species in 1824. All of Agardh's specimens contained *G. olivaceum,* and without careful examination one might think that Agardh had not seen a true *Meridion*.

Since the label on specimen #4088 is not the locality given by Agardh for *M. vernale,* I do not believe we can definitely consider this the type of this species.

It is definite that Agardh was describing a new genus when he described *Meridion* as shown by the type specimens of *M. ovatum.* Furthermore, the 1833 specimens of *M. vernale* which are authenticated specimens, are the same taxon as that which we call *M. circulare* today.

Type species. — Meridion vernale Ag. This is the same as *Meridion circulare* (Grev.) Ag.

1. **Meridion circulare** (Grev.) Ag. var. **circulare**   PL. 2, FIG. 15

Echinella circularis Grev., Mem. Wernerian Nat. Hist. Soc., 4:213, pl. 8, fig. 2. 1822.

Meridion circulare (Grev.) Ag., Consp. Crit. Diat., pt. 3, p. 40. 1831.

Meridion zinkenii Kütz., Flora, 26:396. 1843.

Meridion circulare var. *zinkenii* (Kütz.) Grun., Verh. Zool.-Bot. Ges. Wien, 12:345. 1862.

Frustules forming circular-shaped filaments. Frustules in girdle view with intercalary bands; costae and striae distinctly evident on the valve mantle. Valve clavate; broader apex rounded; narrower one usually slightly swollen, somewhat capitate in shape. Pseudoraphe narrow, more or less distinct. Costae well developed, extending part way or all of the way across the valve. Costae, 3-5 in 10μ. Striae between the costae, 15-16 in 10μ. Length, $12-80\mu$. Breadth, $4-8\mu$.

This species is distinguished by the shape of the valve and the fineness of the costae and striae.

Type locality. — Rivulet near Dumbryden Quarries.

U. S. distribution. — GEOGRAPHICAL: New England States, Middle Atlantic States, Southeastern States, Gulf Coast States, South Central States, East Central States, West Central States, Lakes States, Plains States; Montana, Wyoming, Colorado, Utah, Oregon, California. ECOLOGICAL: Seems to prefer flowing, fresh water.

1. Meridion circulare var. constrictum (Ralfs) V. H.   PL. 2, FIG. 16

Meridion constrictum Ralfs, Ann. Mag. Nat. Hist., 12:458, pl. 18, fig. 2. 1843.
Meridion circulare var. *constrictum* (Ralfs) V. H., Syn. Diat. Belgique, pl. 51,
     figs. 14, 15. 1881. (text, p. 161-combination was made here. 1885.)

Frustules wedge-shaped in girdle and valve view. In valve view the broader apex is capitate. Jelly pore present. The pseudoraphe more or less distinct. Costae, 3-5 in 10μ. Striae, 15-16 in 10μ. Length variable, 12-80μ. Breadth at broadest portion, 4-8μ.

This taxon is distinguished from the nominate variety by the capitate end of the valve.

Grunow (1862) named "*Meridion constrictum*," W. Sm. (1856), *M. constrictum* var. *elongatum*. If this is the same as the typical *M. constrictum*, then this would be the oldest name at the variety rank and would then be the correct name at this rank. I have not been able to find his type specimen of his taxon.

Ehrenberg (1843, p. 416) describes *Gomphonema pupula*, which seems to be this taxon.

Type locality. — Uncertain.

U. S. distribution. — Geographical:New England States, Middle Atlantic States, Southeastern States, East Central States; Wyoming, Utah, Washington, California. Ecological: Similar to that of the nominate variety; tolerant of small amounts of NaCl.

Subfamily FRAGILARIOIDEAE

Hust. *in* Pasch., Süssw.-Fl. Mitteleuropas, Heft 10, Aufl. 2, p. 131. 1930.

This subfamily is characterized by the absence of septa and costae.

KEY TO THE GENERA OF FRAGILARIOIDEAE

1. Valve asymmetrical to transverse axis 2
1. Valve symmetrical to transverse axis 4
    2. Frustules commonly forming star-shaped colonies . . . . *Asterionella* (p. 158)
    2. Frustules occurring individually or forming short filaments 3
3. Margins of valve smooth . . . . *Opephora* (p. 115)
3. Margins of the valve sinuate-dentate . . . . *Amphicampa* (p. 161)
    4. Apical axis of the valve curved 5
    4. Apical axis of the valve straight 7
5. Valve symmetrical to the apical axis 6
5. Valve asymmetrical to the apical axis . . . . *Hannaea* (p. 131)
    6. Central area present . . . . *Synedra* (*cyclopum*) (p. 155)
    6. Central area absent . . . . *Semiorbis* (p. 162)
7. Frustules occurring free or attached, not forming long filaments . . *Synedra* (p. 133)
7. Frustules typically forming long filaments . . . . *Fragilaria* (p. 116)

Genus **Opephora** Petit

Petit, Miss. Sci. Cap Horn, 1882-1883, Bot., vol. 5, p. 130.   1888.

Frustules in girdle view somewhat wedge-shaped. In valve view one apex narrower than the other causing the valve to be asymmetrical to the transverse axis. Apices of the valve rounded. Pseudoraphe variable in width, distinct. Raphe absent. Striae broad; appear to be cross-lineate, sometimes the surface of the striae appear poroid. This structure can be seen more clearly with the electron microscope, and the apparent striae may be single chambers.

This genus can be most easily distinguished by the shape of the valve and the characteristic structure of the striae.

Elmore (1922, p. 47) incorrectly included the species in this genus under *Sceptroneis* Ehr.

In Petit's original description of this genus three species are mentioned: *Fragilaria pacifica* Grun., *Fragilaria pinnata* Ehr. *pro parte,* and *Meridion marinum* Greg. *pro parte.* Since *Fragilaria pacifica* Grun. is the only species, when the genus was originally described, that was not based on specimens which are parts of other species, this species should be the type of the genus. *Fragilaria swartzii* Grun. cannot be the type as Boyer proposes because it was not included in the original description of the genus.

Type species. — Opephora pacifica Grun.

1. **Opephora americana** M. Perag. var. **americana**   PL. 3, FIG. 2

   Opephora americana M. Perag. *in* Temp. & Perag., Diat. Monde Entier, 2nd ed., p. 195.   1910.

Valve elliptical-lanceolate with somewhat attenuated, rostrate, rounded apices. Valve asymmetrical to the transverse axis; one end of the valve broader than the other. Pseudoraphe slightly wider in the middle portion of the valve. Striae somewhat radiate, 5-7 in 10μ. Length, $25\text{-}40\mu$. Breadth, about 11μ.

This taxon is distinguished by the shape of the valve.

Type locality. — U. S. A., Oregon, Klamath County, Swan Lake. (*Isotype*—A-T. & P. no. 365-366.)

U. S. distribution. — Geographical: Known only from the type locality.

2. **Opephora martyi** Hérib. var. **martyi**   PL. 3, FIG. 3

   Opephora martyi Hérib., Diat. Foss. Auvergne, vol. 1, p. 43, pl. 8, fig. 20.   1902.

Frustules in girdle view quadrate; slightly narrower at one end than at the other. Valve ovate with rounded apices, one apex much wider than the other. Pseudoraphe narrow, distinct. Striae broad, 4.5-8 in 10μ. Length, 5-60μ. Breadth in widest portion of the valve, 4-8μ.

This taxon is distinguished by the shape of the valve and its occurrence in fresh water.

Type locality. — [France], Dans un échantillon de Neussargues.

U. S. distribution. — GEOGRAPHICAL: New England States, Middle Atlantic States, Southeastern States, Gulf Coast States, South Central States, East Central States, Lakes States, Plains States, Oregon, California. ECOLOGICAL: Shallow fresh water, in lakes and rivers; mesotrophic water.

3. **Opephora swartzii** (Grun.) Petit var. **swartzii**   PL. 3, FIG. 1

Fragilaria swartzii Grun., Verh. Zool.-Bot. Ges. Wien, 13:143, pl. 5, fig. 7.   1863.
Sceptroneis swartrii Grun. *in* Cl. & Möll., slide no. 257.   1879.
Opephora schwarzii (Grun.) Petit *in* Pell., Diatomées, vol. 2, p. 88, fig. 345.   1889.

Valve linear, clavate with rounded apices. Pseudoraphe fairly wide, distinct. Striae, crossed by bands; almost parallel throughout most of the valve. Striae, 3-4 in 10μ. The structure of the striae of our specimens is more similar to that of Grunow's (*loc. cit.*) than that of Van Heurck's illustration (1881, pl. 44, fig. 24). Length, 44-178μ. Breadth at widest portion, about 10μ.

This taxon is distinguished from other species of this genus with which it might be confused by the coarseness of the striae and the shape of the pseudoraphe.

Our specimens are smaller than the one originally illustrated by Grunow.

Although this species is more often found in marine environments, it does occur in brackish to almost fresh water in Pensacola Bay, Florida.

Type locality. — Inter varias algas ad litora Brasiliae lectas (leg. Cl. Jelinek, Exped. Novara).

U. S. distribution. — GEOGRAPHICAL: North Carolina, Florida. ECOLOGICAL: In slightly brackish to marine water.

Taxa Recorded Since 1960

Opephora ansata Hohn & Hellerm. (recorded by Hohn & Hellerman, 1963).

Genus **Fragilaria** Lyngb.

Lyngb., Tent. Hydrophyt. Danicae, p. 182.   1819.

Frustules forming filaments; septa absent and in all the fresh-water species intercalary bands absent. They are present in a few of the salt water species. Valve symmetrical to the transverse and apical axes. In a few species the valves are tripolar rather than bipolar. Pseudoraphe are present on both valves. They may be narrow or form a broad lanceolate space. The central area is variable in structure, and may be absent. The striae as seen by the light microscope are composed of puncta which are often indistinct.

The chloroplasts are variable in shape and size. The species occurs in the littoral zone as well as in the plankton.

The genus *Fragilaria* is closely related to the genus *Synedra*. Further study may show these two genera should be united. Their main difference is that under natural conditions species of the genus *Fragilaria* form filaments, whereas this is not the case in *Synedra*.

Type species. — *Fragilaria pectinalis* (Müll.) Lyngb.

KEY TO THE SPECIES OF FRAGILARIA

1. Frustules forming filaments in which the frustules are only attached in the middle portion of the valve...[5] *F. crotonensis*
1. Frustules with filaments formed by attachment of the whole surface of the valve, or frustules otherwise associated 2
    2. Valve with unilateral swollen central area...................[4] *F. vaucheriae*
    2. Valve with or without central area; if present, not unilateral and swollen... 3
3. Striae marginal 4
3. Striae not marginal, pseudoraphe narrow linear or forming a linear-lanceolate to lanceolate space 5
    4. Striae, 13 or more in 10μ................................[11] *F. brevistriata*
    4. Striae, less than 10 in 10μ..............................[12] *F. lapponica*
5. Valve tripolar ....[10] *F. pinnata* var. *trigona*
5. Valve bipolar 6
    6. Valve strongly and abruptly swollen in the middle of the valve.......... 7
    6. Valve not so formed or, if swollen, valve trilobed 8
7. Striae, less than 10 in 10μ.............................[8] *F. leptostauron*
7. Striae, 13 or more in 10μ................................[9] *F. construens*
    8. Valve lobed or constricted in the middle portion of the valve............ 14
    8. Valve not lobed or constricted in the middle portion.................... 9
9. Striae, 12 or less in 10μ ....[10] *F. pinnata*
9. Striae finer 10
    10. Margins of the valve with spines.................................... 11
    10. Margins of the valves without spines.................................. 12
11. Apices of the valve strongly attenuated; spines on the valve mantle may not be apparent on the valve surface.........................[6] *F. constricta* f. *stricta*
11. Apices of the valve not strongly attenuated; spines on the valve surface
[7] *F. nitzschioides*
    12. Central area absent 13
    12. Central area present; striae, usually 14 or more in 10μ.......[2] *F. capucina*
13. Striae irregularly placed, that is at different distances from each other; valve capitate ....[1] *F. bicapitata*
13. Striae regularly placed, usually 15 or more in 10μ ....[3] *F. virescens*
    14. Valve constricted at the central area..........[2] *F. capucina* var. *mesolepta*
    14. Valve lobed 15

1. **Fragilaria bicapitata** A. Mayer var. **bicapitata**   PL. 3, FIG. 4

Fragilaria bicapitata A. Mayer, Denkschr. Bayer. Bot. Ges. Regensburg, 13(N.F. 7): 21, pl. 1, fig. 26. 1917.

Valve linear to linear-lanceolate with distinctly capitate apices. Pseudoraphe very narrow. Central area absent. Striae parallel throughout most of the valve, sometimes slightly radiate at the apices. Striae irregularly spaced, often not opposite each other on each side of the pseudoraphe. Striae, 13-17 in 10μ. Length, $10\text{-}55\mu$. Breadth, $3\text{-}5\mu$.

This species is distinguished by the irregularly spaced striae and the shape of the valve.

Type locality. — Uncertain, Bavaria.

U. S. distribution. — GEOGRAPHICAL: New England States; Pennsylvania, Georgia, Montana. ECOLOGICAL: Seems to prefer water of low or medium mineral content; sometimes mesotrophic, often in cool water.

2. **Fragilaria capucina** Desm. var. **capucina**   PL. 3, FIG. 5

Fragilaria capucina Desm., Plant. Crypt. Nord France, 1st ed., Fasc. 10, No. 453. 1825.

Frustules forming long filaments. Valve linear with rounded, somewhat capitate, or somewhat wedge-shaped apices. Pseudoraphe narrow, distinct. Central area usually rectangular, sometimes somewhat rounded in appearance; reaching or almost reaching the margins of the valve. Occasionally the central area is irregularly formed. Striae parallel, 14-18 in 10μ. Length variable, usually $40\text{-}100\mu$, but may be $25\text{-}170\mu$ in length. Breadth, $2\text{-}5\mu$.

This taxon is distinguished by its linear shape and fine striae.

Fragilaria pectinalis (O. Müll.) Lyngb. may be in part, if not completely, synonymous with this species; but it is impossible to be sure from the description and illustrations. If type specimens are found, then this fact can be determined.

Type locality. — Uncertain, Northern France.

U. S. distribution. — GEOGRAPHICAL: New England States, Middle Atlantic States, Southeastern States, South Central States, East Central States, West Central States, Lakes States, Plains States; Montana, Wyoming, Oregon, California. ECOLOGICAL: Seems to prefer slightly alkaline water, indifferent to small amounts of NaCl.

2. **Fragilaria capucina** var. **mesolepta** Rabh.   PL. 3, FIG. 6

Fragilaria mesolepta Rabh., Alg. Sachsens resp. Mitteleuropas, No. 1041. 1861.
Fragilaria capucina var. *mesolepta* Rabh., Fl. Europaea Alg., sect. 1, p. 118. 1864.

Valve linear to linear-lanceolate, constricted at the rectangularly shaped central area. Apices somewhat attenuated, rostrate. Pseudoraphe very narrow. Central area somewhat variable, may be longer than broad or broader than long. Striae parallel, 15-18 in 10μ. Length, 30-35μ. Breadth in narrowest portion of the middle of the valve, 2-4μ.

This taxon is distinguished from other varieties of this species by the constriction in the middle portion of the valve.

The correct name for this taxon at the species level is *Fragilaria bipunctata* Hempr. & Ehr., but *mesolepta* is the correct name as a variety.

Type locality. — In vico Arabiae Tor inter Confervas e Wadi Esle petitas.

U. S. distribution. — GEOGRAPHICAL: New England States, Middle Atlantic States, Southeastern States, South Central States, East Central States, West Central States, Lakes States, Plains States; Montana, Utah, Washington, Oregon, California. ECOLOGICAL: Fresh water, slightly alkaline; sometimes found in slightly brackish water.

3. **Fragilaria virescens** Ralfs var. **virescens**   PL. 3, FIGS. 7-9

Fragilaria pectinalis Ehr., Phys. Abh. Akad. Wiss. Berlin, for 1838:57, pl. 2(1), fig. 7. 1839. (questionable.)
Fragilaria virescens Ralfs, Ann. Mag. Nat. Hist., 12:110, pl. 2, fig. 6. 1843.
Fragilaria aequalis Heib., Consp. Crit. Diat. Danicarum, p. 61, pl. 4, fig. 12. 1863.
Fragilaria virescens var. *producta* (Lagerst.) DeT., Syll. Alg., vol. 2, sect. 1, p. 682. 1891.
Fragilaria aequalis var. *major* Temp. & Perag., Diat. Monde Entier, 2nd ed., p. 194, 1910.

Frustules forming long, straight filaments. Valve with linear or slightly convex margins. Apices attenuate-rostrate. Pseudoraphe very narrow. Central area lacking. Striae fine, usually 15-19 in 10μ. Length, 12-120μ. Breadth, 5-10μ.

This taxon is distinguished by the shape of the valve and the lack of the central area.

Type locality. — Uncertain.

U. S. distribution. — GEOGRAPHICAL: New England States, Middle Atlantic States, Southeastern States, Gulf Coast States, South Central States, East Central States, West Central States, Lakes States, Plains States; Wyoming, Arizona, Washington, Oregon. ECOLOGICAL: Widely distributed in fresh water.

3. Fragilaria virescens var. capitata Østr.   PL. 3, FIG. 10

Fragilaria virescens var. *capitata* Østr., Danske Diat., p. 193, pl. 5, fig. 125. 1910.

Valve linear with distinctly capitate apices. Pseudoraphe narrow, distinct. Jelly pore present at each end of the valve. Striae parallel, 16-17 in 10μ. Length, $28\text{-}60\mu$. Breadth, $4\text{-}6\mu$.

This taxon is characterized by the shape of the valve, particularly the capitate apices.

Østrup erroneously gives in his description, length $5\text{-}10\mu$. However, the illustration is of a specimen 44μ long and 4μ wide.

Type locality. — Utofte Bs. Ferskv.

U. S. distribution. — GEOGRAPHICAL: Middle Atlantic States, Southeastern States.

4. Fragilaria vaucheriae (Kütz.) Peters. var. vaucheriae

PL. 3, FIGS. 14-15

Exilaria vaucheriae Kütz., Linnaea, 8:560, pl. 15, fig. 38. 1833; Alg. Dec., No. 24. 1833.

Synedra vaucheriae (Kütz.) Kütz., Bacill., p. 65, pl. 14(4), figs. 1, 2a, 3. 1844.

Synedra vaucheriae var. *parvula* (Kütz.) Rabh., Fl. Europaea Alg. sect. 1, p. 132. 1864.

Synedra vaucheriae var. *distans* Grun. *in* V. H., Syn. Diat. Belgique, pl. 40, fig. 17. 1881.

Fragilaria intermedia Grun. *in* V. H., Syn. Diat. Belgique, pl. 45, figs. 9-11. 1881.

Fragilaria vaucheriae (Kütz.) Peters., Bot. Not., for 1938 (1/3):167, figs. 1c-g. 1938.

Frustules usually in short or fairly long chains, occasionally occurring singly. Valve linear to linear-lanceolate; narrowed toward the rostrate, rounded apices. Pseudoraphe narrow. Central area usually on only one side of the valve. Striae parallel or slightly radiate, occasionally slightly shortened opposite the central area. Striae, 12-16 in 10μ. Length, $10\text{-}40\mu$, Breadth, $2\text{-}4\mu$.

This taxon is clearly distinguished by its asymmetrical, usually slightly swollen central area.

This taxon, by its occurrence singly or in chains, points up the necessity of uniting the genera *Fragilaria* and *Synedra* which are largely separated by the manner of the frustule growth.

Petersen (1938, p. 164-170) gives an excellent discussion of the systematics and nomenclature of this species. Kützing's illustration (1833b, pl. 15, fig. 38) shows a form with rounded—not rostrate—ends.

Type locality. — In a spring near Weissenfels on *Vaucheria clavata.*

U. S. distribution. — GEOGRAPHICAL: New England States, Middle Atlantic States, Southeastern States, Gulf Coast States, South Central States, East Central States, Lakes States, Plains States; Montana, Wyoming, Colorado, New Mexico, Utah, Oregon, California. ECOLOGICAL: Fresh water, seems to prefer cool water.

4. **Fragilaria vaucheriae** var. **capitellata** (Grun.) Patr. comb. nov.

PL. 3, FIG. 16

Synedra capitellata Grun. *in* V. H., Syn. Diat. Belgique, pl. 40, fig. 26. 1881.
Synedra vaucheriae var. *capitellata* (Grun.) Cl., Jour. Linnean Soc. London, Bot.,
20:314. 1883.

Valve linear-lanceolate; narrowed toward the capitate apices. Pseudoraphe narrow. Central area unilateral, somewhat swollen. Striae, 18-20 in 10μ. Length, 40-55μ. Breadth, 4-6μ.

This taxon is distinguished by the shape of the valve and the fine striae.

Type locality. — Uncertain.

U. S. distribution. — GEOGRAPHICAL: New England States, Middle Atlantic States, Lakes States. ECOLOGICAL: Seems to prefer lakes and ponds.

5. **Fragilaria crotonensis** Kitton var. **crotonensis**   PL. 3, FIGS. 11-12

Fragilaria crotonensis Kitton, Sci.-Gossip, 5:110, fig. 81. 1869.
Synedra crotonensis (Kitton) Cl. & Möll., Diatoms, pt. 3, p. 2, slide no. 128. 1878.
Synedra crotonensis var. *prolongata* f. *belgica* Grun. *in* V. H., Syn. Diat. Belgique,
pl. 40, fig. 10. 1881.
Fragilaria crotonensis var. *prolongata* Grun. *in* V. H., Syn. Diat. Belgique, p. 156.
1885.

Frustules in girdle view linear; swollen at the center, and to a lesser amount, at the ends of the frustule. Frustules attached in the middle portion to form filaments which have a very distinctive appearance. Valve linear; distinctly swollen to a lanceolate shape in the middle portion, and to a lesser extent, at the somewhat capitate apices. Pseudoraphe indistinct. Central area usually rectangular in shape, extending to the margins of the valve or with marginal striae. Striae parallel, 15-18 in 10μ. Length, 40-170μ. Breadth in the middle portion of the valve, 2-4μ.

This taxon is distinguished by the formation of the filaments which remain attached even after cleaning. In valve view the swollen, lanceolate middle portion is the most distinctive characteristic.

Type locality. — U. S. A., Croton water, New York, Dr. Edwards.

U. S. distribution. — GEOGRAPHICAL: New England States, Middle Atlantic States, Southeastern States, Gulf Coast States, South Central States, East Central States, West Central States, Lakes States, Plains States; Montana, Wyoming, Utah, Arizona, Washington, Oregon, California. ECOLOGICAL: A plankton species widely distributed in mesotrophic water; indifferent to small amounts of NaCl.

5. **Fragilaria crotonensis** var. **oregona** Sov.   PL. 3, FIG. 13

Fragilaria crotonensis var. *oregona* Sov., Trans. American Micr. Soc., 77(2):107, pl. 2, figs. 1-3. 1958.

Frustules forming filaments attached by the middle portion of the valve surface. Valve linear-lanceolate, swollen on each side of the central area which is also slightly swollen. Ends of the valve capitate. Pseudoraphe very narrow, becoming a little wider toward the central area. Central area traversed by very faint striae. Striae, 11-14 in 10μ. Length, $90\text{-}120\mu$. Breadth at the central area, $3\text{-}4\mu$.

Sometimes the valve is irregularly constricted in the middle portion of the valve, and swollen on each side of the central area.

This taxon is distinguished from the nominate variety by the bulbous swellings about the central area and the coarser striae.

Type locality. — U. S. A., Oregon, Douglas County, Diamond Lake. (*Holotype*—Cal. Acad. Sci.-3462, Sov. 170-12, Sovereign, 1960.)

U. S. distribution. — GEOGRAPHICAL: Oregon. ECOLOGICAL: In water with pH 8.1-8.8.

6. **Fragilaria constricta** Ehr. var. **constricta**   PL. 3, FIG. 17

Fragilaria ? constricta Ehr., Phys. Abh. Akad. Wiss. Berlin, for 1841:415, pl. 1(1), fig. 21; pl. 3(6), fig. 10. 1843.

Fragilaria constricta Ehr., Mikrogeol., pl. 16(1), figs. 19-20; pl. 16(2), figs. 34-35. 1854.

Fragilaria undata f. *tetranodis* A. Cl., Bih. K. Svenska Vet.-Akad. Handl., 21, Afd. 3(2):35. 1895.

Fragilaria undata var. *lobata* Patr., Farlowia, 2(2):151. 1945.

Frustules in girdle view rectangular; forming irregular filaments, often zigzag. Valve with two or four distinct lobes. If four lobes are present, they are usually not of equal depth because the constriction in the middle of the valve is the deepest. Spines sometimes present on the margins of the valve, but more often evident only on the valve mantle. For this reason they may not be apparent unless the valve is canted so as to show the valve mantle. Pseudoraphe indistinct, often it seems to be absent. Striae indistinctly punctate, parallel; sometimes slightly irregularly placed. Striae, 13-18 in 10μ. Length, $20\text{-}70\mu$. Breadth at widest portion of the valve, $6\text{-}16\mu$.

This taxon is distinguished by the shape of the valve, the indistinct pseudoraphe, and the spines on the margins, if they are apparent.

Originally I believed *Fragilaria undata* of W. Smith did not have spines. However, more thorough examination of his specimens (A—W. Sm. 377) shows spines to be present on the valve mantle although they are not apparent when the valve is flat. Ehrenberg's original description does not mention these spines. Likewise, W. Smith does not mention them in his description of *F. undata.*

This is a species that is very variable in the shape of the valve.

Type locality. — Uncertain.

U. S. distribution. — GEOGRAPHICAL: New England States, Middle Atlantic States, Southeastern States, South Central States, East Central States, West Central States. ECOLOGICAL: Prefers water of low mineral content and usually slightly dystrophic.

6. Fragilaria constricta f. stricta (A. Cl.) Hust. PL. 3, FIG. 18

Fragilaria undata W. Sm., Syn. British Diat., vol. 2, p. 24, pl. 60, fig. 377. 1856.

Fragilaria undata f. *stricta* A. Cl., Bih. K. Svenska Vet.-Akad. Handl., 21, Afd. 3(2):35. 1895.

Fragilaria undata var. *quadrata* Hust. *in* Pasch., Süssw.-Fl. Mitteleuropas, Heft 10, Aufl. 2, p. 144, fig. 149B. 1930.

Fragilaria constricta f. *stricta* (A. Cl.) Hust. *in* Rabh., Kryptog.-Fl. Deutschland, vol. 7(2), no. 1, p. 166, figs. 674d, e. 1931.

Valve short, very broad with parallel sides, narrowing toward the apiculate, rostrate apices. Pseudoraphe indistinct. Central area absent. Short spines irregularly placed on the margins of the valve or on the valve mantle. Striae parallel in the middle portion of the valve and slightly radiate toward the apices. Striae, 16-18 in 10μ. Length, $14\text{-}25\mu$. Breadth, $10\text{-}15\mu$.

This taxon is distinguished by the shape of the valve.

Type locality. — Uncertain.

U. S. distribution. — GEOGRAPHICAL: New England States, Middle Atlantic States. ECOLOGICAL: Seems to prefer slightly acid water of low conductivity.

7. Fragilaria nitzschioides Grun. var. nitzschioides PL. 4, FIG. 1

Fragilaria nitzschioides Grun. *in* V. H., Syn. Diat. Belgique, pl. 44, fig. 10. 1881.

Valve linear with rostrate or somewhat wedge-shaped apices. Pseudoraphe very narrow. Central area absent. Striae parallel or slightly radiate. Short spines present on the margin of the valve. Striae, about 16-20 in 10μ. Short spines, about 8 in 10μ. Length, $15\text{-}52\mu$. Breadth, $3\text{-}5\mu$.

This taxon is distinguished by the short spines on the margin of the valve. These spines can also be seen in girdle view. Sometimes, although recognizable, they are hard to define.

Type locality. — Uncertain.

U. S. distribution. — GEOGRAPHICAL: Gulf Coast States; New York, Indiana.

8. Fragilaria leptostauron (Ehr.) Hust. var. leptostauron

PL. 4, FIG. 2

Biblarium leptostauron Ehr., Mikrogeol., pl. 12, figs. 35-36. 1854.
Staurosira pinnata Ehr., Mikrogeol., pl. 5(2), fig. 24. 1854.
Odontidium? harrisonii W. Sm., Syn. British Diat., vol. 2, p. 18, pl. 60, fig. 373. 1856.
Fragilaria harrisonii (W. Sm.) Grun., Verh. Zool.-Bot. Ges. Wien, 12:368. 1862.
Fragilaria leptostauron (Ehr.) Hust. in Rabh., Kryptog.-Fl. Deutschland, vol. 7(2), no. 1, p. 153, figs. 668a-b. 1931.

Frustules rectangular in girdle view, forming straight or zigzag filaments. Frustules swollen in the middle portion, appearing to be crossed by a band. Valve strongly swollen in the middle portion, giving it a cross shape. Apices rounded. Pseudoraphe distinct, often wider in the middle portion of the valve. Striae coarse, radiate, and crossed by fine lines which are usually 25-30 in 10μ. Striae in the middle portion of the valve often irregular in length. Striae, 5-9 in 10μ. Length, 15-36μ. Breadth in the middle of the valve 10-23μ.

This taxon is distinguished by the shape of the valve and the coarse striae. This species is closely related to Fragilaria construens and F. pinnata.

It is evident from Ehrenberg (Mikrogeol., 1854) that Navicula ? crux Ehrenberg (Inf., 1838) represented more than one taxon (Biblarium leptostauron and Pinnularia crux). Therefore it seems wise to follow Ehrenberg's decision and name this taxon leptostauron—Biblarium leptostauron Ehr. = Fragilaria leptostauron (Ehr.) Hust. Biblarium ? crux = N. crux Ehr. (Ber. Akad. Wiss. Berlin, 1845) may be this taxon, but Ehrenberg (1845) does not indicate this.

Type locality. — Silbergrauer Polirschiefer zwischen Basalt-Tuff bei Cassel.

U. S.. distribution. — Geographical: New England States, Middle Atlantic States, Southeastern States, South Central States, West Central States, Lakes States, Plains States; Montana, Wyoming, Utah, Washington, Oregon, California. Ecological: Common in fresh water, usually in shallow water, often on mud surfaces.

8. Fragilaria leptostauron var. dubia (Grun.) Hust.

PL. 4, FIG. 3

Fragilaria harrisonii var. dubia Grun., Verh. Zool.-Bot. Ges. Wien, 12:368, pl. 7, figs. 8a-d. 1862.
Fragilaria leptostauron var. dubia (Grun.) Hust. in Rabh., Kryptog.-Fl. Deutschland, vol. 7(2), no. 1, p. 154, figs. 668h-i. 1931.

Valve lanceolate to elliptical with acute or rounded apices. Pseudoraphe variable in width, linear to linear-lanceolate. Sometimes the central area is fairly broad, whereas in other specimens it is quite narrow. Striae radiate except in the middle portion of the valve where they are almost parallel. Striae, 6-11 in 10μ. Length, 10-15μ. Breadth at widest portion, 3-7μ.

This taxon seems to be most closely related to variety *rhomboides* Grun.

Grunow's original description indicates that his taxon is very variable in the shape of the valve. Some specimens are elliptical, although the typical ones are similar to the one illustrated, but the apices are not quite as acute and the margins are slightly concave.

Type locality. — . . . aus dem Stienitz See bei Berlin (leg. amic. Reinhardt).

U. S. distribution. — GEOGRAPHICAL: Michigan, Oregon.

9. **Fragilaria construens** (Ehr.) Grun. var. **construens**   PL. 4, FIG. 4

> *Staurosira construens* Ehr., Phys. Abh. Akad. Wiss. Berlin, for 1841:424.   1843.
> *Odontidium tabellaria* W. Sm., Syn. British Diat., vol. 2, p. 17, pl. 34, fig. 291.   1856.
> *Fragilaria construens* (Ehr.) Grun., Verh. Zool.-Bot. Ges. Wien, 12:371.   1862.

Frustules in girdle view rectangular; swollen in the middle portion, giving the appearance of a band across the middle of the frustule. Valve strongly swollen in the middle portion, often somewhat asymmetrical. Ends of the valve rounded, sometimes slightly capitate. Pseudoraphe distinct, linear to linear-lanceolate in shape. Striae radiate throughout most of the valve, crossed by fine lines. Striae 14-18 in 10μ. Length, 7-25μ. Breadth, 5-12μ.

This taxon is very similar in shape to *Fragilaria leptostauron* but differs in that it has much finer striae. This species is highly variable in shape. Further investigations may show that the various varieties are really one continuous series and are not distinct taxa.

Type locality. — Uncertain.

U. S. distribution. — GEOGRAPHICAL: New England States, Middle Atlantic States, Southeastern States, Gulf Coast States, South Central States, East Central States, West Central States, Lakes States, Plains States; Montana, Utah, Washington, Oregon, California. ECOLOGICAL: Seems to prefer slightly alkaline water; often found to be indifferent to chlorides; in the plankton and benthic zones.

9. **Fragilaria construens** var. **binodis** (Ehr.) Grun.   PL. 4, FIG. 7

> (*Fragilaria?*) *binodis* Ehr., Mikrogeol., pl. 5(2), fig. 26; pl. 6(1), fig. 43; pl. 11, fig. 15; (pl. 16(2), fig. 36?).   1854.
> *Fragilaria construens* var. *binodis* (Ehr.) Grun., Verh. Zool.-Bot. Ges. Wien, 12:371. 1862.

Valve constricted in the middle portion with attenuated, rostrate apices. Pseudoraphe narrow, distinct. Central area not clearly differentiated from axial area. Striae parallel, 14-17 in 10μ. Length, 15-35μ. Breadth at widest portion, 3.5-8μ.

This taxon is characterized by the constriction in the middle portion of the valve.

Type locality. — Brenn-Torf aus New Haven, Connecticut [U. S. A.].

U. S. distribution. — GEOGRAPHICAL: New England States; Maryland, Nebraska, Montana, Utah. ECOLOGICAL: Seems to prefer cool, fresh water, can tolerate water with fairly high conductivity.

9. **Fragilaria construens** var. **pumila** Grun.   PL. 4, FIGS. 5-6

> *Fragilaria construens* var. *pumila* Grun. *in* V. H., Syn. Diat. Belgique, pl. **45**, **fig.** 21a. 1881.

Valve elliptical with rounded to rostrate apices. Pseudoraphe distinct, linear to linear-lanceolate in shape. Striae slightly radiate throughout the valve. Striae, 17-18 in 10μ. Length, $10\text{-}20\mu$. Breadth, $3\text{-}5\mu$.

This taxon is distinguished from the nominate variety by its shape. It seems to be most closely related to variety *venter* with which it has been synonymyzed. However, it does differ in the shape of the valve; and the specimens I have seen do not seem to intergrade.

Type locality. — Uncertain.

U. S. distribution. — GEOGRAPHICAL: Connecticut. ECOLOGICAL: Widely distributed with the nominate variety.

9. **Fragilaria construens** var. **venter** (Ehr.) Grun.   PL. 4, FIGS. 8-9

> *Fragilaria venter* Ehr., Mikrogeol., pl. 14, fig. 50; pl. 9(1), figs. 6-7. 1854.
> *Fragilaria construens* var. *venter* (Ehr.) Grun. *in* V. H., Syn. Diat. Belgique, pl. **45**, figs. 21b, 22, 23, 24b, 26a-b. 1881.

Valve variable in shape, from linear-lanceolate, with rostrate apices, to rhombic, with somewhat concave margins, and acute rounded ends. Pseudoraphe distinct, linear to lanceolate in shape. Striae radiate, 14-16 in 10μ. Length, $5\text{-}9\mu$. Breadth, $3\text{-}6\mu$.

This taxon is highly variable in shape, and includes a wide variety of forms. It is somewhat intermediate between *Fragilaria construens* var. *construens* and *F. construens* var. *pumila*.

Ehrenberg (1837, p. 105) lists this taxon as *F. gibba* but does not describe it. Therefore, *F. construens* var. *venter* is the correct name.

Type locality. — Uncertain.

U. S. distribution. — GEOGRAPHICAL: New England States, Southeastern States, South Central States, Gulf Coast States, West Central States, Lakes States, Pennsylvania, Oregon, California. ECOLOGICAL: Widely distributed, seems to prefer water of fairly low nutrient content (oligotrophic to meso-trophic).

10. Fragilaria pinnata Ehr. var. pinnata PL. 4, FIG. 10

Fragilaria pinnata Ehr., Phys. Abh. Akad. Wiss. Berlin, for 1841:415, pl. 3(6), fig. 8. 1843.

Fragilaria elliptica Schum., Schrift. Phys.-Ökon. Ges. Königsberg, 8:52, pl. 1, fig. 5. 1867.

Frustules linear-rectangular to almost quadrate in girdle view. Valve elliptical to linear with rounded apices. Pseudoraphe narrow, sometimes widened to a small lanceolate space at the center of the valve. Striae radiate at the apices, almost parallel in the middle portion of the valve; crossed by fine lines. Striae, 7-12 in 10μ. Fine lines, about 20 in 10μ. Length, $3-35\mu$. Breadth, $2-6\mu$.

This species is distinguished by its coarse striae which are crossed by fine lines. The nominate variety is distinguished from other varieties by its shape.

Type locality. — Uncertain.

U. S. distribution. — GEOGRAPHICAL: New England States, Middle Atlantic States, Southeastern States, Gulf Coast States, South Central States, East Central States, West Central States, Lakes States, Plains States; Montana, Wyoming, Utah, Washington, Oregon, California. ECOLOGICAL: Widely distributed in fresh water.

10. Fragilaria pinnata var. intercedens (Grun.) Hust. PL. 4, FIG. 11

Odontidium mutabile W. Sm., Syn. British Diat., vol. 2, p. 17, pl. 34, fig. 290. 1856.

Fragilaria mutabile (W. Sm.) Grun., Verh. Zool.-Bot. Ges. Wien, 12:368. 1862.

Fragilaria mutabile var. *intercedens* Grun. *in* V. H., Syn. Diat. Belgique, pl. 45, fig. 13. 1881.

Fragilaria pinnata var. *intercedens* (Grun.) Hust. *in* Rabh., Kryptog.-Fl. Deutschland vol. 7(2), no. 2, p. 161. 1931.

Valve linear with rounded ends. Pseudoraphe a broad linear space. Striae coarse, 6-8 in 10μ. Length, usually $15-34\mu$, although shorter forms may be found. Breadth, usually $4-6\mu$.

This taxon is distinguished by the broad central area and the coarse striae. Although it is variable in size, the larger specimens are the more typical ones.

I have not seen any of Grunow's specimens. However, I have seen William Smith's specimens (W. Sm. 290) which seem to be the same taxon as Grunow described and illustrated. Since Grunow's name is the oldest one at this rank, it is the correct one.

Type locality. — Uncertain.

U. S. distribution. — GEOGRAPHICAL: New England States, Middle Atlantic States, Southeastern States, East Central States, Lakes States, Plains States; Oregon, California. ECOLOGICAL: A tolerant fresh-water taxon.

10. Fragilaria pinnata var. lancettula (Schum.) Hust.   PL. 4, FIG. 12

Fragilaria lancettula Schum., Shrift. Phys.-Ökon. Ges. Königsberg, 8:52, pl. 1, fig. 4. 1867.

Fragilaria pinnata var. *lancettula* (Schum.) Hust. *in* A. S., Atlas Diat., pl. 297, figs. 51, 59-64. 1913.

Valve broadly lanceolate with attenuate-rostrate to attenuate-acute ends. Pseudoraphe distinct. Striae crossed by lines which sometimes give them a granulate appearance. Striae, 10-11 in 10μ. Length, $4\text{-}12\mu$. Length-to-breadth ratio, about 2:1.

This taxon is distinguished from the other varieties of this species by the shape of the valve.

Type locality. — Uncertain.

U. S. distribution. — GEOGRAPHICAL: Middle Atlantic States; South Carolina, Florida, Illinois, Utah, Washington, Oregon, California. This taxon probably has been overlooked; otherwise it would have a more continuous distribution. ECOLOGICAL: Fresh to slightly brackish water or water of high conductivity.

10. Fragilaria pinnata var. trigona (Brun. & Hérib.) Hust.

PL. 4, FIG. 13

Fragilaria pacifica var. *trigona* Brun. & Hérib. *in* Hérib., Diat. Auvergne, p. 147, pl. 1, figs. 8-8b. 1893.

Fragilaria pinnata var. *trigona* (Brun. & Hérib. *in* Hérib.) Hust. *in* Rabh., Kryptog.-Fl. Deutschland, vol. 7(2), no. 1, p. 161, figs. 671k-l. 1931.

Valve tripolar. In the center of the valve a small hyaline central area. Striae radiate, 8-12 in 10μ. Length between two poles, as measured by a straight line, $10\text{-}20\mu$.

This taxon is characterized by its tripolar shape.

Type locality. — Deposit marin du puy de Mur.

U. S. distribution. — GEOGRAPHICAL: Oregon.

11. Fragilaria brevistriata Grun. var. brevistriata   PL. 4, FIG. 14

Fragilaria brevistriata Grun. *in* V. H., Syn. Diat. Belgique, p. 157. 1885.
(under name of *Fragilaria brevistriata* var. *subacuta* Grun., pl. 45, fig. 32. 1881, which is not valid.)

Valve linear to linear-lanceolate with subrostrate to rostrate apices. Pseudoraphe a broad, lanceolate space. Striae marginal, slightly radiate. Striae, 13-17 in 10μ. Length, $12\text{-}28\mu$. Breadth, $3\text{-}5\mu$.

This taxon is distinguished from other species by its fine marginal striae. The nominate variety is distinguished from the other varieties by its shape.

Since the species was not described until 1885 in the text of the *Synopsis des Diatomées de Belgique,* the varieties of the species illustrated by Grunow in 1881 are not correct names for those varieties.

Type locality. — Bruxelles (Delogne), fresh water.

U. S. distribution. — GEOGRAPHICAL: New England States, Middle Atlantic States, Southeastern States, Gulf Coast States, East Central States, Lakes States, Plains States; Wyoming, Washington, Oregon, California. ECOLOGICAL: Tolerant of fresh water of a wide range of conductivity.

11. Fragilaria brevistriata var. capitata Hérib.   PL. 4, FIG. 15

> *Fragilaria brevistriata* var. *subcapitata* Grun. *in* V. H., Syn. Diat. Belgique, pl. 45, fig. 33. 1881. (not valid because the nominate variety was not described.)
> *Fragilaria brevistriata* var. *capitata* Hérib., Diat. Foss. Auvergne, vol. 2, p. 92, pl. 12, fig. 18. 1903.

Valve lanceolate with capitate apices. Pseudoraphe a large lanceolate space. Striae slightly radiate. Striae, 14-16 in 10μ. Length, 14-20μ. Breadth, 3-5μ.

This taxon is distinguished from the nominate variety by the rostrate-capitate to capitate apices of the valve. Héribaud states that the apices of the valves of his specimens are more capitate than those of the specimens of Grunow. However, they do not seem to be sufficiently different to consider them separate taxa.

Type locality. — Uncertain.

U. S. distribution. — GEOGRAPHICAL: Texas, Washington. ECOLOGICAL: In the United States it seems to be a much rarer taxon than the nominate variety.

11. Fragilaria brevistriata var. inflata (Pant.) Hust.   PL. 4, FIG. 16

> *Fragilaria inflata* Pant., Resultate Wiss. Erforsch. Balatonsees, vol. 2, pt. 2, sect. 1, p. 79, pl. 9, figs. 219-221. 1902.
> *Fragilaria brevistriata* var. *inflata* (Pant.) Hust. *in* Pasch., Süssw.-Fl. Mitteleuropas, Heft 10, Aufl. 2, p. 145, fig. 152. 1930.

Valve broadly lanceolate with attenuated, rostrate apices. Pseudoraphe a broad lanceolate space. Striae slightly radiate, about 12-16 in 10μ. Length, 10-20μ. Breadth, 3.5-11μ. Length-to-breadth ratio, 2.5:1-4:1.

This variety is distinguished from the other varieties of this species by the shape of the valve.

Type locality. — Seeschlamm bei Siofok.

U. S. distribution. — GEOGRAPHICAL: Maryland, South Carolina, Texas, Nebraska, Washington. ECOLOGICAL: Seems to prefer slightly alkaline water of fairly high conductivity.

12. Fragilaria lapponica Grun. var. lapponica   PL. 4, FIG. 17

Fragilaria lapponica Grun. *in* V. H., Syn. Diat. Belgique, pl. 45, fig. 35. 1881.

Frustules in girdle view linear, rectangular with rounded ends. Valve linear to slightly lanceolate with rounded or somewhat wedge-shaped apices. The pseudoraphe is a large central area. Striae marginal, 6-9 in 10μ. Length, $12\text{-}40\mu$. Breadth, $4\text{-}6\mu$.

This taxon is distinguished in valve view by its large central area and coarse striae.

Hustedt (1931, p. 170) has synonymized *Fragilaria brevistriata* var. *mormonorum* with this taxon. This is a mistake, as variety *mormonorum* has much finer striae and belongs with *F. brevistriata*.

Type locality. — Uncertain.

U. S. distribution. — Geographical: New England States; New Jersey, Texas, Oklahoma. Ecological: Seems to prefer circumneutral water of low mineral content. Indifferent to small amounts of NaCl.

13. Fragilaria sinuata M. Perag. var. sinuata   PL. 4, FIGS. 18-19

Fragilaria sinuata M. Perag. *in* Temp. & Perag., Diat. Monde Entier, 2nd ed., p. 194. 1910.

Valve with triundulate margins and attenuate-rostrate ends. Swelling in the middle portion of the valve larger than near the ends. Pseudoraphe distinct, becoming much wider toward the center of the valve. Striae parallel to slightly radiate. Striae, 11-14 in 10μ. Length, $29\text{-}45\mu$. Breadth of valve at the widest part, to 7μ.

This species is distinguished by the shape of the valve and pseudoraphe.

Boyer (1927a, p. 188) lists a species as *Fragilaria bidens* Heib. However, so far as I can determine from examination of his slides, he has misidentified this taxon.

Type locality. — U. S. A., Oregon, Klamath County, Swan Lake. (*Lectotype*—A-T.&P. 366, 2nd ed., Patrick.)

U. S. distribution. — Geographical: Oregon.

Names of Taxa reported from the U. S. (fresh water) which could not be
verified by a specimen from a public herbarium.

Fragilaria acuta Ehr. (recorded by Ehrenberg, Gratacap and Woodward).
Fragilaria biceps Ehr. (recorded by DeToni).
Fragilaria capucina var. *acuminata* Grun. *in* V. H. (recorded by Boyer).

Fragilaria capucina var. *acuta* Grun. *in* V. H. (recorded by Scheffer and Robinson, and Boyer).

Fragilaria construens var. *exigua* (W. Sm.) Schulz (recorded by Sovereign).

Fragilaria cuneata Ehr. (recorded by Ehrenberg).

Fragilaria diophthalma (Ehr.) Ehr. (recorded by Ehrenberg)—may be *F. capucina.*

Fragilaria elliptica f. *minor* (recorded by Curtis without authority).

Fragilaria eugramma Ehr. (recorded by Ehrenberg).

Fragilaria levis Ehr. (recorded by DeToni).

Fragilaria oxyptera Ehr. (recorded by Ehrenberg).

Fragilaria paradoxa Ehr. (recorded by Ehrenberg).

Fragilaria rhabdosoma Ehr. (recorded by Ehrenberg)—may be *F. capucina.*

Fragilaria rostrata Ehr. (recorded by Ehrenberg).

Fragilaria smithiana Grun. *in* V. H. (recorded by Palmer).

Fragilaria turgens Ehr. (recorded by Curtis).

Names of Taxa for which the original description could not be found

Fragilaria lanceolata (recorded by Curtis, Palmer, Deming).

Taxa Recorded Since 1960[*]

Fragilaria brevistriata var. *inflata* f. *curta* Skv. (recorded by Reimer, 1961).

Fragilaria dibolos Hohn & Hellerm. (recorded by Hohn & Hellerman, 1963).

Fragilaria glebula Hohn & Hellerm. (recorded by Hohn & Hellerman, 1963).

Fragilaria interstincta Hohn & Hellerm. (rec. by Hohn & Hellerman, 1963).

Fragilaria rhodana Hohn & Hellerm. (recorded by Hohn & Hellerman, 1963).

Fragilaria virescens var. *subsalina* Grun. (recorded by Hohn and Hellerman, 1963).

Genus **Hannaea** Patr. gen. nov.

Frustulae facias breves facientes, in conspectu connectivali incurvae, margini ventrali concava, margini ventrali in utrisque lateribus areae centralis tumido; area centrali tumida, centro saepe concava; pseudoraphe praesenti, area centrali tumida, unilaterali; frustula ad axem apicalem asymmetricali, ad axem tranversalem symmetricali.

Frustules forming short bands, in girdle view the frustules are curved.

---

[*] See page 671 for list of additional taxa recorded since 1960.

In valve view the dorsal margin is convex and the ventral margin is concave, but swollen on each side of the central area which is also swollen or smoothly concave except for the swelling of the central area. The pseudoraphe is present and the central area is swollen and evident only on one side of the valve. The frustule is asymmetrical to the apical axis, and symmetrical to the transverse axis.

This genus belongs to the Fragilariaceae. Of the genera of this family, it seems to be most closely related to *Fragilaria* and *Synedra*, from which it differs by the curved shape of the frustule in girdle and valve views.

This is a new genus for those species incorrectly assigned to the genus *Ceratoneis*. The genus *Ceratoneis* was first proposed by Ehrenberg in 1841 (p. 123, pl. 4) for two species: *Ceratoneis closterium*, which is today included in the genus *Nitzschia*; and *Ceratoneis fasciola* which is now recognized as belonging to the genus *Gyrosigma*. In 1844 Kützing expanded the genus to include besides Ehrenberg's species the following: *Ceratoneis laminaris* (*Mastogloia laminaris*), *C. spiralis* (*Nitzschia spiralis* [Kütz.] Rabh.), and *C. arcus* (*C. arcus* today). Grunow in 1862 (p. 343) incorrectly wrote the description of *Ceratoneis* so as to exclude the two species originally placed in it by Ehrenberg and to include the species recognized in this genus today.

It is, therefore, evident that the genus *Ceratoneis* in its present concept cannot stand as it excludes the two species on which it was originally based. I, therefore, propose the name *Hannaea*.

This genus is named in honor of Dr. G. Dallas Hanna of the California Academy of Sciences who is recognized as one of the foremost students of fossil diatoms.

Type species. — *Hannaea arcus* (Ehr.) Patr. comb. nov. This species was originally described by Ehrenberg as *Navicula arcus* (1838, p. 182, pl. 21, fig. 10). It was first mentioned, but not described, by Ehrenberg in 1836 (p. 243).

1. **Hannaea arcus** (Ehr.) Patr. comb. nov., var. **arcus**   PL. 4, FIG. 20

Navicula arcus Ehr., Infusionsthierchen, p. 182, pl. 21, fig. 10.   1838.
Ceratoneis arcus (Ehr.) Kütz., Bacill., p. 104, pl. 6, fig. 10.   1844.

Frustules in girdle view bent, forming short bands. Valve curved, with convex dorsal margin. Ventral margin concave except for the swelling of the unilateral central area. Apices of the valve attenuate-rostrate to somewhat capitate. Central area distinctly swollen, only on the ventral side of the pseudoraphe. Pseudoraphe distinct, narrow. Striae parallel or sometimes slightly radiate toward the apices of the valve. Striae, 13-14 in 10μ at the center to 18 in 10μ at the ends of the valve. Length, usually $15\text{-}150\mu$; Ehrenberg states they may be as short as 4μ. Breadth, usually $4\text{-}7\mu$, but according to Ehrenberg the length is two and one-half to ten times the breadth.

The nominate variety is distinguished by its smoothly concave ventral margin, except for the swollen central area.

This taxon is mentioned by Ehrenberg in 1836, but so far as I can ascertain was not described until 1838.

Type locality. — In mineral Wasser zur Carlsbad.

U. S. distribution. — GEOGRAPHICAL: South Central States, Lakes States, Plains States; Montana, Colorado, Utah, Washington, Oregon, California. ECOLOGICAL: Seems to prefer cool, flowing water, particularly in mountainous regions.

1. **Hannaea arcus** var. **amphioxys** (Rabh.) Patr. comb. nov.

PL. 4, FIG. 21

Ceratoneis amphioxys Rabh., Süssw.-Diat., p. 37, pl. 9, fig. 4. 1853.
Ceratoneis arcus var. amphioxys (Rabh.) Brun., Diat. Alpes Jura, p. 52, pl. 2, fig. 28. 1880.

Valve with convex dorsal margin and ventral margin which is swollen on each side of the abruptly swollen central area, producing a triundulate margin. Apices of valve attenuated, rostrate-capitate, often bent slightly toward the ventral margin. Pseudoraphe narrow, distinct. Central area unilateral, swollen and somewhat attenuated. Striae as in the nominate variety. Length of cord between the two apices, 30-76μ. Breadth at widest portion, usually 4-8μ.

This taxon is distinguished from the nominate variety by the shape of the ventral margin and of the central area. Striae in this variety often a little coarser.

Type locality. — Uncertain.

U. S. distribution. — GEOGRAPHICAL: Tennessee.

Genus **Synedra** Ehr.

Ehr., Phys. Abh. Akad. Wiss. Berlin, for 1830:40. 1832.

Frustules may occur singly or in colonies, never forming long filaments; in girdle view linear, rectangular. In valve view very slender, linear or lanceolate. Pseudoraphe present, central area may or may not be present. A jelly pore is present at one end of the valve. The valve is usually symmetrical to the apical and transverse axes, but there are a few exceptions.

The chloroplasts are variable. Many small plates may be present or there may be two large plate-like structures.

In this book two subgenera, *Synedra* and *Ardissonia*, are considered.

This genus, particularly the subgenus *Synedra*, is very closely related to the genus *Fragilaria.* The only distinction is their manner of growth. Further study may show they should be united.

The species of this genus occur in planktonic or benthic habitats.

Type species. — Synedra ulna (Nitz.) Ehr.

Synedra subgenus SYNEDRA

Most of the species belonging to this subgenus are found in fresh water.

The structure of the frustule is simple. No costae, grooves, or chambered structures are present. A clear area known as the pseudoraphe is found in the apical axis of the valve. A central area may or may not be present. The striae are more or less finely punctate.

KEY TO THE SPECIES OF THE SUBGENUS SYNEDRA

1. Valve with a swollen central area, usually accompanied by a thickening of the wall 2
1. Valve not swollen at the central area 5
  2. Central area unilateral, valve lanceolate . . . . [15] *S. mazamaensis*
  2. Central area bilateral 3
3. Central area always reaching both margins of the valve. 4
3. Central area may reach both margins of the valve or may have short striae on one margin, striae about 17 in 10μ . . . .[14] *S. socia*
  4. Striae distinctly punctate . . . . [16] *S. pulchella*
  4. Striae not distinctly punctate . . . . [13] *S. rumpens*
5. Valve with a linear-lanceolate to lanceolate hyaline central area. 6
5. Valve with narrow pseudoraphe, more or less distinct. 10
  6. Striae usually not opposite each other . . . . [8] *S. demerarae*
  6. Striae opposite each other. 7
7. Ends of the valve attenuate-rostrate 8
7. Ends of the valve not attenuate-rostrate 9
  8. Valve biconstricted, ends of the valve attenuate-rostrate
                                        [10] *S. parasitica* var. *subconstricta*
  8. Valve not biconstricted, ends of the valve attenuated. . . . . [10] *S. parasitica*
9. Striae, less than 15 in 10μ. . . . . [11] *S. fasciculata*
9. Striae, more than 15 in 10μ. . . . . [9] *S. filiformis* var. *exilis*
  10. Apical axis variously curved 11
  10. Apical axis straight 13
11. Apical axis forming an arc of varying degrees of curvature. 12
11. Apical axis sinuous. . . . .[19] *S. longiceps*
  12. Valve forming a distinct arc, lunar shaped, usually less than 100μ
                                                        [22] *S. cyclopum*
  12. Valve forming a slight arc, usually more than 200μ long
                                                        [20] *S. ulna* var. *biceps*
13. Valve very narrow, often with a fragile appearance, central area, if present, distinctly longer than broad 14
13. Valve not needle shaped or very thin; if a great length-to-breadth ratio exists the central area, if present, is usually not longer than broad (exception, no. 20). . 21
  14. Central area never present; striae, more than 20 in 10μ . . . .[4] *S. tenera*
  14. Central area may be absent or present, striae variable in number 15

15. Striae, 20 or more in 10μ; central area, if present, not reaching margins of the valve . . . .[7] S. *famelica*
15. Striae, less than 20 in 10μ. 16
    16. Valve, typically less than 100μ in length. 17
    16. Valve, typically more than 100μ in length; striae, less than 15 in 10μ. 19
17. Valve with more or less capitate apices . . . .[6] S. *amphicephala*
17. Valve without capitate apices. 18
    18. Valve, less than 40μ long; central area usually lacking, if present, very small
                                                  [5] S. *minuscula*
    18. Valve linear to linear-lanceolate, usually over 50μ long; central area variable in size, usually present. . . . .[3] S. *radians*
19. Valve, more than 400μ long; central area absent. . . . .[20] S. *ulna* var. *chaseana*
19. Valve, less than 400μ in length. 20
    20. Length-to-breadth ratio, greater than 30:1. . . . .[2] S. *delicatissima*
    20. Length-to-breadth ratio, 30:1 or less . . . .[1] S. *acus*
21. Valve constricted on one side in the middle of the valve . . . .[12] S. *incisa*
21. Valve not constricted on one side, if constriction present, it is apparent on both sides of the valve. 22
    22. Valve without central area, not constricted. 23
    22. Valve with a central area, may or may not be constricted. 25
23. Ends of the valve rounded, apices not distinct. . . . .[18] S. *gaillonii*
23. Ends of the valve variously shaped. 24
    24. Ends of the valve wedge-shaped, capitate; much wider than main body of valve . . . .[17] S. *capitata*
    24. Ends of the valve much smaller than main body of valve
                                    [20] S. *ulna* var. *amphirhynchus*
25. Valve not constricted in the middle, gradually attenuated to the rostrate ends
                                              [20] S. *ulna*
25. Valve abruptly forming apices; may or may not be constricted in the central portion of the valve. 26
    26. Valve not constricted in the central portion. . . . . .[20] S. *ulna* var. *spathulifera*
    26. Valve constricted in central portion. 27
27. Constriction of the valve very weak. . . . .[20] S. *ulna* var. *contracta*
27. Constriction of the valve strong. 28
    28. Valve abruptly constricted at the central area
                  [20] S. *ulna* var. *oxyrhynchus* f. *mediocontracta*
    28. Valve not abruptly constricted. 29
29. Central area with faint striae crossing it. . . . .[21] S. *goulardi*
29. Central area not crossed by faint striae. . . . .[20] S. *ulna* var. *ramesi*

1. **Synedra acus** Kütz. var. **acus**   PL. 5, FIG. 1

Synedra acus Kütz., Bacill., p. 68, pl. 15, fig. 7. 1844.

Valve lanceolate, tapering to rounded or slightly capitate apices. Pseudoraphe narrow, becoming a little wider toward the middle of the valve. Central area distinct, a little longer than broad. Striae parallel, 11-14 in 10μ. Length, 90-180μ. Breadth, 4.5-6μ. Length-to-breadth ratio, 20:1-30:1.

This taxon is most closely related to *Synedra delicatissima* and S. *radians*. Hustedt (1930, p. 155) has described these species as varieties of

S. acus. However, on careful examination, this taxon differs in its more lanceolate shape of the valve which gives it a coarser appearance. Also the central area is more nearly square and only slightly longer than broad. The central area reaches the margins of the valve. The striae are coarser than in *S. radians.*

Type locality. — Hamburger Moor: Binder.

U. S. distribution. — Geographical: New England States, Middle Atlantic States, Southeastern States, Gulf Coast States, South Central States, East Central States, West Central States, Lakes States, Plains States; Montana, Wyoming, Arizona, Oregon, California. Ecological: A widely distributed species, seems to prefer circumneutral water and water which does not have a very low conductivity. More often found in water of medium hardness.

2. Synedra delicatissima W. Sm. var. delicatissima　　PL. 5, FIG. 2

Synedra delicatissima W. Sm., Syn. British Diat., vol. 1, p. 72, pl. 12, fig. 94.　1853.
Synedra delicatissima var. mesoleia Grun. *in* V. H., Syn. Diat. Belgique, pl. 39, fig. 6.　1881.

Valve linear, needle shaped, tapering a little to the rounded ends. Pseudoraphe very narrow, but distinct. Central area distinct, longer than broad, not reaching the margins of the valve. On the margins of the valve on each side of the central area are very short striae. Striae throughout the valve parallel. Striae, 11-14 in 10μ. Length, $100\text{-}230\mu$. Length-to-breadth ratio, 30:1-50:1.

This taxon is characterized by its needle shape, and the central area which is longer than broad and has very short striae on each margin.

This species is usually rare in collections.

Type locality. — Fresh water. Lough Neagh, Dr. Dickie, 1850. (*Lecto-type*—A-147, W. Sm. 94, Patrick.)

U. S. distribution. — Geographical: New England States, Middle Atlantic States, Gulf Coast States, West Central States, Lakes States. Ecological: This species is usually found in plankton.

2. Synedra delicatissima var. angustissima Grun.　　PL. 5, FIG. 3

Synedra delicatissima var. angustissima Grun. *in* V. H., Syn. Diat. Belgique, pl. 39, fig. 10.　1881.
Synedra acus var. angustissima (Grun.) V. H., Syn. Diat. Belgique, p. 151.　1885.

Valve very long and narrow; because of its delicate structure, it often appears sinuous. Pseudoraphe very narrow. Central area much longer than broad; sometimes clearly rectangular in shape, at other times with an irregular shape. Striae parallel, usually 13-14 in 10μ, sometimes a little finer. Length, usually over 200μ. Length-to-breadth ratio, about 55:1.

This species differs from the nominate variety by its more delicate valve structure and the shape and structure of the central area.

Type locality. — Uncertain, Belgium.

U. S. distribution. — GEOGRAPHICAL: New England States, Middle Atlantic States, Southeastern States, Gulf Coast States, South Central States, East Central States, West Central States, Plains States; New Mexico, Oregon, California. ECOLOGICAL: This species is often found in plankton in water of medium hardness.

3. **Synedra radians** Kütz. var. **radians**   PL. 5, FIG. 4

Synedra radians Kütz., Bacill., p. 64, pl. 14, fig. 7.   1844.

Synedra acus var. *radians* (Kütz.) Hust. *in* Pasch., Süssw.-Fl. Mitteleuropas, Heft 10, Aufl. 2, p. 155, fig. 171.   1930.

Valve linear; narrowing toward the slightly rostrate, rounded apices. Pseudoraphe narrow. Central area of variable size; a little longer than broad or absent. Sometimes the pseudoraphe is just a little wider at the central area. Striae parallel, 15-18 in 10μ. Length, $40\text{-}120\mu$. Breadth at the center of the valve, $2.5\text{-}4\mu$.

Van Heurck on slide no. 220 has very linear specimens of this taxon, whereas on slide no. 312 they are more lanceolate.

This taxon is characterized by its linear needle shape. It differs from *Synedra acus* by its finer striae and narrow, more linear shape. It is similar to S. *delicatissima* W. Sm. in shape, but differs in the fineness of the striae. This taxon is intermediate in shape between S. *acus* and S. *delicatissima*. It is closely related to *Exilaria tenuissima* Bréb. (ms.). I have examined specimens of this taxon from Brébisson's herbarium. Further study may show that these two taxa are the same.

Type locality. — An *Cladophora fracta* bei Tennstädt.

U. S. distribution. — GEOGRAPHICAL: New England States, Middle Atlantic States, West Central States, Lakes States, Plains States; Montana, Wyoming, Utah, Washington, California. ECOLOGICAL: Often found in plankton in slightly alkaline water, often with fairly high conductivity.

4. **Synedra tenera** W. Sm. var. **tenera**   PL. 5, FIG. 5

Synedra tenera W. Sm., Syn. British Diat., vol. 2, p. 98.   1856.

Valve very narrow, linear, tapering to the rounded, slightly inflated ends. Apices not clearly differentiated from the rest of the valve, sometimes slightly rostrate-capitate. Pseudoraphe indistinct. Central area absent. Striae fine, parallel; usually 23-28 in 10μ. Length, $30\text{-}162\mu$. Breadth $1.2\text{-}5\mu$.

This taxon is distinguished by its shape, its lack of central area, and its very fine striae.

I have examined W. Smith's slide no. A-62 from Blarney which seems to be our taxon. Unlike Smith's illustration these specimens sometimes have slightly rostrate-capitate ends.

Type locality. — Uncertain.

U. S. distribution. — GEOGRAPHICAL: Middle Atlantic States; Missouri. ECOLOGICAL: Seems to prefer slow-moving water of low conductivity.

5. Synedra minuscula Grun. var. minuscula   PL. 5, FIG. 6

Synedra minuscula Grun. *in* V. H., Syn. Diat. Belgique, pl. 39, fig. 13. 1881.

In girdle view frustules linear-rectangular. Valve linear, more or less suddenly contracted to form attenuated, rounded ends. Pseudoraphe narrow, distinct. Central area usually lacking; if present, small. Striae parallel, 15-18 in 10μ. Length, 15-39μ. Breadth, 2-3.5μ.

This taxon is characterized by the shape and size of the valve and the lacking, or only poorly developed central area.

Type locality. — Fossile à Franzenbad.

U. S. distribution. — GEOGRAPHICAL: Middle Atlantic States, Southeastern States; Connecticut, Florida, Montana, California. ECOLOGICAL: Seems to prefer cool water.

6. Synedra amphicephala Kütz. var. amphicephala   PL. 5, FIG. 7

Synedra amphicephala Kütz., Bacill., p. 64, pl. 3, fig. 12. 1844.

Frustules in girdle view rectangular; narrower toward the ends. Valve linear to linear-lanceolate, with capitate apices. Pseudoraphe narrow. Central area usually lacking. Striae, 11-16 in 10μ, usually 15-16 in 10μ. Length, 20-75μ. Breadth, 2.5-4μ.

This taxon is distinguished by its linear valve, capitate apices, and narrow pseudoraphe.

Type locality. — In stehendem Wasser bei Thun und Hamburg.

U. S. distribution. — GEOGRAPHICAL: New England States, Middle Atlantic States, Southeastern States, East Central States, West Central States, Lakes States, Plains States; Montana. ECOLOGICAL: Fresh water of variable conductivity.

6. Synedra amphicephala var. austriaca (Grun.) Hust.   PL. 5, FIG. 8

Synedra austriaca Grun. *in* V. H., Syn. Diat. Belgique, pl. 39, figs. 16a-b. 1881.
Synedra amphicephala var. *austriaca* (Grun. *in* V. H.) Hust. *in* Rabh., Kryptog.-Fl. Deutschland, vol. 7(2), no. 2, p. 206, figs. 696b-d. 1932.

Valve more broadly lanceolate than in the nominate variety. Apices attenuated, somewhat capitate. Pseudoraphe narrow. Striae, 13-14 in 10μ. Length, 20-30μ. Breadth, 3-5μ.

This taxon differs from the nominate variety by its more lanceolate shape and less distinctly capitate ends.

Type locality. — Uncertain, Belgium.

U. S. distribution. — GEOGRAPHICAL: Montana. ECOLOGICAL: A cold-water taxon.

7. Synedra famelica Kütz. var. famelica PL. 5, FIG. 9

Synedra famelica Kütz., Bacill., p. 64, pl. 14, fig. 8(1). 1844.

Valve linear to lanceolate, narrowed toward the somewhat attenuate-rostrate ends. Apices sometimes capitate. Pseudoraphe narrow. Central area absent; if present small. Striae, 20-21 in 10μ. Length, 15-40μ. Breadth, 2.5-4μ.

This taxon is characterized by its small size and fine striae.

Type locality. — Im klaren Quellwasser an feinfädigen Algen bei Halle.

U. S. distribution. —GEOGRAPHICAL: North Dakota. ECOLOGICAL: In eutrophic water of high mineral content.

8. Synedra demerarae Grun. var. demerarae PL. 5, FIG. 10

Synedra? demerarae Grun. *in* V. H., Syn. Diat. Belgique, pl. 41, fig. 29. 1881.

Valve lanceolate; narrowed toward the somewhat attenuated, rostrate to slightly capitate apices. Pseudoraphe forming a distinct, lanceolate, clear area. Striae more or less marginal, often not opposite each other. Striae coarse, 8 in 10μ. Length, 37-70μ. Breadth, 3-4μ.

Boyer's specimens are intermediate in shape between Grunow's illustration and those of Pantocsek (1889, p. 64, pl. 26, figs. 383, 386).

This taxon is distinguished by the striae which are marginal and usually not opposite each other, and also by the shape of the valve.

Type locality. — Demerara.

U. S. distribution. — GEOGRAPHICAL: Illinois.

9. Synedra filiformis var. exilis Cl.-Eul. PL. 5, FIG. 11

Synedra filiformis var. *exilis* Cl.-Eul., Acta Soc. Sci. Fennicae, Nov. Ser. B, 2(3):7, fig. 2. 1939.

Valve very narrow, linear-lanceolate. Ends very narrow, somewhat attenuated, rounded. Pseudoraphe or central area lanceolate. Striae continuous throughout the valve. Striae, 22-24 in 10μ. Length, 30-55μ. Breadth, 1.7-3μ.

This taxon is distinguished by the shape and size of the valve and the broad central area.

Type locality. — . . . als Aufwuchs in einem kleinen Bach bei Liina-hamari wenige m. ü. d. Meeresfläche . . .

U. S. distribution. — Geographical: Southeastern States, Gulf Coast States. Ecological: Seems to prefer water of low mineral content.

10. **Synedra parasitica** (W. Sm.) Hust. var. **parasitica**   pl. 5, fig. 12

> *Odontidium? parasiticum* W. Sm., Syn. British Diat., vol. 2, p. 19, supp. pl. 60, fig. 375. 1856.
>
> *Fragilaria? parasitica* (W. Sm.) Grun. *in* V. H., Syn. Diat. Belgique, pl. 45, fig. 30. 1881.
>
> *Synedra parasitica* (W. Sm.) Hust. *in* Pasch., Süssw.-Fl. Mitteleuropas, Heft 10, Aufl. 2, p. 161, fig. 195. 1930.

Valve rhombic-lanceolate with sharply attenuated, somewhat capitate apices. Pseudoraphe linear or linear-lanceolate in shape. Striae fine, 16-19 in 10μ. Length, 10-25μ. Breadth, 3-5μ.

This taxon is characterized by its shape, small size, and fine striations. It grows singly and is often epiphytic on species of *Nitzschia* or *Surirella*.

Cleve-Euler (1953a, p. 56) seems to have confused this taxon with at least two others.

Type locality. — Fresh water; parasitic on *Nitzschia sigmoidea.* Queen's Park, Edinburgh, April and July, 1854, Dr. Greville.

U. S. distribution. — Geographical: New England States, Middle Atlantic States, Southeastern States, Gulf Coast States, East Central States, West Central States, Lakes States, Plains States; California. Ecological: Fresh water, usually epiphytic on other diatoms, in circumneutral, slightly alkaline water; mesotrophic to eutrophic.

10. **Synedra parasitica** var. **subconstricta** (Grun.) Hust.   pl. 5, fig. 13

> *Fragilaria parasitica* var. *subconstricta* Grun. *in* V. H., Syn. Diat. Belgique, pl. 45, fig. 29. 1881.
>
> *Synedra parasitica* var. *subconstricta* (Grun.) Hust. *in* Pasch., Süssw.-Fl. Mitteleuropas, Heft 10, Aufl. 2, p. 161, fig. 196. 1930.

Valve biconstricted; amount of constriction variable. Apices of the valve attenuated, capitate. Pseudoraphe distinct, linear to linear-lanceolate in shape. Striae slightly radiate to almost parallel. Striae, 16-19 in 10μ. Length, 10-23μ. Breadth at widest portion, 4-5μ.

This taxon is distinguished from other varieties of this species by its biconstricted valve.

This variety of Grunow's seems to be the same as that of *Odontidium? parasiticum* var. β W. Sm. (1856, p. 19) although Grunow does not refer to it. I have examined specimens of W. Smith and they are the same as our specimens.

Type locality. — Uncertain.

U. S. distribution. — GEOGRAPHICAL: Middle Atlantic States, East Central States; Missouri. ECOLOGICAL: Epiphytic on other diatoms, often found with the nominate variety.

11. **Synedra fasciculata** (Ag.) Kütz. var. **fasciculata**   PL. 5, FIGS. 17-18

Diatoma fasciculata Ag., Disp. Alg. Sveciae, p. 35.   1812.

Diatoma tabulatum Ag., Consp. Crit. Diat., pt. 4, p. 50.   1832.

Synedra fasciculata (Ag.) *auct. non* Kütz., Bacill., p. 68, exclusive of description. 1844.

Synedra tabulata (Ag.) Kütz., Bacill., p. 68, pl. 15(10), figs. 1-3.   1844.

Synedra affinis Kütz., Bacill., p. 68, pl. 15,   figs. 6, 11; pl. 24(1), fig. 5.   1844.

Frustules usually seen in girdle view in colonies of two to five cells. Girdle very broad. Valve linear, widening a little toward the middle portion; narrower toward the apices which may be rounded or slightly rostrate, rounded. Pseudoraphe distinct, one-third to one-half the breadth of the valve. Central area absent. A distinct jelly pore present near the end of one of the terminal striae. Striae parallel, broad; absent from the tip of the valve, thereby forming a clear area. Striae, 10-14 in 10μ. Length, usually 175-250μ. Breadth, 4-7μ.

The name of this species must be *Synedra fasciculata* since it is the oldest name of the intraspecific taxa. I have examined specimens from Agardh's herbarium (courtesy of Dr. Sven Snogerup) from the type locality, Bastad. Dr. Snogerup states this specimen is in a cover of the special type used by Agardh. The handwriting on the packet is that of C. A. or J. G. Agardh. Dr. Snogerup is not sure whose it is. A portion of the valve of one of these is illustrated, pl. 5, fig. 17. I have also examined specimens of Kützing's *Exilaria fasciculata* Grev. (Alg. Dec. 8, 1833, No. 74). These specimens are part of the species *Synedra pulchella.* Kützing states that his *S. fasciculata* is based on *Diatoma fasciculatum* Ag. (specimens from Jürg.). However, his description does not apply to Agardh's specimen. He does not refer (1844) to *Exilaria fasciculata.*

Synedra tabulata var. *obtusa* Pant. (1889, p. 64, pl. 26, figs. 377, 380) is closely related to this taxon but differs mainly in the number of striae, which are finer, 15-18 in 10μ. As in this taxon, the width of the central area or pseudoraphe is variable.

Type locality. — In plantis marines ad Bastad hieme.

U. S. distribution. — GEOGRAPHICAL: New England States, Middle Atlantic States, Southeastern States, Gulf Coast States, South Central States, Plains States; Wyoming, Arizona, Washington, California. ECOLOGICAL: In water of high conductivity, sometimes slightly brackish.

11. **Synedra fasciculata** var. **truncata** (Grev.) Patr. comb. nov.

PL. 5, FIG. 16

Echinella fasciculata var. *truncata* Grev., Scottish Cryptog. Fl., vol. 1, p. 37, pl. 16, fig. 4. 1823.

Exilaria fasciculata Grev., Scottish Cryptog. Fl., vol. 6, p. 37. 1828.

Synedra fasciculata (Kütz.) Grun. *in* V. H., Syn. Diat. Belgique, p. 153, pl. 41, fig. 15. 1885.

Synedra tabulata var. *fasciculata* (Ag.) Hust. *in* Rabh., Kryptog.-Fl. Deutschland, vol. 7(2), no. 2, p. 218, figs. 710i-l. 1932.

Valve linear-lanceolate; narrowed toward the somewhat wedge-shaped or attenuated apices, which are rounded. Pseudoraphe a broad linear-lanceolate space, but not as broad as in the nominate variety. Striae short, 12-14 in 10μ. Gemeinhardt (1926, p. 25) states 10-15 in 10μ. Length, 20-100μ. Breadth, 4-7μ. Hustedt (1932, p.' 219) states it may be only 3μ wide.

This taxon differs from the nominate variety in that the valve is usually smaller and the length-to-breadth ratio less. Also the pseudoraphe is more lanceolate.

Type locality. — In fresh water, attached to confervae, stems of grass, the Lemnae, etc. Ditches near Edinburgh.

U. S. distribution. — GEOGRAPHICAL: New York, Texas. ECOLOGICAL: In fresh water of high conductivity or somewhat brackish water.

12. **Synedra incisa** Boyer var. **incisa**

PL. 5, FIGS. 14-15

Synedra incisa Boyer, Bull. Torrey Bot. Club, 47:68, pl. 2, fig. 8. 1920.

Frustules flexed in girdle view. Valve linear-lanceolate; asymmetrical to the apical axis by one margin being strongly constricted near the middle of the valve and the other margin being irregular in outline, sometimes constricted. Pseudoraphe narrow. Central area lacking or transverse and variable in size. Striae parallel, 18-20 in 10μ. Length, 23-50μ. Breadth, 3-4μ.

At first glance this species appears as an abnormal form. However, large populations of this diatom with irregular outline have been found several times. This would indicate it is not just an abnormal form. If it is an abnormal form it probably belongs to *Synedra minuscula* Grun. In size, structure of axial and central areas, and number of striae it seems to be related to *S. minuscula.*

In outline it is very similar to *S. affinis* var. *baileyana* Chase *in* Walker and Chase (1886, p. 4) but differs in its finer striae and its ecology, a fresh-water rather than a brackish-water species.

This specimen was selected on a slide which Boyer designated as "type."

Type locality. — U. S. A., Nebraska, Central City; in a water tank. (*Lectotype*—A-Boyer A-6-5, Patrick.)

U. S. distribution. — GEOGRAPHICAL: Pennsylvania, Nebraska.

13. **Synedra rumpens** Kütz. var. **rumpens**   PL. 5, FIG. 19

Synedra rumpens Kütz., Bacill., p. 69, pl. 16, fig. 6(6), figs. 4-5. 1844.

In girdle view frustules linear, narrower toward the ends. Sometimes forms short chains of two to three frustules. Valve linear, attenuated toward the ends. Apices swollen, somewhat capitate. Pseudoraphe narrow. Central area usually a distinct transverse fascia, usually longer than broad; often the valve appears thicker at the central area; not distinctly swollen as in the varieties. Striae parallel; not distinctly punctate. Striae, 18-20 in 10μ. Length, 27-70μ. Breadth, 2-4μ.

The nominate variety is distinguished from the other varieties by the lack of distinct swelling of the valve at the central area. That is, it is only slightly swollen.

This species seems to be related to *Fragilaria vaucheriae* (Kütz.) Peters. This is a quite variable species, and when thoroughly studied, the various varieties may be found in many cases to intergrade.

Type locality. — Im Brackwasser der oldenburgschen Küste.

U. S. distribution. — GEOGRAPHICAL: New England States, Middle Atlantic States, Southeastern States, Gulf Coast States, South Central States, East Central States, West Central States, Lakes States, Plains States; Wyoming, Oregon, California. ECOLOGICAL: Widely distributed in fresh-water lakes or ponds or slow-flowing streams.

13. **Synedra rumpens** var. **familiaris** (Kütz.) Hust.   PL. 5, FIG. 20

Synedra familiaris Kütz., Bacill., p. 68, pl. 15, fig. 12. 1844.
Synedra familiaris f. *parva* Grun. *in* V. H., Syn. Diat. Belgique, pl. 40, fig. 15. 1881.
Synedra familiaris f. *major* Grun. *in* V. H., Syn. Diat. Belgique, pl. 40, fig. 16. 1881.
Synedra pulchella var. *flexella* Boyer, Diat. Philadelphia, p. 49, pl. 12, fig. 2. 1916.
Synedra rumpens var. *familiaris* (Kütz.) Hust. *in* Pasch., Süssw.-Fl. Mitteleuropas,
    Heft 10, Aufl. 2, p. 156, fig. 176. 1930.

Valve linear-lanceolate, swollen on each side of the central area. Apices somewhat capitate. Axial area linear. Central area longer than broad, somewhat swollen. Striae parallel, 18-20 in 10μ; Gemeinhardt (1926, p. 18) states 15-17 in 10μ. Length, 30-80μ. Breadth of the valve in swollen area, 3-4μ.

This taxon is distinguished by the central swellings of the valve or the finer striae.

Elmore (1922, p. 55) has described and figured what he calls *Synedra familiaris* Kütz. His description and illustration do not seem to be this taxon as recognized by most authors. Boyer (1927a, p. 203) considered this taxon as a distinct species and not as a variety of *S. rumpens*. More recent workers have generally considered it as a variety of *S. rumpens*.

Type locality. — An *Cladophora fracta* bei Falaise: Lenormand (Als *Exilaria fasciculata*).

U. S. distribution. — Geographical: New England States, Middle Atlantic States, Southeastern States, South Central States, West Central States, Plains States; Florida, Montana, Arizona, Washington, Oregon, California. Ecological: Widely distributed in circumneutral water.

13. Synedra rumpens var. fragilarioides Grun.   PL. 6, FIG. 1

Synedra rumpens var.? *fragilarioides* Grun. *in* V. H., Syn. Diat. Belgique, pl. 40, fig. 12. 1881.

Valve linear sometimes linear-lanceolate, somewhat swollen on each side of the central area; attenuated to the rounded apices. Pseudoraphe distinct, becoming slightly wider toward the central area. Central area longer than broad, somewhat swollen. This taxon is of variable length-to-breadth ratio, and this fact makes the ends of the valve seem more suddenly attenuated in some specimens than in others. Striae, 10-12 in 10μ. Length, 40-75μ. Breadth at swollen portion of the valve, 3-5μ.

This taxon is distinguished by the central swellings of the valve and the striae which are coarser than those found in most of the other varieties.

Type locality. — Uncertain, Belgium.

U. S. distribution. — Geographical: Middle Atlantic States, Southeastern States; Connecticut, Kentucky, Nebraska, Oregon, California. Ecological: Seems to be of much less frequent occurrence than the other varieties. Prefers waterfalls, springs or brooks; often found in circumneutral water with fairly high conductivity.

13. Synedra rumpens var. scotica Grun.   PL. 6, FIG. 2

Synedra rumpens var.? *scotica* Grun. *in* V. H., Syn. Diat. Belgique, pl. 40, fig. 11. 1881.

Valve linear-lanceolate, having a very slender, rather delicate appearance. Apices slightly capitate or rounded. Pseudoraphe narrow, sometimes not very distinct. Central area swollen, large. Striae parallel, 15-16 in 10μ. Length, 40-60μ. Breadth, 2-3μ.

This taxon is distinguished by its slender, linear-lanceolate valve with the distinctly swollen central area.

Type locality. — Scotland, Kinross.

U. S. distribution. — Geographical: Middle Atlantic States, Southeastern States, South Central States, East Central States, West Central States; Oregon, California. Ecological: Fresh water of low mineral content.

13. **Synedra rumpens** var. **meneghiniana** Grun. PL. 6, FIG. 3

Synedra rumpens var.? *meneghiniana* Grun. *in* V. H., Syn. Diat. Belgique, pl. 40, fig. 13. 1881.

Frustules in girdle view linear; central area swollen. Valve linear to linear-lanceolate with acute, sometimes slightly rostrate ends. Pseudoraphe very narrow, sometimes indistinct. Central area longer than broad, swollen. Striae parallel, 12-13.5 in 10μ. Length, 27-38μ. Breadth, 3-4μ.

This taxon is distinguished from the nominate variety by its coarser striae. It is very similar in shape to the nominate variety.

Type locality. — Battaglia.

U. S. distribution. — GEOGRAPHICAL: Middle Atlantic States, South Central States; South Carolina. ECOLOGICAL: Fresh water of low mineral content.

14. **Synedra socia** Wallace var. **socia** PL. 6, FIGS. 4-6

Synedra socia Wallace, Not. Nat. Acad. Nat. Sci. Philadelphia, No. 331, p. 1, pl. 1, figs. 1A-E. 1960.

Valve linear-lanceolate with attenuate-rostrate apices. Pseudoraphe narrow, distinct. Valve slightly constricted and then swollen in the middle portion in the region of the central area. Central area may reach the margins of the valve on both sides or may have short striae along the margin on one side. Striae parallel, 17 in 10μ. Length, usually 15-28μ. Breadth, 3-4μ.

This taxon is typically much smaller in length-to-breadth ratio than *Synedra rumpens*. It is also more lanceolate in shape. The shape of the valve is similar to that of *Fragilaria vaucheriae*, except for the structure of the central area and the striae, which are much coarser.

This taxon might more correctly be considered a variety of S. *rumpens* since one of the specimens shown by Wallace is very similar to S. *rumpens* var. *familiaris,* however in variety *familiaris* the striae are finer and the length-to-breadth ratio is greater.

This species is closely related to S. *dorsiventralis* O. Müll. (1910, p. 114, figs. 3-5), but it does not have the asymmetrical shape of the valve and is much smaller. Tiffany and Britton (1952, p. 236) list S. *dorsiventralis* O. Müll. as occurring in Illinois, but we have not been able to locate any specimens of this species.

Type locality. — U. S. A., Georgia, Screven County, Savannah River. (*Type Coll.*—A.-G.C. 4036a, Wallace, 1960), (*Lectotype*—A.-G.C. 4036a, Patrick.)

U. S. distribution. — GEOGRAPHICAL: Southeastern States. ECOLOGICAL: Found in circumneutral water of low conductivity.

15. **Synedra mazamaensis** Sov. var. **mazamaensis**   PL. 6, FIG. 7

> *Synedra mazamaensis* Sov., Trans. American Micr. Soc., 77(2):111, pl. 2, figs. 10-15. 1958.

Valve lanceolate, attenuated toward the capitate apices; somewhat swollen in the middle portion of the valve. Pseudoraphe narrow. Central area unilateral; sometimes traversed by very faint striae. Striae appearing slightly radiate toward the apices. Striae, 19-23 in 10μ. Length, $13\text{-}40\mu$. Breadth, $3\text{-}5\mu$.

This taxon is distinguished by its lanceolate shape and the swollen middle portion of the valve.

Sovereign states this species is quite variable in outline, varying from short, compact, relatively wide forms to those relatively long with extremely attenuated ends. In some specimens, longitudinally asymmetrical. This species is related to *Synedra vaucheriae*, but is more lanceolate in the shape of the valve and more finely striated.

Type locality. — U. S. A., Oregon, Crater Lake National Park, Emerald Pool. (*Holotype*—Cal. Acad. Sci.-3463, Sov. 488-11, Sovereign, 1960.)

U. S. distribution. — GEOGRAPHICAL: Washington, Oregon. ECOLOGICAL: Found in water with a pH of 7.2-8.4.

16. **Synedra pulchella** Ralfs *ex* Kütz. var. **pulchella**   PL. 6, FIGS. 10, 12

> *Synedra pulchella* Ralfs *ex* Kütz., Bacill., p. 68, pl. 29, fig. 87. 1844.
> *Synedra pulchella* var. *smithii* (Ralfs) Grun. *in* V. H., Syn. Diat. Belgique, pl. 41, fig. 4. 1881.
> *Synedra pulchella* var. *abnormis* Macchiati, Nuovo Gior. Bot. Italiano, 21:263, fig. 1. 1889.

Frustules in girdle view narrowed toward the ends of the valve. Valve linear-lanceolate with slightly attenuated, rostrate or slightly capitate apices. Pseudoraphe distinct, sometimes widening toward the central area. Central area slightly swollen, reaching the margins of the valve; rectangular to somewhat rounded in shape. Striae distinctly punctate, parallel to sometimes slightly radiate at the ends of the valve. Striae, 12-16 in 10μ, rarely to 20 in 10μ. Length, $33\text{-}150\mu$. Breadth, $5\text{-}8\mu$.

This taxon is distinguished by its shape, its distinctly punctate striae, and its swollen central area.

Type locality. — An Conferven in England.

U. S. distribution. — GEOGRAPHICAL: New England States, Middle Atlantic States, Southeastern States, Gulf Coast States, South Central States, East Central States, West Central States, Lakes States, Plains States; Montana, Nevada, California. ECOLOGICAL: Usually in fresh water of high mineral content, or slightly brackish water.

16. Synedra pulchella var. lacerata Hust. PL. 6, FIG. 11

Synedra pulchellà var. *lacerata* Hust. *in* Gemeinh., Pflanzenforschung, 6:5. 1926.

Valve lanceolate with swollen, somewhat capitate apices. Axial area distinct, broader than in the nominate variety; margins somewhat irregular. Central area swollen, rectangular in shape, extending to the margins of the valve. Striae distinctly punctate, parallel throughout most of the valve, appearing somewhat radiate at the apices. Striae, 16-18 in 10μ. Length, about 100μ. Breadth, 6-7μ.

This taxon is distinguished by the broad, somewhat irregularly formed axial area.

Hustedt *in* Schmidt's Atlas (1913, pl. 300, figs. 32-33) pictured this species but did not describe it. As a result this description is illegitimate.

Type locality. — Viktoriasee.

U. S. distribution. — GEOGRAPHICAL: Florida, Nebraska. ECOLOGICAL: Found in water with high conductivity.

16. Synedra pulchella var. lanceolata O'Meara PL. 6, FIGS. 13-14

Synedra minutissima Kütz. *ex* W. Sm., Syn. British Diat., vol. 1, p. 70, pl. 11, fig. 87. 1853.

Synedra pulchella var. *lanceolata* O'Meara, Proc. Roy. Irish Acad., Ser. 2, 2:304, pl. 28, fig. 20. 1875.

Synedra pulchella var. *minutissima* (Kütz. *ex* W. Sm.) Grun. *in* Cl. & Grun., K. Svenska Vet.-Akad. Handl., Ny Följd, 17(2):107, p. 6, fig. 120. 1880.

Valve lanceolate with acute, rounded apices or apices that are rostrate. Axial area narrow. Central area large, swollen; may be about as long as broad or broader than long. Striae distinctly punctate, 15-20 in 10μ. Length, 18-52μ. Breadth, 6-8μ.

This taxon is distinguished by its lanceolate shape and acute to rostrate apices.

Type locality. — Birkenhead, Cheshire [England]; fresh water.

U. S. distribution. — GEOGRAPHICAL: New England States; North Carolina, Nebraska, California. ECOLOGICAL: Found in water of high mineral content, usually brackish.

17. Synedra capitata Ehr. var. capitata PL. 6, FIG. 15

Synedra capitata Ehr. *in* Poggendorff, Ann. Phys. Chem., Ser. 2, 38:221, pl. 3, fig. 3(1). 1836.

Frustules in girdle view linear. Valve linear with abruptly widened, capitate-wedge-shaped ends. Pseudoraphe distinct. Central area absent. Jelly pore distinct. Striae parallel, slightly radiate near the ends of the valve. Striae, 8-11 in 10μ. Length, 125-500μ. Breadth, 7-10μ.

This taxon is distinguished by the shape of the apices of the valve.

Type locality. — [Italy], . . . Bergmehl von Santa Fiora . . .

U. S. distribution. — GEOGRAPHICAL: New England States, Middle Atlantic States, Gulf Coast States, East Central States, Lakes States, Plains States; Montana, Washington. ECOLOGICAL: Widely distributed in fresh water, often in lakes or slowly flowing rivers.

18. Synedra gaillonii (Bory) Ehr. var. gaillonii   PL. 6, FIG. 16

Navicula (gaillonii) Bory, Encyclop. Method., p. 564. 1824.
Synedra gaillonii (Bory) Ehr., Phys. Abh. Akad. Wiss. Berlin, for 1833:273. 1835.

Girdle view linear, slightly narrower toward the ends. Valve linear, slightly narrower toward the broadly rounded ends. Pseudoraphe narrow, distinct. Central area absent. Jelly pore distinct. Striae parallel, 9-11 in 10μ. Length, 110-270μ. Breadth, 8-11μ.

This taxon is distinguished by its linear shape with broadly rounded ends and its distinct pseudoraphe.

Type locality. — [France], Dieppe.

U. S. distribution. — GEOGRAPHICAL: New York, California. ECOLOGICAL: Brackish water.

19. Synedra longiceps Ehr. var. longiceps   PL. 7, FIG. 11

Synedra longiceps Ehr., Ber. Akad. Wiss. Berlin, for 1845:81. 1845.

Frustules flexuose, linear. Valve linear, curved or sinuous; somewhat swollen just below the styliform apices. Pseudoraphe narrow. Central area reaching the margins of the valve, approximately as long as broad. Striae parallel, 12-14 in 10μ. Length, 170-200μ. Breadth at center of the valve, 5-7μ.

This taxon is distinguished by its sinuous or curved valve and the shape of the apices of the valve. In its general shape it seems to be related to *Synedra capitata*, however, the shape of the apices, the number of striae, and the shape of the central area suggest a relationship to *S. ulna*. Boyer (1927a, p. 203) states that in shape it is similar to some of the sporangial forms of *S. ulna*.

Type locality. — Viva in lacu Mitchigan [Michigan, U. S. A.].

U. S. distribution. — GEOGRAPHICAL: Lake Michigan, Lake Superior. ECOLOGICAL: Fresh water.

20. Synedra ulna (Nitz.) Ehr. var. ulna   PL. 7, FIGS. 1-2

Bacillaria ulna Nitz., Neue Schrift. Naturf. Ges. Halle, 3(1):99, pl. 5. 1817.
Frustulia splendens Kütz., Linnaea, 8:553, fig. 23. 1833.

Synedra bicurvata Beine *ex* Rabh., Fl. Europaea Alg., Sect. 1, p. 129. 1864. Rabh.
    Exsicc. 1405. 1862. (no description).
Synedra lanceolata Kütz., Bacill., p. 66, pl. 30, fig. 31. 1844.
Synedra splendens Kütz., Bacill., p. 66, pl. 14, fig. 16. 1844.
Synedra ulna (Nitz.) Ehr., Ber. Akad. Wiss. Berlin, for 1836:53. 1836.
Synedra ulna var. *lanceolata* Grun., Verh. Zool.-Bot. Ges. Wien, 12:397. 1862.
Synedra ulna var. *splendens* (Kütz.) V. H., Syn. Diat. Belgique, p. 150. 1885.

Valve linear; very gradually attenuated to the rostrate or sometimes somewhat rostrate-wedge-shaped ends. Axial area narrow. Central area not much longer than broad, often almost square. Sometimes very short striae apparent on the margins of the central area. Striae parallel, usually 9-11 in 10μ; Hustedt (1932, p. 198) states sometimes 8-12 in 10μ. Length, usually 75-100μ, however, sometimes as short as 50μ or up to 350μ in length. Breadth, 5-9μ.

This taxon is distinguished from the other varieties by the shape of the apices combined with the shape of the central area.

Synedra splendens is sometimes regarded as a separate variety because of its great length. However, Ehrenberg (1838, p. 211) states that *S. ulna* and *Frustulia splendens* are the same. Since Ehrenberg is probably one of the few people to have seen Nitzsch's and Kützing's specimens, I believe we should follow his conclusions. Certainly from Kützing's Dec. VIII, no. 73, Dec. I, no. 1 they are probably the same taxon, although there is considerable variation in the shape of the apices of the valve.

Type locality. — [Germany], Grundschlamme des Wittenberger Stadtgrabens.

U. S. distribution. — GEOGRAPHICAL: New England States, Middle Atlantic States, Southeastern States, Gulf Coast States, South Central States, East Central States, West Central States, Lakes States, Plains States; Montana, Wyoming, Colorado, Idaho, Utah, Arizona, Oregon, California. ECOLOGICAL: Widely distributed in fresh water.

20. **Synedra ulna** var. **amphirhynchus** (Ehr.) Grun.   PL. 7, FIGS. 6-7

Synedra amphirhynchus Ehr., Phys. Abh. Akad. Wiss. Berlin, for 1841:425, pl. 3(1),
    fig. 25. 1843.
Synedra vitrea Bory *ex* Kütz., Bacill., p. 66, pl. 14, fig. 17. 1844.
Synedra ulna var. *amphirhynchus* (Ehr.) Grun., Verh. Zool.-Bot. Ges. Wien, 12:397.
    1862.
Synedra ulna var. *vitrea* (Bory *ex* Kütz.) V. H., Syn. Diat. Belgique, p. 151. 1885.

Valve linear, suddenly constricted to the attenuate-rostrate or sometimes slightly capitate apices. Pseudoraphe very narrow. Central area absent. Striae parallel, 10-12 in 10μ. Length, usually 180-250μ. Breadth, 4-7μ.

This taxon is characterized by its size, the structure of the ends of the valve, and the lack of a central area.

Van Heurck (1881, pl. 38, fig. 5) and Hustedt (1932, p. 197, fig. e) illustrate specimens of *Synedra* (*ulna* var.) *amphirhynchus* Ehr. and *Synedra ulna* var. *amphirhynchus* (respectively) which have more capitate ends than those given for the original description, or those of Kützing (1844, p. 66). When one compares the original illustration of *S. amphirhynchus* with the original illustration of *S. vitrea*, and with Kützing's illustration of *S. amphirhynchus*, it is evident they all belong to the same taxon.

Type locality. — Uncertain.

U. S. distribution. — GEOGRAPHICAL: Southeastern States; Pennsylvania, Minnesota. ECOLOGICAL: Circumneutral, usually mesotrophic to eutrophic fresh water.

20. Synedra ulna var. chaseana Thomas   PL. 8, FIGS. 1a-b

Synedra ulna var. *chaseana* Thomas *in* Walker & Chase, New and rare diatoms, Ser. 1, p. 4, pl. 2, fig. 3. 1886.
Synedra chaseana (Thomas *in* Walker & Chase) Boyer, Proc. Acad. Nat. Sci. Philadelphia, 78(1), Suppl.:202. 1927.

Valve very long and slender with somewhat capitate ends. Pseudoraphe very narrow. Central area absent. Striae, 7-11 in 10μ. Length, 400-700μ. Breadth, 3-5μ.

This taxon is characterized by its great length and lack of a central area. I have seen the type of this species in the Chicago Academy of Sciences, and we have isotype material at the Academy of Natural Sciences of Philadelphia. It should not be synonymized with *Synedra ulna* var. *danica* (Kütz.) Grun., as Hustedt (1932, p. 200) has done, nor do we consider it a distinct species as Boyer (1927a, p. 202) has made it.

Type locality. — U. S. A., Lake Michigan, Mr. B. W. Thomas.

U. S. distribution. — GEOGRAPHICAL: East Central States; Montana, Lake Michigan. ECOLOGICAL: A plankton species in cool lakes.

20. Synedra ulna var. contracta Østr.   PL. 7, FIG. 3

Synedra ulna var. *contracta* Østr., *in* Bot. Faeröes, pt. 1, p. 281, fig. 47. 1901.

Valve linear with concave margins, appearing somewhat constricted in the middle portion of the valve. Ends of the valve wedge-shaped with attenuate-rostrate apices. Pseudoraphe distinct, abruptly widening into the central area. Central area almost as broad as long, reaching the margins of the valve. Jelly pore evident. Striae parallel throughout most of the valve, slightly radiate at the ends. Striae, 10 in 10μ. Length, 100-120μ. Breadth at widest portion, 7-8μ.

This taxon is most closely related to *Synedra ulna* var. *ramesi* from which it differs by its size, greater length-to-breadth ratio, and shape of the central area. This taxon as well as *S. ulna* var. *ramesi* are closely related to *S. goulardi*.

Type locality. — Found in a gathering from the Faeroes labeled "Green algae from a swamp on Nolsö."

U. S. distribution. — GEOGRAPHICAL: Pennsylvania, North Carolina, Tennessee.

20. **Synedra ulna** var. **danica** (Kütz.) V. H.   PL. 7, FIG. 10

Synedra danica Kütz., Bacill., p. 66, pl. 14, fig. 13. 1844.
Synedra ulna var. *danica* (Kütz.) V. H., Syn. Diat. Belgique, p. 151. 1885.

Valve linear-lanceolate. Ends of the valve swollen, somewhat capitate. Pseudoraphe narrow. Central area transverse, usually not reaching the margins of the valve. Jelly pore present. Striae parallel, 9-10 in 10μ. Length, 120-200μ. Breadth, 5-8μ.

This taxon is distinguished by the shape of the valve and the central area.

Hustedt (1932, p. 200) has synonymized *Synedra ulna* var. *chaseana* Thomas with this taxon. We do not believe this to be correct, as *S. ulna* var. *chaseana* is a much longer, narrower form without a central area and differently shaped apices.

Type locality. — In süssem Wasser der jütischen Halbinsel: Hb. Binder.

U. S. distribution. — GEOGRAPHICAL: New England States, Middle Atlantic States, Southeastern States, Gulf Coast States, South Central States, East Central States, West Central States, Lakes States, Plains States; Montana, Colorado, New Mexico, Arizona, Oregon, California. ECOLOGICAL: Often in plankton in circumneutral fresh water, indifferent to small amounts of salt.

20. **Synedra ulna** var. **biceps** (Kütz.) Kirchn.   PL. 8, FIGS. 2a-b

Synedra biceps Kütz., Bacill., p. 66, pl. 14(18); pl. 14(21), fig. 1. 1844.
Synedra longissima W. Sm., Syn. British Diat., vol. 1, p. 72, pl. 12, fig. 95. 1853.
Synedra ulna var. *biceps* (Kütz.) Kirchn. in Cohn, Kryptog, Fl. Schles., p. 208. 1878.
Synedra ulna var. *longissima* (W. Sm.) Brun, Diat. Alpes Jura, p. 126, pl. 4, fig. 21. 1880.

Frustules and valve curved. Valve linear, narrowed toward the swollen, rounded ends. Pseudoraphe narrow, often indistinct. Central area usually lacking. W. Smith's specimens have no central area. Striae, 8-12 in 10μ. Length, 200-600μ. Breadth, 5-7μ.

This taxon is distinguished by its great length, curvature of the valve, and swollen, rounded ends. In length it is similar to *Synedra ulna* var. *chaseana* which is much narrower and not curved.

Brun states his taxon is the same as *S. longissima* W. Sm. However, W. Smith's name was superfluous when published and, therefore, had no standing.

Type locality. — Pond in Botanic Garden, Belfast, 1950, Dr. Dickie.

U. S. distribution. — GEOGRAPHICAL: New England States, Middle Atlantic States, Southeastern States, East Central States, Lakes States, Plains States; Montana, Wyoming. ECOLOGICAL: Seems to prefer cool, fresh water.

20. **Synedra ulna** var. **obtusa** V. H.   PL. 7, FIG. 9

Frustulia aequalis Kütz., Linnaea, 8:546, pl. 14, fig. 30. 1833.
Synedra obtusa W. Sm., Syn. British Diat., vol. 1, p. 71, pl. 11, fig. 92. 1853.
Synedra ulna var. *obtusa* (W. Sm.) V. H., Syn. Diat. Belgique, p. 151. 1885.

Valve linear with rounded or slightly swollen apices. Pseudoraphe narrow. Central area variable in size, not reaching the margins of the valve. Jelly pore well developed. Striae parallel, 8-11 in 10μ. Length, $150-200\mu$. Breadth, $6-8\mu$.

This taxon is distinguished by its broad apices which are scarcely differentiated from the main part of the valve. It has a greater length-to-breadth ratio than the nominate variety, and its central area is less well developed.

William Smith states his taxon is the same as specimens of *Synedra aequalis* Kütz. (1849, p. 45) sent to him by Brébisson. However, they are not the same as *S. aequalis* illustrated by Kützing (1844, pl. 14, fig. 14) which Kützing considered the same as the species listed in *Species Algarum*. (Kützing cites *Die kieselschaligen Bacillarien oder Diatomeen* reference to illustrate his taxon in *Species Algarum*.) Although W. Smith's name may have been superfluous when published, it is the oldest one at the variety rank.

Type locality. — Uncertain.

U. S. distribution. — GEOGRAPHICAL: East Central States; Montana. ECOLOGICAL: Although Boyer (1927a, p. 200) says of *Synedra obtusa* W. Sm., "Fresh water. Not uncommon.", there are neither specimens in his collection nor records from the United States to substantiate this statement. Seems to prefer cool water.

20. **Synedra ulna** var. **oxyrhynchus** f. **mediocontracta** Hust.   PL. 7, FIG. 4

Synedra oxyrhynchus var. *medioconstricta* Forti, Atti Reale Ist. Veneto, 69:1299. 1910.

Synedra ulna var. *oxyrhynchus* f. *mediocontracta* Hust. *in* Rabh., Kryptog.-Fl. Deutschland, vol. 7(2), no. 2, p. 199, fig. 691B (r). 1932.

This taxon differs from *Synedra ulna* var. *oxyrhynchus* by the abrupt constriction of the valve in the central area. Striae, 11 in 10μ. Length, 50-100μ. Breadth, 6μ at the central constriction and 8μ in the broadest portion.

Type locality. — Nel sedimento più leggero del saggio raccolto sulle colline dei Soddo.

U. S. distribution. — GEOGRAPHICAL: Tennessee. ECOLOGICAL: Seems to prefer circumneutral water of low conductivity.

20. **Synedra ulna** var. **ramesi** (Hérib.) Hust. PL. 6, FIG. 9

Synedra ramesi Hérib., Diat. Foss. Auvergne, vol. 2, p. 80, pl. 11, fig. 28. 1903.
Synedra ulna var. *ramesi* (Hérib.) Hust. *in* Pasch., Süssw.-Fl. Mitteleuropas, Heft 10, Aufl. 2, p. 152, fig. 163. 1930.

Valve linear with margins concave in the middle portion of the valve; slightly swollen near the narrow, attenuated, rostrate apices. Pseudoraphe narrow, distinct, widening into a large central area which extends to the margins of the valve. Central area longer than broad. Striae indistinctly punctate, parallel except near the ends of the valve where they are often curved, slightly radiate. Striae, usually 10-12 in 10μ; Hustedt's illustration (*loc. cit.*) has 14-16 in 10μ. Length, 45-55μ; Hustedt's illustration is of a specimen 30μ long. Breadth at widest portion, 7-8μ; Hustedt's illustration is about 5μ wide.

Hustedt (1932, p. 199) has synonymized this taxon with *Synedra ulna* var. *contracta* Østr. which is larger, has a different length-to-breadth ratio, and has a central area of different shape.

Type locality. — Uncertain.

U. S. distribution. — GEOGRAPHICAL: New England States, Middle Atlantic States, Southeastern States, Gulf Coast States, South Central States, Plains States; Montana, New Mexico, California.

20. **Synedra ulna** var. **spathulifera** (Grun.) V. H. PL. 7, FIG. 8

Synedra spathulifera Grun. *in* V. H., Syn. Diat. Belgique, pl. 38, fig. 4. 1881.
Synedra ulna var. *spathulifera* (Grun.) V. H., Syn. Diat. Belgique, p. 151. 1885.

Frustules in girdle view with ends of the frustules wider than the middle portion. Valve linear, somewhat swollen near the ends of the valve. Apices wedge-shaped, rounded; ends of the valve, therefore, appear spatulate in shape. Pseudoraphe narrow. Central area variable in size, but not extending to the margins of the valve. Jelly pore evident. Striae parallel throughout the valve or sometimes slightly radiate at the apices. Striae, 10-12 in 10μ. Length, 100-160μ. Breadth, 6.5-8μ.

This taxon is characterized by the spatulate ends of the valve, and the central area which does not reach the margins of the valve.

Type locality. — Deurne près d'Anvers.

U. S. distribution. — Geographical: New England States, Middle Atlantic States, Southeastern States, East Central States, West Central States, Lakes States; Montana, California. Ecological: Seems to prefer cool, fresh water.

20. **Synedra ulna** var. **subaequalis** (Grun.) V. H.   pl. 7, fig. 5

Synedra subaequalis Grun. *in* V. H., Syn. Diat. Belgique, pl. 38, fig. 13. 1881.
Synedra ulna var. *subaequalis* (Grun.) V. H., Syn. Diat. Belgique, p. 151. 1885.

Valve linear, slightly narrowed at the somewhat rostrate ends. Pseudoraphe very narrow. Central area usually absent; if present, small. Striae, 7-9 in 10μ. Length, 200-250μ. Breadth, 3-5μ.

This taxon is distinguished from *Synedra ulna* var. *longissima* in that the ends of the valve are narrower than the middle, and the length-to-breadth ratio is greater. Also it is usually shorter than *S. ulna* var. *longissima* and has striae that are a little coarser. A central area may be present also. The valve without a central area differs from such valves of *S. ulna* var. *danica* in that the valve is linear—not linear-lanceolate—and it is typically longer than *S. ulna* var. *danica*.

Type locality. — Eaux douces—Bruxelles (Delogne).

U. S. distribution. — Geographical: New England States, Middle Atlantic States, East Central States, Plains States; Montana, Washington. Ecological: Seems to prefer water of fairly low mineral content.

21. **Synedra goulardi** Bréb. var. **goulardi**   pl. 6, fig. 8

Synedra goulardi Bréb. *in* Cl. & Grun., K. Svenska Vet.-Akad. Handl., Ny Följd, 17(2):107, pl. 6, fig. 119. 1880.

Valve constricted in the middle portion; somewhat swollen toward the wedge-shaped ends which become rostrate or subcapitate. Pseudoraphe distinct, narrow. Central area about as broad as long. Striae faint, but present throughout the central area; parallel or slightly radiate at the ends. The radiate appearance of the striae at the ends seems, in some cases, to be due to whether you are examining the inside rather than the outside of the valve. Striae, 10-11 in 10μ. Length, 57-80μ. Breadth of the valve in widest portion, 8-10μ.

This taxon is distinguished from *Synedra ulna* var. *ramesi* which it resembles in many characteristics by the presence of faint striae throughout the central area.

Type locality. — Uncertain.

U. S. distribution. — GEOGRAPHICAL: Middle Atlantic States, Gulf Coast States, South Central States, East Central States. ECOLOGICAL: Often found in warm water.

22. **Synedra cyclopum** Brutschy var. **cyclopum** PL. 8, FIGS. 6-7

Synedra cyclopum Brutschy, Internat. Rev. Ges. Hydrobiol., 10:284, fig. 11. 1922.

Valve somewhat curved or arched, linear to linear-lanceolate in shape; narrowed to the rounded or somewhat capitate ends. Pseudoraphe narrow. Central area absent or lanceolate to elliptical in shape, not reaching the margins of the valve. Striae parallel, opposite each other. Striae, 14 in 10μ at the center of the valve to 18 in 10μ toward the apices of the valve. Length, $25\text{-}93\mu$. Breadth, $3\text{-}4\mu$.

This taxon is distinguished by its curved valve and the shape of the central area.

Type locality. — Uncertain.

U. S. distribution. — GEOGRAPHICAL: Montana, Wyoming. ECOLOGICAL: Often attached to crustacea in cool water.

22. **Synedra cyclopum** var. **robustum** Schulz PL. 8, FIG. 8

Synedra cyclopum var. *robustum* Schulz, Ber. Westpreus. Bot.-Zool. Vereins, 53(7): 26, pl. 4, figs. 12-13. 1931.

Valve slightly arcuate, narrowing toward the rostrate to rostrate-capitate ends. Pseudoraphe narrow; widening a little toward the central area which is a broad transverse area. Length of the central area greater than width. A jelly pore sometimes distinct toward one end of the valve. Striae parallel or slightly radiate toward the ends of the valve. Striae, 16-20 in 10μ. Length, $45\text{-}86\mu$. Breadth, $5\text{-}7\mu$.

This variety is distinguished from the nominate variety by its more robust appearance.

The only specimens we have seen are those of Sovereign from Upper Klamath Lake, Oregon.

Type locality. — U. S. A., Wisconsin, Delavan Lake.

U. S. distribution. — GEOGRAPHICAL: Wisconsin, Oregon. ECOLOGICAL: Found in water with a pH of 7.1-8.4.

Names of Taxa reported from the U. S. (fresh water) which could not be verified by a specimen from a public herbarium.

Synedra acuta Ehr. (recorded by Ehrenberg).

Synedra dicephala (recorded by Palmer. Also we cannot find the original description).

Synedra dorsiventralis Müll. (recorded by Britton).
Synedra longissima W. Sm. (recorded by Jelliffe).
Synedra oxyrhynchus var. *undulata* Grun. (recorded by Boyer).
Synedra parallelogram (recorded by Palmer. Also we cannot find the original description).
Synedra pulchella f. *major* Grun. *in* V. H. (recorded by Curtis).
Synedra tenuissima Kütz. (recorded by Eddy).
Synedra ulna var. *capitata* Ehr. (recorded by Galtsoff. Also we cannot find the original description).

Taxa Recorded Since 1960[*]

Synedra actinastroides Lemmerm. (rec. by Whitford & Schumacher, 1963).
Synedra acutissimus (recorded by Lackey *in* Jackson, 1964).
Synedra nana Meist. (recorded by Williams & Scott, 1962).
Synedra netronoides Hohn (recorded by Hohn, 1961).
Synedra ulna var. *oxyrhynchus* (recorded by Blum, 1963).

Names of Taxa which were misidentified or are of uncertain application

Synedra hyalina = *Nitzschia putrida* Beneche.
Synedra scalaris = *Nitzschia scalaris* (Ehr.) W. Sm.
Synedra ulna var. *constricta* recorded by Forest. He probably meant *Synedra ulna* var. *genuina* f. *constricta* A. Mayer (*S. ulna* f. *constricta*). We were not able to find Forest's specimen. *Synedra ulna* var. *oxyrhynchus* f. *constricta* recorded by Silva & Sharp is probably the same taxon.
Synedra ulna var. *delicatissima* (recorded by Lackey).
Synedra ulna var. *radians* (recorded by Lackey).
Synedra valens Ehr. = *Nitzschia valens* (Ehr.) Ralfs.

Synedra subgenus ARDISSONIA (De Not.) Hust.

Hust. *in* Rabh., Kryptog.-Fl. Deutschland, vol. 7(2), no. 2, p. 225.   1932.

The species belonging to this subgenus are marine to brackish-water species. Three are included in this book because they have been found in brackish waters in estuaries of rivers.

This subgenus differs from the *Eusynedra* in the structure of the frustules. The valve has both apical and transverse ribs. The transverse ribs divide the valve into chambers which may be internally open or closed. The longitudinal ribs may divide these transverse chambers into smaller ones. Thus the size of the chambers depends on the placement of the longitudinal ribs. The pseudoraphe or clear area typically found in the

---

[*] See page 671 for list of additional taxa recorded since 1960.

apical axis of the valve of the *Eusynedra* is replaced by a rib. Between the transverse ribs, the surface of the valve (surface of the chambers) has punctate striae. In some species the chambered structure of the valve is poorly developed.

De Notaris in 1871 (p. 95) erected the monotypic genus *Ardissonea* for *Synedra robusta* Pritch.

KEY TO THE SPECIES OF THE SUBGENUS ARDISSONIA

1. Longitudinal lines very near the margins of the valve, often indistinct . . [1] S. *fulgens*
1. Longitudinal lines distinct, more or less removed from the margins of the valve . . . 2
    2. Chambered structure of the valve not well developed, rows of pores absent
                                                           [2] S. *crystallina*
    2. Chambered structure of the valve well developed, rows of pores on the valve
       surface distinct . . . . [3] S. *robusta*

1. **Synedra fulgens** (Grev.) W. Sm. var. **fulgens**   PL. 8, FIGS. 5a-c

Exilaria fulgens Grev., Scottish Cryptog. Fl., vol. 5, p. 291, figs. 1-2. 1827.
Synedra fulgens (Grev.) W. Sm., Syn. British Diat., vol. 1, p. 74, pl. 12, fig. 103. 1853.

Valve linear, with a central swelling, and swollen ends. Pseudoraphe usually indistinct; if distinct, very narrow. Longitudinal line near margin of the valve, sometimes hard to recognize. Costae, usually 14-16 in 10μ; Hustedt (1932, p. 230) states there may be as few as 12 in 10μ. A single row of fine puncta between the ribs. Length, 170-450μ. Breadth, 10-15μ.

This taxon is most easily distinguished by the shape of the valve and the longitudinal ribs which are very close to the margin of the valve.

Type locality. — On various small algae in the sea, in spring and summer. Appin, Capt. Carmichael.

U. S. distribution. — GEOGRAPHICAL: New England States, Middle Atlantic States; California. ECOLOGICAL: In brackish to marine water, often found in estuaries.

2. **Synedra crystallina** (Ag.) Kütz. var. **crystallina**   PL. 8, FIGS. 4a-c

Diatoma crystallina Ag., Syst. Alg., p. 3. 1824.
Synedra crystallina (Ag.) Kütz., Bacill., p. 69, pl. 16, fig. 1. 1844.

Valve linear, slightly swollen in the middle portion and at the rounded ends. Pseudoraphe usually indistinct. A single longitudinal rib distinct, near each margin of the valve. Transapical ribs, 8-12 in 10μ. A row of puncta between the ribs. Length, 160-300μ; Hustedt (1932, p. 233) gives length to 700μ. Breadth, 8-15μ; Hustedt (1932, p. 233) gives breadth to 20μ.

This taxon is distinguished by the distinct longitudinal rib near each of the margins of the valve, and the shape of the valve.

This taxon was misidentified by H. L. Smith on slide no. 578 as *Synedra superba* W. Sm.

Agardh states this taxon is the same as *Echinella fasciculata* Lyngb. However, this name has already been used for another species of *Diatoma* by Agardh (1812, p. 35). Agardh, therefore, calls this taxon *Diatoma crystallina* and bases it on Lyngbye's *Echinella fasciculata*.

Type locality. — Habitat in Sinu Othiniensi.

U. S. distribution. — GEOGRAPHICAL: Massachusetts, Florida. ECOLOGICAL: Brackish water.

3. **Synedra robusta** Ralfs var. **robusta**   PL. 8, FIGS. 3a-c

Synedra robusta Ralfs *in* Pritch., Hist. Infusoria, 4th ed., p. 789, pl. 8, fig. 3. 1861.

Valve broadly linear, narrowed toward the broadly rounded ends. Longitudinal ribs usually three, sometimes more on the valve surface. Transapical ribs, 7-8 in 10μ. Valve surface composed of the chambers formed by the longitudinal and transverse ribs. The former each open by a pore on the external surface of the valve. These pores are more or less in the center of the chamber in the median rows. On the lateral rows of the chambers, the pores are located near the margins of the valve. The outer walls are covered with fine puncta. Length, $200\text{-}520\mu$. Breadth, $30\text{-}40\mu$.

This taxon is distinguished by the number and position of the longitudinal ribs, the number of the transverse ribs, and the position of the pores of the chambers. It is closely related to *Synedra formosa* Hantz.

Type locality. — Algae, Corsica.

U. S. distribution. — GEOGRAPHICAL: South Carolina. ECOLOGICAL: Slightly brackish, warm water.

Genus **Asterionella** Hass.

Hass., Micr. Exam. Water, p. 10, pl. 2(2), fig. 5. 1850.

Frustules usually forming star-shaped colonies. Frustules in valve or girdle view with the apices of unequal size. No septa or intercalary bands present. In valve view one apex larger than the other, capitate; the other may be capitate or of variable shape. Valve symmetrical to the long axis. Pseudoraphe narrow, often indistinct. Striae fine.

This genus is distinguished by the shape of the colonies of the frustules, the lack of septa and intercalary bands, and the asymmetry of the frustules in girdle or valve view to the transverse axis.

This genus is typically found in plankton.

Hassal did not distinguish the description of the genus from that of the type species, *Asterionella formosa.*

Type species. — *Asterionella formosa* Hass.

1. **Asterionella bleakeleyi** W. Sm. var. **bleakeleyi**   PL. 9, FIG. 6

Asterionella bleakeleyi W. Sm., Syn. British Diat., vol. 2, p. 82. 1856.

Frustules in girdle view unequally inflated at the ends, slightly swollen in the middle portion. In valve view the end of the frustule attached to the other diatoms of the colony is larger, more distinctly capitate than the opposite end of the valve. Shape of the valve linear; often somewhat swollen in the middle. Pseudoraphe very narrow; the striae are very fine. Length, 45-65μ.

This taxon is distinguished by the shape of the valve and by its habitat.

Type locality. — Marine, Harwich.

U. S. distribution. — GEOGRAPHICAL: New England States, Middle Atlantic States, Southeastern States; Washington. ECOLOGICAL: Often found in estuaries of rivers or bays, brackish to marine water.

2. **Asterionella formosa** Hass. var. **formosa**   PL. 9, FIGS. 1-3

Asterionella formosa Hass., Micr. Exam. Water, p. 10, pl. 2(2), fig. 5. 1850.
Asterionella formosa var. *subtilis* Grun. *in* V. H., Syn. Diat. Belgique, pl. 51, fig. 21. 1881.
Asterionella formosa var. *subtilissima* Grun. *in* V. H., Syn. Diat. Belgique, pl. 51, fig. 24. 1881.

Frustules forming star-shaped colonies. The end of the frustule attached to the other members of the colony broader than the rest of the frustule. Valve linear, a little narrower toward the ends of the valve. Apices of the valve capitate; the end attached to the other frustules of the colony much larger, strongly capitate; the opposite apex much smaller, often not so distinctly capitate. Pseudoraphe very narrow, often indistinct. Striae fine, 24-28 in 10μ. Length, 40-130μ. Breadth, 1-3μ.

This taxon is distinguished by the size of the frustules and the apices of the valve being very unequal in size.

Type locality. — Thames at Brentford, drinking water of Grand Junction Company.

U. S. distribution. — GEOGRAPHICAL: New England States, Middle Atlantic States, Southeastern States, South Central States, East Central States, West Central States, Lakes States, Plains States; Montana, Wyoming, Utah, Washington, Oregon, California. ECOLOGICAL: A planktonic species most often found in mesotropic or eutrophic water.

2. Asterionella formosa var. gracillima (Hantz.) Grun. PL. 9, FIG. 4

Diatoma gracillimum Hantz. *in* Rabh., Alg. Sachens resp. Mitteleuropas, No. 1104. 1861.

Asterionella gracillima (Hantz.) Heib., Consp. Crit. Diat. Danicarum, p. 68, pl. 6, fig. 19. 1863.

Asterionella formosa var. *gracillima* (Hantz.) Grun. *in* V. H., Syn. Diat. Belgique, pl. 51, fig. 22. 1881.

Valve linear to linear-lanceolate. Capitate ends of variable, unequal size, but more similar in size than in the nominate variety. Striae fine, 20-27 in 10μ. Length, $35\text{-}90\mu$. Breadth, $2\text{-}3\mu$.

This variety is distinguished from the nominate variety by its smaller size and the capitate ends of the valve which are more similar in size. This variety typically has its best development in the winter time.

A. Mayer (1937, p. 73) discusses the opinion of various workers as to the systematic status of this taxon.

Type locality. — Elbufer im grossen Gehege bei Dresden, November, 1860.

U. S. distribution. — GEOGRAPHICAL: New England States, Middle Atlantic States, Southeastern States, South Central States, East Central States, West Central States, Lakes States; California. ECOLOGICAL: Seems to prefer cool to cold water.

3. Asterionella ralfsii W. Sm. var. ralfsii PL. 9, FIG. 5

Asterionella ralfsii W. Sm., Syn. British Diat., vol. 2, p. 81. 1856.

Frustules in girdle view shorter, relatively broader than in *Asterionella formosa* Hass. One end of the frustule in girdle view distinctly broader than the other. In valve view one end capitate; the other smaller, rounded. Striae about 32 in 10μ. Length, $20\text{-}50\mu$. Breadth in the middle portion of the valve in girdle view, about 3μ. The specimens I have seen from the United States have a delicate appearance and in girdle view are not as broad as the European specimens.

This taxon is distinguished by its typically small size, very fine striae and the shape of the valve.

Ross (1956, p. 79) gives an excellent account of this species.

Type locality. — Uncertain. *Diatoma stellare* Ralfs Mss. ad specim in Hérib. Jenn. (B.M. 24422). Probably Dolgelly.

U. S. distribution. — GEOGRAPHICAL: New England States, Middle Atlantic States. ECOLOGICAL: This variety seems to prefer fairly shallow ponds and water of very low mineral content which is more or less rich in humates (dystrophic) and has a low pH.

Genus **Amphicampa** Ehr. *ex* Ralfs

Ehr. *ex* Ralfs *in* Pritch., Hist. Infusoria, 4th ed., p. 765.   1861.

Frustules in girdle view without septa or intercalary bands. Valve straight or slightly curved. Dorsal margin convex. Ventral margin straight or slightly concave. Dorsal and ventral margins of the valve sinuate-dentate. Pseudoraphe present near the ventral margin. Striae indistinctly punctate, fine. Kolbe (1956) considers the vertical line near the end of the valve which seems to be formed by the fusion of puncta, a primitive raphe.

This genus is distinguished by the shape of the valve, which is straight or slightly curved, and its sinuate-dentate margins. It is closely related to the genus *Semiorbis*.

Although Rabenhorst (1864, p. 75) attributes this genus to Ehrenberg, 1849, a thorough search of the literature does not reveal the description. Ehrenberg seems to have used this genus name first in the *Mikrogeologie* (1854). On page 373 (text) he creates a new division of the genus *Eunotia* for *E. eruca* and *E. mirifica*. On plate 33 he lists, in the legend of the plate, these two species as belonging to the genus *Amphicampa*. However, since two species are shown, we cannot treat one of them as the description of the genus as could be done if it were a monotypic genus. The first generic description seems to be that of Ralfs (*loc. cit.*). Although Ehrenberg in 1854 refers to the *Ber. Akad. Wiss. Berlin*, for 1844, an examination of this volume reveals no reference to this genus or these species.

Type species. — *Amphicampa mirabilis* (Ehr.) Ralfs.

1. **Amphicampa mirabilis** Ehr. *ex* Ralfs var. **mirabilis**   PL. 9, FIGS. 8-9

Amphicampa mirabilis Ehr. *ex* Ralfs *in* Pritch., Hist. Infusoria, 4th ed., p. 765. 1861.

Valve with convex dorsal and straight or slightly concave ventral margins. Both margins with three to six sinuous dentations giving the valve its characteristic appearance. Apices rostrate. Pseudoraphe distinct, near the ventral margin. Jelly pore evident at one end of the valve. Striae punctate, more distinct in the large than in the small specimens. Striae in the large specimens, 8-10 in 10μ; in the small specimens, up to 15 in 10μ. Length, 29-93μ.

This species is distinguished by the number of its sinuous dentations. Ralfs says that it is the same species as *Amphicampa eruca* Ehr.

Ehrenberg (1854, pl. 33 (7), figs. 1, 2) illustrated this species and *A. eruca*. However, since he did not define the genus, the nomenclature starts with Ralfs.

Type locality. — Fossile e terra mexicana tiga.

U. S. distribution. — GEOGRAPHICAL: Nebraska, California.

Genus **Semiorbis** Patr. gen. nov.

Frustulibus sine septis aut fasciis. Valva incurva et in una specie posita in hoc genere semicircula in forma. Marginibus dorsalibus et ventralibus parallelis aut paene parallelis. Lineis nullis hyalinis aut pseudoraphe praesentibus. Nodulibus terminalibus inopiis. Striis punctatis obscure; nullis costis praesentibus. Species sola in hoc genere fibras semper fere non format.

Frustules without septa or intercalary bands. Valve curved, and in the one species placed in this genus, semicircular in shape. Dorsal and ventral margins parallel, or almost parallel. No hyaline lines or pseudoraphe present. Terminal nodules lacking. Striae indistinctly punctate; no costae present. The one species of this genus does not typically form filaments.

This genus is distinguished from *Amphicampa* by the parallel margins of the valve which are without crenulations or undulations. It is distinguished from the genus *Eunotia* by the lack of terminal nodules. In other characteristics it superficially resembles some species of *Eunotia*.

Kolbe (1956) states that in the only species in this genus a raphe is present at the ends of the valve. He states it is very difficult to see in valve view. Certainly most workers have not seen it. If Kolbe (1956) is correct, this genus should be regarded as belonging to the Eunotiales.

Grunow *in* Van Heurck (1881) described the genus *Pseudoeunotia* by illustrating two species, *P. doliolus* (Wall.) Grun. and *P. hemicyclus* (Ehr.) Grun. He did not indicate which species was the type. Subsequent workers have determined that these two species differ in several characteristics, and as Hustedt *in* Rabenhorst (1931) points out, they should not be considered as belonging to the same genus. In *P. doliolus* the valve has costae separated by double rows of puncta, and in *P. hemicyclus* only striae composed of an indistinct row of puncta are present. In *P. doliolus* the frustules typically grow in filaments, whereas in *P. hemicyclus* this is not the case. Hustedt has typified the genus *Pseudoeunotia* by *P. doliolus*. He placed *P. hemicyclus* in the genus *Amphicampa* Ehr. *ex* Ralfs. However, this is not correct for this species is very different from the species described by Ralfs which typify that genus.

Peragallo (1884) only treats the species *P. doliolus*, and Van Heurck (1896) only treats *P. hemicyclus*. Thus, Hustedt (*loc. cit.*) seems to be the first to consider critically both species and typify *Pseudoeunotia* by one of them.

I want to acknowledge the help of Mr. Ross of the British Museum in helping me to work up the data pertinent to the description of this genus.

Type species. — Semiorbis hemicyclus Ehr.

1. Semiorbis hemicyclus (Ehr.) Patr. comb. nov., var. hemicyclus

PL. 9, FIG. 7

Synedra hemicyclus Ehr., Ber. Akad. Wiss. Berlin, for 1840:217. 1840.

Eunotia hemicyclus (Ehr.) Ralfs *in* Pritch., Hist. Infusoria, 4th ed., p. 763. 1861.

Pseudoeunotia hemicyclus (Ehr.) Grun. *in* V. H., Syn. Diat. Belgique, pl. 35. fig. 23. 1881.

Amphicampa hemicyclus (Ehr.) Karst. *in* Engl. & Prantl, Nat. Pflanzenfam., vol. 2(2), p. 268, fig. 353. 1928.

Valve semicircular with dorsal and ventral margins almost parallel. Apices of the valve somewhat attenuated, rostrate. Terminal nodules absent. Raphe, if present as Kolbe (1956) states, is indistinct in valve view. Striae indistinctly punctate, 9-10 in 10μ; not interrupted by a hyaline line. Length of the cord between the two apices, 20-40μ. Breadth, 3-5μ.

This taxon is most easily distinguished by the shape of the valve.

Type locality. — Fossiles ad Degernfors Sueciae.

U. S. distribution. — GEOGRAPHICAL: New England States, Middle Atlantic States. ECOLOGICAL: Bogs and ponds; seems to prefer cool water of low mineral content. Sometimes found in water rich in humates.

Fig. 1. *Tabellaria fenestrata*, valve view A-G.C. 5308, Wyoming, Fremont Co.
Fig. 2. *Tabellaria fenestrata*, girdle view A-G.C. 5308, Wyoming, Fremont Co.
Fig. 3. *Tabellaria quadrisepta*, valve view A-G.C. 46351a, New Jersey, Burlington Co.
Fig. 4. *Tabellaria flocculosa*, valve view A-V.H. 346, (Norway), Dovrefields Mountains.
Fig. 5. *Tabellaria flocculosa*, girdle view A-V.H. 347, Belgium, Paliseul.
Fig. 6. *Tabellaria binalis* A-Boyer 547, New Hampshire, Grafton Co.
Fig. 7. *Tetracyclus elliptica* A-T. & P. 365, Oregon, Klamath Co.
Fig. 8. *Tetracyclus emarginatus* A-225, W.Sm., Gap of Dunloe.
Fig. 9. *Tetracyclus lacustris* A-T. & P. 366, Oregon, Klamath Co.

Abbreviations of Slide Numbers Used in Text and Plates Explanations

A-G. C. = Academy of Natural Sciences of Philadelphia—General Collection
Cal. Acad. Sci. = California Academy of Sciences
Ag. Herb. = Agardh Herbarium
N.Y.B.G. = New York Botanical Garden
B. M. = British Museum
Univ. Bot. Mus. Lund = University Botanical Museum of Lund, Sweden

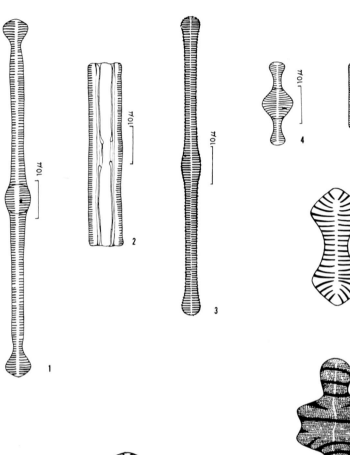

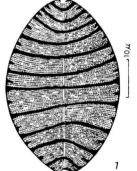

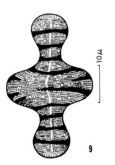

166

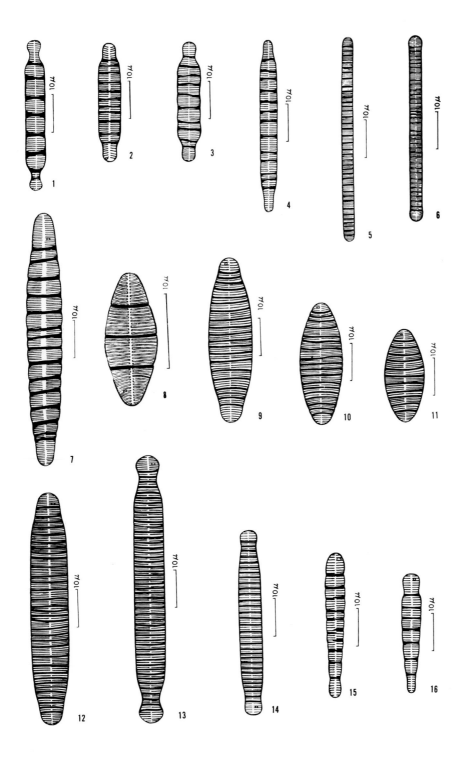

168

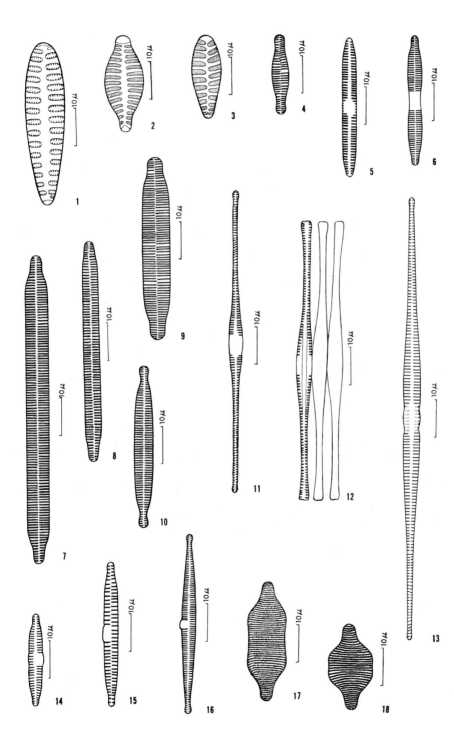

PLATE 4

Fig. 1. *Fragilaria nitzschioides* A-G.C. 8043a, Florida, Santa Rosa Co.

Fig. 2. *Fragilaria leptostauron* A-V.H. 316, (England), Hull.

Fig. 3. *Fragilaria leptostauron* var. *dubia* Cal. Acad. Sci.-3475, Sov. 67-20, Oregon, Crater Lake.

Fig. 4. *Fragilaria construens* A-T. & P. 216, Connecticut, Hartford Co.

Fig. 5. *Fragilaria construens* var. *pumila* A-T. & P. 216, Connecticut, Hartford Co.

Fig. 6. *Fragilaria construens* var. *pumila* A-T. & P. 341, Connecticut, Hartford Co.

Fig. 7. *Fragilaria construens* var. *binodis* A-G.C. 5708, Nebraska, Keya Paka Co.

Fig. 8. *Fragilaria construens* var. *venter* A-V.H. 190, Belgium, Anvers.

Fig. 9. *Fragilaria construens* var. *venter* A-G.C. 46346, Pennsylvania, Brandy-wine.

Fig. 10. *Fragilaria pinnata* A-G.C. 5165, Wyoming, Albany Co.

Fig. 11. *Fragilaria pinnata* var. *intercedens* A-193, W.Sm. 290, England, Sussex, Plumpton.

Fig. 12. *Fragilaria pinnata* var. *lancettula* A-G.C. 6776a, Utah, Cache Co.

Fig. 13. *Fragilaria pinnata* var. *trigona* Cal. Acad. Sci.-3463, Sov. 488-11, Oregon, Crater Lake National Park, Emerald Pool.

Fig. 14. *Fragilaria brevistriata* A-Boyer 905, New Jersey, Weequachick Lake.

Fig. 15. *Fragilaria brevistriata* var. *capitata* A-V.H. 318, Belgium, Brussels.

Fig. 16. *Fragilaria brevistriata* var. *inflata* A-G.C. 5877, Nebraska, Dodge Co.

Fig. 17. *Fragilaria lapponica* A-Boyer 905, New Jersey, Weequachick Lake.

Fig. 18. *Fragilaria sinuata* A-Boyer 902, Oregon, Swan River.

Fig. 19. *Fragilaria sinuata* A-T. & P. 366, Oregon, Klamath Co. (drawing of Lectotype).

Fig. 20. *Hannaea arcus* comb. nov. A-V.H. 281, Belgium, Rochehaut.

Fig. 21. *Hannaea arcus* var. *amphioxys* comb. nov. A-G.C. 43733, Tennessee, Blount Co.

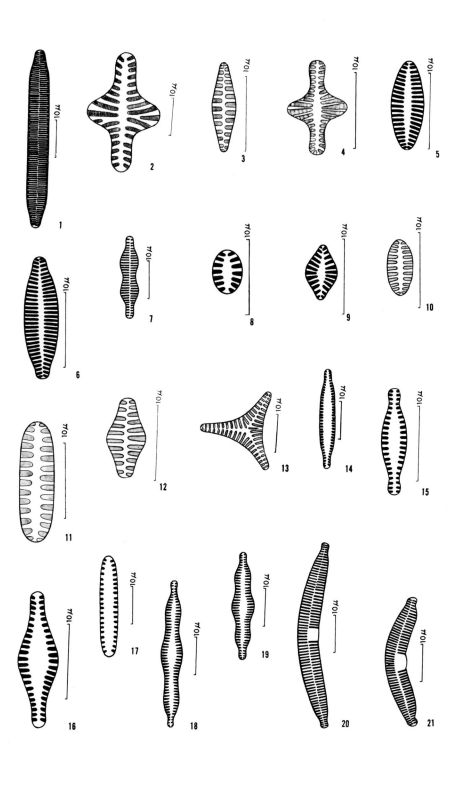

172

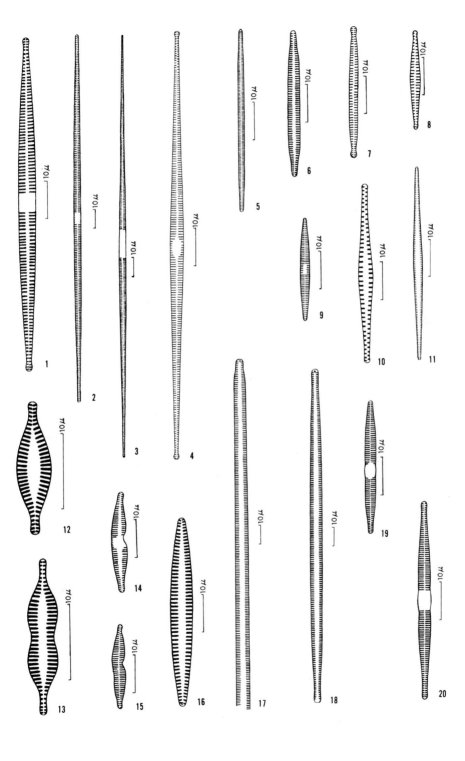

174

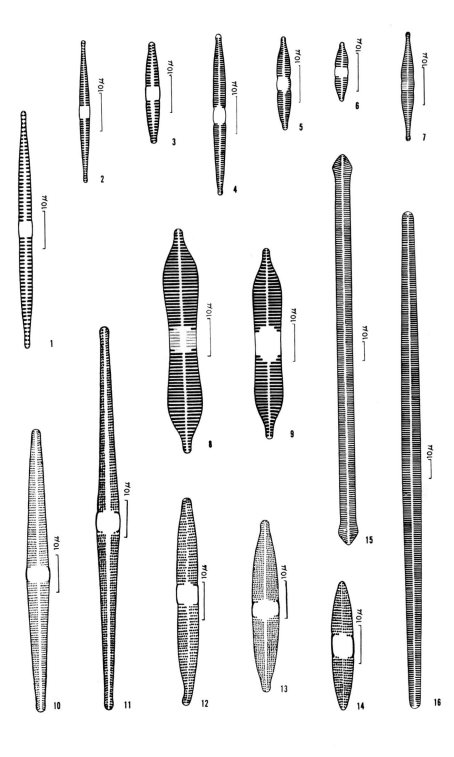

Fig. 1.   *Synedra ulna* A-Kütz. Dec. 1, No. 1, Weissenfels.

Fig. 2.   *Synedra ulna* A-Kütz. Dec. 8, No. 73, Leucopetram.

Fig. 3.   *Synedra ulna* var. *contracta* A-G.C. 2444, Tennessee, Blount Co.

Fig. 4.   *Synedra ulna* var. *oxyrhynchus* f. *mediocontracta* A-G.C. 2444, Tennessee, Blount Co.

Fig. 5.   *Synedra ulna* var. *subaequalis* A-V.H. 286, Belgium, Brussels (Isotype).

Fig. 6.   *Synedra ulna* var. *amphirhynchus* A-G.C. 4728a, Pennsylvania, Montgomery Co.

Fig. 7.   *Synedra ulna* var. *amphirhynchus* A-G.C. 3682a, South Carolina, Kershaw Co.

Fig. 8.   *Synedra ulna* var. *spathulifera* A-G.C. 5328, Montana, Missoula Co.

Fig. 9.   *Synedra ulna* var. *obtusa* A-G.C. 5342, Montana, Missoula Co.

Fig. 10.   *Synedra ulna* var. *danica* A.-V.H. 288, (Great Britain), Cumbrae.

Fig. 11.   *Synedra longiceps* A-H.L.Sm. 563, H. L. Smith states this is original material. Mackinaw, Lake Superior (Isotype).

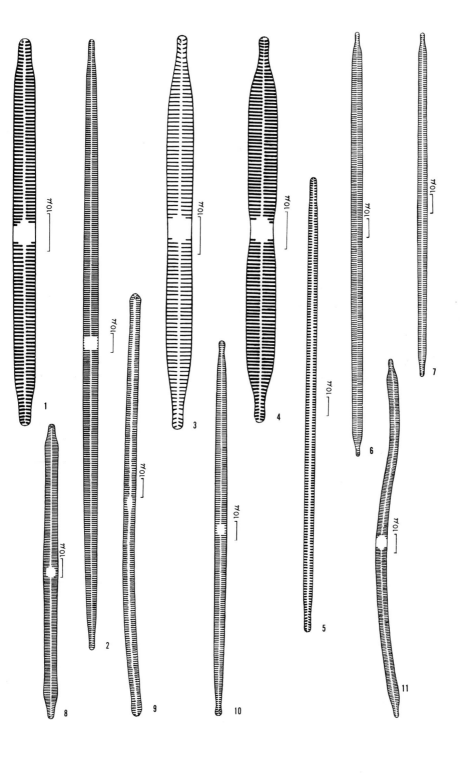

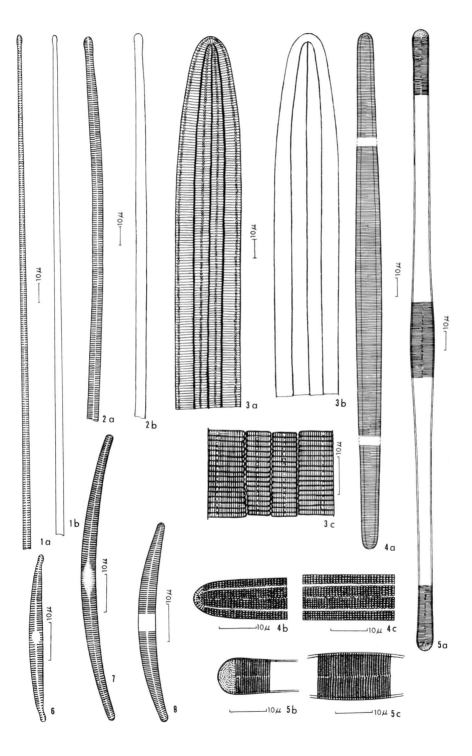

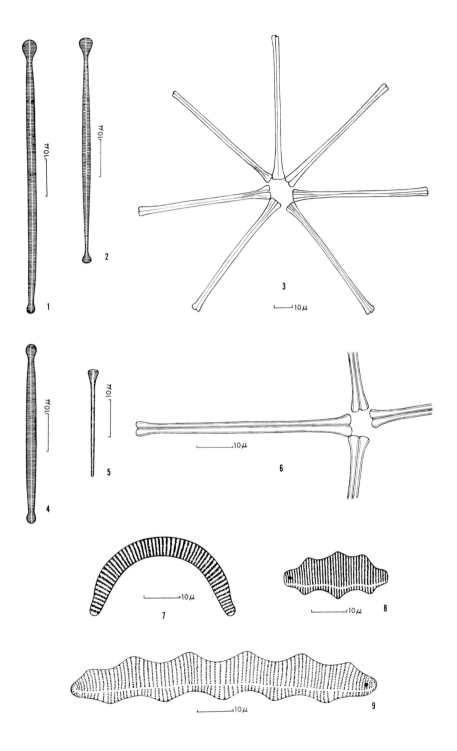

Order **EUNOTIALES**

Silva *in* R. A. Lewin, Physiol. and Biochem. Algae, Appendix A, pp. 831, 835.   1962.

This order is characterized by one or both of the valves having a short, often rudimentary raphe. A central nodule is absent. The terminal nodules are variable in size. The apical axis may be straight or curved. The valves may be asymmetrical or symmetrical to the transverse axis. A jelly pore is often evident. The chloroplasts are typically two large plates. The species included in this book belong to one family, the Eunotiaceae.

Family **EUNOTIACEAE**

Hust. *in* Pasch., Süssw.-Fl. Mitteleuropas, Heft 10, Aufl. 2, p. 56.   1930.

This family has the same characteristics as described for the order. The genera belonging to this family divide themselves into two subfamilies, the *Peronioideae* and the *Eunotioideae*.

The type genus of this family is *Eunotia* Ehr. This family to date has only been found in fresh water, and usually in oligotrophic or dystrophic water.

Subfamily EUNOTIOIDEAE

Hust *in* Pasch., Süssw.-Fl. Mitteleuropas, Heft 10, Aufl. 2, p. 165.   1930.

Frustules free living or in filamentous colonies. Apical axis of the valve somewhat bent; dorsal margin convex, ventral margin straight or concave. Valve symmetrical or asymmetrical to the transverse axis. Polar nodules more or less well developed; a short raphe present in the nodule, sometimes extending into the valve, and usually into the valve mantle. Three genera (*Eunotia, Desmogonium,* and *Actinella*) belonging to this subfamily are included in this book.

KEY TO THE GENERA OF EUNOTIOIDEAE

1. Valve asymmetrical to the transverse axis ....*Actinella* (p. 222)
1. Valve symmetrical or almost symmetrical to the transverse axis 2
    2. Valve with short, small spines present on the ventral and the dorsal margins of the valve ....*Desmogonium* (p. 221)
    2. Valve typically without spines, if spines present they are on the dorsal margin only
                           Eunotia (p. 183)

Genus **Eunotia** Ehr.

Ehr., Ber. Akad. Wiss. Berlin, for 1837:44.   1837.

The species of this genus live singly or form filaments. In girdle view they are rectangular in shape. In valve view they are asymmetrical to the longitudinal or apical axis. Usually the dorsal margin is more or less convex, while the ventral margin is straight or somewhat concave. The raphe is short and often apparent only in valve view at the terminal nodules. The terminal nodules may be located at the ends of the valve or on the ventral margin. In the various species the size and shape of the terminal nodules may vary considerably. Often a clear line or pseudoraphe is located near the ventral margin and connects the terminal nodules.

The striae are parallel throughout most of the valve and usually indistinctly punctate. A character often used in separating species is whether they are parallel or radiate about the terminal nodules.

In instances where species of this genus are found in filaments, they often resemble very closely some species of *Fragilaria*. They can be separated from *Fragilaria* by the presence of the terminal nodules which can be seen in girdle view near the ends of the valves.

The species of this genus are usually found in water with a low calcium and chloride content. They are frequent in oligotrophic or dystrophic water. Certain species are typically found in association with moss and in bogs. Most species are more commonly found in soft-water rivers and lakes.

This genus as originally described by Ehrenberg (1837, p. 44) contained species which we now recognize as belonging to both the genera *Epithemia* and *Eunotia*. The present concept of this genus is typified by *Eunotia arcus* Ehr. which was one of the species Ehrenberg described at the same time he described the genus. Boyer (1927a, p. 215) has designated this species as the type of the genus.

When Ehrenberg described this genus it contained only those species of *Eunotia*, as recognized today, which do not form filaments. Those species which do form filaments were placed in the genus *Himantidium*. Today the genus *Himantidium* Ehr. (1840, p. 17) is synonymized with this genus.

Type species. — *Eunotia arcus* Ehr.

KEY TO THE SPECIES OF EUNOTIA

1. Dorsal margin without swellings or humps 2
1. Valve with swellings or undulations on dorsal or ventral margins or both 32
    2. A line extends from the terminal nodules toward the center of the valve
                                                            [1] *E. flexuosa*
    2. Terminal nodule without such a line 3
3. Apices of the valve distinctly separated from the main body of the valve 20
3. Apices of valve otherwise formed 4
    4. Frustules very narrow and linear, more than 27 times as long as broad; ends
       long and thinly drawn out and slightly recurved dorsally . . . . . . [4] *E. naegelii*
    4. Frustules broader in relation to length 5
5. Frustules with apices inflated, wedge-capitate in shape 6
5. Frustules otherwise formed 7
    6. Valve usually widened in the middle . . . . [5] *E. formica*
    6. Valve not widened in the middle, very long . . . . [6] *E. tautoniensis*

7. Valve strongly arched 8
7. Valve straight or only slightly to moderately arched 9
    8. Small forms, under 50μ............................... [32] *E. elegans*
    8. Very large robust forms, more than 100μ.................. [12] *E. clevei*
9. Ends somewhat capitate or drawn out, terminal nodules distinct.......... 10
9. Valve gradually narrowed toward rounded apices, or apices of the valve truncately rounded; ends not separated from main body of the valve.............. 15
    10. Ends more or less capitate, dorsal and ventral margin almost parallel...... 11
    10. Ends of the valve slightly narrowed........................... 14
11. Striae, 16 or more in 10μ.. 12
11. Striae, may be 15 in 10μ, typically less........................... 13
    12. Valve less than 50μ long, typically less than 40μ............ [30] *E. tenella*
    12. Valve more than 50μ long .... [8] *E. lapponica*
13. Frustule wall thickly silicified in valve view under ordinary light microscope, appearing as a heavy black line............................ [9] *E. valida*
13. Frustule wall not so formed.............................. [2] *E. glacialis*
    14. Valve slender, linear, terminal nodules a short distance from the apices of the valve, ends of the valve sometimes slightly recurved........ [35] *E. fallax*
    14. Not so slender, terminal nodule at or very close to apices of the valve. Frustules in girdle view often with internal septa............. [26] *E. soleirolii*
15. Margins of the valve parallel, ends truncately rounded.......... [10] *E. parallela*
15. Margins of the valve parallel in some species, in others not parallel, ends not truncately rounded.. 16
    16. Ends of the valve almost the same width as the center of the valve may be distinct... 17
    16. Valve narrowed toward apices, ends not differentiated from main body of the valve 18
17. Terminal striae distinctly radiate about terminal nodule, length-to-breadth ratio less than 10:1 .... [31] *E. vanheurckii*
17. Terminal striae parallel or only slightly radiate about terminal nodule, length-to-breadth ratio 6:1-25:1 .... [3] *E. curvata* and var.
    18. Dorsal margin angular, thus giving the valve a more or less triangular appearance .... [42] *E. trinacria*
    18. Dorsal margin smoothly curved; valve not having a triangular appearance 19
19. Ends of the valve acute, or somewhat rounded; striae, 13 or more in 10μ at the center of the valve .... [28] *E. incisa*
19. Ends of the valve rounded; striae at the center of the valve, 12 in 10μ or less .... [16] *E. monodon*
    20. Ends of the valve distinctly capitate or truncate 21
    20. Ends of the valve drawn out, narrower than the valve at the central area 29
21. Size variable, striae usually 8-14 in 10μ 22
21. Striae, more than 14 in 10μ, usually much finer in small species 25
    22. Ends of the valve truncate, sometimes slightly capitate, dorsal margin strongly convex .... [11] *E. praerupta*
    22. Ends of the valve distinctly capitate, large species 23
23. Ends of the valve on the dorsal margin angular, somewhat wedge-shaped; narrower than the middle portion of the valve 24
23. Ends of the valve smoothly capitate, almost the same width as the main body of the valve .... [15] *E. maior*
    24. Valve not appearing arched .... [13] *E. indica*
    24. Valve having an arcuate appearance .... [34] *E. arcus*
25. Margin almost parallel 26
25. Margin usually not parallel, dorsal margin strongly convex 28

47. Length-to-breadth ratio, usually about 6:1; striae punctate
[16] *E. monodon* var. *constricta*
47. Length-to-breadth ratio, usually about 4:1; striae indistinctly punctate
[17] *E. zygodon*
   48. Dorsal margin with two abrupt, somewhat angular, swellings [46] *E. bactriana*
   48. Dorsal margins with two rounded swellings or undulations 49
49. Dorsal margin strongly convex 50
49. Dorsal margin not strongly convex 53
   50. Ends of the valve truncate 51
   50. Ends of the valve protracted, somewhat capitate or rostrate 52
51. Apices of the valve obliquely cut off, terminal nodules large . . . . . . [18] *E. suecica*
51. Apices of the valve truncate . . . . [11] *E. praerupta* var. *bidens*
   52. Striae at the center of the valve, usually 10-12 in 10μ . . . . [24] *E. diodon*
   52. Striae at the center of the valve, more than 12 in 10μ, usually 15-18 in 10μ
[22] *E. bidentula*
53. Ends of the valve protracted, rounded . . . . [25] *E. pectinalis* var. *minor*
53. Ends of the valve obliquely capitate . . . . [34] *E. arcus* var. *bidens*
   54. Ventral margin straight or slightly concave 55
   54. Ventral margin distinctly concave 57
55. Ends of the valve rounded, not distinctly set off from main body of the valve
[44] *E. perminuta*
55. Ends of the valve distinctly set off from main body of the valve 56
   56. Ends protracted, terminal nodules at some distance from the apices
      of the valve, undulations distinct . . . . [23] *E. hexaglyphis*
   56. Ends of the valve capitate, undulations not well developed
[42] *E. trinacria* var. *undulata*
57. Length-to-breadth ratio 2.5:1-4:1; dorsal margin strongly convex 58
57. Length-to-breadth ratio greater than this, valve with variable number of
dorsal undulations 59
   58. Valve with three undulations . . . . [19] *E. triodon*
   58. Valve with more than three undulations . . . . [20] *E. serra* var. *diadema*
59. Ends of the valve protracted; small forms . . . . [45] *E. quaternaria*
59. Ends of the valve not protracted nor distinctly set off from the rest of the valve
[20] *E. serra*

1. **Eunotia flexuosa** Bréb. *ex* Kütz. var. **flexuosa**   PL. 10, FIG. 1

Eunotia flexuosa Bréb. *ex* Kütz., Sp. Alg., p. 6. 1849.

Frustules linear in girdle view. Valve linear, usually slightly arched, somewhat swollen to form more or less capitate ends. Width of the valve at the ends usually a little greater than at the center. Terminal nodules very distinct, at or very near the ends of the valve on the ventral margin. An appendage of the raphe extends toward the center of the valve from the dorsal margin of the terminal nodules. Jelly pore at one apex of the valve. Striae equidistant, indistinctly punctate. Striae, usually 15-19 in 10μ. Length, 90-300μ. Breadth, 2-5μ. Hustedt (1932, p. 312, fig. 778) states that the striae are 14-18 in 10μ. Cleve-Euler (1953a, p. 93) says that the striae are distinctly punctate, 11-20 in 10μ; length, 80-300μ; breadth, 1.5-8μ.

This diatom is easily recognized by its linear appearance and the lines extending toward the center of the valve from the terminal nodules. The presence of a jelly pore is also characteristic of this species as well as in *Eunotia formica* and *E. tautoniensis*. Through these species the genus *Eunotia* seems to be related to *Desmogonium*.

Eunotia biceps Ehr. (1843, pp. 373, 413) may be the same as this taxon, but it is impossible to be sure. Ehrenberg's figure resembles a sponge spicule more than a diatom.

Type locality. — France, Falaise.

U. S. distribution. — GEOGRAPHICAL: New England States, Middle Atlantic States, Southeastern States, Gulf Coast States, South Central States, East Central States, Lakes States; Montana, Wyoming, California. ECOLOGICAL: It has its best development in acid to circumneutral waters of low mineral content, where the current is slow. Especially found in lakes, ditches, swamps, and ponds.

1. **Eunotia flexuosa** var. **eurycephala** Grun.   PL. 10, FIG. 2

> *Eunotia flexuosa* var. ? *eurycephala* Grun. *in* V. H., Syn. Diat. Belgique, pl. 35, fig. 8.   1881.

Valve longer in proportion to breadth than in the nominate variety; in girdle view linear. Ends of the valve distinctly capitate, much wider than the middle portion of the valve. Striae parallel except at the ends where they are somewhat radiate. Striae, 13-18 in 10μ. Length, $80\text{-}265\mu$. Breadth, $1.5\text{-}4\mu$.

This variety is easily distinguished from the nominate variety by the distinctly swollen, capitate ends.

Type locality. — Uncertain, Belgium.

U. S. distribution. — GEOGRAPHICAL: Alabama; probably fossil.

2. **Eunotia glacialis** Meist. var. **glacialis**   PL. 10, FIG. 3

> *Himantidium gracile* Ehr., Phys. Abh. Akad. Wiss. Berlin, for 1841:417, pl. 2(1), fig. 9, pl. 3(1), fig. 41.   1843.
> *Eunotia gracilis* (Ehr.) Rabh., Fl. Europaea Alg., Sect. 1, p. 72.   1864.   [non *E. gracilis* W. Sm. (1853).]
> *Eunotia glacialis* Meist., Beitr. Kryptog.-Fl. Schweiz, 4(1), p. 85, pl. 10, figs. 2-3. 1912.

Frustules in girdle view rectangular. Valve linear; arcuate. At the ends the dorsal and ventral margins reflexed, somewhat swollen to form capitate ends. Degree of capitateness seems to vary. Terminal nodules distinct on the ventral margin. Striae, 9-14 in 10μ. Length, $15\text{-}130\mu$. Breadth, $3\text{-}6\mu$. Cleve-Euler (1953a, p. 92) states that the valves may be 220μ in length.

This species is characterized by its long, slender appearance, but it is not as long and slender as *Eunotia naegelii*.

Type locality. — French Guiana, Cayenne, Martinique I.?

U. S. distribution. — GEOGRAPHICAL: New England States, Middle Atlantic States, Southeastern States, Gulf Coast States, East Central States, West Central States, Plains States; Washington. ECOLOGICAL: As most *Eunotia* species, it is found in acid to circumneutral water of low mineral content, usually in cool water.

3. **Eunotia curvata** (Kütz.) Lagerst. var. **curvata** PL. 10, FIG. 4

Synedra lunaris Ehr., Phys. Abh. Akad. Wiss. Berlin, for 1831:87. 1832.

Exilaria curvata Kütz., Alg. Dec., No. 112. 1834.

Ceratoneis lunaris (Ehr.) Grun. *in* Rabh., Beitr. Nähr. Kenntn. Verbr. Alg., Heft 2, p. 7. 1865.

Eunotia lunaris (Ehr.) Grun. *in* V. H., Syn. Diat. Belgique, pl. 35, figs. 3-4. 1881.
    (non *Eunotia lunaris* Bréb. *ex* Rabh., El. Europaea Alg., sect. 1 p. 69. 1864.)

Eunotia lunaris var. *bilunaris* Grun. *in* V. H., Syn. Diat. Belgique, pl. 35, fig. 6B. 1881.

Eunotia lunaris var. *excisa* Grun. *in* V. H., Syn. Diat. Belgique, pl. 35, fig. 6C. 1881.

Eunotia curvata (Kütz.) Lagerst., Öfv. K. [Svenska] Vet.-Akad. Förh., 41(2):61. 1884.

Valve usually lunate or arcuate in shape, sometimes almost straight; usually gradually narrowed toward rounded, sometimes slightly swollen ends. Dorsal and ventral margins parallel. Terminal nodules small, raphe indistinct. A thin line occasionally is seen extending from the terminal nodules toward the center of the valve. The overall contour of the valve has a smooth appearance. Striae, 13-18 in 10μ. Length, $20\text{-}150\mu$. Breadth, $3\text{-}6\mu$.

This species is characterized by its lunate appearance and the small terminal nodules. It often produces abnormal forms which have the margins indented in various ways. These have been described as varieties (var. *excisa* and var. *bilunaris*).

Type locality. — Germany, Berlin.

U. S. distribution. — GEOGRAPHICAL: New England States, Middle Atlantic States, Southeastern States, Gulf Coast States, South Central States, East Central States, West Central States, Lakes States, Plains States; Montana, Wyoming, Washington, California. ECOLOGICAL: This species is widely distributed in water of low mineral content; commonly found in acid water, but may be in slightly alkaline water. Often it has its best development in swamps or shallow ponds, but also found in streams and rivers.

3. **Eunotia curvata** var. **capitata** (Grun.) Woodhead and Tweed

PL. 10, FIG. 5

Synedra lunaris var. *capitata* Grun., Verh. Zool.-Bot. Ges. Wien, 12:389. 1862.
Eunotia lunaris var. *capitata* (Grun.) Hust., Süssw.-Diat. Deutschlands, p. 25. 1909.
Eunotia curvata var. *capitata* Woodhead and Tweed, Northwest Nat. 1954:103.

Very similar in shape to the nominate variety of the species except for the capitate ends of the valve. Length-to-breadth ratio usually less than that of the species. Valve narrows toward the capitate ends. Terminal nodules often more distinct than in the species. Striae, 13-16 in 10μ. Length, 40-115μ. Breadth, 3-5μ.

Type locality. — [Austria], Praterlacken . . . einige Orte in Mähren.
U. S. distribution. — GEOGRAPHICAL: Middle Atlantic States. ECOLOGICAL: Found in oligotrophic water.

4. **Eunotia naegelii** Migula var. **naegelii**   PL. 10, FIG. 6

Synedra alpina Naeg. *ex* Kütz., Sp. Alg., p. 43. 1849.
Eunotia naegelii Migula *in* Thomé, Fr. Deutschland, Band 2(1), p. 203. 1907.

Valve slightly arched, narrowly lanceolate; narrowed toward rounded or somewhat capitate ends. In general appearance the valve is long, slender. Terminal nodules and raphe distinct, but usually small. Striae, 14-20 in 10μ. Length, 45-130μ. Breadth, 1.5-3.5μ.

This species is quite similar to *Eunotia curvata* from which it differs in its greater length-to-breadth ratio, 27:1 or more. It also has a greater length-to-breadth ratio than *E. glacialis*. The ends of the valve do not follow the general contour of the valve and thus appear to bend back.

This species is often called *Eunotia alpina* (Naeg.) Hust. This name is illegitimate as it is a later homonym.

Type locality. — [Switzerland], In Helvetia.
U. S. distribution. — GEOGRAPHICAL: Pennsylvania, Tennessee, Indiana; not common. ECOLOGICAL: This species seems to prefer acid water of low mineral content.

5. **Eunotia formica** Ehr. var. **formica**   PL. 10, FIG. 7

Eunotia formica Ehr., Phys. Abh. Akad. Wiss. Berlin, for 1841:414. 1843.

Valve usually linear, sometimes slightly bent; swollen in the middle, particularly on the ventral margin. Amount of swelling on the dorsal margin varies from none at all to very pronounced. Ends usually broader than the main body of the valve, wedge-capitate in shape. Terminal nodules very distinct, on the ventral margin of the valve. A jelly pore is apparent at one of the apices. Striae parallel, often not equidistant; in many cases broken near the ventral margin, resulting in the formation of a line that is usually evident over the swelling in the middle of the valve. Striae, 8-12 in 10μ at the center of the valve, more numerous at the ends. Length, $40-160\mu$. Breadth, $7-13\mu$.

A. Berg (1939, p. 452) has described some small forms that certainly are not typical for the species as generally found in the United States. They probably represent abnormal or atypical individuals. Typically this species is easily recognized by its wedge-capitate ends and the swelling at the center of the valve. In many characteristics it is quite similar to *Eunotia tautoniensis* Hust. *ex* Patr., but differs from the latter by the presence of a swollen median area and a valve that is typically straighter than is the case in *E. tautoniensis*.

Type locality. — Uncertain.

U. S. distribution. — GEOGRAPHICAL: New England States, Middle Atlantic States, Southeastern States, Gulf Coast States, East Central States, Lakes States, Plains States; Washington, California. ECOLOGICAL: It is typically found in acid to circumneutral soft water, standing or usually slow-flowing water.

6. Eunotia tautoniensis Hust. *ex* Patr. var. **tautoniensis**   PL. 10, FIG. 8

Eunotia tautoniensis Hust. *ex* Patr., Farlowia, 2(2):163. 1945.

Valve arcuate-elongate. Ends wedge-capitate in shape. Terminal nodules distinct. Jelly pore apparent at one of the valve apices. Striae equidistant, 12-14 in 10μ at the center of the valve, to 17 in 10μ at the ends. Length, $94-257\mu$. Breadth, $5-10\mu$.

This species is very similar to *Eunotia formica* described above. However, it differs from it in that the valve is more curved and the swelling is absent in the middle portion of the valve.

This species was invalidly published by Hustedt *in* A. Schmidt, *Atlas Diat.*, pl. 291, figs. 1-3, 1913.

Type locality. — U. S. A., Massachusetts, Taunton.

U. S. distribution. — GEOGRAPHICAL: New England States, Middle Atlantic States. ECOLOGICAL: This species has been found in cool water of low mineral content.

7. Eunotia rostellata Hust. *ex* Patr. var. **rostellata**   PL. 10, FIG. 9

Eunotia rostellata Hust. *ex* Patr., Farlowia, 2(2):163. 1945.

Ventral margin strongly concave; dorsal margin convex. Two margins almost parallel, thus giving the valve a lunate appearance. Ends of the valve distinct, formed by the valve narrowing rather abruptly at the ends, thus producing a somewhat attenuated appearance. Terminal nodules distinct, somewhat removed from the apices of the valve. Striae parallel, 14-16 in 10μ at the center, to 17-18 in 10μ at the ends. Length, 46μ. Breadth, 4-5μ.

This diatom is easily recognized by its lunate appearance and its somewhat attenuated ends.

Type locality. — U. S. A., Nevada, Kings River.

U. S. distribution. — GEOGRAPHICAL: Pennsylvania, Nevada. ECOLOGICAL: Found in cool, acid water.

8. **Eunotia lapponica** Grun. *ex* A. Cl. var. **lapponica**   PL. 10, FIG. 10

Eunotia lapponica Grun. *ex* A. Cl., Bih. K. Svenska Vet.-Akad. Handl., 21, Afd. 3(2):29, pl. 1, figs. 29-30. 1895.

Frustules in girdle view rectangular, with rounded ends. Ventral margin of valve slightly concave, somewhat swollen at the ends; dorsal margin convex but almost parallel to ventral margin, narrowing toward the apices to form capitate-truncate ends. Terminal nodules large; raphe distinct in the clear area. Position of the terminal nodules somewhat variable; the clear area of the terminal nodules usually extending to the ends of the valve. Striae parallel, somewhat variable, usually 16-22 in 10μ. Length, 50-100μ. Breadth, 6-8μ.

This diatom is easily recognized by the generally linear appearance of the valve, the large terminal nodules, and the fineness of the striae.

Type locality. — Kvikkjokk, Njunnats, Jokkmolsk, Kamajolsk, Njammats, Tjukksbakken, Gellivare.

U. S. distribution. — GEOGRAPHICAL: Connecticut. Only known from Bethany Bog. ECOLOGICAL: Found in northern Europe in mountain areas, in springs and bogs.

9. **Eunotia valida** Hust. var. **valida**   PL. 10, FIG. 11

Eunotia valida Hust. *in* Pasch., Süssw.-Fl. Mitteleuropas, Heft 10, Aufl. 2, p. 178, fig. 299. 1930.

Frustules in girdle view rectangular. Ventral margin concave, dorsal margin convex. Margins of the valve almost parallel. Ends of the valve rounded, somewhat capitate; sometimes slightly reflexed. Terminal nodules large, on ventral margin at the apices of the valve. Striae, 11-15 in 10μ. Length, 30-150μ. Breadth, 3.5-7.5μ.

This species is characterized by its linear appearance and its wall, which is much thicker than in most diatoms. Thus, the valve appears to be surrounded by a heavy, dark line.

Type locality. — Häufig an überrieselten Felsen der Edmundsklamm in der Böhmischen Schweiz.

U. S. distribution. — GEOGRAPHICAL: Middle Atlantic States, Southeastern States; Tennessee. ECOLOGICAL: Prefers cool, acid water.

10. Eunotia parallela Ehr. var. parallela PL. 10, FIG. 12

Eunotia parallela Ehr., Phys. Abh. Akad. Wiss. Berlin, for 1841:414. 1843.
Eunotia angusta Cl.-Eul., K. Svenska Vet.-Akad. Handl., Fjärde Ser., 4(1):81,
figs. 407b, c, f. 1953. (questionable.)

Dorsal and ventral margins of the valve parallel. Valve varying from almost straight to more or less arched; rounded at the apices. Ends indistinguishable from rest of the valve. Terminal nodules small, distinct, near apices of the valve. Striae parallel, may be slightly radiate over terminal nodule. Hustedt (1932, p. 302) states that the striae may vary from 8-16 in 10μ. Length, usually 50-150μ. Breadth, 5-15μ. Ehrenberg (1854, pl. 4(3), fig. 16) shows one specimen that is 226μ long.

This species is distinguished by the parallel margins of the valve and the rounded ends.

Cleve-Euler (1953a, pp. 81, 83) divides this species into two. Under the typical form of *Eunotia angusta* she places *E. parallela* var. *angusta* Grun. (1884, p. 100) and *E. parallela* f. *angustior* Grun. *in* V. H. (1881, pl. 34, fig. 16). This species, she states, has the ends of the valve simply rounded. She states that the ends of the valve in *E. parallela* Ehr. are rounded and somewhat set off from the main body of the valve.

I have carefully examined the ends of the valve in Ehrenberg's plates in *Mikrogeologie* (1854: pl. 2(2), fig. 24; pl. 3(2), fig. 11; pl. 3(4), fig. 15; pl. 4(3), fig. 16). They do not seem to be differentiated from the main body of the valve as Cleve-Euler describes them. I, therefore, do not believe that Cleve-Euler's specimens of *E. angusta* belong to another species.

Type locality. — Uncertain, U. S. A.

U. S. distribution. — GEOGRAPHICAL: New England States. ECOLOGICAL: In cool to cold water, often associated with *Sphagnum*.

11. Eunotia praerupta Ehr. var. praerupta PL. 10, FIG. 14

Eunotia praerupta Ehr., Phys. Abh. Akad. Wiss. Berlin, for 1841:414. 1843.
Eunotia praerupta var. *curta* Grun. *in* V. H., Syn. Diat. Belgique, pl. 34, fig. 24.
1881.

Frustules in girdle view, rectangular. Ventral margin usually slightly concave at the center, straight at the ends of the valve; sometimes almost straight throughout the entire length. Dorsal margin convex; narrowed, often reflexed at the ends to form truncate, somewhat capitate apices. Dorsal margin sometimes not so formed and the ends are truncate-rostrate. Terminal nodules distinct, at the ends of the valve, extending upward along the apices. Striae parallel, 6-13 in 10μ. Length, 20-100μ. Breadth, 4-15μ. Length-to-breadth ratio, 5:1-7:1.

This species can easily be recognized by the convexity of the dorsal margin and by the characteristic truncate-rostrate to slightly capitate ends. Cleve-Euler (1953a, p. 114) assigns the illegitimate name *Eunotia praemonos* to this taxon.

Type locality. — Uncertain, U. S. A.

U. S. distribution. — Geographical: New England States, Middle Atlantic States, Southeastern States, Gulf Coast States, South Central States, East Central States; Montana, Wyoming, Colorado, California. Ecological: Usually in northern or mountainous localities in acid to circumneutral water.

11. Eunotia praerupta var. bidens (Ehr.) Grun. PL. 10, FIG. 13

Eunotia bidens Ehr., Phys. Abh. Akad. Wiss. Berlin, for 1841:413. 1843.

Eunotia praerupta var. *bidens* (Ehr.) Grun. *in* Cl. & Grun., K. Svenska Vet.-Akad. Handl., Ny Földj, 17(2):109. 1880.

Eunotia praerupta var. *bidens* f. *minor* Grun. *in* V. H., Syn. Diat. Belgique, pl. 34, fig. 22. 1881.

Eunotia praerupta var. *bidens* f. *compressa* Berg, Bot. Not., for 1939:458, pl. 4, fig. 177. 1939.

This variety has the same characteristics as the species except that the dorsal margin has two undulations. The shape of the apices may vary from rounded-truncate to rectangularly-truncate, sometimes slightly concave at the truncated ends.

Type locality. — Uncertain, U. S. A.

U. S. distribution. — Geographical: New England States, Middle Atlantic States, Southeastern States, Gulf Coast States, Lakes States; Montana, Wyoming, Washington. Ecological: In water of low mineral content, often found associated with moss; pH, acid to circumneutral.

11. Eunotia praerupta var. inflata Grun. PL. 10, FIG. 15

Eunotia praerupta var. *inflata* Grun. *in* V. H., Syn. Diat. Belgique, pl. 34, fig. 17. 1881.

This variety differs from the nominate variety of the species in that the dorsal margin is very convex. Ventral margin almost straight or slightly concave. Ends often somewhat more rounded, more rostrate; not as angularly truncate as in the typical forms. Some forms of this variety with capitate-truncate ends. Length-to-breadth ratio, 2.5:1-4:1. Striae variable, 5-8 in 10μ at the center to 9-12 in 10μ at the ends. Length, 25-60μ. Breadth, 10-15μ.

Grunow's varieties *curta* and *inflata* seem to intergrade. They are characterized by being short, broad forms.

Type locality. — Uncertain, Belgium.

U. S. distribution. — Geographical: Middle Atlantic States; Montana, Wyoming. Ecological: Seems to prefer acid, cool water, associated with moss.

12. Eunotia clevei Grun. var. clevei   PL. 11, FIG. 1

Eunotia clevei Grun. *in* Cl., Acta Soc. Fauna Fl. Fennica, 8(2):55, pl. 3, figs. 13-16. 1891.

Ventral margin concave. Dorsal margin strongly convex. Two margins not parallel. Valve narrowed toward rounded, slightly capitate ends. The ends are formed by the dorsal margin being slightly reflexed, whereas the ventral margin is smooth. Terminal nodules large, formed around the ends of the raphe which is reflexed in the apices of the valve. Raphe distinct in the clear area of each nodule. A clear line formed by the interruption of the raphe connects the two terminal nodules. Striae distinctly punctate, 12-18 in 10μ. Puncta composing the striae are likewise, 12-18 in 10μ. Length, $100-340\mu$. Breadth, $22-40\mu$.

This species is very distinctive, easily recognized by its large size, coarsely punctate striae, and large terminal nodules. It is most often found in recent fossil deposits. However, since it is doubtful that it is always fossil, it is included in this book.

This species was first named in 1879 in the pamphlet and on the slide label of Cl. & Möll., No. 140, but it is neither described, nor designated from other species on the slide.

A. Cleve-Euler (1953a, p. 132) states that in girdle view the frustules are lanceolate in shape with small spines. This view of the frustules we have not observed.

Type locality. — Uncertain.

U. S. distribution. — Geographical: New Jersey, Washington, Oregon (fossil?).

13. Eunotia indica Grun. var. indica   PL. 11, FIG. 2

Eunotia indica Grun. *in* Rabh., Beitr. Nähr. Kenntn. Verbr. Alg., Heft 2, p. 5, pl. 1, fig. 7. 1865.

Ventral margin concave, recurved at the ends. Dorsal margin strongly convex; suddenly recurved at the ends to form capitate, wedge-shaped apices. Ends of valve broad. Terminal nodules on ventral margin large, very close to the apices of the valve. Striae indistinctly punctate, 10-14 in 10μ. Length, usually $50-100\mu$. Breadth, $10-14\mu$. Length-to-breadth ratio, usually 5:1-7:1. Cleve-Euler (1953a, p. 120) gives striae, 8-12 in 10μ; length, $30-110\mu$; breadth, $5.5-15\mu$.

This species differs from *Eunotia maior* in the distinctive shape of the ends of the valve, and in the length-to-breadth ratio which gives this diatom a chunkier appearance than the long slender *E. maior*.

Type locality. — Banka Island.

U. S. distribution. — Geographical: Maine, Pennsylvania. Ecological: In cool lakes and streams.

14. **Eunotia luna** Ehr. var. **luna**   pl. 11, fig. 3

Eunotia luna Ehr., Ber. Akad. Wiss. Berlin, for 1845:77.   1845.

Valve lunate. Dorsal margin convex, gradually narrowed toward the rounded ends. Ventral margin undulate with an abrupt swelling at the center of the valve. Terminal nodules at the apices of the valve on the ventral margin. Striae parallel, 8-10 in 10μ. Length, $70\text{-}85\mu$. Breadth at the center of the valve, $14\text{-}15\mu$.

This diatom has been found rarely in the United States. It is easily distinguished by the smooth dorsal and the undulate ventral margins.

Type locality. — Fossilis in Oregonia [U. S. A.].

U. S. distribution. — Boyer states fresh water, New England States; New Jersey. The specimen illustrated was a single mount made by Ward and was from the United States with no further indication of locality.

15. **Eunotia maior** (W. Sm.) Rabh. var. **maior**   pl. 11, fig. 5

Himantidium majus W. Sm., Syn. British Diat., vol. 2, p. 14, pl. 33, fig. 286.   1856.
Eunotia majus (W. Sm.) Rabh., Fl. Europaea Alg., sect. 1, p. 72.   1864.
Eunotia monodon var. *maior* (W. Sm.) Hust. *in* Pasch., Süssw.-Fl. Mitteleuropas,
    Heft 10, Aufl. 2, p. 186, fig. 255.   1930.

A large linear species. Ventral margin concave, sometimes slightly swollen at the center. Dorsal margin convex, parallel to the ventral margin. Ends of the valve capitate, rounded at the apices, almost as broad as the main body of the valve. Terminal nodules large, near the ends of the valve. Striae parallel at the center of the valve, radiate at the ends. Striae, 8-14 in 10μ. Length, $35\text{-}220\mu$. Breadth, $6\text{-}15\mu$. Length-to-breadth ratio, usually 10:1-12:1.

This species is distinguished by its linear appearance and the rounded, capitate ends which are almost as wide as the main body of the valve.

Some authors have treated this species as a variety of *Eunotia monodon* Ehr. However, since this seems to be a basic taxon about which there is considerable variation, I think it more logical to consider this a separate species and the other forms varieties.

A. Berg (1939, p. 450) has united a variety of forms which he considers belong to *E. maior*. Cleve-Euler (1953a, p. 120) to some extent has followed

Berg. This great variety of forms is not encountered in the United States. Cleve-Euler recognizes *E. maior* and *E. monodon* as two separate species.

From the specimens we have seen, the union of *E. indica* and *E. monodon* with the *E. maior* taxon does not seem advisable. *E. maior* is a long slender species with rounded, capitate ends which are almost as wide as the valve in its middle portion. The striae easily resolve into puncta. However, the ends of *E. monodon* are not so clearly set apart from the ends of the valve, and the species does not have the long, linear appearance.

A large part of the confusion about *E. maior* and *E. monodon* results from the fact that Ehrenberg (1843) has shown two figures representing different taxa under the name *E. monodon*. One of the figures shown (pl. 2(5), fig. 7) is *E. monodon* as set forth below. The other figure (pl. 3(3), fig. 3) is the common concept of *E. maior* as here described. We believe that Van Heurck (1881, pl. 33, fig. 3; pl. 34, fig. 14) has correctly separated these two taxa. *Eunotia indica*, which has capitate, wedge-shaped ends, is easily separated from the typical *E. maior* complex. It is characteristically a tropical species.

Type locality. — Ireland, Killarney, Gap of Dunloe.

U. S. distribution. — GEOGRAPHICAL: New England States, Middle Atlantic States, Southeastern States, Gulf Coast States, South Central States, East Central States, Lakes States, Plains States; Wyoming, Washington, California. ECOLOGICAL: Seems to prefer slightly acid water with low mineral content; found in swamps, bogs, lakes, and flowing water.

15. **Eunotia maior** var. **ventricosa** A. Cl. PL. 11, FIG. 4

Eunotia maior var. *ventricosa* A. Cl., Bih. K. Svenska Vet.-Akad. Handl., 21, Afd. 3(2):27, pl. 1, fig. 37. 1895.
Eunotia stevensonii Boyer, Bull. Torrey Bot. Club, 47:69, pl. 2, figs. 12-13. 1920.

Characterized by a strong swelling or undulation on the ventral margin in the middle of the valve. Terminal nodules at the ends of the valve. Striae interrupted near the ventral margin to form a clear line, which may be seen extending from one terminal nodule to the other or may be apparent only in the region of the ventral swelling. Striae, 9-11 in 10μ. Length, 88-113μ. Breadth, except in the region of the ventral swelling, 9-11μ.

Type locality. — Uncertain, Sweden, Lule Lappmark.

U. S. distribution. — GEOGRAPHICAL: New England States, Middle Atlantic States; Washington. ECOLOGICAL: Fresh, slightly acid water of low conductivity.

16. **Eunotia monodon** Ehr. var. **monodon**   PL. 11, FIG. 6

Eunotia monodon Ehr., Phys. Abh. Akad. Wiss. Berlin, for 1841:414, pl. 2(5),
    fig. 7. [*non* pl. 3(3), fig. 3]. 1843.
Himantidium monodon Ehr., Phys. Abh. Akad. Wiss. Berlin, for 1841:417, pl. 4(1),
    fig. 10; pl. 4(5), fig. 6. 1843. (synonymy questionable.)

Frustules rectangular in girdle view. Ventral margin concave. Dorsal
margin more strongly convex so that the two margins of the valve are not
parallel. Valve slightly narrowed toward rounded, but not protracted or
capitate ends. Terminal nodules distinct, on ventral margin a short distance from the apices of the valve. Striae indistinctly punctate, slightly
radiate about the terminal nodules. Striae, 8-12 in 10μ. Length, $35\text{-}90\mu$.
Breadth, $7\text{-}15\mu$.

This species is often confused with *Eunotia maior*. This confusion was
partially due to Ehrenberg who figured both forms under the name *E.
monodon*. *Eunotia maior* can be separated easily from *E. monodon* because
in the former the ends are distinctly capitate and set off from the main body
of the valve. In *E. monodon* the ends are only very slightly separated by a
narrowing of the valve.

Type locality. — West Indies, Guadeloupe.

U. S. distribution. — GEOGRAPHICAL: New England States, Middle Atlantic States, Southeastern States, Gulf Coast States, South Central States;
Wyoming, Colorado, New Mexico, Washington. ECOLOGICAL: This species
is most commonly found in swamps in cool to cold water which is acid
and high in humates.

16. **Eunotia monodon** var. **constricta** Cl.-Eul.   PL. 11, FIG. 7

Eunotia monodon var. *constricta* Cl.-Eul., K. Svenska Vet.-Akad. Handl., Fjärde
    Ser., 4(1):118, fig. 455f. 1953.

Ventral margin concave. Dorsal margin convex with two undulations.
Valve of equal width except for the undulations. Ends as broad as main
body of the valve, rounded at the apices. Terminal nodules large, on ventral margin. Striae, 8-14 in 10μ. Length, 95μ. Breadth, $7\text{-}16\mu$. According
to Cleve-Euler, measurements are as in *Eunotia monodon* var. *hybrida*:
length, 76μ; breadth, $15\text{-}16\mu$, but differs by the presence of an undulate,
dorsal margin.

The valve is more arcuate than in the nominate variety, and the dorsal
margin has two distinct undulations. This diatom does not belong to the
same taxon as *Himantidium bidens* Greg. (1854, p. 100, pl. 4, fig. 21).
Hustedt (1932, p. 306, fig. 772) illustrates a diatom which he calls *E. monodon* var. *bidens* (Greg.) W. Sm. His taxon seems to be similar to some of

Gregory's illustrations of *Himantidium bidens*. It is not the same as Cleve's or our taxon and should be placed with *E. major* not with *E. monodon*.

Type locality. — Finnish Lappland, probably Vaskojoke.

U. S. distribution. — GEOGRAPHICAL: Georgia, Florida; may be fossil. ECOLOGICAL: This species prefers warm, acid water.

17. **Eunotia zygodon** Ehr. var. **zygodon**   PL. 11, FIG. 8

Eunotia zygodon Ehr., Phys. Abh. Akad. Wiss. Berlin, for 1841:415, pl. 2(1), fig. 6. 1843.

Ventral margin concave, particularly at the center of the valve. Dorsal margin strongly convex with two swellings or undulations. Ends of the valve broad, rounded; as wide as the general body of the diatom. Terminal nodules large, lobed; located a short distance from the apices on the ventral margin. Striae more or less distinctly punctate as *Eunotia maior* var. *bidens* and *E. maior* var. *ventricosa*. Striae, 12-14 in 10μ. Length, $50\text{-}125\mu$. Breadth at broadest part of swelling, $24\text{-}25\mu$; at narrowest portion, $18\text{-}22\mu$.

As pointed out by Hustedt (1937a, p. 172), this species is quite similar to the variable *E. monodon*; however, it differs in that the undulations in *E. zygodon* are swellings which distinctly increase the breadth of the valve. As illustrated in A. Schmidt's *Atlas der Diatomaceen-Kunde,* there are many recognized varieties of this species.

Type locality. — French Guiana, Cayenne.

U. S. distribution. — GEOGRAPHICAL: This is typically a tropical South American species. It has been found in Florida in collections which did not have enough data to be sure whether they were living or fossil; New Jersey, Alabama.

18. **Eunotia suecica** A. Cl. var. **suecica**   PL. 11, FIG. 9

Eunotia suecica A. Cl., Bih. K. Svenska Vet.-Akad. Handl., 21, Afd. 3(2):29, pl. 1, fig. 31, 32? 1895.

Valve arcuate. Dorsal margin with two distinct swellings or undulations, dividing the dorsal margin into about two equal parts. Ends variable, about half the width of the valve at the broadest point of the undulation, broadly rostrate and truncate. Apices squarely cut off, thus giving a very characteristic appearance. Ventral margin slightly concave or arched. Ends of the valve following the contour of the ventral margin. Terminal nodules at the ends of the valve, extending upward along the apices; somewhat variable in size. Striae parallel, 10-14 in 10μ. Length, $25\text{-}40\mu$. Breadth, $10\text{-}20\mu$.

Type locality. — Uncertain.

U. S. distribution. — Geographical: Pennsylvania, South Carolina. Ecological: This is a cool-water species.

19. Eunotia triodon Ehr. var. triodon   PL. 12, FIG. 1

Eunotia pentodon Ehr., Ber. Akad. Wiss. Berlin, for 1837:45. 1837.
Eunotia triodon Ehr., Ber. Akad. Wiss. Berlin, for 1837:45. 1837.

Ventral margin of the valve concave, curved upwards at the apices.
Dorsal margin strongly convex with three dorsal undulations. Ends of the,
valve protracted, about one-half the width of the valve at the center of
the undulations; rounded at the apices. Raphe clearly apparent near the
ends of the valve, ending in terminal nodules which are located centrally
at the ends of the valve a short distance from the apices. A clear line formed
by the absence of puncta in the striae often apparent near the ventral margin. Striae indistinctly punctate, somewhat radiate about the terminal
nodules, variable as to density. Ehrenberg describes them as 11-12 in 10μ;
Hustedt states 15-20 in 10μ. Our specimen has striae, 14-16 in 10μ. Length,
35-120μ. Breadth, 14-20μ.

Although this species was first described in 1837 by Ehrenberg, a
much more complete description is given in *Infusionsthierchen* (1838, p.
192, pl. 21, fig. 24).

Type locality. — Zu Brot verbachnes Bergmehl von den Grenzen Lapplands in Schweden.

U. S. distribution. — Geographical: New England States, Middle Atlantic States, Southeastern States, Gulf Coast States; Washington. Ecological: Prefers oligotrophic to somewhat acid water.

20. Eunotia serra Ehr. var. serra   PL. 12, FIG. 2

Eunotia serra Ehr., Ber. Akad. Wiss. Berlin, for 1837:45. 1837.
Eunotia bisoctonaria Ehr., Ber. Akad. Wiss. Berlin, for 1840:209. 1840.
Eunotia decaodon Ehr., Ber. Akad. Wiss. Berlin, for 1840:209. 1840.
Eunotia endecaodon Ehr., Ber. Akad. Wiss. Berlin, for 1840:209. 1840.
Eunotia enneodon Ehr., Ber. Akad. Wiss. Berlin, for 1840:209. 1840.
Eunotia heptodon Ehr., Ber. Akad. Wiss. Berlin, for 1840:209. 1840.
Eunotia icosodon Ehr., Ber. Akad. Wiss. Berlin, for 1840:210. 1840.
Eunotia octodon Ehr., Ber. Akad. Wiss. Berlin, for 1840:209. 1840.
Eunotia serrulata Ehr., Ber. Akad. Wiss. Berlin, for 1840:209. 1840.
Eunotia septena Ehr., Phys. Abh. Akad. Wiss. Berlin, for 1841: pl. 4(2), fig. 13.
    1843.
Eunotia polyodon Ehr., Ber. Akad. Wiss. Berlin, for 1845:77. 1845.
Eunotia hendecaodon Ehr., Mikrogeol., pl. 4(1), fig. 19. 1854.
Eunotia dodecaodon Ehr., Mikrogeol., pl. 4(1), fig. 20. 1854.
Eunotia prionotus Ehr., Mikrogeol., pl. 17(1), fig. 41. 1854.

Eunotia quindenaria Ehr., Mikrogeol., pl. 17(1), fig. 42. 1854.

Eunotia scalaris Ehr., Mikrogeol., pl. 17(1), fig. 44. 1854.

Eunotia quatuordenaria Ehr., Mikrogeol., pl. 33(10), fig. 6. 1854.

Eunotia tredenaria Ehr., Mikrogeol., pl. 33(10), fig. 9. 1854.

Eunotia undenaria Ehr., Mikrogeol., pl. 33(10), fig. 12. 1854.

Eunotia robusta Ralfs *in* Pritch., Hist. Infusoria, 4th ed., p. 763. 1861. (in part).

Eunotia robusta var. *polyodon* Meist., Beitr. Kryptog.-Fl. Schweiz, 4(1), pl. 11, fig. 1. 1912.

Frustules in girdle view rectangular; in valve view having a long, narrow appearance. Ventral margin straight at the ends, more or less concave toward the center of the valve. Dorsal margin convex with from four to twenty or more undulations. Length of the valve seems to vary as the number of undulations. Apices of the valve rounded, not distinctly differentiated from the main body of the valve. Terminal nodules distinct, on ventral margin, a short distance from the apices of the valve. Striae distinctly or indistinctly punctate. On the dorsal margin there may be a few short striae, but they are not as numerous as in the variety *diadema*. Striae parallel, radiate over the terminal nodules.. Striae, usually 10-12 in 10µ at the center, to 14 in 10µ at the ends. Length, 50-150µ. Length-to-breadth ratio, 6:1-9:1.

This taxon has been called invalidly *Eunotia robusta* Ralfs in recent literature. Patrick (1958, p. 9) discusses the nomenclature of this taxon.

Type locality. — N. Sweden, Degernfors; Bergmehl.

U. S. distribution. — GEOGRAPHICAL: New England States, Middle Atlantic States, Gulf Coast States; Colorado, California. ECOLOGICAL: Oligotrophic or dystrophic water.

20. **Eunotia serra** var. **diadema** (Ehr.) Patr.   PL. 12, FIG. 3

Eunotia diadema Ehr., Ber. Akad. Wiss. Berlin, for 1837:45. 1837.

Eunotia tetraodon Ehr., Infusionsthierchen, p. 192, pl. 21, fig. 25. 1838.

Eunotia heptaodon Ehr., Mikrogeol., pl. 17(1), fig. 34. 1854.

Eunotia diadema var. *tetraodon* (Ehr.) Cl.-Eul., K. Svenska Vet.-Akad. Handl., Fjärde Ser., 4(1):125, fig. 462a. 1953.

Eunotia diadema var. *intermedia* Cl.-Eul., K. Svenska Vet.-Akad. Handl., Fjärde Ser., 4(1):125, fig. 464g. 1953.

Eunotia diadema var. *densior* Cl.-Eul., K. Svenska Vet.-Akad. Handl., Fjärde Ser., 4(1):126, fig. 464f. 1953.

Eunotia serra var. *diadema* (Ehr.) Patr., Not. Nat. Acad. Nat. Sci. Philadelphia, No. 312, p. 10, fig. 11. 1958.

Ventral margin of the valve concave. Dorsal margin strongly convex with four or more undulations, most typically four. Ends of the valve protracted, about one-half the breadth of the valve at its broadest part. Terminal nodules on the ventral margin of the valve. Striae distinctly punctate, somewhat radiate. Many shorter striae which do not extend through the breadth of the valve are present on the dorsal margin. Striae near ventral margin, 10-15 in 10μ. Length, 21-85μ. Length-to-breadth ratio, 2.5:1-4:1.

This taxon is considered a distinct species rather than a variety by many workers. However, the general shape of the valve, the type of terminal nodules, and the characteristics of the striation place this in the same species as *Eunotia serra*.

Type locality. — Zu Brot verbachnes Bergmehl von den Grenzen Lapplands in Schweden.

U. S. distribution. — Geographical: New England States; Utah. Ecological: Like the species found in oligotrophic or dystrophic water, usually cool. Often found in swamps or bogs.

21. **Eunotia obesa** var. **wardii** Patr.   PL. 12, FIG. 4

Eunotia obesa var. *wardii* Patr., Not. Nat. Acad. Nat. Sci. Philadelphia, No. 312, p. 4, fig. 4. 1958.

Ventral margin strongly concave. Dorsal margin strongly convex, with two large humps or swellings. Terminal nodules on ventral margin extending upward to almost the center of the end of the valve, forming an oblong space. Nodules a short distance from the apices of the valve. Striae indistinctly punctate; radiate about the terminal nodules, somewhat radiate in the dorsal swellings. Shorter striae often present, extending from the dorsal margin, Striae, 12-14 in 10μ at the center of the valve to 17 in 10μ at the ends. Length of cord extending from one end of the valve to the other, about 62μ. Breadth of the valve at the center of the swellings, 19.5μ.

This variety differs from the nominate variety of the species in that the valve has a longer, more graceful appearance. The ends of the valve are not as swollen and are more distinctly set off from the rest of the valve.

P. T. Cleve (1900, p. 277) mentions and illustrates a variety of *Eunotia obesa* Cl. from Mobile, Alabama, but he does not name it. Our variety appears to be the same as the one shown by Cleve.

Type locality. — U. S. A., Alabama, Mobile, Spring Hill.

U. S. distribution. — Geographical: Known only from the type locality. From the numbering system of Ward's collection used by the New York Botanical Garden, it appears that this may be a locality for fossil diatoms.

22. **Eunotia bidentula** W. Sm. var. **bidentula**   PL. 12, FIG. 5

Eunotia bidentula W. Sm., Syn. British Diat., vol. 2, p. 83. 1856.

Ventral margin straight. Dorsal margin very convex with two swellings or undulations. Ends of the valve produced or attenuated; somewhat capitate on dorsal margin, straight on ventral margin. Ends variable in breadth. Striae parallel at the center of the valve, somewhat radiate toward the ends. Striae, 15-18 in 10μ. Length, $20\text{-}50\mu$. Breadth, $6\text{-}14\mu$.

W. Smith does not say anything about the position of the terminal nodules. However, I have examined specimens from W. Smith's original Braemer collection [W. Sm. A-1 (lectotype)], and they are the same taxon as our specimen. Hustedt (1932, fig. 744) illustrates specimens which have the terminal nodules at the ends of the valve and one which has nodules as in our specimens. Van Heurck (1881, pl. 34, fig. 28) illustrates a variety of this species which has the terminal nodules on the ventral margin removed from the ends of the valve as in our specimens.

I have checked Ehrenberg's original description of *E. camelus*, and I agree with W. Smith that it is not this taxon.

Type locality. — Fresh water [Scotland] Braemer, August 1854, Dr. Balfour.

U. S. distribution. — GEOGRAPHICAL: New England States, Middle Atlantic States, Southeastern States. ECOLOGICAL: This species seems to have its best development in cold water. It is an acidophil.

23. **Eunotia hexaglyphis** Ehr. var. **hexaglyphis**   PL. 12, FIG. 6

> *Eunotia hexaglyphis* Ehr., Mikrogeol., pl. 16(1), fig. 34; pl. 16(2), fig. 24. 1854.
> *Eunotia pentaglyphis* Ehr., Mikrogeol., pl. 17(1), fig. 32. 1854. [pl. 16(2), fig. 22 appears to be a different taxon.]
> *Eunotia tetraglyphis* Ehr., Mikrogeol., p. 172. 1854.

Ventral margin straight or slightly concave. Dorsal margin undulate, depth of the undulations variable. Apices of the valve narrowly protracted, slightly bent in a downward direction. Terminal nodules near base of the protracted apices, thus somewhat removed from the ends of the valve. Length of the valve variable, depending on the number of dorsal undulations. Striae, 12-15 in 10μ. Length, $33\text{-}80\mu$ or more. Breadth, $6\text{-}11\mu$.

The most obvious characteristic of this taxon is the structure of the apices which are narrowly protracted and slightly bent, sometimes slightly capitate, always less than one-half the greatest breadth of the valve, and often quite narrow. It is the shape of the apices and the position of the terminal nodules which distinctly separates this species from *Eunotia robusta*, *E. triodon*, and *E. tridentula*.

Van Heurck (1881, pl. 34, fig. 33) lists this species as *E. polyglyphis* Grun. var. *hexaglyphis*. I have been unable to find Grunow's original description of *E. polyglyphis*. Hustedt (1932, p. 294) describes *E. polyglyphis* and cites Grunow as the authority. This name is illegitimate for this taxon since the name of the taxon should be one of Ehrenberg's original names. For this reason *E. hexaglyphis* Ehr. is selected as the valid name for this taxon. *E. pentaglyphis* Ehr. and *E. tetraglyphis* Ehr. are listed as synonyms.

Type locality. — Zu Brod verbachnes Bergmehl von den Grenzen Lapplands in Schweden.

U. S. distribution. — Geographical: New England States; Wyoming, Nevada, California. Ecological: Common in cool mountainous areas.

24. **Eunotia diodon** Ehr. var. **diodon**   PL. 12, FIG. 7

> *Eunotia diodon* Ehr., Ber. Akad. Wiss. Berlin, for 1837:45.   1837.
> *Eunotia diodon* f. *minor* Grun. *in* V. H., Syn. Diat. Belgique, pl. 33, fig. 5.   1881.

Ventral margin slightly concave. Dorsal margin strongly convex with two undulations; abruptly narrowed at the ends of the valve which are rostrate, rounded at the apices. Apices about half the width of the valve at its widest part. Large terminal nodules on ventral margin at the apices of the valve. Striae parallel, 10-12 in 10μ at the center, to 14-16 in 10μ at the ends. Length, 10-80μ. Breadth, 5-15μ.

This species is easily separated from *Eunotia maior* var. *bidens* in that in this species the ends of the valve are much narrower than the central part of the valve.

Type locality. — Zu Brod verbacknes Bergmehl von den Grenzen Lapplands in Schweden.

U. S. distribution. — Geographical: New England States, Middle Atlantic States, Southeastern States, Gulf Coast States, West Central States, Lakes States, Plains States. Ecological: This species is an acidophil preferring cool water.

25. **Eunotia pectinalis** (O. F. Müll.?) Rabh. var. **pectinalis**
PL. 12, FIGS. 8, 10

> *Conferva pectinalis* O. F. Müll., Nova Acta Acad. Sci. Imp. Petropolitane 3(Hist.):
>   91, pl. 1, figs. 4-7.   1788.   (questionable.)
> *Eunotia pectinalis* (Dillw.) Rabh., Fl. Europaea Alg. sect. 1, p. 73.   1864.
> *Eunotia pectinalis* f. *elongata* V. H., Syn. Diat. Belgique, pl. 33, fig. 16.   1881.
> *Eunotia pectinalis* var. *stricta* (Rabh.) V. H., Syn. Diat. Belgique, pl. 33, fig. 18.
>   1881.

Frustules rectangular in girdle view. Valve elongate, slightly curved or bent. Ventral margin straight or slightly concave, sometimes slightly swollen at the center. Dorsal margin straight or slightly convex, sometimes slightly swollen at the center of the valve; usually almost parallel to ventral margin. Valve narrowed toward broadly attenuated, truncately rounded ends. Width of the ends somewhat variable as to its ratio to the width of the middle of the valve. Terminal nodules distinct, near the apices of the valve. Striae parallel, slightly radiate at the ends; usually coarser at the center than at the ends of the valve. Striae, 7-12 in 10μ at the center of the valve, to 14 in 10μ at the ends of the valve. Length, 17-140μ. Breadth, 5-10μ.

This is quite a variable taxon. The varieties which are recognized represent the extremes of series of variations from the typical form. In time a complete series of variable individuals may bridge the variation from the typical forms to the named varieties.

Rabenhorst gave Dillwyn as the authority for this specific name. However, Dillwyn gives O. F. Müller as the authority in his citation of this name. It is impossible to be sure from the original description and plates that either O. F. Müller or Dillwyn actually was working with this taxon.

Type locality. — In scaturiginibus Germaniae et Daniae. (Müller).

U. S. distribution. — GEOGRAPHICAL: New England States, Middle Atlantic States, Southeastern States, Gulf Coast States, South Central States, East Central States, Lakes States; Utah, California. ECOLOGICAL: It is most commonly found in the cooler regions or in the northern or central parts of the United States. It prefers water of a low mineral content, and oligotrophic to eutrophic.

25. **Eunotia pectinalis** var. **ventricosa** Grun.   PL. 12, FIG. 9

Eunotia ventralis Ehr., Phys. Abh. Akad. Wiss. Berlin, for 1841:414. 1843. [a typographical error p. 414, *F. ventralis;* on p. 375, *Eunotia ventralis*.]
Eunotia pectinalis var. *ventricosa* (Ehr.) Grun. *in* V. H., Syn. Diat. Belgique, pl. 33, fig. 19B. 1881.
Eunotia pectinalis var. *ventralis* (Ehr.) Hust., Abh. Naturw. Ver. Bremen, 20(2): 276, pl. 3, figs. 26-27. 1911.

Valve arcuate, dorsal margin slightly concave in the middle of the valve, ventral margin with a distinct swelling at the center of the valve. Valve narrowed toward the broadly attenuated, rostrate ends. A clear line formed by a break in the striae often seen near the ventral margin in the region of the ventral swelling. Range of length, breadth, and striae number as in the species.

This variety differs from *Eunotia pectinalis* var. *undulata* in that the dorsal margin is not undulate; also the valve is more arcuate than in variety *undulata*.

Van Heurck (*loc. cit.*) published the combination *E. pectinalis* var. *ventricosa* Grun. for "*E. ventricosa* Ehr.," a name we have been unable to find in the literature. Possibly he meant *E. ventricosa* Grun.

Type locality. — U. S. A., New York, West Point; fossil.

U. S. distribution. — GEOGRAPHICAL: New England States, Middle Atlantic States, Southeastern States, Gulf Coast States, West Central States, Plains States. ECOLOGICAL: Often found with the species.

25. **Eunotia pectinalis** var. **undulata** (Ralfs) Rabh.   PL. 12, FIG. 11

Fragilaria pectinalis var. *undulata* Ralfs, Ann. Mag. Nat. Hist., 12:108, pl. 2, fig. 3d. 1843.

Himantidium undulata W. Sm., Syn. British Diat., vol. 2, p. 12, pl. 33, fig. 281. 1856.

Eunotia pectinalis var. *undulata* (Ralfs) Rabh., Fl. Europaea Alg., sect. 1, p. 74. 1864.

Valve usually linear, slightly arched with three or more undulations on the dorsal margin; one distinct swelling on the ventral margin at the center of the valve. Ends broadly attenuate, truncately rounded approximately half as broad as the valve at its center. Terminal nodules distinct, a short distance from the ends of the valve. Striae parallel at the center; more distant at the center than at the ends of the valve. A clear line formed by a break in the striae often found near the ventral margin. The range of striae number, of the length, and of the width is the same as in the nominate variety of the species.

This variety is easily distinguished by the many undulations of the dorsal margin and the central swelling of the ventral margin. This variety is quite variable in outline.

Ralfs describes a form of this variety in which the ends are attenuated and very narrow. There are only three dorsal undulations. The width of the value in proportion to the length is much greater than is usually found in this taxon. The form pictured by Ralfs, so far as we know, has not been found in the United States. Therefore, our illustration is of the more usual form.

Type locality. — Wales, Drws Ardudwy near Barmouth.

U. S. distribution. — Geographical: New England States, Middle Atlantic States, Southeastern States; Florida (?). Ecological: This variety prefers circumneutral water of low mineral content.

25. **Eunotia pectinalis** var. **recta** A. Mayer *ex* Patr.   PL. 12, FIG. 12

Eunotia pectinalis var. *recta* A. Mayer *ex* Patr., Farlowia, 2(2):161.   1945.

Ventral margin straight or slightly concave. Dorsal margin convex. Valve narrowed at rostrate-capitate ends. Striae parallel, 15-18 in 10μ. Length, 15-25μ. Breadth, 3-4μ.

This variety is mainly distinguished from the nominate variety and *Eunotia pectinalis* var. *minor* by the shape of the apices, the relatively larger terminal nodules, and the smaller size.

A. Mayer (1917, p. 69, pl. 1, figs. 37-38) illustrated, but did not describe this variety which he attributed to Rabenhorst. Since an extensive search of the literature has revealed no description by Rabenhorst, A. Mayer's publication is probably invalid.

Type locality. — Bavaria, Fichtelgebirge, am Südostabhange der Kösseine in einer Höhe von ca. 700 m. Das Material wurde kleinen Wasserläufen entnommen, die sich auf etwas sumpfigem Untergrunde dahinschlängelten.

U. S. distribution. — GEOGRAPHICAL: This variety is rare in the U. S. A. The only record in our collection is from Davy's Run, Monroe Co., Pennsylvania. ECOLOGICAL: In water with a very low mineral content.

25. **Eunotia pectinalis** var. **minor** (Kütz) Rabh.   PL. 12, FIGS. 13-14

> *Himantidium minus* Kütz., Bacill., p. 39, pl. 16, fig. 10.   1844.
> *Himantidium veneris* Kütz., Bacill., p. 40, pl. 30, fig. 7.   1844.   (at least in part.)
> *Eunotia impressa* Ehr., Mikrogeol., pl. 3(4), fig. 20; pl. 14, fig. 66.   1854.
> *Eunotia pectinalis* var. *minus* (Kütz.) Rabh., Fl. Europaea Alg., sect. 1, p. 74.
>   1864.
> *Eunotia pectinalis* var. *impressa* O. F. Müll., Forschungsber. Biol. Stat. Plön, 6:59.
>   1898.
> *Eunotia pectinalis* var. *minor* f. *impressa* (Ehr.) Hust. in Pasch., Süssw.-Fl. Mittel-
>   europas, Heft 10, Aufl. 2, p. 182, fig. 239.   1930.

Ventral margin slightly concave. Dorsal margin distinctly convex, often with two shallow undulations. Valve somewhat narrower at the ends than at the center. Apices of the valve rounded; somewhat narrower but not distinctly set off from the main body of the valve. Terminal nodules near, but not at the ends of the valve; distinct but not large. Striae straight; almost perpendicular to ventral margin at the center of the valve, but somewhat curved at the ends. Striae, usually 14-16 in 10μ at the center, to about 20 in 10μ at the ends. Length, 20-60μ. Breadth, 4-7μ.

Ehrenberg in *Mikrogeologie* (1854, pl. 14, fig. 66) indicates the striae as 7-8 in 10μ. Often the striae on Ehrenberg's drawings are simply filled in and do not seem to indicate the true number. Since no other workers record such a low number of striae for this taxon, it is inferred that this is the case in Ehrenberg's drawings.

The specimens of this variety with the smooth dorsal margin differ from *Eunotia pectinalis* var. *stricta* mainly in the fact that this variety has much finer striae.

A full discussion of the synonymy of *E. impressa* Ehr. and *Himantidium minus* Kütz. has been given by Patrick (1958, pp. 5-6).

Type locality. — [Germany], Unter Süsswasseralgen bei Jever: Koch!

U. S. distribution. — GEOGRAPHICAL: New England States, Middle Atlantic States, Southeastern States, Gulf Coast States, South Central States, East Central States, West Central States, Lakes States; Montana, Washington, California. ECOLOGICAL: Found in acid to circumneutral water; tolerates more calcium than many species of *Eunotia*.

26. Eunotia soleirolii (Kütz.) Rabh. var. soleirolii   PL. 13, FIGS. 1-2

Himantidium soleirolii Kütz., Bacill., p. 39, pl. 16, fig. 9.   1844.
Eunotia soleirolii Kütz., Rabh., Fl. Europaea Alg., sect. 1, p. 74.   1864.
Eunotia pectinalis var. *soleirolii* (Kütz.) V. H., Syn. Diat. Belgique, p. 143.   1885.

Valve linear; arcuate. Ends not differentiated clearly from the main part of the valve. Striae, 12-14 in 10μ. Length, 30-65μ. Breadth, 3-4μ.

The only distinguishing characteristics often given this taxon are the internal septae which seem to be a result of an abnormal division of the frustule. However, Kützing describes and illustrates the valve as linear-lunate in shape. This shape of the valve distinguishes this species from the smaller forms of *Eunotia pectinalis* (Müll.?) Rabh.

The nomenclature of this species has been discussed by Patrick (1958, p. 11). I wish to designate the lectotype of this species: a specimen from Kützing's herbarium No. 27 (B. M. 17865).

Type locality. — In Bergwassern auf Corsica! Duby (Biasoletto!).

U. S. distribution. — GEOGRAPHICAL: New Hampshire, New Jersey.

27. Eunotia sudetica O. Müll. var. sudetica   PL. 13, FIG. 3

Eunotia sudetica O. Müll., Forschungsber. Biol. Stat. Plön, 6:59, pl. 3, figs. 25-26. 1898.

Ventral margin straight or slightly concave. Dorsal margin strongly convex. Ends indistinguishable or, as in illustration, with a rostrate, somewhat attenuated appearance. Terminal nodules distinct, located at some distance from the apices of the valve. Striae, 8-13 in 10μ. Length, usually 15-50μ. Breadth, 5-9μ. Cleve-Euler (1953a, p. 110) states that specimens may be 60μ long.

In shape this species is very similar to *Eunotia incisa* and is undoubtedly related to it. It differs mainly in that this is a coarsely striated form, usually 8-11 in 10μ, whereas *E. incisa* is more finely striated, 13-17 in 10μ. The ends of the valve are usually definitely narrower than the main body of the valve, whereas in *E. incisa* they are not differentiated from the main body.

Type locality. — Germany, Riesengebirge, Kochel (Teich) I, Kochel (Teich) III.

U. S. distribution. — GEOGRAPHICAL: Southeastern States; Pennsylvania. ECOLOGICAL: Acid to circumneutral water.

28. Eunotia incisa W. Sm. *ex* Greg. var. incisa   PL. 13, FIG. 4

Himantidium veneris Kütz., Bacill., p. 40, pl. 30, fig. 7.   1844.   (probably not this species.)
Eunotia incisa W. Sm. *ex* Greg., Quart. Jour. Micr. Sci., 2:96, pl. 4, fig. 4.   1854.
Eunotia veneris (Kütz.) DeT., Syll. Alg., vol. 2, sect. 2, p. 794.   1892.   (probably not this species.)

Frustules in girdle view rectilinear. Frustules in valve view with straight ventral margin, convex dorsal margin. Apices of the valve usually acute, sometimes rounded; undifferentiated from main portion of the valve. Terminal nodules removed from the ends of the valve; distinct, at some focuses appearing as a notch in the ventral margin. Striae more distant at the center of the valve than at the ends. Striae, 13-17 in 10μ. Length, 15-50μ. Breadth, 4-7μ.

This species is characterized by the apices of the valve being undifferentiated from the main body of the valve and by the very fine striae.

Eunotia incisa var. *obtusiuscula* Grun. *in* V. H. (1881, pl. 34, fig. 35B, Type slide 271) is a definite taxon and should be considered a variety of this species. *E. incisa* var. *obtusa* Grun. *in* A. Cl. (1895, p. 30) does not belong to this taxon. It appears to be a variety of *E. vanheurckii* Patr.

The nomenclature of this species has been discussed by Patrick (1958, p. 3). Specimens of Kützing's *Himantidium veneris* which I have seen in Kützing's herbarium are *E. pectinalis* var. *minor.*

Type locality. — Scotland, Island of Mull; diatomaceous earth.

U. S. distribution. — GEOGRAPHICAL: New England States, Middle Atlantic States, Southeastern States, Gulf Coast States; California. ECOLOGICAL: In water low in dissolved minerals particularly calcium, although this diatom will tolerate more calcium than most *Eunotia* species. Often found in clear, cool water in association with moss.

29. **Eunotia carolina** Patr. var. **carolina**   PL. 13, FIG. 5

Eunotia carolina Patr., Not. Nat. Acad. Nat. Sci. Philadelphia, No. 312, p. 2, fig. 9. 1958.

Frustules rectangular in girdle view. Ventral margin of the valve straight. Dorsal margin strongly convex at the center of the valve; narrowed toward the ends, which are protracted and rounded at the apices. Terminal nodules distinct, on the ventral margin at some distance from the apices of the valve. Striae parallel, only slightly radiate about terminal nodules; indistinctly punctate. Striae, 13-14 in 10μ at the center, to 18-20 in 10μ at the ends. Length, 32μ. Breadth, 6.5μ.

In general shape this species resembles some of the varieties of *Eunotia pectinalis*. However, the dorsal margin is much more convex and the ends are more narrowly protracted. It also differs from *E. sudetica* in its more narrowly protracted ends and finer striae.

Type locality. — U. S. A., Georgia, near the mouth of Upper Three Runs, a tributary of the Savannah River below Augusta.

U. S. distribution. — GEOGRAPHICAL: Known only from the type locality. ECOLOGICAL: In dystrophic water.

30. **Eunotia tenella** (Grun.) Cl. var. **tenella**   PL. 13, FIG. 6

Eunotia arcus var.? *tenella* Grun. *in* V. H., Syn. Diat. Belgique, pl. 34, figs. 5-6. 1881.

Eunotia tenella (Grun.) A. Cl., Bih. K. Svenska Vet.-Akad. Handl., 21, Afd. 3(2): 33. 1895.

Ventral margin slightly concave. Dorsal margin varies in its degree of convexity. Margins sometimes almost parallel, in others the valve appears swollen in the middle portion. Dorsal margin narrows toward rostrate, rounded or somewhat capitate ends. Terminal nodules distinct, on the ventral margin close to the apices. Striae, 14-16 in 10μ at the center, to 20 in 10μ at the ends. Length, $6-37\mu$. Breadth,, $2-4\mu$.

This species is differentiated from *Eunotia arcus* by the shape of the ends of the valve and the finer striation. The distinct terminal nodules are also a characteristic diagnostic character.

Type locality. — Uncertain, Belgium.

U. S. distribution. — GEOGRAPHICAL: New England States, Middle Atlantic States, Southeastern States, South Central States; California. ECOLOGICAL: This species, as most of the other species of *Eunotia*, prefers somewhat acid, soft waters.

31. **Eunotia vanheurckii** Patr. var. **vanheurckii**   PL. 13, FIG. 7

Eunotia faba (Ehr.) Grun. *in* V. H., Syn. Diat. Belgique, pl. 34, fig. 34. 1881. (text, p. 143. 1885.) [non *Eunotia faba* Ehr. 1838.]

Eunotia vanheurckii Patr., Not. Nat. Acad. Nat. Sci. Philadelphia, No. 312, p. 12, fig. 12. 1958.

In girdle view frustules rectangular in shape. Ventral margin straight or slightly concave; often thickened about halfway between the center and the apices of the valve. Dorsal margin convex. Valve gradually narrows at the rounded ends. Ends of the valve not distinctly set off by a narrowing of the valve or by the dorsal or ventral margins being more convex or concave than in the main contour of the valve. Striae parallel at the center, becoming somewhat radiate at the ends; more widely spaced at the center than at the ends of the valve. Terminal nodules distinct, of moderate size; may be near, or a short distance behind the apices of the valve. Striae, 13-18 in 10μ at the center, to 15-20 in 10μ at the ends. Length, $26-60\mu$. Breadth, $5-9\mu$.

The frustules sometimes show an inner shell as commonly found in *Eunotia soleirolii* (Kütz.) Rabh.

The species is characterized by the ends of the valve being undifferentiated from the main body of the valve and by the thickening on the ventral margin. This species has often been incorrectly called *E. faba* (Ehr.) Grun.

Patrick (1958, p. 12) discusses the nomenclature of this taxon.

Type locality. — Mascarene Islands, Bourbon (Réunion); Kieselguhr.

U. S. distribution. — Geographical: Maine, Pennsylvania. Ecological: Ponds, lakes, and swamps. In soft, somewhat dystrophic water.

31. **Eunotia vanheurckii** var. **intermedia** (Krasske *ex* Hust.) Patr.

pl. 13, fig. 8

Eunotia pectinalis var. *minor* f. *intermedia* Krasske *ex* Hust. *in* Rabh., Kryptog.-Fl. Deutschland, vol. 7(2), no. 2, p. 298, figs. 763 1-o. 1932.

Eunotia vanheurckii var. *intermedia* (Krasske *ex* Hust. *in* Rabh.) Patr., Not. Nat. Acad. Nat. Sci. Philadelphia, No. 312, p. 14, fig. 13. 1958.

Ventral margin straight, wall thickened in areas halfway between the center of the valve and the ends. Dorsal margin convex. Ends not distinctly formed, but confluent with the rest of the valve. Terminal nodules distinct, near the ends of the valve. Striae parallel, 14-16 in 10μ at the center of the valve, more numerous toward the ends. Length, $15\text{-}40\mu$. Breadth, about $4\text{-}5\mu$.

This taxon was considered by Hustedt as a form of variety *minor* of *Eunotia pectinalis*. He speaks of the similarity of this form to *Eunotia faba*, which was synonymyzed with *E. vanheurckii* by Patrick (1958, p. 12).

When one examines Hustedt's illustrations and specimens it is clear that this taxon should be placed with *E. vanheurckii* rather than with *E. pectinalis*. The characteristic ends of the valve of *E. pectinalis* are not present. The shape of the valve is like that of *E. vanheurckii* rather than *E. pectinalis*. The thickenings of the wall on the ventral margin are similar to those of *E. vanheurckii* and are not found in *E. pectinalis*. The striae number is more similar to that of *E. vanheurckii* than to *E. pectinalis*.

Type locality. — None given by Hustedt. Krasske (1932, p. 101) gives: In moss in melting snow at Kalser Tauren (Alps).

U. S. distribution. — Geographical: Tennessee. Ecological: Prefers characteristically oligotrophic water.

32. **Eunotia elegans** Østr. var. **elegans**

pl. 13, fig. 9

Eunotia elegans Østr., Danske Diat., p. 172, pl. 5, fig. 105. 1910.

Valve strongly arched, ends straight; thus the general contour of the valve strongly reflexed at the ends. Margins of the valve parallel. Dorsal margin swollen to form capitate ends. Terminal nodules small, near the ends of the valve. Striae parallel, 18-24 in 10μ. The length of the valve is very hard to measure, because the valve is so strongly arched. Length, $28\text{-}35\mu$. Breadth, $2\text{-}3\mu$. Hustedt (1931, p. 287) gives span width $29\text{-}70\mu$; breadth $2\text{-}5\mu$.

This species is easily recognized by the strongly arched valve with almost straight ends. It can be easily overlooked because it is very hyaline.

Type locality. – Denmark.

U. S. distribution. – Geographical: Pennsylvania, South Carolina. Ecological: Prefers cool, slightly acid water of low conductivity.

33. Eunotia septentrionalis Østr. var. septentrionalis   PL. 13, FIG. 10

Eunotia septentrionalis Østr., Medd. om Grønland, 15:274, pl. 1, fig. 10.   1898.

Arched appearance in valve view. Ventral margin concave; gradually recurved toward ends, producing apices which are somewhat reflexed. Dorsal margin strongly convex, usually not parallel to the ventral margin; almost straight near the center, thus giving the valve a flattened appearance. Ends of the valve slightly reflexed, rostrate-capitate in shape. Terminal nodules on the ventral margin at the ends of the valve, fairly large. Striae, 16-20 in 10μ. Length, 18-25μ. Breadth, 4-6μ.

This species is quite similar in many characteristics to *Eunotia tenella*. It differs in that the valve is typically more arched than in *E. tenella*. Also the ends are more distinctly separated from the main body of the valve and are typically slightly reflexed.

Type locality. – [East Greenland], Sjelden, D. O.

U. S. distribution. – Geographical: Middle Atlantic States. Ecological: In cool, acid water low in mineral content.

34. Eunotia arcus Ehr. var. arcus   PL. 13, FIG. 11

Eunotia arcus Ehr., Ber. Akad. Wiss. Berlin, for 1837:45.   1837.
Himantidium arcus (Ehr.) Ehr., Ber. Akad. Wiss. Berlin, for 1840:212.   1840.
Eunotia arcus var. *curta* (Grun.) Schönf., Diat. Germaniae, p. 116.   1907.

Frustules in girdle view rectangular. Ventral margin almost straight or concave. Dorsal margin convex. Margins of some specimens almost parallel; in others dorsal margin much more convex than ventral margin is concave, producing a swollen appearance. Dorsal margin strongly bent back at ends, causing the ends to be sharply cut off from the main body of the valve and giving them a strongly angular, capitate appearance. Ventral margin smooth, thus formation of the capitate ends is produced on the dorsal side of the valve. In some small forms the ends are formed mainly by a narrowing of the valve, giving a rostrate appearance. The capitate ends of the valve have an angular appearance. Terminal nodules large and distinct, located at the ends of the valves on the ventral margin. Striae sometimes variable, not equidistant from each other. Striae, 11-14 in 10μ. Length, 17-90μ. Breadth, 3-9μ.

This species is easily characterized by the angular, capitate ends and the large terminal nodules at the apices of the valve.

Cleve-Euler recognizes a great many varieties of this species. Since many of these seem to intergrade, I have recognized only those American varieties which appear to be distinct.

Type locality. — N. Sweden, Degernfors; Bergmehl.

U. S. distribution. — Geographical: New England States, Middle Atlantic States, Southeastern States, Gulf Coast States, South Central States, East Central States, West Central States, Lakes States, Plains States; Wyoming, New Mexico. Ecological: This species grows in the presence of calcium. In this respect it differs from most of the species of *Eunotia* which are calciphobes; pH, acid to circumneutral.

34. Eunotia arcus var. bidens Grun. PL. 13, FIG. 12

Eunotia arcus var. *bidens* Grun. *in* V. H., Syn. Diat. Belgique, pl. 34, fig. 7. 1881.

The main difference between this variety and the nominate variety is the two undulations on the dorsal margin. In size and striae number it is similar.

Type locality. — Uncertain, Belgium.

U. S. distribution. — Geographical: New England States, Middle Atlantic States, Southeastern States, South Central States, East Central States. Ecological: Slightly acid or circumneutral water of low conductivity.

34. Eunotia arcus var. uncinata (Ehr.) Grun. PL. 13, FIG. 13

Eunotia uncinata Ehr., Phys. Abh. Akad. Wiss. Berlin, for 1841:414. 1843.

Eunotia arcus var. *uncinata* (Ehr.) Grun. *in* V. H., Syn. Diat.. Belgique, pl. 34, fig. 13. 1881. (text, p. 142. 1885.)

This variety differs from the species in that the valve is more arched and the length-to-breadth ratio is a little greater. Terminal nodules on the ventral margin a short distance from the apex of the valve. Striae, usually 10-11 in 10μ at the center, sometimes finer at the ends.

Type locality. — U. S. A., Maine, Blue Hill Pond; fossil.

U. S. distribution. — Geographical: New England States, Middle Atlantic States. Ecological: Fresh, slightly acid water of low conductivity.

34. Eunotia arcus var. fallax Hust. PL. 13, FIG. 14

Eunotia arcus var. *fallax* Hust. *in* Pasch., Süssw.-Fl. Mitteleuropas, Heft 10, Aufl. 2, p. 175, fig. 219. 1930.

Valve with slightly concave ventral margin and distinctly convex dorsal margin. The apices of the valve capitate, somewhat reflexed. Terminal nodules large, on the ventral margin of the valve. Striae coarse, 8-10 in 10μ. Length, 25-40μ. Breadth, 6-7μ.

This variety is distinguished from the nominate variety by its coarse striae and usually smaller size.

Type locality. — Uncertain.

U. S. distribution. — Geographical: New England States, Middle Atlantic States. Ecological: Prefers acid water of low nutrient content.

35. Eunotia fallax A. Cl. var. fallax   PL. 13, FIG. 15

> *Eunotia fallax* A. Cl., Bih. K. Svenska Vet.-Akad. Handl., 21, Afd. 3(2):33, pl. 1, fig. 35. 1895.

Frustules in girdle view rectangular, narrow. In valve view ventral margin almost straight, dorsal margin slightly convex. The apices of the valve strongly capitate, and somewhat reflexed, giving the valve a very characteristic appearance. Terminal nodules distinct, on the ventral margin at the end of the valve. Striae, 14-18 in 10μ. Length, 15-40μ. Breadth, 2-4μ.

This taxon seems to be most closely related to *Eunotia arcus* var. *fallax* Hust. from which it differs by its greater length-to-breadth ratio, and the valve is almost straight and not distinctly arched as in *E. arcus* var. *fallax* Hust. Hustedt (1932, p. 288) gives the striae as being coarser than in the A. Cl. description which states striae 14-15 in 10μ. Our specimens have the striae to 18 in 10μ.

Type locality. — Uncertain.

U. S. distribution. — Geographical: Pennsylvania. Ecological: Seems to prefer cool, somewhat acid water.

36. Eunotia nymanniana Grun. var. nymanniana   PL. 13, FIG. 16

> *Eunotia nymanniana* Grun. *in* V. H., Syn. Diat. Belgique, pl. 34, fig. 8. 1881.

Ventral margin almost straight or slightly concave; dorsal margin more convex so that the margins are almost but not quite parallel. Dorsal margin abruptly reflexed to form the strongly capitate ends. At the apices the ends are obliquely truncate, thus giving the general structure of the ends an angular appearance. Terminal nodules are large, distinct, and at the apices of the valve on the ventral margin. Striae parallel, slightly radiate at ends. Striae, 15-25 in 10μ, usually 18 in 10μ. Length, 15-45μ. Breadth, 3-6μ. Length-to-breadth ratio, 7.5:1-5:1.

This species is very similar in shape to *Eunotia fallax* A. Cl. It differs mainly in that the striae are much finer. Hustedt has synonymized this species with *E. exigua* var. *compacta* (1932, p. 286). Cleve-Euler (1953a, p. 106) states that Hustedt has confused two taxa which seem to be distinct.

Eunotia nymanniana as found in the United States is a more slender, straighter species than *E. exigua*.

Type locality. — Uncertain, Belgium.

U. S. distribution. — GEOGRAPHICAL: Pennsylvania. ECOLOGICAL: In water of low mineral content.

37. **Eunotia exigua** (Bréb. *ex* Kütz.) Rabh. var. **exigua**

PL. 13, FIGS. 17-18

Himantidium exiguum Bréb., *ex* Kütz., Sp. Alg., p. 8. 1849.
Eunotia paludosa Grun., Verh. Zool.-Bot. Ges. Wien, 12:336, pl. 6, fig. 10. 1862.
Eunotia exigua (Bréb. *ex* Kütz.) Rabh., Fl. Europaea Alg., sect. 1, p. 73. 1864.

Ventral margin concave. Dorsal margin usually more strongly convex. Margins of the valve usually not parallel. Valve gradually broadened toward the center. Dorsal margin strongly reflexed to form capitate, more or less truncate ends. Terminal nodules on ventral margin at the apices of the valve. Striae parallel, 20-25 in 10μ. Length, 10-26μ, Breadth, 2-4μ. Length-to-breadth ratio usually 4:1-6:1.

This species differs from *Eunotia nymanniana* Grun. and *E. fallax* A. Cl. in that in this species the frustules in valve view are more arcuate, and the length-to-breadth ratio is less. The ends of the valve are more rounded and less angular than in *E. nymanniana* Grun. and much more distinct from the rest of the valve than in *E. fallax* A. Cl.

Type locality. — In Gallia.

U. S. distribution. — GEOGRAPHICAL: New England States, Middle Atlantic States, Southeastern States, Gulf Coast States, South Central States, East Central States. ECOLOGICAL: Often found associated with mosses in acid water of low mineral content. Also found in bogs, springs, and small streams.

38. **Eunotia rabenhorstii** var. **monodon** Grun.   PL. 13, FIG. 19

Eunotia rabenhorstii var. *monodon* Grun. *in* V. H., Syn. Diat. Belgique, pl. 35, fig. 12B. 1881.

Dorsal margin of the valve almost parallel to the ventral margin except for an abrupt swelling at the center of the valve. At the ends the dorsal margin reflexed to form the broadly capitate apices. Ventral margin concave, swollen near the ends. Terminal nodules distinct, at the ends of the valve, extending upward along the apices. Striae parallel, 12 in 10μ at the center, to 17 in 10μ at the ends. Length, 20-30μ. Breadth, at the broadest position, 6-8μ.

Type locality. — Brazil?: Bresil.

U. S. distribution. — Geographical: Only known from the Savannah River, Aiken County, South Carolina. Ecological: This is a river low in mineral content but eutrophic in general characteristics.

39. **Eunotia gibbosa** Grun. var. **gibbosa**   PL. 14, FIG. 1

Eunotia gibbosa Grun. *in* V. H., Syn. Diat. Belgique, pl. 35, fig. 13. 1881.

Valve strongly bilobed with a more or less symmetrical appearance. Both dorsal and ventral margins strongly undulate. Ends wedge-shaped and rounded, in some specimens somewhat rostrate. Terminal nodules large, on the ventral margin of the wedge-shaped ends. Striae parallel in the center, radiate at the ends; short striae sometimes irregularly present on the dorsal margin. Striae near the ventral margin often interrupted to form a clear line. Striae, 10-12 in 10μ at the center, more numerous at the ends, sometimes 16 in 10μ. Length, 23-50μ. Breadth, 11-16μ at widest part. Length-to-breadth ratio at the lobes, usually 2:1-3:1.

Type locality. — Uncertain.

U. S. distribution. — Geographical: This species has been recorded in the United States only from the Adirondack Mountains, New York.

40. **Eunotia meisteri** Hust. var. **meisteri**   PL. 14, FIG. 2

Eunotia meisteri Hust. *in* Pasch., Süssw.-Fl. Mitteleuropas, Heft 10, Aufl. 2, p. 179, fig. 230. 1930.

Ventral margin straight or only slightly arched, undulate or smooth. Dorsal margin strongly convex, giving the valve a swollen appearance; strongly reflexed at the ends to produce a capitate appearance. Ends of the valve capitate, slightly rounded or truncate at the apices. Terminal nodules distinct, on the ventral margin near the apices of the valve. Striae parallel at the center, radiate about the terminal nodules at the ends. Striae, about 21 in 10μ. Length, 12-16μ. Breadth, 3-4μ.

This species can be differentiated from *Eunotia microcephala* in that the striae are radiate rather than parallel over the terminal nodules. Also *E. microcephala* is much more slender in appearance than *E. meisteri*.

Type locality. — Überrieselten Felsen in der Sächsischen Schweiz.

U. S. distribution. — Geographical: Middle Atlantic States; South Carolina, Tennessee, Montana. Ecological: Prefers acid water.

41. **Eunotia microcephala** Krasske *ex* Hust. var. **microcephala**
PL. 14, FIG. 3

Eunotia microcephala Krasske *ex* Hust. *in* Rabh., Kryptog.-Fl. Deutschland, vol. 7(2), no. 2, p. 290, figs. 756a-b. 1932.

Ventral margin undulate, more or less concave at the center, slightly swollen toward the ends. Dorsal margin strongly convex in the middle, without undulations. Ends protracted, capitate, roundly cut off at the apices. Terminal nodules on the ventral margin at the apices of the valve. Striae parallel—not radiate—about the terminal nodules. Striae, 18-22 in 10μ. Length, 9-15μ. Breadth, 2-3μ.

This species differs from *Eunotia meisteri* in its undulate ventral margin; whereas the ventral margin in *E. meisteri* is smooth or only very slightly undulate, never concave at the center of the valve. It differs in shape from *E. perpusilla* in its strongly convex, smooth dorsal margin. A definitive characteristic of this species, which separates it from many of the small *Eunotias*, is that the striae are parallel or almost parallel—not radiate—about the terminal nodules.

Type locality. — Alps, Stubachtale; in moors and swamps among liverworts and algae.

U. S. distribution. — GEOGRAPHICAL: Pennsylvania, North Carolina, Tennessee. ECOLOGICAL: This species seems to prefer living among mosses in oligotrophic or dystrophic cool water.

42. **Eunotia trinacria** Krasske var. **trinacria** PL. 14, FIG. 4

Eunotia trinacria Krasske, Bot. Arch., 27:349, fig. 1. 1929.

Valve triangular in appearance. Ventral margin straight. Dorsal margin convex, pointed at the center of the valve to produce a triangular appearance. Ends rounded, not separated from the main body of the valve. Terminal nodule on ventral margin, close to the apices of the valve. Striae a little closer at the ends than at the center of the valve. Striae, 17-22 in 10μ. Cleve-Euler (1953a, p. 103) gives 18-30 in 10μ. Length, 7-15μ. Hustedt (1932, p. 285) states that the length may be 4-40μ. Breadth, 2-3μ.

Type locality. — Charakterform überrieselter Felsen des Elbsandsteingebirges: . . . und ziemlich häufig im Priessnitzgrund.

U. S. distribution. — GEOGRAPHICAL: Middle Atlantic States; California. ECOLOGICAL: Prefers cool, somewhat acid water.

42. **Eunotia trinacria** var. **undulata** Hust. PL. 14, FIG. 5

Eunotia trinacria var. *undulata* Hust. in Pasch., Süssw.-Fl. Mitteleuropas, Heft 10, Aufl. 2, p. 176, fig. 222. 1930.

This variety differs from the nominate variety of the species in that the ends are clearly defined, capitate-truncate in shape. The dorsal margin, as in the nominate variety, is pointed at the center of the valve, but differs in that the margin is slightly undulate producing a wavy appearance. Striae and general proportions as in the species. Length-to-breadth ratio usually greater than in the species.

This taxon is clearly separated from *Eunotia microcephala* var. *tridentata* by the ventral margin, which is smooth and not thickened or undulated.

Type locality. — An nassen Felsen in der sächsischen Schweiz.

U. S. distribution. — Geographical: Pennsylvania. Ecological: Prefers cool, somewhat acid water.

43. Eunotia perpusilla Grun. var. perpusilla   pl. 14, fig. 6

Eunotia perpusilla Grun. *in* V. H., Syn. Diat. Belgique, pl. 34, fig. 31. 1881.

Ventral margin slightly swollen near each apex, giving the margin an undulate appearance. Siliceous wall appears to be thicker over each swelling than is characteristic of the rest of the valve. Dorsal margin slightly undulate, number of undulations varies. Ends distinctly separated from the rest of the valve; much narrower, may be slightly capitate. Terminal nodules distinct but small. Striae, 16-20 in 10μ. Length, 16-20μ. Breadth, 3-4μ.

The nomenclature of this species has been discussed by Patrick (1958, pp. 7-8).

Type locality. — Uncertain, Belgium.

U. S. distribution. —Geographical: New England States; Montana. Ecological: Found in cool, acid water of low mineral content.

44. Eunotia perminuta (Grun.) Patr. var. perminuta   pl. 14, figs. 7-8

Eunotia tridentula var.? *perminuta* Grun. *in* V. H., Syn. Diat. Belgique, pl. 34, fig. 29. 1881.
Eunotia perminuta (Grun.) Patr., Not. Nat. Acad. Nat. Sci. Philadelphia, No. 312, p. 7, fig. 6. 1958.

Valve linear; triundulate dorsal margin; broadly rounded ends. Striae, 14-19 in 10 μ. Length, 10-24μ. Breadth, 3-4μ. Length-to-breadth ratio, 3:1-6:1.

Van Heurck (1881, pl. 34, fig. 30) shows a specimen which appears to be slightly undulate on the ventral margin. This, however, is not typical for this taxon.

Eunotia perminuta (Grun.) differs from *E. quaternaria* in the length-to-breadth ratio, the general shape of the valve which is more curved in *E. quaternaria*, and the apices which are much broader in relation to the breadth of the valve than is the case in *E. quaternaria*. Thus the apices do not appear to be distinctly separated from the rest of the valve as is the case in *E. quaternaria*.

This taxon differs from *E. perpusilla* in that the ventral margin is smooth, not undulate. However, in some specimens, it does appear to be slightly thickened near the ends of the valve. The apices are broad and usually are almost as wide as the central portion of the valve, whereas in *E. perpusilla* they are much narrower and distinctly separated from the main portion of the valve.

Type locality. — Uncertain, Belgium.

U. S. distribution. — Geographical: Southeastern States; New York, Montana, Wyoming, Colorado. Ecological: Found in water of low mineral content.

45. **Eunotia quaternaria** Ehr. var. **quaternaria**   pl. 14, fig. 10

Eunotia quinaria Ehr., Phys. Abh. Akad. Wiss. Berlin, for 1841:414, pl. 2(1), fig. 12. 1843.

Eunotia quaternaria Ehr., Phys. Abh. Akad. Wiss. Berlin, for 1841:414, pl. 2(1), fig. 13. 1843.

Eunotia tridentula Ehr., Phys. Abh. Akad. Wiss. Berlin, for 1841:414, pl. 2(1), fig. 14. 1843.

Eunotia tridentula var. *quadridentata* A. Mayer, Denkschr. Bayer. Bot. Ges. Regensburg, 13(N.F. 7):25, pl. 1, fig. 59. 1917.

Ventral margin more or less concave. Dorsal margin convex with three to five undulations. Ends of the valve much narrower than main body of the valve, having a truncate to slightly capitate appearance. Terminal nodules on the ventral margin of the valve at the apices. Striae indistinctly punctate, 10-14 in 10μ. Length, $30\text{-}40\mu$.. Breadth, $6\text{-}9\mu$.

This species is characterized by its convex, undulating dorsal margin and its slightly attenuated rostrate apices.

Patrick (1958, p. 8) has discussed the nomenclature of this species.

Type locality. — [French Guiana], Cayenne.

U. S. distribution. — Geographical: New York, Pennsylvania, Montana, Washington. Ecological: Seems to prefer acid water.

46. **Eunotia bactriana** Ehr. var. **bactriana**   pl. 14, fig. 9

Eunotia bactriana Ehr., Mikrogeol., pl. 16(1), figs. 29-30. 1854.

Ventral margin of the valve concave, somewhat swollen at the ends. Dorsal margin convex with two abrupt swellings, one near each end of the valve. Valve narrows at capitate-truncate ends. Terminal nodules large, at the ends of the valve on ventral margin. Striae parallel, 15-18 in 10μ. Length, $30\text{-}40\mu$. Breadth, $3\text{-}6\mu$.

This species is easily recognized by the two abrupt swellings on the dorsal margin, the capitate-truncate ends, and the large terminal nodules.

Type locality. — N. Sweden, Degernfors; fossil from Bergmehl.

U. S. distribution. — Geographical: New England States; New Jersey, Washington. Ecological: This species seems to prefer cool water of low mineral content.

Names of Taxa reported from the U. S. (fresh water) which could not be verified by a specimen from a public herbarium

Eunotia arcus var. *plicata* (Brun) Hérib. (recorded by Tempère and Peragallo).

Eunotia batavica f. *gamma* Berg (recorded by Berg).

Eunotia camelus f. *dentata* Berg (recorded by Berg).

Eunotia depressa Ehr. (recorded by Ehrenberg).

Eunotia fallax var. *gracillima* Krasske (recorded by Hohn).

Eunotia formica f. *alpha* Berg (recorded by Berg).

Eunotia formica f. *beta* Berg (recorded by Berg).

Eunotia gracilis f. *major* (M. Perag.) Hérib. (recorded by Héribaud).

Eunotia gratella f. *beta* Berg (recorded by Berg).

Eunotia kocheliensis O. Müll. (recorded by Hohn).

Eunotia major f. *compacta* Berg (recorded by Berg).

Eunotia major f. *excelsa* Berg (recorded by Berg).

Eunotia major f. *plectrum* Berg (recorded by Berg).

Eunotia nodosa Ehr. (recorded by Bailey), may be *E. pectinalis* var. *undulata.*

Eunotia paradoxa Ehr. (recorded by Ehrenberg).

Eunotia pectinalis f. *didymodon* (Grun.) Berg (recorded by Berg).

Eunotia praerupta-nana Berg (recorded by Berg).

Eunotia prionotus Ehr. (recorded by Ehrenberg).

Eunotia pseudo-parallela f. *alpha* Berg (recorded by Berg).

Eunotia sphaerula Ehr. (recorded by Ehrenberg).

Eunotia tetraodon f. *minuta* Berg (recorded by Berg).

Names of Taxa reported from the U. S. which were misidentified or for which we cannot find original descriptions.

Eunotia amphioxys Ehr. = *Hantzschia amphioxys* Grun. (recorded by Bailey).

Eunotia cygnus Ehr. according to Mills probably an *Epithemia* (recorded by Palmer).

Eunotia elongata Rabh. cannot find original description (recorded by Terry).

Eunotia gibba Ehr. probably *Epithemia gibba* (recorded by Bailey).

Eunotia librile Ehr. probably *Epithemia librile* (*Epithemia turgida* var. *granulata*) (recorded by Bailey).

Eunotia lunula Ehr. according to Habershaw *Epithemia lunula* (recorded by Curtis).

Eunotia ternaria Ehr. cannot find original description.

Taxa Recorded Since 1960[*]

Eunotia lunaris var. *subarcuata* (Naeg.) Grun. (recorded by Hohn and Hellerman, 1963).

Eunotia robusta var. *diadema* (recorded by Thomasson, 1962).

Eunotia torula Hohn (recorded by Hohn, 1961).

Genus **Desmogonium** Ehr.

Ehr. *in* Schomburgk, Reisen Britisch—Guiana Jahren 1840-1844, vol. 3, p. 539.   1848.

Frustules rectangular in girdle view; often forming more or less zigzag filaments. Valve slightly curved, symmetrical to the transverse axis. Terminal nodules distinct on the ventral margin of the valve, variable in size. Jelly pore usually evident at both ends of the valve. Short, small spines evident on both margins of the valve.

This genus is closely related to the genus *Eunotia* from which it mainly differs in its manner of growth and the presence of short spines on both margins of the valve.

This genus is very common in the tropics, in strongly acid water.

Type species. — Desmogonium guianense Ehr.

1. **Desmogonium rabenhorstianum** var. **elongatum** Patr.

PL. 14, FIG. 15

Desmogonium rabenhorstianum var. *elongatum* Patr., Not. Nat. Acad. Nat. Sci. Philadelphia, No. 59, p. 3, figs. 1-3.   1940.

Valve very long, narrow, with large swollen ends. The valve is slightly curved. Apices rounded to slightly wedge-shaped. Terminal nodules distinct on the ventral margin of the swollen end. Jelly pores apparent. Striae distinctly punctate, fine. Striae, 16-19 in 10μ. Marginal spines in the valve, about 5 in 10μ. Length, $140\text{-}240\mu$. Breadth, $5\text{-}7\mu$.

This variety is distinguished from the nominate variety by its great length and broadly swollen, rounded ends. It differs from *Desmogonium kurtiana* (Grun.) Patr. by the shape of the ends of the valve and its great length.

Type locality. — "In irrigation ditch below Lagòa Poranga. Bucu, For-

---

[*] See page 671 for list of additional taxa recorded since 1960.

taleza, Drouet 1506, 1507" [Ceará, Brazil]. (*Holotype*—A-G.C. 25416a, Patrick, 1940.)

U. S. distribution. — Geographical: Florida. Ecological: Seems to prefer warm somewhat dystrophic water.

Genus **Actinella** Lewis nom. cons. non Persoon   1807

Lewis, Proc. Acad. Nat. Sci. Philadelphia, 15:343.   1864.
Tibiella Bessey, Trans. American Micro. Soc., 21:77.   1899.

Frustules solitary or forming star-shaped colonies by the attachment of the smaller ends of the frustules. In girdle view frustules subcuneate or linear, often with margins slightly concave in the middle portion. Valve with one apex much larger than the other. Terminal nodules present. A jelly pore present near one or both apices. Valve distinctly striated. Short spines present on the margins of the valve.

The species of this genus are most easily distinguished from each other by the shape of the apices of the valve.

This genus seems to be most closely related to the genera *Desmogonium* and *Eunotia.*

The species of this genus are usually found in acid water. Most of the species are found in semitropical or tropical waters. The type species of the genus is an exception.

Type species. — *Actinella punctata* Lewis.

1. **Actinella punctata** Lewis var. **punctata**   pl. 14, fig. 14

Actinella punctata Lewis, Proc. Acad. Nat. Sci. Philadelphia, 15:343, figs. 5a-c.
    1863.
Tibiella punctata (Lewis) Patr., Not. Nat Acad. Nat. Sci. Philadelphia, No. 28,
    p. 10.   1939.

Frustules forming star-shaped colonies. In girdle view frustules linear, slightly cuneate with one end much more swollen than the other. Valve linear, arcuate; one end very swollen, with a terminal indentation which resembles the end of the tibia bone. Valve gradually tapers to the other end which is rounded, slightly swollen. Terminal nodules on the ventral margin. Jelly pores present. Striae parallel at the center of the valve, becoming radiate at the apices. Small spines evident on the margins of the valve. Striae, 15-17 in 10μ. Length, $65\text{-}100\mu$. Breadth in middle portion of the valve, $4\text{-}6\mu$.

Type locality. — U. S. A., New Hampshire, Saco Pond, on the surface of mud. (*Lectotype*—A-Feb. 2372, Patrick.)

U. S. distribution. — Geographical: New England States, Middle Atlantic States, Southeastern States. Ecological: Seems to prefer bogs and ponds in water high in humates (dystrophic).

Subfamily PERONIOIDEAE

Hust. *in* Pasch., Süssw.-Fl. Mitteleuropas, Heft 10, Aufl. 2, p. 165. 1930.

Frustules in girdle view and valve view wedge-shaped without intercalary bands or septa. A narrow pseudoraphe extending the length of the valve. Raphe short, present near each apex of one valve, and on the other valve may be present near both apices, or very rudimentary. A single genus *Peronia* is included in this book.

Genus **Peronia** Bréb. & Arn. nom. cons. non (De la Roche in) Redouté 1812

Bréb. & Arn. *ex* Kitton, Quart. Jour. Micr. Sci., New Ser., 8:16. 1868.

Frustules in girdle view wedge-shaped, without intercalary bands or septa. Valve linear-wedge-shaped with rounded apices. On one valve short raphe extending from each apex; no true central nodule present. between the median ends of the raphe a clear linear area. The other valve with a linear pseudoraphe, sometimes a very short raphe extending from one apex, maybe hardly evident. Striae parallel, absent from the apices. Indistinct "costae-like" striae sometimes present. Valve asymmetrical to the transverse axis.

Type species. — *Gomphonema fibula* Bréb. *ex* Kütz. [= *Peronia fibula* (Bréb. *ex* Kütz.) Ross.]

1. **Peronia fibula** (Bréb. *ex* Kütz.) Ross var. **fibula**   PL. 14, FIG. 13

Gomphonema fibula Bréb. *ex* Kütz., Sp. Alg., p. 65. 1849.
Peronia erinacea Bréb. & Arn. *ex* Kitton, Quart. Jour. Micr. Sci., New Ser., 8:16. 1868.
Meridion erinaceum (Bréb. & Arn.) H. L. Sm., Spec. Typ. 239. 1874.
Sceptroneis fibula (Bréb.) Elm., Univ. Nebraska Stud., 21(1/4):47, pl. 2, figs. 51-53. 1922.
Peronia fibula (Bréb. *ex* Kütz.) Ross, Ann. Mag. Nat. Hist., Ser. 12, 9:78. 1956.

Frustules in girdle view wedge-shaped, forming curved or circular filaments. Nodules of the raphe evident. Valve wedge-shaped. Sides of the valve linear, slightly constricted below the rounded end of the broader apex; valve tapering toward the narrow, rounded apex. A true short raphe present at one or both ends of the valve. Terminal nodules very small or indistinct. A very narrow hyaline area present between the two segments of the raphe. If the raphe is at only one end of the valve or absent, this area (pseudoraphe) often very narrow or indistinct. Sometimes it appears as if certain striae which are irregularly spaced are heavier than the others. Striae parallel, 13-20 in 10μ. Length, $16\text{-}70\mu$. Breadth, $2.5\text{-}5\mu$.

The irregular thickening of the striae seems to occur in some valves and not in others.

This taxon is characterized by the shape of the valve and the variable structure of the raphe.

Type locality. — Prope Falaise legit Amic. de Brébisson.

U. S. distribution. — GEOGRAPHICAL: Delaware, South Carolina, Florida, South Dakota, Nebraska. ECOLOGICAL: Fresh, shallow water.

2. **Peronia intermedium** (H. L. Sm.) Patr. comb. nov., var. **intermedium**
PL. 14, FIGS. 11-12

> *Meridion intermedium* H. L. Sm., American Quart. Micr. Jour., 1:12, pl. 3, fig. 2. 1878.

Frustules in girdle view wedge-shaped; striae of variable thickness. Valve clavate with the apices rounded; valve gradually tapering from the broader apex to the opposite narrower apex. Pseudoraphe very indistinct. Striae, 22-24 in 10μ. Striae of irregular thickness which are "costae-like" in appearance irregularly spaced. Length, $25\text{-}75\mu$. Breadth at widest portion of the valve, $6\text{-}10\mu$.

This species differs from *Meridion circulare* by its finer striae and the much less distinct "costae-like" striae which are often hard to see in valve view.

H. L. Smith states that *Peronia erinacea* is related to this species as this species is related to *Meridion circulare*. However, the presence of terminal nodules which are clearly evident in girdle view shows that this species belongs to *Peronia* rather than *Meridion*.

Type locality. — U. S. A., Tennessee, Knoxville. (*Lectotype*—A-H.L.Sm. 238, Patrick.)

U. S. distribution. — GEOGRAPHICAL: Tennessee, Iowa, Michigan.

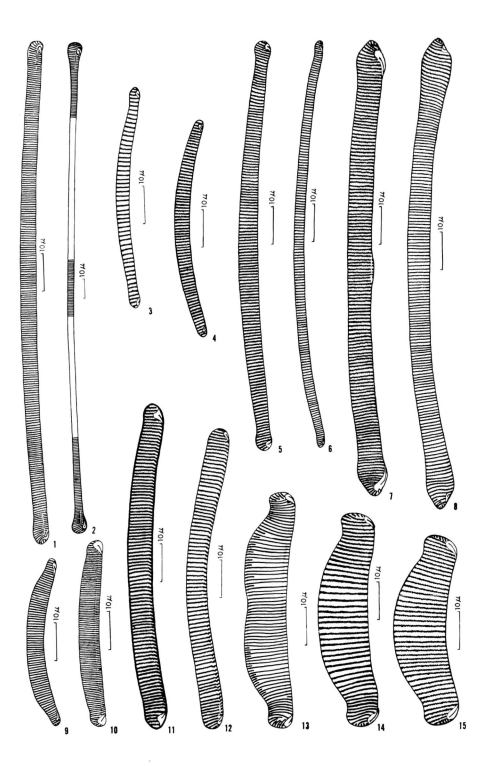

PLATE 11

Fig. 1.   *Eunotia clevei* A-Boyer E-3-18, Finland, Sodankyla.
Fig. 2.   *Eunotia indica* A-G.C. 2182, Pennsylvania, Monroe Co., Pocono Lake.
Fig. 3.   *Eunotia luna* N.Y.B.G.-Ward C-4-16.
Fig. 4.   *Eunotia maior* var. *ventricosa* A-Boyer 778, New Hampshire, Sullivan Co.
Fig. 5.   *Eunotia maior* A-189, W.Sm. 286, Scotland, Braemar.
Fig. 6.   *Eunotia monodon* A-V,H. 548, Connecticut, Wellington, fossil deposit.
Fig. 7.   *Eunotia monodon* var. *constricta* A-G.C. 2557, Florida, Mascotte.
Fig. 8.   *Eunotia zygodon* A-Boyer T-5-17, Alabama, Mobile Co., Citronella.
Fig. 9.   *Eunotia suecica* A-G.C. 2198, Pennsylvania, Pike Co., Shohola Falls.

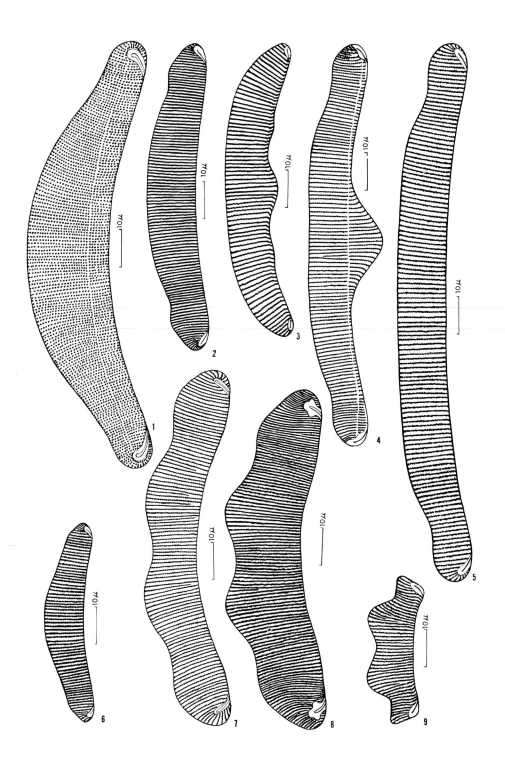

PLATE 12

Fig. 1. *Eunotia triodon* A-V.H. 263, Sweden, Lillhaggjon.
Fig. 2. *Eunotia serra* A-V.H. 274, Norway.
Fig. 3. *Eunotia serra* var. *diadema* A-V.H. 274, Norway.
Fig. 4. *Eunotia obesa* var. *wardii* N.Y.B.G.-Ward C-7-17, Alabama, Mobile, Spring Hill.
Fig. 5. *Eunotia bidentula* A-G.C. 4302a, Connecticut, New Haven Co., Bethany Bog.
Fig. 6. *Eunotia hexaglyphis* A-H.L.Sm. 160, Sierra Nevada, King's River.
Fig. 7. *Eunotia diodon* A-Cl. & Möll. 300, New Zealand, Rotorua Lake.
Fig. 8. *Eunotia pectinalis* A-H.L. Sm. 193, Florida.
Fig. 9. *Eunotia pectinalis* var. *ventricosa* A-G.C. 5624, Nebraska, Kearney Co.
Fig. 10. *Eunotia pectinalis* A-Boyer 929, Connecticut, Fall Mountain.
Fig. 11. *Eunotia pectinalis* var. *undulata* A-V.H. 265, England.
Fig. 12. *Eunotia pectinalis* var. *recta* A-G.C. 2113, Pennsylvania, Monroe Co., Davy's Run.
Fig. 13. *Eunotia pectinalis* var. *minor* A-G.C. 2168, Pennsylvania, Monroe Co., Wier Lake.
Fig. 14. *Eunotia pectinalis* var. *minor* A-V.H. 484, (Great Britain), England.

230

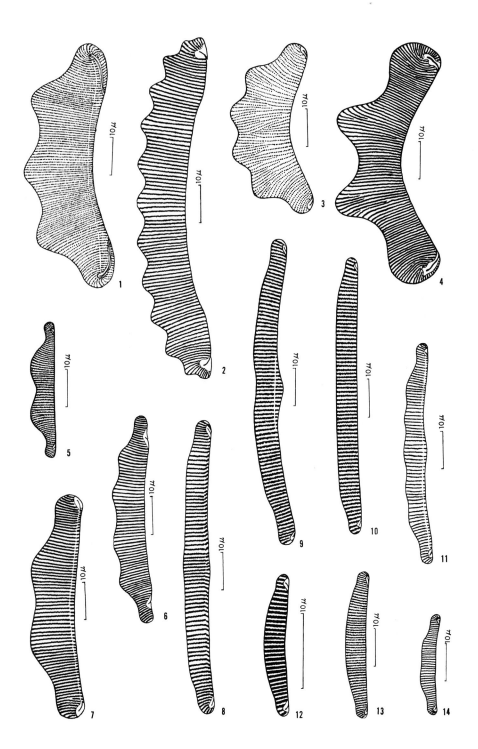

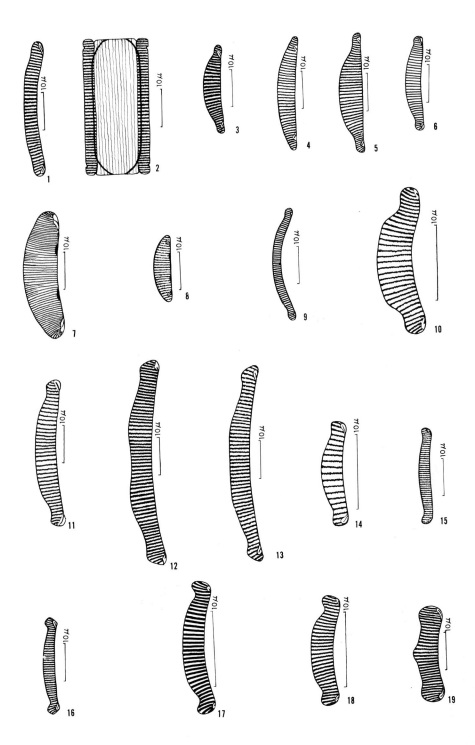

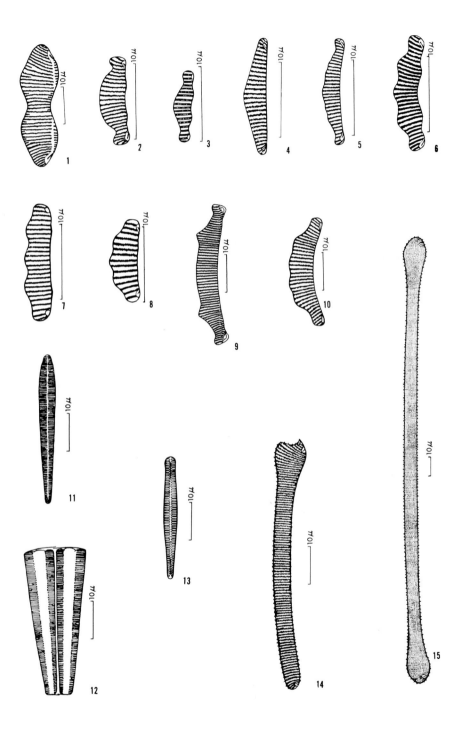

Order **ACHNANTHALES**

Silva *in* Lewin, Physiol. & Biochem. Algae, p. 836. 1962.

Frustules with a fully developed raphe on one valve and an axial space (pseudoraphe) on the apposing valve. In some instances this latter valve has polar rudiments of a raphe, but the branches are short and extend less than half way to the middle portion of the valve.

Family **ACHNANTHACEAE**

Kütz., Bacill., p. 74. 1844. (as *Achnantheae*)

Frustules individual or united in groups of varying number. Most forms are epiphytic. The frustules grow adnate, stalked, or in colonies or chains.

Valves linear, lanceolate, to elliptical, usually bent or arched apically or transapically. Intercalary bands, septa, and pseudosepta rare.

Although the genus *Rhoicosphenia* is rather distinct in this family, being heteropolar to the transverse axis, the line of distinction between the genera *Achnanthes* and *Cocconeis* is more difficult to draw. Almost any characteristic chosen can be shown either to have some exception or to merge. The separation presented here is similar to that used by Cleve (1895, pp. 163, 168) to separate *Cocconeis* from his various other divisions of the *Achnanthes*.

Forms will undoubtedly occur which do not clearly satisfy any one category, but it is hoped that this present division will reduce the number of those doubtful forms to a minimum. Certainly with a separation based primarily on the valve shape and growth habit, which has been common in the past, the area of uncertainty has been considerable.

Subfamily **COCCONEIOIDEAE**

Schütt *in* Engl. & Prantl, Natürl. Pflanzenfam., Teil 1, Abt. 1b, p. 121. 1896. (as *Achnantheae-Cocconeideae*)

Valves elliptical. One valve with fully developed raphe; opposing valve with pseudoraphe. Internal intercalary band often present. Pseudoraphe valve moderately to strongly convex (transversely). Frustules uncommon in girdle view, not distinctly bent (apically). Cells growing individually, adnate to the substrate with raphe valve in contact with the substrate.

Two of the three genera listed by Hustedt (1932, p. 319) under the Cocconeioideae (*Anorthoneis* and *Campyloneis*) are marine and are, therefore, not considered in this work.

Genus **Cocconeis** Ehr.

Ehr., Phys. Abh. Akad. Wiss. Berlin, for 1835:173.   1837.

Valves elliptical; without produced or protracted and distinct ends. Pseudoraphe valve[*1] mostly moderately to strongly convex; raphe valve convex to more nearly flat. Opposing valves usually with different striae pattern and/or structure. Raphe valve[*2] with a marginal and/or submarginal hyaline area (ring). In many cases there is noted a rather broad, more highly refractive band around the margin of the raphe valve which seems to correspond with the presence of an attached intercalary-like band (probably the structure referred to by Cleve as a loculiferous rim). These occasionally may be seen unattached to the valve; sometimes they have rudimentary chamber-like projections. The valve length-to-breadth ratio is usually about 2:1 or less and does not appear to exceed 2.5:1.

The raphe valve striae are usually punctate; those of the pseudoraphe valve vary more from punctate to areolate. On both valves the striae tend to become more or less distinctly curved-radiate toward the extremities, the high point of the curve being in the direction of the valve center.

Members of this genus appear to be epiphytic, particularly on other algae and higher aquatic plants, and grow individually appressed to the substrate, not in chains or on stalks. They are sometimes found in plankton samples but probably only as a result of having been physically separated from their substrate.

Type species. — *Cocconeis scutellum* Ehr. [Designated by Boyer, 1927.]

KEY TO THE SPECIES OF COCCONEIS

1. Pseudoraphe valve with coarse striae—not exceeding 10 in 10μ—which are broken into 1 to 3 large rectangular segments ....[1] *C. disculus*
1. Pseudoraphe valve with finer striae—not less than 14 in 10μ (as measured along pseudoraphe) **2**
    2. Raphe valve striae interrupted one-third to about one-half the distance from axial area to valve margin by a longitudinal hyaline space; central area present, irregularly or laterally expanded **3**
    2. Raphe valve striae may be interrupted marginally or submarginally but not as above. Central area small, orbicular or absent **4**
3. Raphe valve with transversely expanded narrow rectangular central area, longitudinal "line" dissecting striae narrow, well defined ....[4] *C. klamathensis*
3. Raphe valve with small, irregular (subcircular to angular) central area, longitudinal "line" dissecting striae broader, irregular in outline and dissipating toward valve center ....[6] *C. rugosa*

[*1] Abbreviated as: PRV.
[*2] Abbreviated as: RV.

4. Puncta on pseudoraphe valve small along axial area, increasing in size to large coarse puncta toward the valve margin . . . . [5] *C. fluviatilis*

4. Puncta on pseudoraphe valve not varying markedly in size as above 5

5. Pseudoraphe valve highly arched, raphe valve with marginal hyaline area
[2] *C. pediculus*

5. Pseudoraphe valve not highly arched, almost flat; raphe with marginal and submarginal hyaline area . . . . [3] *C. placentula* & vars.

1. **Cocconeis disculus** (Schum.) Cl. var. **disculus**   PL. 15, FIGS. 1-2

Navicula diaculus Schum., Schrift. Phys.-Ökon. Ges. Königsberg, 5:21, pl. 2, fig. 23. 1864.

Cocconeis disculus (Schum.) Cl. *in* Cl. & Jentzsch, Schrift. Phys.-Ökon. Ges. Königsberg, 22:129, 139. 1882.

Valve relatively flat, elliptical or very slightly elongate-elliptical. *Raphe valve* with rim evident at valve margin. Axial area narrow, linear. Central area very small or lacking. Raphe filiform; proximal raphe ends slightly broadened, rounded, and close; distal ends straight. Striae curved radiate; finely but discernably punctate. *Pseudoraphe valve* with linear to linear-lanceolate pseudoraphe. Striae radiate, broken into large coarse dashes of which there are only one to about three comprising each stria. Striae, about 22 in 10μ (RV); 7-9 in 10μ (PRV). Length, 17-25μ. Breadth, 11-16μ.

Characterized best by the large, coarse dashes comprising the striae on the pseudoraphe valve.

This taxon, at its lower size range, may be confused with the usual concept of *Cocconeis diminuta* but the pseudoraphe valve striae do not exceed about 9 in 10μ, whereas on *C. diminuta* the pseudoraphe valve striae are 13-14 in 10μ. The raphe valve striae on *C. diminuta* are also finer.

Without type material it is difficult to delineate *C. diminuta*. Based only on Pantocsek's illustrations and description the diatom that Hustedt has illustrated represents a different diatom. The possibility is great, however, that Pantocsek saw a complete frustule but missed the raphe valve striae, considering the striae on that valve to be the same as on the pseudoraphe valve.

Up to 1960 no records of *C. diminuta* from the United States had been confirmed; therefore, it is not included in this section.

Schumann may have observed *C. disculus* in much the same way as Pantocsek did *C. diminuta*, thus placing it in *Navicula*. Observed material (A-G.C. 11985) from one of the two original localities, Domblitten, shows clearly several frustules of a *Cocconeis* fitting the description of Hustedt. When both valves are present, the diatom does indeed appear like a *Navicula*, for the raphe valve striae are virtually impossible to see.

Type locality. — Europe, Im Kalkmergel des Spirding und von Domblitten.

U. S. distribution. — Geographical: Florida, Iowa. Ecological: Reported from springs and lakes; insufficiently known.

2. Cocconeis pediculus Ehr. var. pediculus   pl. 15, figs. 3-4

Cocconeis pediculus Ehr., Infusionsthierchen, p. 194, pl. 21, fig. 11. 1838.
Cocconeis communis Heib., Consp. Crit. Diat. Danicarum, p. 98. 1863. (*pro parte*)

Valve strongly arched, broadly elliptical or somewhat rhombic-elliptical. Intercalary band (as an inner chamber) occasionally seen. *Raphe valve* with narrow, linear axial area terminating in a small semicircular clear space near the valve extremities. Central area small, circular to somewhat irregular. Raphe filiform, proximal ends close, extending into the central area; distal ends straight, terminating at the small semicircular space near the valve extremities, Striae curved-radiate, finely but distinctly punctate. Striae not extending completely to the valve margin, but interrupted by a narrow, clear marginal area which is continuous around the valve much as a rim. *Pseudoraphe valve* with very narrow, linear pseudoraphe. Central area lacking. Striae also curved radiate, faintly etched as a shallow trough, with distantly placed conspicuous puncta. Puncta arranged in longitudinally undulating rows. Striae, about 20 in 10μ along the axial area, 16-17 in 10μ near the margins (RV); 18 in 10μ along the axial area, 15-16 in 10μ near the margins (PRV). Length, $11\text{-}30\mu$; Hustedt (1930, p. 189) gives 56μ. Breadth, $6\text{-}20\mu$; Hustedt (*loc. cit.*) gives 37μ.

Due to the curvature of the valve the striae count is lower in number near the margins than it is along the axial area.

Type locality. — Germany, Berlin.

U. S. distribution. — Geographical: New England States, Middle Atlantic States, Southeastern States, Gulf Coast States, South Central States, East Central States, West Central States, Lakes States, Plains States; Montana, Wyoming, New Mexico, Idaho, Utah, Arizona, California. Ecological: A widespread eurytopous species; epiphytic on many aquatic plants and other objects, but not often found in large numbers. Considered by some as resistant to moderate amounts of organic pollution; alkaliphil, and salt "indifferent."

3. Cocconeis placentula Ehr. var. placentula   pl. 15, fig. 7

Cocconeis placentula Ehr., Infusionsthierchen, p. 194. 1838.

Valve elliptical to somewhat linear-elliptical. Intercalary band with rudimentary short extensions into the valve cavity often in evidence. *Raphe valve* with very narrow axial area; central area small, more or less oval. Raphe filiform; proximal ends close, distal ends straight, terminating at inner hyaline ring. Striae curved radiate, finely punctate, interrupted near the margin by a hyaline area. A second hyaline area encircles the valve at the margin isolating a short, striate submarginal area. *Pseudoraphe valve* with very narrow, linear pseudoraphe. Central area not well distinguished. Striae also curved-radiate, finely punctate. Puncta forming many close longitudinal rows which are undulate. Striae, 20-23 in 10μ (RV); 24-26 in 10μ (PRV). Length, $10\text{-}70\mu$. Breadth, $8\text{-}40\mu$.

Best distinguished from *Cocconeis pediculus* by the relatively flat valves and the presence of two hyaline areas—one marginal, one submarginal—encircling the raphe valve near the margin instead of one (marginal) area in *C. pediculus*.

Features of the pseudoraphe valve are used to distinguish the subordinate taxa in this complex. The arrangement and nature of the puncta on the pseudoraphe valve, unfortunately for the taxonomist, are quite variable. Geitler (1932, pp. 109-133) has shown differences which appear in the reproductive cycle of some of the varieties, but these are of limited value in the straight morphological approach where culturing is not practical.

The separation used here is based, in part, on the original descriptions of Cleve (1895, pp. 169-170), Van Heurck (1885, p. 133), Hustedt (1930, pp. 189-190; 1933, pp. 347-350), and on personal observations.

Type locality. — Germany, bei Berlin—auf Vaucherien und Lemna-Wurzeln. . . .

U. S. distribution. — GEOGRAPHICAL: New England States, Middle Atlantic States, Southeastern States, Gulf Coast States, South Central States, East Central States, West Central States, Lakes States, Plains States; Montana, Wyoming, New Mexico, Utah, Arizona, Washington, Oregon, California. ECOLOGICAL: A widespread eurytopous species epiphytic on aquatic plants and other objects. More commonly found in circumneutral to alkaline waters (alkaliphil?); apparently salt "indifferent" but not observed in great numbers in slightly brackish waters.

3. **Cocconeis placentula** var. **euglypta** (Ehr.) Cl.   PL. 15, FIG. 8

Cocconeis euglypta Ehr., Mikrogeol., pl. 34(6 A), fig. 2. 1854.
Cocconeis placentula var. *euglypta* (Ehr.) Cl., K. Svenska Vet.-Akad. Handl., Ny Földj, 27(3):170. 1895.[91]

Striae on pseudoraphe valve broken into a series of two to four (very large forms with five) conspicuous "dashes" forming as many irregular

---

[91] This volume was received by the British Museum (Natural History) and the Academy of Natural Sciences in 1896.

longitudinal hyaline spaces or ribs; also coarser than the nominate variety. *Raphe valve* as in the nominate variety. Striae, 19-23 in 10μ (RV); 19-20 in 10μ (PRV). Length, 10-50μ. Breadth, 8-30μ.

The length-to-breadth ratio in this variety often appears greater than that of variety *lineata*. At present it is difficult to say whether or not this is a constant feature. See discussion under variety *lineata* for further comment on this taxon.

Ehrenberg reported this diatom (as *C. euglypta*) in 1853, but simply listed it as new without a description The earliest valid publication I can find is, as listed above, in his 1854 work.

Type locality. — Florida; Dunkelbraunes sandiges Uferland des Salakchopko [U.S.A.].

U. S. distribution. — Geographical: New England States, Middle Atlantic States, Southeastern States, Gulf Coast States, South Central States, East Central States, West Central States, Lakes States, Plains States; Montana, Utah, Arizona, Oregon, California. Ecological: As the nominate variety.

3. **Cocconeis placentula** var. **lineata** (Ehr.) V. H.   pl. 15, figs. 5-6

> *Cocconeis lineata* Ehr., Phys. Abh. Akad. Wiss Berlin, for 1847, pl. 5(1), fig. 10; pl. 5(2), fig. 44. 1849.
> *Cocconeis placentula* var. *lineata* (Ehr.) V. H., Syn. Diat. Belgique, p. 133. 1885.

Striae on pseudoraphe valve fewer in number than in the nominate variety. The puncta are more distant forming several (up to 12) distinct longitudinal undulating hyaline lines. Striae, 19-23 in 10μ (RV); 19-20 in 10μ (PRV). Length, 10-70μ. Breadth, 8-40μ.

Included in this taxon are the forms with distinctly rounded individual puncta as well as those with puncta prolonged into short dashes with the punctum usually defined at the mid point of the "dash." In either case the longitudinal hyaline rows defined are several and the "dashes" are not as long or distinct as in variety *euglypta*.

Type locality. — Europe, Scirocco-Staub von Genua; Scirocco-Staub von Lyon.

U. S. distribution. — Geographical: New England States, Middle Atlantic States, Southeastern States, Gulf Coast States, South Central States, East Central States, West Central States, Lakes States, Plains States; Wyoming, Arizona, Washington, Oregon, California. Ecological: As the nominate variety.

4. **Cocconeis klamathensis** Sov. var. **klamathensis**   pl. 15, figs. 9-10

> *Cocconeis klamathensis* Sov., Trans. American Micr. Soc., 77(2):112, pl. 2, figs. 16-17. 1958.

Valve elliptical, strongly arched. *Raphe valve* with narrow, linear axial area. Central area expanded into a narrow, linear area extending about two-fifths of the valve width. Raphe filiform, slightly broader toward the proximal ends; distal ends straight, subterminal. Striae somewhat curved, radiate, punctate; separated into an outer and inner portion by a convex, narrow hyaline space on both sides about midway to the valve margin. A broad hyaline ring present at the margin. *Pseudoraphe valve* with narrow, linear pseudoraphe. Central area barely evident, circular. Striae curved-radiate except at the center where they are approximately parallel, punctate; the puncta appearing as short dashes. A submarginal line apparent around the valve. Striae, about 20 in 10μ at the valve margins, 24 in 10μ toward the axial area (RV); 26-29 in 10μ (PRV). Length, 15-36μ. Breadth, 13-25μ.

Best distinguished by the intermediate hyaline line on the raphe valve interrupting the striae pattern.

Type locality. — U.S.A., Oregon, Upper Klamath Lake. (*Holotype*— Cal. Acad. Sci.—3464, Sov. 204.9, Sovereign, 1960.)

U. S. distribution. — GEOGRAPHICAL: Oregon, California. ECOLOGICAL: Insufficiently known.

5. **Cocconeis fluviatilis** Wallace var. **fluviatilis**   PL. 15, FIGS. 11-12

> *Cocconeis fluviatilis* Wallace, Not. Nat. Acad. Nat. Sci. Philadelphia, No. 331, p. 2, pl. 1, figs. 2a-b. 1960.

Valve elliptical, relatively flat. *Raphe valve* with narrow, linear axial area. Central area not apparent as such. Raphe filiform; proximal raphe ends close, distal ends terminating at hyaline ring. Striae nearly parallel at mid-valve becoming radiate and curved-radiate near the extremities, finely but distinctly punctate. Striae interrupted submarginally by a rather broad hyaline ring. *Pseudoraphe valve* with narrow, linear pseudoraphe; no central area. Striae coarsely punctate, radiate to curved-radiate near the extremities. Puncta elongate; as a dash toward the margins, becoming smaller and more rounded at the pseudoraphe. Striae, 12 in 10μ at the valve margins; 16 in 10μ along the axial area (both valves). Length, 15-34μ. Breadth, 9-19μ.

Best distinguished by the characteristics of the puncta on the pseudoraphe valve, as described.

Type locality. — U.S.A., South Carolina, Allendale Co., Savannah River (*Holotype*—A-G.C. 3872b, Wallace, 1960).

U. S. distribution. — GEOGRAPHICAL: Middle Atlantic States, Southeastern States, Gulf Coast States; California. ECOLOGICAL: Although found most commonly in fresh water of coastal area streams, it appears to be tolerant of some salt intrusion for it is sometimes found in appreciable numbers in the slightly brackish portions of these streams.

6. Cocconeis rugosa Sov. var. rugosa   PL. 15, FIGS. 13-14

> *Cocconeis rugosa* Sov., Trans. American Micr. Soc., 77(2):112, pl. 3, figs. 34-35. 1958.

Valve elliptical, moderately arched. *Raphe valve* with narrow, linear axial area. Central area small, irregular in shape. Raphe filiform, broadening toward proximal ends which protrude into the central area; distal raphe ends straight, subterminal. Striae curved, radiate, punctate. Puncta interrupted by an irregular hyaline space on either side of the axial area. Broad hyaline ring encircling the valve at the margin. *Pseudoraphe valve* with narrow, linear, or linear-lanceolate pseudoraphe. Central area extremely small or lacking. Striae curved, radiate except few at the center which may be parallel, punctate. Marginal portion of the striae slightly differentiated as a rim-like area. Striae, 14-16 in 10μ at valve margin (mid valve), 18-23 along axial area (RV); about 16 in 10μ at valve margin (mid valve), 20 in 10μ along axial area (PRV). Length, 18-63μ. Breadth, 12-52μ.

Type locality. — U.S.A., Oregon, Emerald Pool (Crater Lake area). (*Holotype*—Cal. Acad. Sci.—3465, Sov. 488.12, Sovereign, 1960.)

U. S. distribution. — GEOGRAPHICAL: Oregon. ECOLOGICAL: Insufficiently known.

Names of Taxa reported from the U. S. (fresh water) which could not be verified by a specimen from a public herbarium.

Cocconeis amygdalina (Bréb.) Grun. (recorded by Tempere & Peragallo and Palmer).
Cocconeis diminuta Pant. (recorded by Sovereign).
Cocconeis thumensis A. Mayer (recorded by Sovereign and Young *in* Hohn).
Cocconeis limbata Ehr. (recorded by Ehrenberg).
Cocconeis pellucida Hantz. (recorded by Gray and Boyer).
Cocconeis pinnata Greg. (recorded by Boyer).
Cocconeis distans Greg. (recorded by Galtsoff).
Cocconeis scutellum f. *parva* Grun. *in* V. H. (recorded by Ward).
Cocconeis transversalis Greg. (recorded by Ward).

Names of taxa reported from the U. S. which are of uncertain application.

Cocconeis mormonorum Ehr. (recorded by DeToni).
Cocconeis oblonga Kütz. (recorded by Ehrenberg).
Cocconeis praetexta Ehr. (recorded by Ehrenberg and Eddy).
Cocconeis undulata Ehr. (recorded by Ehrenberg).

Taxa Recorded Since 1960

Cocconeis delalineata Hohn (recorded by Hohn, 1961).

Cocconeis delapunctata Hohn (recorded by Hohn, 1961).

Cocconeis diminuta Pant. (recorded by Stoermer, 1962 and Hohn, 1961).

Cocconeis inusitatus Hohn (recorded by Hohn, 1961).

Cocconeis patrickiae Reim. (recorded by Reimer, 1962, not *ii* as originally published).

Subfamily **ACHNANTHOIDEAE**

Schütt *in* Engl. & Prantl, Natürl. Pflanzenfam., Teil 1, Abt. 1b, p. 120. 1896. [as *Achnanthoideae—Achnantheae*]

Frustules in girdle view more or less bent (apically) as a shallow "U" or "V" shape. Cells growing more commonly as stipitate epiphytes or in chains. Valves mostly linear or lanceolate, occasionally elliptical. One valve with fully developed raphe, opposing valve with pseudoraphe or with a rudimentary raphe near the valve ends. Intercalary band occasionally present but not common. Pseudoraphe valve flat or only slightly convex (transversely).

Genus **Achnanthes** Bory

Bory, Dict. Class. Hist. Nat., 1:79-80. 1822.

Frustules in girdle view rectangular with a more or less pronounced bend at the center making this view somewhat "U" or "V" shaped. Valves mostly lanceolate or linear-lanceolate but may occasionally become linear-elliptical or elliptical. Valves may be moderately convex but more often are only slightly convex to essentially flat surfaces. Opposing valves usually with similar striae pattern but some may be markedly different (e.g., *Achnanthes clevei* Grun.). Some taxa are distinguished by the presence of a horseshoe-shaped area on one side of the pseudoraphe valve. When present, this is diagnostic for the genus. Raphe and pseudoraphe straight and median, marginal or submarginal, diagonal and/or sigmoid. Striae coarsely to finely, singly to doubly punctate (or areolate), or puncta not apparent with the light microscope. Striae mostly radiate or parallel. Those which are curved-radiate may have the high point of the curve away from the direction of the valve center (*A. peragalli* Brun & Hérib. *in* Hérib., RV) or toward the direction of the valve center [*A. flexella* (Kütz.) Brun, PRV].

Members of this genus are more commonly stipitate or adherent in groups although some are probably individual epiphytic or free-living frustules.

With this separation of *Achnanthes* from *Cocconeis* it would become necessary to transfer several taxa presently in *Cocconeis* to *Achnanthes*. In the present work this is necessary for only one fresh-water taxon report confirmed from the United States (*Cocconeis hustedtii* Krasske).

Only one subgenus is considered in this work—*Achnanthidium*. The concept of this subgenus, however, is altered from that presented by either Hustedt (1933, pp. 418, 419) or Cleve-Euler (1953b, pp. 15, 49), in that it encompasses their interpretation of the subgenera *Microneis* and most of *Achnanthidium*. Most of the species considered under the genus *Eucocconeis* are also included in the subgenus *Achnanthidium* as defined. The presence of a sigmoid raphe, although distinct and extreme in some forms does not seem to be diagnostic for a separate group. Nearly all degrees of raphe curvature can be noted from the distinctly sigmoid raphe of *A. flexella* to the subtle curvature seen in *A. exigua*.

With the present interpretation, the species originally placed in *Achnanthidium* by Kützing (i.e., *A. microcephalum, A. delicatulum*) are again a part of that category. One of these species has been selected as the type—*A. microcephalum*.

The subgenus *Achnanthes* represented by brackish- to marine-water forms is not represented in the taxa presented here. It is mainly characterized by the type and arrangement of the areolae in double rows. Thus, the valve has an alternating series of broad and narrower transverse ribs. The fine structure of the areolae may also prove to be diagnostic.

The species *A. brevipes* was placed by P. T. Cleve (1895, p. 193), Hustedt (*op. cit.*, pp. 424, 425), and others in *Achnanthidium;* but it appears that the valve structure is quite similar to that of *A. longipes*, there being areolae in double rows. These can be seen on *A. brevipes* with the light microscope. They are more distinct on the pseudoraphe valve than on the raphe valve. Accordingly *A. brevipes* would be included in the subgenus *Achnanthes*. Helmcke and Krieger (1961, p. 23) point out the similarities in valve fine structure between *A. longipes* and *A. brevipes*.

The species *A. coarctata, A. temperei,* and *A. inflata* are somewhat intermediate in character and it is with some reservation that I place them in this subgenus. The axial area of the pseudoraphe valve is eccentric in these three taxa just as in the subgenus *Achnanthes*. Nevertheless, the puncta (or areolae), although rather large, do not appear to be of the same type as is characteristic of those in the subgenus *Achnanthes*, nor do they appear in double rows separated by a partition. Further study may indicate that a separate subgeneric classification is warranted for species of this kind.

Type species. — *Echinella stipitata* Lyngb. [according to Boyer, who considers it as possibly *A. brevipes* Ag.].

Achnanthes subgenus ACHNANTHIDIUM (Kütz.) Hust.

Kütz., Bacill., p. 75. 1844.

Striae singly (rarely doubly) punctate, lineate or undifferentiated as seen in the light microscope. In a few cases the striae become quite coarsely punctate (areolate?), but, if so, the areolae do not appear in double rows.

I am designating the type for this subgenus as follows:

Type species. — Achnanthidium microcephalum Kütz. [= *A. microcephala* (Kütz.) Grun.]

KEY TO THE SPECIES OF ACHNANTHES

1. Pseudoraphe valve with a horseshoe-shaped clear area on one side in the middle portion of the valve 2
1. Pseudoraphe valve without such an area 11
    2. Striae on both valves about the same in number; raphe valve striae, not exceeding about 22 in 10μ at the valve extremities 3
    2. Raphe valve striae noticeably finer than those on pseudoraphe valve; raphe valve striae, about 28 in 10μ near the valve extremities 9
3. Horseshoe-shaped area (PRV) narrower at valve margin than at axial area, striae parallel or very slightly radiate . . . . [27] *A. chilensis* var. *subaequalis*
3. Horseshoe-shaped area (PRV) wider at valve margin than at axial area, striae moderately to strongly radiate 4
    4. Valves elliptical; margins distinctly convex throughout 5
    4. Valves elongate; margins not distinctly convex throughout, straight or concave in some places 6
5. Raphe valve with diamond-shaped central area; striae, 15-18 in 10μ (RV)
                                     [24] *A. lanceolata* var. *omissa*
5. Raphe valve with more transversely expanded central area; striae, 11-14 in 10μ (RV)
                                   [24] *A. lanceolata* (smaller forms)
    6. Valves with broadly rounded somewhat conical apices not distinguished from valve body . . . . [24] *A. lanceolata* (larger forms)
    6. Valves with apices variously distinguished from valve body 7
7. Valves with substrate to rostrate ends . . . . [24] *A. lanceolata* var. *dubia*
7. Valves with distinctly capitate ends . . . . [24] *A. lanceolata* var. *haynaldii*
7. Valves with apiculate ends 8
    8. Raphe valve with large quadrangular central area
                          [24] *A. lanceolata* var. *lanceolatoides*
    8. Raphe valve with diamond-shaped central area . [24] *A. lanceolata* var. *apiculata*
9. Striae on pseudoraphe valve, about 15 in 10μ near the center to 18 in 10μ near the ends; valve ends short, substrate . . . . [26] *A. peragalli* var. *parvula*
9. Striae on pseudoraphe valve, about 17 in 10μ near the center to 20 in 10μ near the ends; valve ends long, rostrate to capitate or apiculate 10
    10. Valve ends protracted, rostrate to capitate . . . . [26] *A. peragalli*
    10. Valve ends narrow, apiculate . . . . [26] *A. peragalli* var. *fossilis*
11. Striae on both valves broken into distinct puncta or areolae 12
11. Striae on one or both valves finely punctate, lineate or appearing solid 16

12. Pseudoraphe central; valve ends narrow, beaked, the beaks curving slightly in opposing directions .... [30] *A. curvirostrum*

12. Pseudoraphe lateral or not apparent in valve view; valve ends neither produced into narrow beaks nor curved in opposite directions 13

13. Valves with parallel or slightly concave margins, pseudoraphe valve with conspicuous terminal nodules .... [29] *A. temperei*

13. Valves with undulate sides, no terminal nodules apparent on pseudoraphe valve .. 14

   14. Valves with convex (tumid) central portion; puncta, not exceeding 12 in 10μ in either valve 15

   14. Valves with slightly constricted middle portion making valve body twice undulate; puncta, 14-18 in 10μ on both valves .... [28] *A. coarctata*

15. Valve margins twice strongly concave forming large, bulbous ends.... [31]*A. inflata*

15. Valve margins not, or only weakly (twice) concave forming large, broadly rounded rostrate ends .... [31] *A. inflata* var. *elata*

   16. Raphe valve with transverse central space reaching both margins, stauroid.. 17

   16. Raphe valve with central area variously shaped including those with a unilateral expansion to the valve margin, but striae present somewhere on one or both sides of central area 23

17. Striae on pseudoraphe valve, not exceeding about 23 in 10μ near the ends and usually coarser at the center 18

17. Striae on pseudoraphe valve finer, 24-27 in 10μ at the center becoming about 30 in 10μ near the ends 22

   18. Valves with protracted, distinctly rostrate to capitate ends 19

   18. Valves with only subtilely distinguished ends or with extremities not at all set off from the valve body 21

19. Valve margins concave at the center of the valve..... [8] *A. exigua* var. *constricta*

19. Valve margins parallel to slightly convex at the center of the valve 20

   20. Striae on raphe valve fine, 30-34 in 10μ .... [8] *A. exigua* var. *heterovalva*

   20. Striae on raphe valve coarser, 24-25 in 10μ .... [8] *A. exigua*

21. Striae on both valves coarse, 14 in 10μ .... *A. stewartii*

21. Striae on both valves finer, 19 or more in 10μ ...... [9] *A. hungarica* var. *hungarica*

   22. Striae distinctly radiate; raphe valve with relatively broad, expanding stauroid area .... [5] *A. affinis*

   22. Striae slightly radiate to parallel, raphe valve with narrow, linear stauroid area (this diatom has a shortened stria at the margins on either side of the central area but they are sometimes difficult to see) .... [2] *A. linearis*

23. Raphe valve with alternately longer and shorter striae at the center of the valve.. 24

23. Raphe valve not as above, central striae of equal length or irregular but not a series of distinctly long and short striae 26

   24. Raphe valve with sigmoid axial area and raphe; pseudoraphe valve with 20-26 striae in 10μ .... [11] *A. flexella*

   24. Raphe valve with straight axial area and raphe; pseudoraphe valve with 10-15 striae in 10μ 25

25. Valves with protracted rostrate ends .... [22] *A. clevei* var. *rostrata*

25. Valves with conical extremities, not produced into rostrate ends..... [22] *A. clevei*

   26. Pseudoraphe valve with axial and central areas uniting into a broad lanceolate space occupying one-half or more of the total valve width at the center 27

   26. Pseudoraphe valve with linear to narrow lanceolate pseudoraphe (occupying less than one-half of total valve width at the center) and/or distinct central area 31

27. Valves more or less elliptical, raphe valve with distinct central area 28
27. Valves elongate, raphe valve with axial and central areas uniting into a lanceolate
space (sometimes with a unilateral extension of the central area to the margin) . 30
    28. Striae at the center of the valve, 17-22 in 10μ, indistinctly punctate or
    lineate 29
    28. Striae at the center of the valve, about 27 in 10μ, not noticeably punctate
    or lineate . . . . [12] A. marginulata
29. Raphe valve striae, 17-19 in 10μ at the center of the valve becoming 20-22 in
10μ near the ends . . . . [16] A. hustedtii
29. Raphe valve striae finer, 22-24 in 10μ at the center of the valve becoming about
28 in 10μ near the ends . . . . [13] A. levanderi
    30. Central space occupying about two-thirds of the valve width, axial space
    remaining broad toward valve extremities . . . . [15] A. gibberula
    30. Central space extended as unilateral area to valve margin or, if not, occupy-
    ing only about one-half of the valve width; axial space narrowing sharply,
    becoming linear, near valve ends . . . . [25] A. grimmei
31. Raphe valve with single pore off the end of one central stria . . . . [6] A. wellsiae
31. Raphe valve without pore as described above 32
    32. Both valves with unilateral central stauroid area extending from central
    area, distal raphe ends and enclosing axial area curved in opposite directions
                                  [10]A. lapponica var. ninckei
    32. Valves without unilateral area as described above; distal raphe ends and
    enclosing axial area curved in the same direction, straight or indistinct but
    not curved in opposite directions 33
33. Striae on both valves relatively few in number, 10-18 in 10μ, not exceeding 18 in
10μ at any point on the valve face 34
33. Striae on one or both valves not less than 20 in 10μ and always more numerous
than this at some point on the valve surface, 22-40 in 10μ 40
    34. Valves with distinctly produced rostrate to capitate ends 35
    34. Valves lanceolate to elliptical, ends not distinguished from the valve body . . 36
35. Striae broad, frequently subconical with widest part at the valve margin, central
area orbicular or somewhat irregular, but distinct . . . . [23] A. hauckiana var. rostrata
35. Striae narrow, of equal breadth throughout, central area quite small, indistinct
or lacking . . . . [19] A. lemmermanni
    36. Striae on pseudoraphe valve punctate, puncta interrupted on both sides by
    a longitudinal line (clear space) . . . . [21] A. lewisiana
    36. Striae on pseudoraphe valve lineate or appearing smooth, not interrupted
    by longitudinal line (clear space) 37
37. Valves elliptical 38
37. Valves lanceolate . . . . [23] A. hauckiana
    38. Valves small, about $5\text{-}11\mu$ long, $3.5\text{-}5\mu$ wide; raphe valve with small, ovoid
    central area or none at all 39
    38. Valves larger, $14\text{-}17\mu$ long, $7\text{-}8\mu$ wide; raphe valve with narrow rectangular
    central area . . . . [17] A. stewartii
39. Valves with strongly obtuse margins and striae appearing smooth or, under
optimum lighting, very finely lineate . . . . [23] A. hauckiana (smaller forms)
39. Valves with slightly convex margins and distinctly lineate striae . . . . [20] A. pinnata
    40. Raphe valve with rather large expanding central area bordered by several
    shortened striae 41
    40. Both valves with small, central area, or none at all 42

41. Pseudoraphe valve with large central area tapering gradually into abbreviated pseudoraphe; and with striae, 24-26 in 10µ ......[14] *A. sublaevis* var. *crassa*

41. Pseudoraphe valve with linear to linear-lanceolate pseudoraphe; no distinct central area; and with striae, 12-14 in 10µ ....[18] *A. saxonica*

    42. Valves with parallel sides and rounded—not attenuated or otherwise contoured—extremities ....[2] *A. linearis* var. *pusilla*

    42. Valves with slightly to moderately convex sides, slightly attenuated or with ends at least somewhat distinguished from the valve body 43

43. Striae on both valves, about 20 in 10µ at the center of the valve, indistinctly lineate or indistinctly punctate 44

43. Striae on both valves, 24 to 30 in 10µ at the center of the valve, not noticeably punctate or lineate 45

    44. Central striae radiate, distal raphe ends appearing straight.......[3] *A. nollii*

    44. Central striae parallel, distal raphe ends curved subterminally in the same direction ....[7] *A. deflexa*

45. Raphe valve with striae, about 24 in 10µ just above and below the central area, becoming 29-30 in 10µ at the ends 46

45. Raphe valve with striae, 28-30 in 10µ just above and below central area, becoming 34-38 in 10µ at the ends 47

    46. Valves short, less than 10µ in length, striae slightly finer (30 in 10µ) near extremities of pseudoraphe valve ....[2] *A. linearis* f. *curta*

    46. Valves, 10-20µ long; striae near extremities of pseudoraphe valve, about 26 in 10µ ....[2] *A. linearis*

47. Striae on pseudoraphe valve fine, 30 in 10µ at the center of the valve to about 38 in 10µ near the ends and slightly to moderately radiate.......[4] *A. minutissima*

47. Striae on pseudoraphe valve coarser, about 26 in 10µ at the center of the valve to about 32 in 10µ near the ends and very slightly radiate.......[1] *A. microcephala*

1. Achnanthes microcephala (Kütz.) Grun. var. microcephala

PL. 16, FIGS. 1-2

Achnanthidium microcephalum Kütz., Bacill., p. 75, pl. 3, figs. 13, 19. 1844.
Achnanthes microcephala (Kütz.) Grun. *in* Cl. & Grun., K. Svenska Vet.-Akad. Handl., Ny Földj, 17(2):22. 1880.

Valve linear-lanceolate with subcapitate to capitate ends. *Raphe valve* with narrow, linear axial area and small central area of variable shape. Central area usually about one-half the valve breadth at the center. Raphe filiform; proximal ends not noticeably distinctive; distal ends indistinct, but appearing to curve slightly in the same direction. Striae slightly radiate, becoming more numerous toward the ends; central striae sometimes slightly broader than the remaining striae and spaced to give the impression of a small stauros; puncta not apparent. *Pseudoraphe valve* with narrow, linear pseudoraphe; central area small or lacking. Striae character as on the raphe valve slightly radiate or approaching parallel; only slightly coarser than those of the raphe valve. Striae, 28 in 10µ near the center, becoming about 34 in 10µ toward the ends (RV); 26 in 10µ near the center, becoming about 32 in 10μ toward the ends (PRV). Length, 8-26μ. Breadth, 2-3μ.

Distinguished from the more capitate forms of *Achnanthes minutissima* by the coarser striae on the pseudoraphe valve. In populations observed from this country, the smaller forms of *A. minutissima* seem to lose the distinct end, whereas the end can be distinguished at least to some degree in the very small forms of *A. microcephala*.

This taxon has often been confused with *A. minutissima* and in some cases even with the *A. exilis* of Kützing. Certainly when these populations are mixed, it is no easy task to separate all forms adequately.

At present, I am following the available information from the original description and, generally, the concept of Hustedt and others for this taxon. Examination of Kützing's original material may help to confirm or revamp this concept.

A careful study of the actual amplitude of variation in these taxa should also prove very helpful.

Type locality. — Uncertain, . . . Nordhausen! Hamburg! Schleusingen! Halle! Stuttgart! Thun! Triest! Genua! Falaise, Berlin. . . .

U. S. distribution. — GEOGRAPHICAL: New England States, Middle Atlantic States, East Central States, Lakes States; Texas, Nebraska, Arizona, California. ECOLOGICAL: Apparently rather eurytopic, but not as commonly encountered as *A. minutissima*. Found mostly at higher pH values 6.5-8.5 and probably to be considered as an alkaliphil.

2. **Achnanthes linearis** (W. Sm.) Grun. var. **linearis**   PL. 16, FIGS. 3-4

Achnanthidium lineare W. Sm., Ann. Mag. Nat. Hist., Ser. 2, 15:8, pl. 1, fig. 9. 1855.

Achnanthes linearis (W. Sm.) Grun. *in* Cl. & Grun., K. Svenska Vet.-Akad. Handl., Ny Följd, 17(2):23. 1880.

Valve linear or slightly linear-elliptical with broad, obtusely rounded extremities, sometimes subtilely distinguished as broad, subrostrate ends. *Raphe valve* with narrow, essentially linear, axial area which narrows slightly near valve extremities; central area usually narrow and stauroid but varying according to the length of one or two central striae. Raphe filiform; proximal raphe ends not protruding into the central area; distal ends indistinct but apparently straight. Striae slightly radiate, not noticeably punctate or lineate. *Pseudoraphe valve* with narrow, linear pseudoraphe. Central area lacking or only a small, linear elliptical space. Striae as on the raphe valve. Striae, about 24-26 in 10μ at the center, becoming about 28-29 in 10μ toward the ends (RV); 23-26 in 10μ at the center, becoming 28-29 in 10μ at the ends (PRV). Length, 10-20μ. Breadth, 2.5-3.5μ.

Best distinguished from *Achnanthes microcephala* by its more linear shape, less distinct ends, and slightly coarser striae; from *A. affinis* by its shape and the lack of a complete stauros.

There are several small *Achnanthes* species (especially *A. linearis, A. affinis, A. microcephala,* and *A. minutissima*) which all appear very similar upon casual observation. Rather great care must be taken to keep them separate when they appear as a mixed population. There is a need for continued taxonomic and morphological work in this area to determine the accuracy of the present separation.

The diatom illustrated by Hustedt (1933, p. 378, text figs. 821a-b) is not typical of the shape this diatom assumes in the collections I have seen from the United States; neither is it typical of the specimens from the Lasswade material (A-Feb. 3120, Feb. 3447, J. W. Bail. 1020, and W. Sm. 218). The later illustrations of Hustedt *in* A. S. *Atlas* (1937d, pl. 412, figs. 19-23) are much closer to the Lasswade material of Greville.

Type locality. — Uncertain. Fresh water. Fountain of Vaucluse; Lasswade near Edinburgh. . . .

U. S. distribution. — Geographical: Middle Atlantic States; Oregon. Ecological: Apparently pH "indifferent" and halophobe, but little reliable data are available for ecological comment.

2. **Achnanthes linearis** f. **curta** H. L. Sm.   pl. 16, figs. 13-14

Achnanthes linearis f. *curta* H. L. Sm. *in* Boyer, Diat. Philadelphia, p. 59, pl. 16, figs. 16-17. 1916.

Smaller than the nominate variety and with slightly more radiate striae than variety *linearis*. The shape varies from that of the nominate variety to one with a slightly gibbous center. Striae, about 24 in 10μ at the center, becoming about 30 in 10μ at the ends on both valves. Length, 4 to about 8μ. Breadth, 2.4-3μ.

It is quite possible that such populations are degenerative clones of the species incapable of regaining their normal size.

Type locality. — U.S.A., New Jersey, Elm, sides of a greenhouse tank.

U. S. distribution. — Geographical: New Jersey, North Carolina. Ecological: Insufficiently known.

2. **Achnanthes linearis** var. **pusilla** Grun.   pl. 16, figs. 5-6

Achnanthes (*linearis* var.?) *pusilla* Grun. *in* Cl. & Grun., K. Svenska Vet.-Akad. Handl., Ny Följd, 17(2):23. 1880.

Differs in shape and striae number from the nominate variety. Valve with parallel sides and broadly rounded extremities not distinguished from the valve body. Striae slightly coarser than those of variety *linearis*. Striae,

20-23 in 10μ at the center, becoming 26-27 in 10μ toward the ends (RV); 18-22 in 10μ at the center, becoming 26-27 in 10μ toward the ends (PRV). Length, 13-17μ. Breadth, 3-4μ.

Athough I have not seen the type of this taxon, our specimens do agree with those of Nordstedt (A-Cl. & Möll. 186) and of Van Heurck (A-V. H. 140).

Type locality. – Finshőe, Norwegen (Nordstedt).

U. S. distribution. – GEOGRAPHICAL: Pennsylvarria. ECOLOGICAL: Found so far only from small, fast-flowing circumneutral streams in Pennsylvania.

3. **Achnanthes nollii** Bock var. **nollii**   PL. 16, FIGS. 7-8

Achnanthes nollii Bock *in* Bock & Bock, Nachr. Naturw. Mus. Aschaffenburg, 38:54-56, pl. 2, figs. 1-2; pl. 5, figs. 7-9. 1953.

Valve elliptical-lanceolate to linear-lanceolate. Ends varying from obtusely rounded, not set off from valve body (smaller forms) to protracted, subcapitate or capitate (larger forms). *Raphe valve* with narrow axial area, broadening only slightly to form a small longitudinally rhombic central area. Raphe filiform; proximal ends slightly enlarged, distal ends appearing straight. Striae slightly radiate in the middle portion of the valve becoming parallel toward the ends; central striae broader and farther apart than the remaining striae, sometimes one or two striae are shortened; indistinctly lineate. *Pseudoraphe valve* with linear pseudoraphe, sometimes slightly widened at the center, but no distinct central area present. Striae slightly radiate at the center; slightly broader and farther apart than the finer, more parallel striae toward the ends, also indistinctly lineate. A few short interposed striae occasionally noted. Striae, 20-22 in 10μ at the center, becoming about 35 in 10μ toward the ends on both valves. Length, 9-20μ. Breadth, 3.5-5μ.

Type locality. – Germany, Freigerichtsee bei Kahl am Main.

U. S. distribution. – GEOGRAPHICAL: Kentucky. ECOLOGICAL: Insufficiently known. Single record from a relatively hard-water, alkaline (pH 7.6-7.8) stream.

4. **Achnanthes minutissima** Kütz. var. **minutissima**   PL. 16, FIGS. 9-10

Achnanthes minutissima Kütz., Linnaea, 8:578, pl. 16, fig. 54. 1833; Alg. Dec. 8, No. 75. 1833.

Achnanthes minutissima var. *cryptocephala* Grun. *in* V. H., Syn. Diat. Belgique, pl. 27, figs. 41-44. 1880.

Achnanthes minutissima f. *curta* Grun. *in* V. H., Syn. Diat. Belgique, pl. 27, figs. 35-36. 1880.

Valve linear-elliptical with obtusely rounded substrate to capitate ends. *Raphe valve* with narrow, linear axial area and narrow, somewhat irregularly shaped, central area occupying up to about one-half the total width of the valve in the middle portion. Raphe filiform; proximal raphe ends rather close, distal ends curving subtilely in the same direction. Striae slightly to moderately radiate, becoming more numerous toward the ends. One or two shorter striae on either side of the central area sometimes spaced slightly farther apart than the remaining striae. *Pseudoraphe valve* with narrow, linear axial area, slightly broadened in the middle portion of the valve or with an occasional shortened stria at the center, but with no distinct central area as such. Striae character and direction as on the raphe valve. Striae, 30-32 in 10μ at the center, becoming 36-38 in 10μ near the ends (both valves). Length, $5-40\mu$. Breadth, $2-4\mu$.

Very similar to *Achnanthes microcephala*, especially the somewhat capitate forms. Distinguished from *A. microcephala* by the slightly finer and more strongly radiate striae. The central area of *A. minutissima* is mostly somewhat irregular in shape, whereas in *A. microcephala* the central area tends to be more clearly orbicular.

I am in agreement with Hustedt's remark (1933, p. 377) that the separate concept of variety *cryptocephala* is better "aufzugeben," and have, therefore, included it here as part of variety *minutissima*.

In my opinion, the presence of one or two shorter and slightly broader striae on either side of the raphe valve central area is not diagnostic for either taxon discussed above.

Type locality. — Germany, An *Zygnema* mit *Exilaria crystallina* in einem Graben bei Aschersleben, im Juni.

U. S. distribution. — GEOGRAPHICAL: New England States, Middle Atlantic States, Southeastern States, Gulf Coast States, South Central States, East Central States, West Central States, Lakes States, Plains States; Montana, Utah, Arizona, Nevada, Oregon, California. ECOLOGICAL: A very widespread taxon to be found throughout the country. Eurytopic, Euryŏk. Found at very wide range of pH, but has appeared here in largest numbers in waters with a pH about 6.5-9.0. Oligohalobe, probably "indifferent."

5. **Achnanthes affinis** Grun. var. **affinis**   PL. 16, FIGS. 11-12

   Achnanthes affinis Grun. *in* Cl. & Grun., K. Svenska Vet.-Akad. Handl., Ny Földj, 17(2):20. 1880.

Valve linear-lanceolate with broad, obtusely rounded substrate to rostrate ends. *Raphe valve* with a narrow axial area and a stauroid central area, reaching to the valve margins. Raphe filiform, proximal raphe ends terminating at the stauros, distal ends indistinct. Striae slightly to moderately radiate throughout. *Pseudoraphe valve* with narrow, linear pseudoraphe which occasionally widens somewhat in the center of the valve, but does not form a distinct central area. Striae slightly radiate throughout. Striae, about 27 in 10μ in the middle portion, becoming about 30 in 10μ near the ends on both valves. Length, $14\text{-}23\mu$. Breadth, $3\text{-}4\mu$.

Distinguished from *Achnanthes minutissima* by the distinct stauros on the raphe valve and the coarser striae near the valve ends.

Some of the distribution records reported in the literature for this taxon, as well as related taxa such as *A. minutissima, A. microcephala* and others, are questionable, for their small size, together with their variability, often makes positive identification quite difficult.

Type locality. — Belgium.

U. S. distribution. — GEOGRAPHICAL: New England States, Middle Atlantic States, Southeastern States, South Central States, East Central States, Lakes States, Plains States; Colorado, Arizona, Oregon, California. ECOLOGICAL: A eurytopous species more often reported from circumneutral to alkaline waters, alkaliphil(?).

6. **Achnanthes wellsiae** Reim. nom. nov., var. **wellsiae** PL. 16, FIGS. 15-17

> *Achnanthes solea* Hust., Bot. Not. for 1952, (4):389, figs. 60-61. 1952. [*nom. illegit.*]

Valve linear to linear-elliptical with cuneate extremities which are slightly beaked. *Raphe valve* with narrow axial area; central area very small or lacking. Single pore present at the center, at end of one slightly shortened central stria. Raphe filiform; proximal raphe ends close; distal ends curving slightly in the same direction at the extreme end. Striae radiate. *Pseudoraphe valve* with narrow, linear to linear-lanceolate pseudoraphe; no central area. Striae radiate as the raphe valve. Striae, 22-24 in 10μ (RV); 20-22 in 10μ (PRV). Length, $10\text{-}27\mu$. Breadth, $4.8\text{-}6\mu$.

Best distinguished by the small central pore just at the end of one central stria.

The striae are actually very finely punctate (lineate), but without extremely good resolution this cannot be seen.

The name *Achnanthes solea* was used by Zimmermann (1917, p. 5) for a quite different entity than that of Hustedt. For this reason it is necessary to erect a new name for Hustedt's taxon. This diatom is named for Miss Evelyn Wells who did most of the original library research for this publication.

Type locality. — Norway, Snigsfjord, Asevåg.

U. S. distribution. — GEOGRAPHICAL: Texas. ECOLOGICAL: Has appeared so far only from slightly brackish-water areas of the Gulf Coast in East Texas.

7. **Achnanthes deflexa** Reim. sp. nov.   PL. 16, FIGS. 18-20

Valvis lineari-ellipticalibus usque ellipticalibus. Apicibus non aut solum leniter prolatis. Raphovalvae area axiali angusta; area centrali parva aut inopia. Raphi filiformi, apicibus proximalibus densis, apicibus distalibus in eodem cursu declinatis. Striis parallelis aut leniter radiatis, obscure punctatis. Pseudoraphovalvae pseudoraphi angusto-lineari, area centrali indistincta. Striis illis raphovalvae similibus. Striis in media parte 20-22 in 10μ, in ambabus valvis 28-30 in 10μ. Longitudine 7-25μ, latitudine 3.8-4.5μ.

Valve linear-elliptical to elliptical with extremities varying from subtilely protracted subrostrate to obtusely rounded, not protracted. *Raphe valve* with narrow, linear axial area curving at the ends; central area small, elongate-elliptical or lacking. Raphe filiform; proximal raphe ends close; distal ends curved or deflected in the same direction, subterminal. Striae parallel or very slightly radiate. Indistinctly punctate; more distant at the center of the valve than at the ends. *Pseudoraphe valve* with narrow, linear pseudoraphe; no distinct central area. Striae parallel or slightly radiate; indistinctly punctate. Striae, 20-22 in 10μ at the center, becoming about 28-30 in 10μ near the ends on both valves. Length, 7-25μ. Breadth, 3.8-4.5μ.

This diatom has often been confused with *Achnanthes linearis*. It is best distinguished from *A. linearis* by the characteristic of the distal raphe ends and the indistinctly punctate striae.

Upon careful focusing with oblique light the individual puncta can be seen but they are so close together that they have been described as one usually observes them, i.e., indistinctly punctate.

Achnanthes deflexa is deceptively similar to *A. arcus* Hust. (1942d, p. 38, text figs. 44-48) especially as regards the striae and raphe structure. It fails, however, to meet the description of Hustedt in the following respects: (1) One of the most important diagnostic features of *A. arcus* as given by Hustedt is the strongly arcuate shape of the frustule in girdle view. In *A. deflexa* the girdle view varies from nearly straight to only slightly arcuate and, in certain views, the frustule is seen to recurve at the ends; (2) The raphe valve striae of *A. arcus* are described as being slightly radiate and finer (34 in 10μ) than on the pseudoraphe valve where they are parallel and 29 to 32 in 10μ throughout. *A. deflexa* has striae changing in number from 20 in 10μ at the center to about 28 to 30 in 10μ near the ends on both valves, and they are parallel to slightly radiate on both valves; (3) The length of Hustedt's diatom is given as 24 to 30μ long and 5 to 6μ wide. *A. deflexa* varies from 8 to 25μ in length with auxospores measuring about 26 to 28μ. The breadth varies from 3.8 to 4.5μ; and (4) *A. deflexa* is more linear-elliptical to elliptical with shorter subrostrate ends or only rounded extremities, whereas *A. arcus* is indicated as linear with relatively longer, subrostrate to rostrate ends.

Type locality. – U.S.A., Indiana, Marshall Co., Lake Maxinkuckee, east side of the lake. (*Holotype*–A G.C. 1931, Reimer.)

U. S. distribution. – GEOGRAPHICAL: Middle Atlantic States; Indiana, Oklahoma, Utah. ECOLOGICAL: Found in moderately hard waters of lakes, streams, and springs (alkaliphil?). Probably a rather widely distributed species.

8. **Achnanthes exigua** Grun. var. **exigua**   PL. 16, FIGS. 21-22

> *Stauroneis exilis* Kütz., Bacill., p. 105, pl. 30, fig. 21. 1844. [non *A. exilis* Kütz., 1833.]
>
> *Achnanthes exigua* Grun. *in* Cl. & Grun., K. Svenska Vet.-Akad. Handl., Ny Följd, 17(2):21. 1880.

Valve broadly linear or linear-elliptical with nearly quadratic valve body and distinctly set off, protracted rostrate ends. *Raphe valve* with narrow axial area, flaring abruptly into the central area. Central area extending to the valve margins as a flattened rectangle or slightly expanding toward the valve margins, stauroid. Raphe filiform; proximal raphe ends broader than the raphe branch, not extending beyond the striae bordering the central area; distal ends subtilely curved in opposite directions. Striae radiate except at the ends where they may be either slightly radiate or parallel. *Pseudoraphe valve* with narrow, linear or somewhat linear-lanceolate pseudoraphe. Central area lacking or a small flattened rectangle caused by occasional shortening of one or two striae at the center; striae slightly radiate, at the ends either slightly radiate or parallel. Striae, 24-25 in 10μ (RV); 20-22 in 10μ (PRV). Length, 7-17μ. Breadth, 4.5-6μ.

Distinguished from similar-shaped species of *Achnanthes* by the sharply defined quadrangular valve body and the stauros-like central area on the raphe valve; from its varieties by the shape or the striae number as given.

Stauroneis quadrata Hérib. (1903, p. 14) probably belongs here in synonymy, but without an illustration of both valves it is difficult to know with any degree of certainty just where it belongs.

Elmore (1922, p. 96, pl. 12, figs. 461-462) described and illustrated a diatom which he called *Stauroneis parvula* Jan. but which seems to be much more like the raphe valve of *A. exigua*. Examination of his slide (N.Y.B.G.-Elm. 700) from one of the localities mentioned (labelled *Stauroneis parvula*) reveals a rather large population of *A. exigua*. *S. parvula* is the only diatom listed on the slide label. It is quite probable that Elmore's other records of *S. parvula* are also to be referred to *A. exigua*.

Type locality. – In süssem Wasser der Insel Trinidad.

U. S. distribution. — GEOGRAPHICAL: New England States, Middle Atlantic States, Southeastern States, Gulf Coast States, South Central States, East Central States, West Central States, Lakes States, Plains States; Colorado, California. ECOLOGICAL: A rather widespread lake form, but also to be found in rivers and streams. Occurs frequently in aquarium tanks. Alkaliphil, eurythermal, euryphotic.

8. **Achnanthes exigua** var. **constricta** (Grun.) Hust.   PL. 16, FIGS. 23-24

Stauroneis exilis var.? *constricta* Grun. *in* Reise Novara, Bot., vol. 1, pp. 20-21. 1870.

Cocconeis exigua var. *constricta* Torka, Zeitschr. Naturw. Abt. Posen, Geol. 16(1/5): 131, fig. 3a. 1909.

Achnanthes exigua var. *constricta* (Grun.) Hust. *in* Schroeder, Hedwigia, 63(2): 145, pl. 1, figs. 7-8. 1922.

Valve with constriction at the center. Other features as described for the nominate variety except for a tendency of the striae on the raphe valve to become slightly more numerous than in variety *exigua*. Striae, 25-27 in 10μ (RV); 22 in 10μ (PRV). Length, 7-17μ. Breadth, 4.5-6μ.

Further studies may prove that this taxon varies enough to be the transition bridging the nominate variety and variety *heterovalva*.

Type locality. — Im Wahiria-See auf Taïti.

U. S. distribution. — GEOGRAPHICAL: Pennsylvania, Florida. ECOLOGICAL: Insufficiently known; often found on aquarium walls, etc.

8. **Achnanthes exigua** var. **heterovalva** Krasske   PL. 16, FIGS. 25-26

Achnanthes exigua var. *heterovalva* Krasske, Bot. Arch., 3(4):193, figs. 9a-b. 1923.

Achnanthes exigua var. *heterovalvata* Krasske *ex* Hust. *in* Pasch., Süssw.-Fl. Mitteleuropas, Heft 10, Aufl. 2, p. 202, text fig. 228. 1930.

Raphe valve with finer striae than in the nominate variety; valve sides may or may not be slightly constricted at the center. Other features as described for variety *exigua*. Striae, 30 in 10μ, becoming about 34 in 10μ near the ends (RV); 22 in 10μ (PRV). Length, 10-15μ. Breadth, 5-6μ.

Type locality. — Germany, Hesse, Kassel; Wand eines Schul-Aquariums der Bürgerschule 5.

U. S. distribution. — GEOGRAPHICAL: New England States, Middle Atlantic States, Gulf Coast States, East Central States, West Central States, Plains States; Montana, Utah, Arizona, Oregon, California. ECOLOGICAL: As the nominate variety.

9. Achnanthes hungarica (Grun.) Grun. var. hungarica

Achnanthidium hungaricum Grun., Verh. Zool.-Bot. Ges. Wien, 13:146, pl. 4, figs. 8a-c. 1863.
Achnanthes hungarica (Grun.) Grun. *in* Cl. & Grun., K. Svenska Vet.-Akad. Handl., Ny Följd, 17(2):20. 1880.

Valve linear-elliptical to linear-lanceolate with obtuse, subcuneate apices which are sometimes set off by a subtile constriction of the valve margins. *Raphe valve* with narrow, linear axial area. Central area a broad, widening stauros-like space reaching one or both margins; one side of the central area usually broader than the opposite side. Raphe filiform, proximal ends rather close, rounded and somewhat broader than the raphe branch; distal ends curving slightly in opposite directions. Striae slightly radiate throughout, lineae difficult to resolve. *Pseudoraphe valve* with narrow pseudoraphe; shorter striae in the middle portion form a very weak central area. Striae slightly radiate. Striae, 19-23 in 10μ on both valves. Length, $14\text{-}45\mu$. Breadth, $6\text{-}8\mu$.

Best distinguished by the peculiar configuration of the raphe valve central area.

Type locality. — [Europe], . . . ad litora meridionalia lacus Peisonis Hungariae, in lacunis parvis inter radicula Lemnarum.

U. S. distribution. — GEOGRAPHICAL: Middle Atlantic States, Southeastern States, Gulf Coast States, East Central States, West Central States, Lakes States, Plains States; Montana, Oregon, California. ECOLOGICAL: Lakes and ponds; occasionally in flowing water, but not found in large numbers. Alkaliphil. Considered by Hustedt (1957, p. 246) as "β-saprophytisch" when present in large numbers.

10. Achnanthes lapponica var. ninckei (Guerm. & Mang.) Reim. comb. nov.

Achnanthes ninckei Guerm. & Mang., Österreichische Bot. Zeitschr., 100(4/5):541, pl. 1, figs. 10-11. 1953.

Valve moderately arched, short-lanceolate to elliptical. Longer forms with produced, rostrate ends; shorter forms with obtusely rounded extremities—not set off from the valve body. *Raphe valve* with narrow, linear axial area expanding slightly near the central area, deflecting in opposite directions quite near the ends forming a sigma. Central area a more or less unilateral expanding fascia; opposite side with slightly broader striae which are irregular or alternately longer and shorter. Raphe filiform, proximal ends only slightly broadened; distal ends curved in opposite directions. Striae radiate throughout, broader at the middle portion of the

valve, becoming narrower and more numerous toward the ends; not noticeably punctate or lineate except in larger forms where the puncta are seen
in the larger central striae. *Pseudoraphe valve* with narrow, linear pseudoraphe; central area large, oval or quadrangular with a unilateral fascia
extending to the margin on one side only. Striae radiate throughout,
broader and shorter at the center, becoming narrower and more numerous
toward the ends—not noticeably punctate or lineate. Striae, 20-24 in 10μ
at the center, becoming 28-32 in 10μ toward the ends (RV); about the
same as the raphe valve except perhaps slightly finer near the ends (PRV).
Length, 9-24μ. Breadth, 5-7μ.

Most readily distinguished from the nominate variety by the presence
of a unilateral central area on both valves. To date (1960) I have not been
able to verify any specimens of the nominate variety from this country.

It is possible that *A. aretasii* Mang. *in* Bourr. & Mang. (1954, p. 19,
pl. 2, figs. 16a-c) also belongs here in synonymy.

In my opinion this diatom has too many similarities to *A. lapponica*
to consider it anything other than a variety thereof.

Type locality. — Bretenoux (Lot), Cère (France).

U. S. distribution. — GEOGRAPHICAL: Maryland, Utah. ECOLOGICAL: Insufficiently known.

11. **Achnanthes flexella** (Kütz.) Brun var. **flexella**   PL. 16, FIGS. 31-32

> *Cymbella? flexella* Kütz., Bacill., p. 80, pl. 4, fig. 14, (?) pl. 6, fig. 8. 1844.
> *Achnanthidium flexellum* Bréb. *in* Kütz., Sp. Alg., p. 54. 1849.
> *Cocconeis thwaitesii* W. Sm., Syn. British Diat., vol. 1, pp. 21-22, pl. 3, figs. 33a,
>   b, d. 1853.
> *Achnanthes flexella* (Kütz.) Brun, Diat. Alpes Jura, p. 29, pl. 3, fig. 21. 1880.
> *Cocconeis flexella* (Kütz.) Cl., K. Svenska Vet.-Akad. Handl., Ny Földj, 27(3):179.
>   1895.
> *Eucocconeis flexella* (Kütz.) Hust. *in* Pasch., Süssw.-Fl. Mitteleuropas; Heft 10,
>   Aufl. 2, p. 193, text fig. 270. 1930.

Valve highly arched and somewhat twisted; elliptical to elliptical-
lanceolate with extremities varying from those obtusely rounded, not distinguished from the valve body, to those somewhat produced into broadly
rostrate ends. *Raphe valve* with narrow, diagonally sigmoid axial area;
central area small, oval. Raphe filiform; sigmoid, proximal raphe ends
small, bulbous, well within the central area; distal raphe ends terminating
on opposite sides of the valve ends, at the base of produced ends. Striae
radiate throughout, slightly wider and less numerous in the middle portion
where they are alternately long and short; striae finely punctate. *Pseudoraphe valve* with narrow, straight or only slightly deflected axial area;
central area rather large, ovoid to nearly rectangular. Striae parallel at the

center of the valve, radiate toward the ends; finely but less obscurely punctate than the raphe valve. Striae, 17-20 in 10μ at the center, becoming about 25 in 10μ, then 28-30 in 10μ at the ends (RV); 20-23 in 10μ at the center, becoming 24-26 in 10μ toward the ends (PRV). Cleve (1895, p. 179) gives 16 in 10μ (PRV). Length, 20-50μ; Hustedt (1930, p. 193) gives length, 80μ. Breadth, 10-18μ; Hustedt (*loc. cit.*) gives breadth, 26μ.

Distinguished best from *Achnanthes lapponica* by the more diagonal raphe and by the proximal raphe ends extending well into the the central area.

Due to the relative shortness and the extreme arch of the valve, the striae are rather difficult to count accurately which may account, in part, for the wide range of striae number given by various authors.

Boyer (1927b, p. 249) reports a *Cocconeis minuta* (Cl.) Cl. from the United States. This name has been placed in synonymy with *A. flexella* by several authors. Boyer's material (A-Boyer, T-5-15) appears to be only larger, more elliptical forms of *A. flexella*. Up to the present time I have not seen any forms from the United States which agree with Cleve's *Achnanthidium minutum*. Specimens from Cleve's original material (A-G.C. 12045) show *A. minutum* to be a quite different taxon from *A. flexella*.

Type locality. — Switzerland, In Quellwasser bei Thun.

U. S. distribution. — GEOGRAPHICAL: New England States, Middle Atlantic States, East Central States, Lakes States; Kentucky, Montana. ECOLOGICAL: More commonly found in lakes, ponds, and bogs or in water courses draining such areas; pH "indifferent" (or acidophil?).

12. **Achnanthes marginulata** Grun. var. **marginulata** PL. 17, FIGS. 1-2

Achnanthes marginulata Grun. *in* Cl. & Grun., K. Svenska Vet.-Akad. Handl., Ny Följd, 17(2):21. 1880.

Valve elliptical to elliptical-lanceolate with obtusely rounded extremities; larger forms with slightly produced, broadly subrostrate ends. *Raphe valve* with narrow, linear axial area; central area broadly elliptical to almost rectangular, occupying about three-quarters of the total distance across the valve center. Raphe filiform; proximal raphe ends situated slightly within the central area; distal ends straight. Striae radiate throughout, not noticeably punctate or lineate. *Pseudoraphe valve* with axial and central areas uniting to form a large, lanceolate space. Striae radiate, a few shorter striae interposed at or near the center of the valve; striae not noticeably punctate or lineate. Striae, 27-30 in 10μ (RV); about 24 in 10μ at the center, becoming about 28 in 10μ at the ends (PRV). Length, 10-21μ. Breadth, 4-8μ.

Best distinguished by the broad central area on the raphe valve together with the large central space on the pseudoraphe valve.

Most specimens seen from this country are more typically elliptical as pl. 17, figs. 1 & 2, although a few more lanceolate forms like those of Hustedt (1930, p. 203, text fig. 299) have been noted.

Type locality. — Norway, Memerutungen.

U. S. distribution. — Geographical: South Carolina, Colorado, Utah. Ecological: Has appeared more commonly in relatively soft, slightly acid to circumneutral waters.

13. **Achnanthes levanderi** Hust. var. **levanderi**   pl. 17, figs. 3-4

> *Achnanthes levanderi* Hust. *in* Rabh., Kryptog.-Fl. Deutschland, vol. 7(2), no. 3, p. 404, text fig. 856. 1933.

Valve broadly linear-elliptical to elliptical; extremities broadly rounded, often nearly flat, not distinguished from the valve body. *Raphe valve* with narrow axial area and elliptical to rectangular central area. Raphe filiform; striae radiate throughout, indistinctly lineate. *Pseudoraphe valve* with broadly elliptical-elongate central space and abbreviated narrow axial area near each end, or both areas united into an elongate-elliptical space. Striae radiate, indistinctly lineate, slightly coarser than on the raphe valve. Striae, 22-24 in 10μ in the middle portion, becoming about 28 in 10μ near the ends (RV); 21-22 in 10μ in the middle portion, becoming about 25 in 10μ near the ends (PRV). Length, $6-9\mu$. Breadth, $4-5\mu$.

This taxon is very similar to *Achnanthes marginulata* but can be distinguished by its coarser central striae and fine puncta (appearing as indistinct lineae). The central area of the raphe valve is smaller than that of *A. marginulata* and has a tendency to be slightly asymmetrical. Finally, *A. levanderi* is a smaller form, not known to exceed 9μ in length.

Forms observed in this country conform more exactly in shape to Hustedt's illustration *in A. S. Atlas* (1936a, pl. 407, figs. 75-76) in that they are more nearly rectangular than elliptical. However, inclusion in *Achnanthes didyma* Hust.—not reported from the United States—is obviated best by the quite radiate striae on the raphe valve.

Type locality. — Finland, Vesijärvi, Tümpel am Ostfluss des Wuokatti!

U. S. distribution. — Geographical: Utah. Ecological: Insufficiently known; to date recorded only from this locality in the Rockies.

14. **Achnanthes sublaevis** var. **crassa** Reim. var. nov.   pl. 17, figs. 5-6

Striae crassiores quam illae varietatis *sublaevis*, 24-26 in 10μ. Longitudo, $9-12\mu$. Latitudo, $5-5.5\mu$.

Valve linear-elliptical with gibbous center and quite broadly rostrate ends. *Raphe valve* with narrow, linear axial area; central area variable from broadly elliptical to rectangular, sometimes broader on one side. Raphe filiform; proximal ends slightly protruding into the central area; distal ends straight. Striae radiate throughout, obscurely punctate. *Pseudoraphe valve* with axial and central areas uniting to form a broad central space which tapers to a narrow axial portion near each end. Striae as on the raphe valve. Striae, 24-26 in 10μ on both valves. Length, 9-12μ. Breadth, 5-5.5μ.

Best distinguished by the broad, rostrate ends and the gibbous center.

With the exception of the coarser striae this diatom is identical with the nominate variety. Hustedt (1936b, p. 180) gives the striae count as "etwa 30 in 10μ." His figures in A. S. *Atlas* (1936a, pl. 409, figs. 74-82) measure about 32 in 10μ. None of our specimens show striae this fine.

Type locality. — U.S.A., New Jersey, Mercer Co., Assunpink Creek. (*Holotype*—A.G.C. 44716a, Reimer.)

U. S. distribution. — GEOGRAPHICAL: Known only from the type locality. ECOLOGICAL: Insufficiently known. Found once in a relatively soft-water stream with a pH of 6.8.

15. Achnanthes gibberula Grun. var. gibberula PL. 17, FIGS. 7-8

Achnanthes gibberula Grun. *in* Cl. & Grun., K. Svenska Vet.-Akad. Handl., Ny Följd, 17(2):22. 1880.

Valve linear-lanceolate with gibbous center and obtusely rounded, rostrate to occasionally subcapitate extremities. *Raphe valve* with filiform raphe. Proximal raphe ends straight or sometimes appearing deflected in the same direction; distal ends curving in the same direction at the ends. Axial and central areas forming a broad, linear-lanceolate space. Striae slightly radiate, more distant at the center. *Pseudoraphe valve*; pseudoraphe forming a broad, lanceolate space. Striae about the same distance apart throughout; individual striae sometimes lacking at the center. Striae, about 22 in 10μ at the center, becoming about 26 in 10μ toward the ends on both valves. Length, 15-28μ. Breadth, 4-5μ.

Best distinguished by the gibbous center and the characteristic broad, lanceolate space formed by the union of the axial and the central areas.

The variety *angustior* Grun. *in* Cl. (1895, p. 184) probably should be retained as a variety. Van Heurck's specimens of variety *angustior* (A.-V.H. 139) are not only narrower, but they have coarser striae (16 in 10μ at the center to 20 in 10μ toward the ends); and the valves are generally shorter (down to about 8μ) than in the nominate variety. Such forms have not been seen from this country.

Type locality. — East Indies, In Thermen, Ostindiens.

U. S. distribution. — Geographical: Wyoming. Ecological: Thus far identified only from hot springs in the above locality. May be restricted to springs and thermal streams(?).

16. Achnanthes hustedtii (Krasske) Reim. comb. nov., var. hustedtii

pl. 17, figs. 9-10

Cocconeis hustedtii Krasske, Bot. Arch., 3:193, text figs. 10a-b. 1923.

Valve relatively flat, linear or oblong-elliptical. *Raphe valve* with linear axial area. Central area broad-oval or rectangular. Raphe straight, becoming slightly broader toward the valve center; proximal raphe ends distant, rounded; distal ends indistinct but appearing straight over the ends. Striae radiate, indistinctly lineate. *Pseudoraphe valve* with broad lanceolate space, or pseudoraphe. Striae as on the raphe valve except shorter. Striae, 17-19 in 10μ, becoming about 20-22 near the ends on both valves. Length, 12-17μ. Breadth, 5-7μ.

Best distinguished from the similar appearing *Achnanthes marginulata* by its more elliptical shape and coarser striae.

Type locality. — Germany, Kassel, Wand eines Schulaquariums . . . beobachtet.

U. S. distribution. — Geographical: Pennsylvania. Ecological: More often found in riffle and waterfalls areas (aerophilous?), alkaliphil.

17. Achnanthes stewartii Patr. var. stewartii

pl. 17, figs. 11-12

Achnanthes stewartii Patr., Farlowia, 2(2):169-170, pl. 2, figs. 1-3. 1945.

Valve elliptical. *Raphe valve* with narrow axial area. Central area narrow-rectangular, one or two striae at the margins. Raphe filiform; proximal ends enlarged, rounded; distal ends straight. Striae rather broad, curved-radiate, lineate, indistinctly doubly punctate (difficult to resolve). *Pseudoraphe valve* with narrow, linear pseudoraphe. No definite central area; one or two shortened striae at the center. Striae as on the raphe valve. Striae, about 14 in 10μ on both valves. Length, 14-17μ. Breadth, 7-8μ.

Distinguished from *Achnanthes pinnata* by its larger size, the shortened striae on the raphe valve forming a narrow rectangular central area, and by the double row of puncta distinguishable with the light microscope.

Type locality. — U.S.A., Pennsylvania, Pike Co., Lake Wallenpaupack tributary. (*Holotype*—A.G.C. 2194, Patrick, 1945.)

U. S. distribution. — Geographical: Middle Atlantic States; Georgia, Tennessee. Ecological: Insufficiently known.

18. **Achnanthes saxonica** Krasske var. **saxonica**   PL. 17, FIGS. 13-14

Achnanthes saxonica Krasske *in* Hust. *in* Rabh., Kryptog.-Fl. Deutschland, vol. 7(2), no. 3, p. 403, text fig. 854B. 1933.

Valve elliptical with broad, obtusely rounded extremities. *Raphe valve* with very narrow axial area. Central area transversely expanded, at least one-half the breadth of the valve, somewhat rectangular. Proximal raphe ends terminating at the margin of the central area, slightly broader than remainder of filiform raphe. Striae radiate throughout, finely lineate. *Pseudoraphe valve* with linear to linear-lanceolate pseudoraphe; no distinct central area. Striae slightly radiate, sometimes parallel at the center, more or less distinctly lineate. Striae, 22-24 in 10μ (RV); 12-14 in 10μ (PRV). Length, 8-13μ. Breadth, 4-5μ.

Features of the raphe are very difficult to determine when the frustule is intact unless good lenses and optimum oblique light are applied.

Type locality. — Germany, Erzgebirge, an überieselten Steinen und in nassen Moosrasen.

U. S. distribution. — GEOGRAPHICAL: California. ECOLOGICAL: Insufficiently known.

19. **Achnanthes lemmermanni** Hust. var. **lemmermanni**
PL. 17, FIGS. 15-16

Achnanthes lemmermanni Hust. *in* Rabh., Kryptog.-Fl. Deutschland, vol. 7(2), no. 3, p. 390, fig. 837. 1933.

Valve body oblong-elliptical with slightly to rather strongly convex sides; narrowing abruptly to produced, subcapitate or capitate ends. *Raphe valve* with narrow, linear axial area. Central area small, indistinct, or lacking. Raphe filiform, proximal raphe ends slightly enlarged. Striae distinct, radiate, usually becoming parallel at the ends, indistinctly lineate. *Pseudoraphe valve* with narrow, lanceolate pseudoraphe formed by union of the axial and the central areas. Striae as on the raphe valve. Striae, 16-18 in 10μ on both valves. Length, 10-15μ. Breadth, 4.5-5μ.

Although Hustedt (*loc. cit.*) describes the sides as nearly parallel, his illustrations show a variation from nearly parallel to rather strongly convex sides. I have seen specimens from this country varying between both extremes although our specimens appear more commonly with strongly convex sides. At present there seems to be no reason to keep these variants separate.

Type locality. — Germany, in der Wumme (einem Nebenfluss der Weser) bei Bremen!

U. S. distribution. — Geographical: Virginia, South Carolina, California. Ecological: Found, so far, only from fresh to slightly brackish waters in coastal areas (probably oligohalobe-"indifferent").

20. **Achnanthes pinnata** Hust. var. **pinnata**   PL. 17, FIGS. 17-18

Achnanthes pinnata Hust. *in* Hedin, Southern Tibet, vol. 6, pt. 3, p. 123, pl. 9, figs. 15-18. 1922.

Valve elliptical with parallel to slightly convex sides and obtusely rounded extremities. *Raphe valve* with narrow axial area; central area lacking. Raphe filiform, proximal ends slightly enlarged, distal ends appearing straight. Striae radiate, rather broad, lineate. *Pseudoraphe valve* with narrow, linear to linear-lanceolate pseudoraphe; no distinct central area. Striae radiate, rather broad, lineate. Striae, 14-18 in 10μ on both valves. Length, 5-9μ. Breadth, 3.5-5μ.

As pointed out by Hustedt *in* Hedin (*loc. cit.*), this diatom can readily be confused with *Fragilaria pinnata* since the raphe is easy to overlook. The smaller, more narrow valve plus the finer striae distinguish it readily from elliptical forms of *Achnanthes hauckiana*.

Type locality. — Tibet, prope lacum "TSO-Ngombo" castra CXXXIV (1901).

U. S. distribution. — Geographical: Middle Atlantic States, Southeastern States, South Central States, East Central States; California. Ecological: Reported mostly from streams and rivers; alkaliphil(?).

21. **Achnanthes lewisiana** Patr. var. **lewisiana**   PL. 17, FIGS. 19-20

Achnanthes lewisiana Patr., Farlowia, 2(2):168, pl. 1, figs. 2-3. 1945.

Valve linear-elliptical to elliptical with obtusely rounded ends. *Raphe valve* with axial and central areas united into a linear-lanceolate space; no central area differentiated. Raphe straight, filiform; proximal ends close; distal ends curving very slightly in the same direction. Striae slightly radiate. *Pseudoraphe valve* with axial and central areas united into a linear-lanceolate space. Striae punctate, interrupted by a longitudinal space on both sides. Striae, 15-18 in 10μ on both valves. Length, 7-15μ. Breadth, 4-4.6μ.

The fine lineae of the raphe valve striae are only visible under quite optimal light conditions and would not ordinarily be seen. This feature has been deleted from the diagnosis and the illustration.

Type locality. – U.S.A., Pennsylvania, Pike County, Shohola Falls (*Holotype*–A-G.C. 2210, Patrick, 1945).

U. S. distribution. – GEOGRAPHICAL: Pennsylvania. ECOLOGICAL: Insufficiently known.

22. **Achnanthes clevei** Grun. var. **clevei**   PL. 17, FIGS. 21-22

> *Achnanthes clevei* Grun. *in* Cl. & Grun., K. Svenska Vet.-Akad. Handl., Ny Földj, 17(2):21. 1880.

Valve lanceolate to elliptical-lanceolate. Apices varying from not protracted, obtusely rounded, to slightly protracted and broadly subtruncate. *Raphe valve* with narrow, linear-lanceolate axial area. Central area variable, lacking to irregularly orbicular. Raphe filiform, broadening slightly toward the proximal ends. Striae strongly radiate, finely punctate; alternately longer and shorter on both sides of the central area. *Pseudoraphe valve* with narrow, linear to linear-lanceolate pseudoraphe. No distinct central area present. Striae parallel at the center to slightly radiate toward the ends of the valve, coarsely punctate; puncta larger than on the raphe valve. Striae, 18-24 in 10μ (RV); 9-15 in 10μ (PRV). Puncta, 24-27 in 10μ (RV); 18-22 in 10μ (PRV). Length, 10-30μ. Breadth, 5-9μ.

Type locality. – [Sweden], Westergötland.

U. S. distribution. – GEOGRAPHICAL: New England States, Middle Atlantic States, Southeastern States, Gulf Coast States, South Central States, East Central States, West Central States; Oregon, California. ECOLOGICAL: Common in lakes and rivers at higher pH values (alkaliphil).

22. **Achnanthes clevei** var. **rostrata** Hust.   PL. 17, FIGS. 23-24

> *Achnanthes clevei* var. *rostrata* Hust. *in* Pasch., Süssw.-Fl. Mitteleuropas, Heft 10, Aufl. 2, p. 204, fig. 295. 1930.

Differs from the species by having distinctly protracted, rostrate ends. Other characteristics as in the nominate variety. Striae, 23-26 in 10μ (RV); 10-15 in 10μ (PRV). Puncta, 24-27 in 10μ (RV); 18-22 in 10μ (PRV). Length, 10-30μ. Breadth, 5-9μ.

Type locality. – [Europe], uncertain.

U. S. distribution. – GEOGRAPHICAL: New England States, Southeastern States, West Central States. ECOLOGICAL: As the nominate variety.

23. **Achnanthes hauckiana** Grun. var. **hauckiana**   PL. 17, FIGS. 25-32

> *Achnanthes hauckiana* Grun. *in* Cl. & Grun., K. Svenska Vet.-Akad. Handl., Ny Földj, 17(2):21-22. 1880.

Achnanthes hauckiana var. *elliptica* Schulz *in* Hust. *in* Pasch., Süssw.-Fl. Mitteleuropas, Heft 10, Aufl. 2, p. 202.   1930; Illust.: Bot. Arch., 13:191, text fig. 39.
1926.

Valve broadly elliptical to elliptical-lanceolate. Extremities varying
from broad, obtusely rounded, not distinguished from the valve body
(smaller forms) to slightly protracted, subrostrate ends (larger forms).
Raphe valve with narrow, linear axial area; central area usually orbicular,
but sometimes of irregular configuration. Raphe filiform, proximal ends
broader than the raphe axis. Striae coarse, rather broad, often wider at
the valve margin, especially the central striae; radiate. *Pseudoraphe valve*
with linear to linear-lanceolate pseudoraphe, formed by union of the axial
and the central areas; no distinct central area as such. Striae coarse and
rather broad, less distinctly wedge-shaped than those of the raphe valve,
parallel or only slightly radiate. Striae, 10-12 in 10μ, becoming 12-15 in
10μ near the ends on both valves. Length, 9-31μ. Breadth, 5-9μ.

A taxon quite variable in shape. Best distinguished by the coarse
striae, at least some of which are usually wedge-shaped or conical; the
broad portion of the striae is at the valve margin. The striae are actually
resolved into fine lineae, but since these are difficult to see even under
oil immersion they are excluded from the description and illustrations.

There seems to be no good grounds to separate variety *elliptica* from
the nominate variety. Examination of large populations of *Achnanthes
hauckiana* frequently shows a complete series encompassing both forms.
Such a series is illustrated in pl. 17, figs. 25-32.

This species has often been identified from this country as *A. delicatula*. To date I can verify no records of *A. delicatula* from the United
States. There is some rather puzzling information in the literature about
A. delicatula and its exact delineation is not clear. Van Heurck has
figured a form he calls *A. delicatula* (1880, pl. 27, figs. 3-4) which does
not have long, rostrate ends as shown by Kützing. One of Van Heurck's
slides, A-V.H. 234, which he cites for this taxon, has specimens which are
lanceolate in shape and with only slightly set off subtruncate ends. Another slide, A-V.H. 11, has specimens with rather protracted, rostrate to
apiculate ends which better resemble the Kützing illustration. The illustration of Hustedt resembles those on V.H. 11, but he shows rather narrow
striae, not broad and sometimes tapering as the V.H. specimens. Future
check of the Kützing material may throw some light on the identity and
variability of *A. delicatula*.

Type locality. — [Italy], In den Reka Quellen bei Triest.

U. S. distribution. — GEOGRAPHICAL: Middle Atlantic States, Southeastern States, Gulf Coast States, South Central States, East Central States,
West Central States; California. ECOLOGICAL: Found most commonly in

slightly to moderately brackish water, also reported from inland fresh-water areas with relatively high specific conductivity.

23. **Achnanthes hauckiana** var. **rostrata** Schulz   PL. 17, FIGS. 33-34

Achnanthes hauckiana var. *rostrata* Schulz *in* Hust. *in* Pasch., Süssw.Fl. Mittel-europas, Heft 10, Aufl. 2, p. 202. 1930; Illust.: Bot. Arch., 13:191, text fig. 40. 1926.

Valve not attaining the larger size of the nominate variety, with elliptical to orbicular valve body and distinctly protracted, rostrate ends. Striae often not quite as broad as in the nominate variety. Other features as described for *Achnanthes hauckiana*. Striae, 12-14 in 10μ on both valves. Length, $10-15\mu$. Breadth, $5-6\mu$.

Schulz (*loc. cit.*) published a quite adequate illustration of this taxon, but did not describe it. According to Art. 32 of the *International Code of Botanical Nomenclature* this constitutes an invalid publication. The first valid use of this combination that can be found is that of Hustedt.

This variety appears to be much less common than variety *hauckiana*.

Type locality. — [Europe], Danziger Bucht.

U. S. distribution. — GEOGRAPHICAL: Gulf Coast States; California. ECOLOGICAL: When found, it is usually associated with the nominate variety and probably has similar ecological characteristics.

24. **Achnanthes lanceolata** Bréb.*ex* Kütz. var. **lanceolata**

PL. 18, FIGS. 1-10

Achnanthes lanceolata Bréb. *ex* Kütz., Bot. Zeit., 4(13):247. 1846.
Achnanthidium lanceolatum Bréb. *in* Kütz., Sp. Alg., p. 54. 1849.
Achnanthidium lanceolatum var. *inflata* A. Mayer, Ber. Naturw. Ver. Regensburg, 14:81, pl. 14, fig. 35. 1913.
Achnanthes lanceolata var. *ventricosa* Hust., Arch. Hydrobiol., 10:64, pl. 2, fig. 32. 1914.

Valve elliptical to lanceolate with broad, obtusely rounded extremi-ties. *Raphe valve* with narrow, linear axial area; central area broad, rectangular. Raphe filiform, becoming slightly broader toward rounded proximal ends; distal ends curving in the same direction over the ends (indistinct in smaller forms). Striae slightly radiate; center striae short, marginal, irregular in number and occasionally lacking on one side. *Pseudoraphe valve* linear to linear-lanceolate, interrupted centrally on one side by a horseshoe-shaped clear area. Axial and central areas forming a linear-lanceolate space. Striae slightly radiate. Striae, 11-14 in 10μ on both valves. Length, $12-31\mu$. Breadth, $4.5-8\mu$.

The striae are actually subtilely lineate, but because this is not readily visible even under oil immersion the characteristic has been deleted from the diagnosis and the illustration.

This very common, polymorphic species has been discussed and re-classified by Kolbe (1927, pp. 46-49), Hustedt (1933, pp. 410-411), and several others. No attempt is being made here to do the same for the whole complex, but certain points have come out in this study which should be mentioned.

From the variation of *Achnanthes lanceolata* (pl. 18, figs. 1-10) found in the Brébisson material from Falaise, A-Feb. 3119, I am of the opinion that Hustedt's variety *ventricosa* is only a larger specimen of *A. lanceolata*. Further, some forms which commonly have been referred to variety *elliptica* also belong here. The variety *elliptica* of Cleve is undoubtedly something quite different from the elliptical forms shown in pl. 18, figs. 7-10. See the discussion under variety *omissa* for further comment.

Type locality. — [France], Falaise.

U. S. distribution. — Geographical: New England States, Middle Atlantic States, Southeastern States, Gulf Coast States, South Central States, East Central States, West Central States, Lakes States, Plains States; Montana, Wyoming, Colorado, New Mexico, Utah, Arizona, Nevada, Washington, Oregon, California. Ecological: A quite common species occurring under a wide range of ecological conditions. Observed especially in rather well-aerated flowing waters (?rheophil) of neutral to alkaline pH (pH, ?indifferent or alkaliphil); does not seem to appear in large numbers under conditions of heavy organic enrichment.

24. **Achnanthes lanceolata** var. **apiculata** Patr. 　　PL. 18, FIGS. 24-25

> *Achnanthes lanceolata* var. *apiculata* Patr., Farlowia, 2(2):167, pl. 1, figs. 4-5. 1945.

Valve elliptical with apiculate ends. Striae on the raphe valve more strongly radiate and often undulate. Central striae broader and coarser than in the nominate variety; also central area is broadly orbicular to diamond-shaped, not subrectangular as in variety *lanceolata*. Other features as in the nominate variety. Striae, 6-8 in 10μ at the center of the valve, becoming 10-12 in 10μ toward the ends (RV); 10-12 in 10μ (PRV). Length, $20\text{-}32\mu$. Breadth, $10\text{-}11\mu$.

This variety is quite distinct, being characterized not only by its shape but also by the features on the raphe valve as described above.

Type locality. — U.S.A., Pennsylvania, Pike Co., Shohola Falls. (*Holotype*—A-G.C. 2190, Patrick, 1945.)

U. S. distribution. — GEOGRAPHICAL: Middle Atlantic States, Southeastern States; Florida, Tennessee. ECOLOGICAL: Found most often in soft-water streams.

24. **Achnanthes lanceolata** var. **dubia** Grun.   PL. 18, FIGS. 11-15

Achnanthes lanceolata var. *dubia* Grun. *in* Cl. & Grun., K. Svenska Vet.-Akad. Handl., Ny Följd, 17(2):23. 1880.
Achnanthidium rostrata Østr., Bot. Tidsskr., 25:35, pl. 1, fig. 11. 1903.
Achnanthes lanceolata var. *rostrata* (Østr.) Hust., Abh. Naturw. Ver. Bremen, 20(2):279, pl. 3, figs. 34a-b. 1911.

Valve more broadly elliptical and with protracted, subrostrate to rostrate ends. Striae, 10-14 (17) in 10μ. Length, 8-16μ. Breadth, 3.6-5μ.

Some of the smaller cells of this variety approach an elliptical shape, but remain subtilely subrostrate, pl. 18, fig. 15. Patrick reports having seen specimens identified as *A. lanceolata* var. *rostrata* with 17 striae in 10μ (RV).

Type locality. — Uncertain, . . . Buchberg in Unterösterreich. Belgien.

U. S. distribution. — GEOGRAPHICAL: New England States, Middle Atlantic States, Southeastern States, Gulf Coast States, South Central States, East Central States, West Central States, Plains States; Montana, Wyoming, Utah, California. ECOLOGICAL: As the nominate variety.

24. **Achnanthes lanceolata** var. **haynaldii** (Istv.-Schaarsch.) Cl.
PL. 18, FIGS. 20-21

Achnanthes haynaldii Schaarsch., Magyar Növenytani Lapok, 5(50):20. 1881.
Achnanthes lanceolata var. *haynaldii* (Schaarsch.) Cl., Diatomiste, 2(17):99, pl. 7, figs. 14a-b. 1894.
Achnanthes lanceolata var. *capitata* O. Müll., Bot. Jahrb., 43(4):8, pl. 1, figs. 6-7. 1909.

Valve body elliptical-lanceolate or nearly elliptical with protracted, capitate ends. Other features as in the nominate variety. Striae, about 14 in 10μ on both valves. Length, 15-28μ. Breadth, 4.5-5.5μ.

Forms less than about 15μ in length have not been noted for this taxon as is otherwise true in variety *lanceolata* and variety *dubia*. The broader, capitate ends and generally larger size best distinguish this taxon from variety *dubia*.

I do not quite see the direct connection between this diatom and the nominate variety as Hustedt does (1933, p. 411) and, therefore, elect to retain it as a variety and not a form. In such a case it becomes necessary to accept the earliest epithet, variety *haynaldii*. Even though Schaarschmidt considered several forms of *Achnanthes lanceolata* in his description of *A.*

haynaldii and their varieties, his description of the species itself indicates (i.e., capitate ends) that he was considering this taxon.

Type locality. — [Ecuador?], In fluentibus m. Antisana.

U. S. distribution. — GEOGRAPHICAL: New England States, Middle Atlantic States, Southeastern States, Gulf Coast States; Kansas, Wyoming, Washington, California. ECOLOGICAL: Insufficiently known; often found associated with the nominate variety.

24. **Achnanthes lanceolata** var. **lanceolatoides** (Sov.) Reim. comb. nov.
PL. 18, FIGS. 18-19

> *Achnanthes lanceolatoides* Sov., Trans. American Micr. Soc., 77(2):115, pl. 2, figs. 18-19. 1958.

Valve elliptical-lanceolate with short, subrostrate or somewhat apiculate ends. *Raphe valve* with large, subquadrate central area. Striae, 11-14 in 10μ on both valves. Length, 22-35μ. Breadth, 10-12μ.

In my opinion, the features of this diatom do not differ enough from *A. lanceolata* to warrant a separate specific classification. The central area is bordered by short striae in much the same fashion as in variety *haynaldii*. The character of the striae does not seem to differ significantly. This variety is similar in shape and size to variety *apiculata,* but is readily distinguished from it by the rectangular—not diamond-shaped—central area. The significance of the four striae remnants in the central area (Sovereign's specimen) is not known.

Type locality. — U.S.A., Oregon, Crater Lake. (*Holotype*—Cal. Acad. Sci.-3466, Sov. 498.8, Sovereign, 1960.)

U. S. distribution. — GEOGRAPHICAL: Oregon. ECOLOGICAL: Insufficiently known. Sovereign (*loc. cit.*) finds it "scarce" in two samples with pH 8.1 and pH 8.

24. **Achnanthes lanceolata** var. **omissa** Reim. var. nov.
PL. 18, FIGS. 16-17

Valvae ellipticae, area centrali rhaphe valvae scutulata; striis paulum tenuioribus, 15 usque ad 18 in 10μ versus apices (Rhaphovalva); 13 usque ad 15 versus apices (Pseudoraphovalva). Longitudo valvarum 9-15μ, latitudo valvarum 6-6.5μ.

Valve broadly elliptical (oval) similar in shape to the shorter forms of the nominate variety. Differs principally in that the raphe valve has finer striae and a smaller, somewhat diamond-shaped central area. Striae, 15 in 10μ at the center of the valve to 18 in 10μ at the ends (RV); 13 in 10μ at the center to 15 in 10μ at the ends (PRV). Length, 9-15μ. Breadth, 6-6.5μ.

There is a tendency for this diatom to have more strongly curved striae than the nominate variety. Some of the smaller forms of variety *lanceolata* also have slightly curved striae but not to the degree shown by variety *omissa*.

This diatom is similar to Cleve's (1891, p. 51) *Achnanthes lanceolata* var. *elliptica* and, indeed, may often have been interpreted as a part thereof by other workers.

In checking the identity of some small specimens from Iowa which resembled Hustedt's illustrations and description of *A. lanceolata* var. *elliptica* Cl., it became necessary to examine some material of Cleve from the type locality (A-G.C. 12045). On this slide the same diatom was found which occurred in the Iowa collection, but it differed slightly from the diagnosis of Cleve.

Another *Achnanthes* was seen in Cleve's material which fits his diagnosis much more satisfactorily. The two are similar in appearance but closer observation shows some basic differences. The diatom in Cleve's material which I believe is his variety *elliptica* has rather coarse-appearing striae which are doubly punctate under the light microscope in much the same fashion as *A. stewartii*. This is not the case with the Iowa *Achnanthes* (variety *omissa*). The striae on the pseudoraphe valve of variety *omissa* are slightly less in number, and the valve itself is slightly more narrow than given by Cleve for variety *elliptica*. Even though the striae of *A. lanceolata* appear two to several times punctate under the electron microscope they give a solid or, under oblique light, a straight, finely lineate appearance rather different from that of variety *elliptica* of Cleve.

Schulz (1926, p. 192, figs. 41a, c) illustrates a diatom considered by him to be variety *elliptica* Cl. and shows the striae broken into coarse lines. Hustedt (1933, p. 411) speaks of "Struktureigentümlichkeiten" for variety *elliptica*. Hustedt's illustration is so presented that it is difficult to know whether he has Cleve's variety *elliptica* in mind or the variety *omissa*. He does not show, however, the shortened striae at the inner margin of the horseshoe-shaped area as is common to Cleve's specimens and which may be diagnostic. Cleve-Euler (1932, p. 55) considered variety *elliptica* of Cleve as a distinct species (thus creating a later homonym, for *A. elliptica* was used by Schumann in 1867, p. 63, pl. 2, fig. 27) which she retained in her later work (1953b, p. 16). In this same work she also uses the category *A. lanceolata* (gamma) *elliptica* Schulz for a diatom which somewhat resembles variety *omissa*, but which is probably not the same as Schulz's diatom. These names have no standing and must be rejected.

In my opinion variety *omissa* is distinct from Cleve's variety *elliptica*. I have not seen the latter in collections from this country.

Type locality. — U.S.A., Iowa, Dickinson Co., Lake West Okoboji, west side of Pillsbury Point, on rock at 1.5 meters depth. (*Holotype*—A-G.C. 8526, Reimer.)

U. S. distribution. — Geographical: Iowa. Ecological: Insufficiently known.

25. Achnanthes grimmei Krasske var. grimmei   pl. 18, figs. 22-23

Achnanthes grimmii Krasske, Abh. Ber. Ver. Naturk. Cassel, 56:30, pl. 1, fig. 10. 1925.

Valve linear to elliptical-lanceolate with broad, obtusely rounded, rostrate to subcapitate ends—not well set off from the valve body. *Raphe valve* with axial area broadening considerably toward the middle portion of the valve, forming a lanceolate space along the central axis. Central area a one-sided space extending to the margin which occasionally may be lacking according to Hustedt (1933, p. 400). Raphe filiform, not distinct; proximal ends broader than remainder of the raphe branches; distal ends curved slightly in the same direction. Striae slightly radiate throughout. *Pseudoraphe valve* with narrow axial area at extremities broadening into a lanceolate space as on the raphe valve. Central area as on the raphe valve. Striae slightly radiate throughout, coarser than on the raphe valve. Striae, 18-20 in 10μ at the center of the valve, becoming gradually finer toward the ends where the last few are 32 or more in 10μ (RV), Hustedt gives to 40 in 10μ (1933, p. 400); striae, 18-22 in 10μ at the center, becoming about 25 in 10μ near the ends (PRV). Length, 10-20μ. Breadth, 3-4μ.

Best distinguished from *Achnanthes affinis* by the lanceolate axial areas and the coarse striae at the center. Under optimum light conditions the striae appear indistinctly lineate, but since this feature is not ordinarily visible under oil immersion it has been deleted from the diagnosis and the illustration.

Type locality. — Uncertain, . . . haüfig in Mineralquellen des Gebietes . . . Nieder//Hessens [Germany].

U. S. distribution. — Geographical: Washington. Ecological: Found, so far, only from mineral springs.

26. Achnanthes peragalii Brun & Hérib. var. peragalii

pl. 19, figs. 1-2

Achnanthes peragalii Brun & Hérib. *in* Hérib., Diat. Auvergne, p. 50, pl. 1, fig. 4. 1893.

Valve broadly elliptical with protracted, rostrate to capitate ends. *Raphe valve* with filiform raphe; proximal raphe ends close; distal ends indistinct. Axial area narrow, expanding slightly at the central area;

central area an expanding rectangle. Striae strongly radiate, slightly curved. Central striae somewhat farther apart and of varying length. *Pseudoraphe valve* with lanceolate pseudoraphe of variable expansion, narrowing sharply at either end. Striae slightly radiate, more distant than on the raphe valve; interrupted on one side by a horseshoe-shaped clear area which is also of variable shape, but is broader at the valve margin. Striae, 23 in 10μ at the center, becoming about 27 in 10μ toward the ends (RV); 17 in 10μ at the center, becoming about 20 in 10μ near the ends (PRV). Length, 12-18μ. Breadth, 6-9μ.

Best distinguished by its nearly circular valve body and rostrate to capitate ends.

Hustedt says the raphe at the distal ends curves in opposite directions. I have never seen the diatom lying flat enough to be able to resolve this feature clearly. Also the pseudoraphe seems to vary considerably. In some specimens it is rather broad; in other cases it is nearly linear. This is quite analogous to the situation in Hustedt's concept of *Achnanthes oestrupii.* For further comment see the discussion under *A. peragalli* var. *parvula.*

Type locality. — [France], Puy-de-Dôme. Bords de l'étang de Chancelade; sur diverses algues filamenteuses (Montel).

U. S. distribution. — GEOGRAPHICAL: New England States, Middle Atlantic States, Southeastern States; Oregon. ECOLOGICAL: Reported mostly from lakes and smaller streams; pH "indifferent" (?).

26. **Achnanthes peragalli** var. **fossilis** Temp. & Perag.   PL. 19, FIGS. 3-5

Achnanthes peragalli var. *fossilis* Temp. & Perag., Diat. Monde Entier, 2nd ed., p. 113. 1909.

Ends short, apiculate—not rostrate to capitate as in the nominate variety. Other features the same. Striae, 22-23 in 10μ at the center, becoming about 27 in 10μ toward the ends (RV); 16 in 10μ at the center, becoming about 20 in 10μ near the ends (PRV). Length, 8-17μ. Breadth, 7-8.5μ.

This diatom may well be a part of the nominate variety, or only a form of it. I can, however, find no clear intergrades between the two. In the specimens I have seen the ends are either clearly (shorter) apiculate or (longer) rostrate to capitate. Smaller forms, 8-10μ long, still maintain this distinction. It seems best to retain this name until the problems in this and closely related taxa are thoroughly investigated.

The Tempère and Peragallo specimens (A-T.&P. 212) have a quite narrow pseudoraphe, but in other collections (i.e., A-G.C. 44254a) this area can be either narrow or broad. In a few cases there appear to be rudimentary extensions of the striae delimiting both a broad and a narrow pseudoraphe.

Type locality. — U.S.A., Connecticut, Tamarack Swamp.

U. S. distribution. — GEOGRAPHICAL: Southeastern States; Connecticut. ECOLOGICAL: Insufficiently known.

26. Achnanthes peragalli var. parvula (Patr.) Reim. comb. nov.

PL. 19, FIGS. 6-7

Achnanthes oestrupii var. *parvula* Patr., Farlowia, 2(2):169, pl. 1, figs. 6, 7. 1945.

Valve elliptical with short, subrostrate ends. Striae slightly more numerous than in the nominate variety. Other features the same. Striae, about 22 in 10μ at the center, becoming 28 in 10μ near the ends (RV); 15 in 10μ at the center, becoming about 18 in 10μ near the ends (PRV). Length, 9-12μ. Breadth, 6μ.

I cannot find sufficient differences between *A. oestrupi* var. *parvula* Patr. and *A. peragalli* Brun to warrant their continued separation under different specific epithets.

The circumscription and relationships of the species *Achnanthes oestrupii* (Cl.-Eul.) Hust. and *A. peragalli* Brun & Hérib. *in* Hérib. need to be examined further. Hustedt's diagnoses of these species (1930, p. 207; 1933, pp. 411-412) leave little other than shape and a "double-horseshoe" (*A. oestrupii*) as distinguishing features. Having seen this latter feature vary in *A. peragalli* from present and distinct to completely absent, I have little "faith" in it here as a distinctive characteristic. Unfortunately Cleve-Euler's type for *A. lanceolata* var. *oestrupii* (1922, p. 53) is based on a description and illustration of the pseudoraphe valve only (Østrup, 1899, p. 52, pl. 2, fig. 14). I have seen neither the Hollerup material nor any later illustration or discussion of the complete frustule from this original material.

Type locality. — U.S.A., Pennsylvania, Pike Co., Shohola Falls. (*Holotype*—A-G.C. 2209, Patrick, 1945.)

U. S. distribution. — GEOGRAPHICAL: Pennsylvania, South Carolina. ECOLOGICAL: Found to date only in relatively soft-water streams.

27. Achnanthes chilensis var. subaequalis Reim. var. nov.

PL. 19, FIGS. 8-9

Striae raphovalvae crassiores quam illis varietatis *chilensis.* Striae, 20-22 in 10μ (RV); 18-20 in 10μ (PRV). Longitudo, 8-14μ. Latitudo, 3-4μ.

Valve linear to linear-lanceolate with protracted, subcapitate to capitate ends. *Raphe valve* with narrow, linear axial area; no central area. Raphe distinct, filiform. Proximal raphe ends close; distal ends indistinct, but appearing straight. Striae parallel to slightly radiate. *Pseudoraphe valve* with the axial and the central areas united into a narrow, lanceolate space. Distinct tapering horseshoe-shaped area on one side at the valve center, narrower portion at the valve margin. Striae, likewise, parallel or slightly radiate. Striae, 20-22 in 10μ (RV); 18-20 in 10μ (PRV). Length, 8-14μ. Breadth, 3-4μ.

Distinguished from the *Achnanthes lanceolata* group primarily by the tapering horseshoe-shaped area; the portion at the margin being narrower—not wider—than the portion bordering the pseudoraphe.

Best distinguished from the nominate variety by the coarser striae on the raphe valve. Hustedt (1927, p. 238) gives about 30 in 10μ for the raphe valve striae and 20 in 10μ for the pseudoraphe valve striae. In this variety the striae number almost the same on both valves.

There is a tendency for the striae on the raphe valve to be slightly radiate towards the valve ends and parallel at the center of the valve, although exceptions can be found in any population. Under extremely good conditions of lighting the striae appear lineate, but due to the subtilty of this characteristic, it is not included in the diagnosis nor the illustration.

It is possible that variety *subaequalis* is the same as the invalidly published *A. harrisonii* (Cholnoky, 1959, p. 7).

In my opinion there are too many morphological similarities between this diatom and *A. chilensis* to consider it anything other than a variety thereof.

Type locality. — U.S.A., Florida, Santa Rosa Co., Escambia River, scraping off *Scirpus* sp. (*Holotype*—A-G.C. 4451a, Reimer.)

U. S. distribution. — GEOGRAPHICAL: Gulf Coast States. ECOLOGICAL: So far found only in slightly brackish- to fresh-water parts of coastal streams in the above area.

28. **Achnanthes coarctata** (Bréb. *in* W. Sm.) Grun. var. **coarctata**

PL. 19, FIGS. 10-11

Achnanthidium coarctatum Bréb. *in* W. Sm., Ann. Mag. Nat. Hist., Ser. 2,15:8, pl. 1, fig. 10. 1855.
Achnanthes coarctata (Bréb. *in* W. Sm.) Grun. *in* Cl. & Grun., K. Svenska Vet.-Akad. Handl., Ny Földj, 17(2):20. 1880.

Valve linear-elliptical; constricted at the center of the valve and produced with broadly rounded, truncate ends. Valve surface arched. *Raphe valve* with linear axial area; central area a rectangular stauros reaching the margins. Raphe recurved near the proximal ends. Proximal raphe ends abruptly rounded, not protruding into the central area; distal ends curving in the same direction. Striae radiate throughout, distinctly punctate. *Pseudoraphe valve* with submarginal to marginal, narrow pseudoraphe.

Striae irregularly parallel at the center of the valve becoming radiate, in some cases curved-radiate or nearly semicircular, near the ends; distinctly punctate as the raphe valve. Striae, 13-15 in 10μ (RV); 10-14 in 10μ (PRV). Puncta, 14-18 in 10μ on both valves. Length, $20\text{-}48\mu$. Breadth, $7\text{-}12\mu$.

Smaller and more finely structured than *Achnanthes temperei*. Also readily distinguished from *A. temperei* by the rostrate ends and the lack of large terminal nodules.

This taxon may have an earlier name, but information at hand is not sufficient to warrant a change at the moment. Ehrenberg (1843, p. 422, pl. 1(2), fig. 12b) describes a similar looking form from Chile as *Stauroneis constricta*. Later in *Mikrogeologie* (1854, pl. 34 (5B), figs. 1-2) he describes an *Achnanthes binodis* from Africa which also looks similar. If it can be established that either of these is to be included here, the earliest name will have to be adopted.

William Smith (*loc. cit.*) cites an earlier reference to *A. coarctatum* (Kütz., 1849, p. 54), but the name does not appear in Kützing's work at all. Therefore, the original citation must be that of Wm. Smith as given.

Type locality. — Uncertain . . . France, Cave near Royat; England, Grassmere, Westmorland.

U. S. distribution. — GEOGRAPHICAL: New England States, Middle Atlantic States, Southeastern States; Florida, Ohio, Oregon. ECOLOGICAL: Aerophil, often found on soil, rocks, mosses, etc.; occasionally found in flowing water; pH "indifferent."

29. **Achnanthes temperei** M. Perag. var. **temperei**   PL. 19, FIGS. 12-13

> *Achnanthes temperei* M. Perag. *in* Temp. & Perag., Diat. Monde Entier, 2nd ed., p. 100. 1908.
> *Achnanthepyea temperei* M. Perag., Deux. Exped. Antarctic Française, 1908-1910, Bot., Diat., p. 13, pl. 1, figs. 35-37. 1921.

Valve linear-lanceolate with cuneate extremities and a slight to moderate constriction of the center. *Raphe valve* with linear axial area; central area a rectangular stauros extending to the margins. Raphe branch twice twisted (lateral); proximal raphe ends rounded, bulbous; distal ends curving in the same direction. Striae areolate, coarse; parallel or slightly radiate. *Pseudoraphe valve* with narrow, linear, submarginal to marginal pseudoraphe which ends at the large terminal nodules. Striae as on the raphe valve. Areolae rows, 8-10 in 10μ on both valves. Length, 38 to about 75μ. Breadth, $12\text{-}15\mu$.

Best distinguished from *Achnanthes brevipes* Ag. to which it is related, by the large terminal nodules on the pseudoraphe valve.

The diatom listed by Cleve & Möller on their slide no. 204 as "*A. contracta* var." (from Oakland, California) appears to be a part of this taxon.

Type locality. — U.S.A., Connecticut, Quinnipiac River, Davis Pit.

U. S. distribution. — GEOGRAPHICAL: Connecticut, Texas, California. ECOLOGICAL: Distributed from extreme upper- to middle-tidal portions of coastal rivers.

30. Achnanthes curvirostrum Brun var. curvirostrum

PL. 19, FIGS. 14, 19

Achnanthes curvirostrum Brun, Diatomiste, 2, pl. 16, figs. 84-85. 1895.

Valve broadly elliptical to linear-lanceolate with narrow, protracted, apiculate or subrostrate to rostrate ends. Ends slightly to moderately curved or "bent" in opposite directions. *Raphe valve* with narrow axial area, thickened as a siliceous rib and curving slightly, in sigmoid fashion, into the ends. Central area circular with distinct central nodule. Raphe filiform toward extremities, but broader toward the bulbous proximal raphe ends. Distal raphe ends curved in opposite directions. Striae radiate, distinctly punctate. *Pseudoraphe valve* with narrow pseudoraphe, curving slightly at the ends in sigmoid fashion. Central area very small and circular, or lacking. Striae radiate, distinctly punctate. Striae, 11 in 10μ, becoming 14 in 10μ near the ends (RV); 12 in 10μ (PRV). Brun shows about 7 in 10μ striae (PRV). Puncta, 18-20 in 10μ (RV); 16 in 10μ (PRV). Length, 25-50μ. Breadth, 13-16μ.

Distinguished by the characteristic curved or "bent" ends.

Our specimens vary from the illustrations of J. Brun (*loc. cit.*) in that the striae on the pseudoraphe valve measure about 12 in 10μ instead of about 7 in 10μ as in Brun's fig. 85. Examination of the following slide: A-T.&P. 949, Morris Cove, Connecticut, U.S.A., Sondage, shows all pseudoraphe valves with about 12 striae in 10μ. It is possible either that the striae count does vary as low as 7 in 10μ on the pseudoraphe valve or that Brun counted the striae at the margins where the count does go below 10 in 10μ.

Type locality. — U.S.A., Mories Cove, Connecticut, U. S. (Tempère) Sondage.

U. S. distribution. — GEOGRAPHICAL: Gulf Coast States; Connecticut, Virginia. ECOLOGICAL: Insufficiently known; found to date in slightly to moderately brackish water.

31. Achnanthes inflata (Kütz.) Grun. var. inflata

PL. 19, FIGS. 15-16

Stauroneis inflata Kütz., Bacill., p. 105, pl. 30, fig. 22. 1844.
Achnanthes ventricosa Ehr., Mikrogeol., p. 266, pl. 1(2), figs. 9-10; pl. 1(3), figs. 18a-c, (?) 19a-d. 1854. [*non A. ventricosa* Kütz. 1844.]
Achnanthes inflata (Kütz.) Grun. *in* Reise Novara, Bot., vol. 1, p. 7. 1870.

Valve in outline twice strongly concave forming a gibbous center, and two long, capitate extremities. Valve surface highly arched and longitudinally undulate. *Raphe valve* with linear, slightly sinuous axial area flaring into a widening stauros central area. Raphe sinuous as the axial area, twice recurved; proximal raphe ends rounded, not protruding into the central fascia; distal ends curving in the same direction. Striae slightly radiate, composed of large distinct puncta. *Pseudoraphe valve* with narrow, linear, eccentric pseudoraphe, submarginal to marginal; no central area. Striae parallel except at the ends where they become curved, radiate; composed of large distinct puncta as on the raphe valve. Striae, 10-13 in 10μ (RV); 9-11 in 10μ (PRV). Puncta, 10-12 in 10μ (RV); about 9 in 10μ (PRV). Length, $30\text{-}65\mu$. Breadth, $10\text{-}18\mu$.

The well known diatomist, R. Ross of the British Museum of Natural History, has done considerable work on this taxon. In a letter to the senior author, he indicates that the name *inflata* has been incorrectly applied to this diatom. Having seen neither the Kützing material nor other type material at Ross' disposal which bear on the problem, I am not as qualified to make a reasonable judgment at this time and, therefore, yield to his publication of these findings.

Type locality. — [Caribbean Islands], Insel Trinidad.

U. S. distribution. — Geographical: Gulf Coast States; New Jersey, Georgia, Washington(?). Ecological: Found in neutral to alkaline waters and can withstand some salt intrusion (oligohalobe-"indifferent").

31. Achnanthes inflata var. elata (Leud.-Fortm.) Hust.

PL. 19, FIGS. 17-18

Navicula elata Leud.-Fortm., Mém. Soc. Emul. Côtes-du-Nord, 15:187. 1878.
Achnanthes inflata var. *elata* (Leud.-Fortm.) Hust., Arch. Hydrobiol. Suppl., 15(2): 206, pl. 14, figs. 12-13. 1937.

Valve linear to linear-elliptical with less gibbous center than the nominate variety, and with long, subrostrate to rostrate extremities forming only one distinct undulation. Other features as in the nominate variety. Striae, 10-13 in 10μ (RV); 9-11 in 10μ (PRV). Puncta, 10-12 in 10μ (RV); about 9 in 10μ (PRV). Length, $30\text{-}50\mu$; Hustedt gives 96μ (1937b, p. 206). Breadth, $10\text{-}16\mu$; Hustedt gives 21μ (*loc. cit.*).

Larger forms as reported by Hustedt have not been seen from this country.

Type locality. — Ceylon.

U. S. distribution. — Geographical: Texas. Ecological: As the nominate variety.

Names of Taxa reported from the U. S. (fresh water) which could not be verified by a specimen from a public herbarium.

Achnanthes americana Cl. (recorded by Boyer).
Achnanthes biasolettiana (?Kütz.) Grun. (recorded by Curtis and Boyer).
Achnanthes calcar Cl. (recorded by Sovereign).
Achnanthes conspicua A. Mayer (recorded by Hohn and Silva).
Achnanthes conspicua var. *brevistriata* Hust. (recorded by Silva).
Achnanthes didyma Hust. (recorded by Sovereign).
Achnanthes dispar Cl. (recorded by Hohn).
Achnanthes exilis Kütz. (recorded by Curtis, Chase, and Tiffany & Britton).
Achnanthes hudsonis Grun. *in* V. H. (recorded by Curtis and DeToni).
Achnanthes oestrupi (A. Cl.) Hust. (recorded by Sovereign).
Achnanthes pachypus Mont. (recorded by Ehrenberg).
Achnanthes trinodis (W. Sm.) Grun. (recorded by Curtis).
Cocconeis minuta Cl. (*Achnanthes?*) (recorded by Boyer).

Names of taxa reported from the U. S.
which are of uncertain application

Achnanthes delicatula (Kütz.) Grun. (recorded by Cleve, Boyer and Hohn).

Taxa Recorded Since 1960

Achnanthes biporoma Hohn & Hellerm. (recorded by Hohn & Hellerman, 1963).
Achnanthes chlidanos Hohn & Hellerm. (recorded by Hohn & Hellerman, 1963).
Achnanthes detha Hohn & Hellerm. (recorded by Hohn & Hellerman, 1963).
Achnanthes lanceolata var. *bimaculata* Hust. (recorded by Hohn, 1961).
Achnanthes lapponica (Hust.) Hust. (recorded by Reimer, 1962).
Achnanthes laterostrata Hust. (recorded by Hohn & Hellerman, 1963).
Achnanthes minutissima var. *macrocephala* Hust. (recorded by Hohn & Hellerman, 1963).
Achnanthes minutissima var. *robusta* Hust. (recorded by Hohn & Hellerman, 1963).
Achnanthes monela Hohn & Hellerm. (recorded by Hohn & Hellerman, 1963).
Achnanthes prava Sov. (recorded by Sovereign, 1963).
Achnanthes ricula Hohn & Hellerm. (recorded by Hohn & Hellerman, 1963).
Achnanthes rupestoides Hohn (recorded by Hohn, 1961).
Achnanthes subatomus Hust. (recorded by Hohn & Hellerman, 1963).
Achnanthes subhudsonis var. *kraeuselii* Choln. (recorded by Hohn and Hellerman, 1963).

Genus **Rhoicosphenia** Grun.

Grun., Verh. Zool.-Bot. Ges. Wien, 10:511. 1860.

Frustules attached to a substrate by a stalk. Both valve and girdle views appear wedge-shaped although some valves are nearly symmetrical and assume a more nearly linear-lanceolate shape. In girdle view the frustule is bent or bowed. Thus there is a concave and a convex valve, the former having a completely developed raphe, the latter having only rudimentary raphe slits near the extremities. The raphe valve has a central nodule which is clearly seen in girdle view. Both valves possess a well-developed pseudoseptum at each end. Striae are parallel or radiate and finely punctate. The puncta are arranged rather close so that under the light microscope they appear (and are described here) as lineate.

Type species. — Gomphonema curvatum Kütz., [= *Rhoicosphenia curvata* (Kütz.) Grun. *ex* Rabh.]

1. **Rhoicosphenia curvata** (Kütz.) Grun. *ex* Rabh. var. **curvata**

PL. 20, FIGS. 1-5

Gomphonema curvatum Kütz., Linnaea, 8:567, pl. 16, fig. 51. 1833.
Rhoicosphenia curvata (Kütz.) Grun. *ex* Rabh., Fl. Europaea Alg., pp. 112, 342. 1864.
Rhoicosphenia curvata var. *subacuta* M. Schmidt *in* A. S., Atlas Diat., pl. 213, figs. 6-7. 1899.
Rhoicosphenia curvata var. *major* Cl., K. Svenska Vet.-Akad. Handl., Ny Földj, 27(3):165. 1895.

Valve variable in outline from clavate to linear-lanceolate, clearly heteropolar to nearly isopolar. Valve extremities bluntly to narrowly rounded, not distinguished from valve body. *Raphe valve* (concave valve) with narrow, linear axial area and small elongate central area. Raphe filiform; proximal ends slightly enlarged, distal ends indistinct. Striae slightly radiate, sometimes becoming parallel towards the ends. Central striae broader and less numerous than those near the ends. Striae lineate. *Rudimentary raphe valve* (convex valve) with narrow, linear axial area and no central area. Rudimentary raphe short; branch extending from foot pole about one-sixth to one-fifth the length of the valve; branch extending from head pole even shorter, usually about one-half the length of the lower raphe branch and sometimes difficult to see. Striae generally parallel, but may appear somewhat radiate near the extremities; lineate as on the raphe valve. Central striae slightly broader and less numerous than those near the ends. Striae, 9-15 in 10μ at the center, becoming 16-20 in 10μ near the ends (RV); about 11-13 in 10μ at the center, becoming 16-18 in 10μ near the ends (RRV). Length, 12-75μ. Breadth, 4-8μ.

Although Grunow, in erecting the genus *Rhoicosphenia*, indicated the type as *Gomphonema curvatum*, he did not actually make the combination *Rhoicosphenia curvata*. As near as I can determine this combination was first made in Rabenhorst (1864, *loc. cit.*).

Type locality. — Germany; exact locality uncertain.

U. S. distribution. — Geographical: New England States, Middle Atlantic States, Southeastern States, South Central States, East Central States, West Central States, Lakes States, Plains States; Montana, Wyoming, Colorado, New Mexico, Utah, Washington, Oregon, California. Ecological: A widespread species more commonly found in alkaline flowing waters (alkaliphil, rheophil?), not characteristic of lower gradients of coastal rivers and probably to be considered as "oligohalobe."

Names of Taxa reported from the United States (fresh water) which could not be verified by a specimen from a public herbarium.

Rhoicosphenia curvata var. *gracilis* M. Schmidt *in* A. S.

284

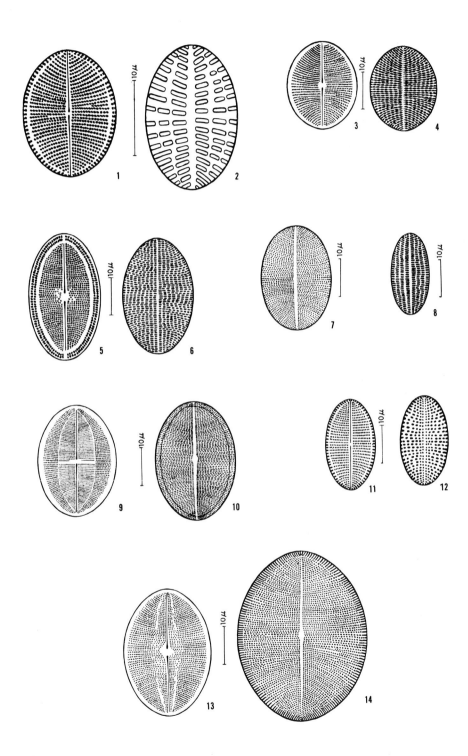

PLATE 16

Fig. 1 – 2. *Achnanthes microcephala* A-Boyer G-7-11, Pennsylvania, Ithan, Fountain in Evans Arboretum.

Fig. 3 – 4. *Achnanthes linearis* A-Feb. 3120, Scotland, Lasswade.

Fig. 5 – 6. *Achnanthes linearis* var. *pusilla* A-G.C. 2115, Pennsylvania, Monroe Co., Davy's Run, open sun, running water, on or enmeshed in weeds.

Fig. 7 – 8. *Achnanthes nollii* A-G.C. 45843a, Kentucky, Mühlenberg Co., Green River.

Fig. 9 –10. *Achnanthes minutissima* A-Kütz. Dec. 8, No. 75, Ad Zygnema ad Aschersleben.

Fig. 11 –12. *Achnanthes affinis* A-G.C. 6695a, Arizona, Havasu Canyon, Supi [Supai].

Fig. 13 –14. *Achnanthes linearis* f. *curta* A-Boyer A-5-4, New Jersey, Elm, sides of a greenhouse tank.

Fig. 15 –17. *Achnanthes wellsiae* nom. nov. A-G.C. 8077, Texas, Orange Co., Sabine River.

Fig. 18 –20. *Achnanthes deflexa* sp. nov. A-G.C. 1931, Indiana, Marshall Co., Lake Maxinkuckee, east side of the lake (drawing of Holotype.)

Fig. 21 –22. *Achnanthes exigua* A-G.C. 5702, Nebraska, Hamilton Co., Platte River near Grand Island, floating at edge of pond.

Fig. 23 –24. *Achnanthes exigua* var. *constricta* A-Boyer Z-4-19, Pennsylvania, Philadelphia Co., Philadelphia, from a bottle of water kept three years.

Fig. 25 –26. *Achnanthes exigua* var. *heterovalva* A-G.C. 44811, Maryland, Frederick Co., Monocacy River.

Fig. 27 –28. *Achnanthes hungarica* A-G.C. 5345, Montana, Missoula Co., three miles SW of Missoula, soil algae by lake.

Fig. 29 –30. *Achnanthes lapponica* var. *ninckei* comb. nov. A-G.C. 6776a, Utah, Cache Co., Stream Mill Creek.

Fig. 31 –32. *Achnanthes flexella* A-H.L.Sm. 7, France, Moulins.

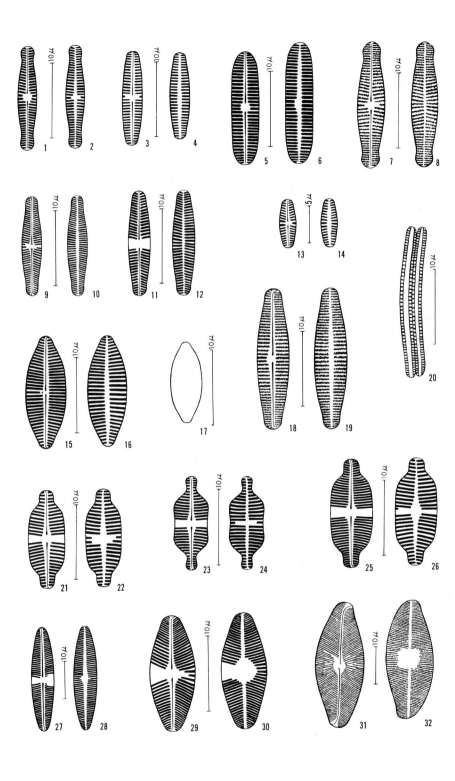

PLATE 17

Fig. 1 – 2. *Achnanthes marginulata* A-G.C. 5140, Colorado, Long's Peak, in shallow streamlet.

Fig. 3 – 4. *Achnanthes levanderi* A-G.C. 6776b, Utah, Cache Co., Stream Mill Creek.

Fig. 5 – 6. *Achnanthes sublaevis* var. *crassa* var. nov. A-G.C. 44716a, New Jersey, Mercer Co., Assunpink River (drawing of Holotype).

Fig. 7 – 8. *Achnanthes gibberula* A-Boyer O-7-10, Wyoming, Yellowstone Park.

Fig. 9 –10. *Achnanthes hustedtii* comb. nov. A-G.C. 45009, Pennsylvania, Lititz Creek.

Fig. 11 –12. *Achnanthes stewartii* A-G.C. 2194, Pennsylvania, Pike Co., Lake Wallenpaupack (drawing of Holotype).

Fig. 13 –14. *Achnanthes saxonica* A-G.C. 8523, California, Contra Costa Co., San Joaquin River.

Fig. 15 –16. *Achnanthes lemmermanni* A-G.C. 7051a, California, Contra Costa Co., San Joaquin River.

Fig. 17 –18. *Achnanthes pinnata* A-G.C. 43939a, Maryland, Frederick Co., Potomac River.

Fig. 19 –20. *Achnanthes lewisiana* A-G.C. 2210, Pennsylvania, Pike Co., Shohola Falls, scraping from rock (drawing of Holotype).

Fig. 21 –22. *Achnanthes clevei* A-G.C. 4592a, Virginia, Scott Co., Clinch River.

Fig. 23 –24. *Achnanthes clevei* var. *rostrata* A-G.C. 4181a, Canada, Ontario, Greville Co., St. Lawrence River.

Fig. 25 –32. *Achnanthes hauckiana* A-G.C. 6565b, Texas, Orange Co., Sabine River.

Fig. 33 –34. *Achnanthes hauckiana* var. *rostrata* A-G.C. 6565b, Texas, Orange Co., Sabine River.

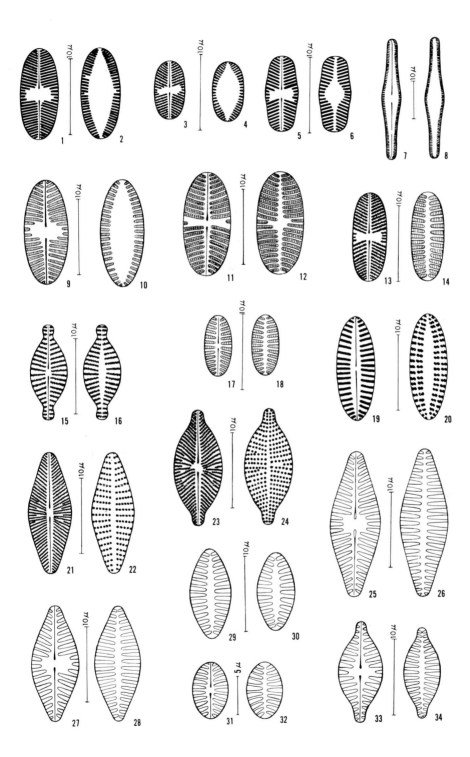

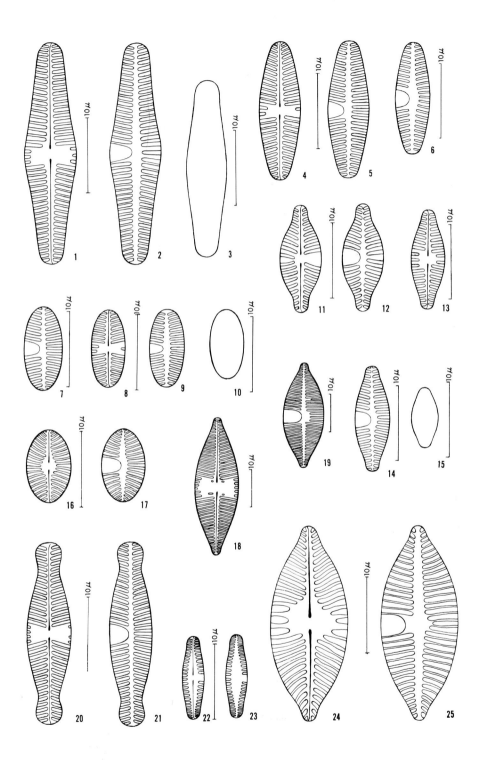

PLATE 19

Fig. 1 – 2. *Achnanthes peragalli* A-G.C. 2200, Pennsylvania, Pike Co., Shohola Falls.

Fig. 3 – 4. *Achnanthes peragalli* var. *fossilis* A-T. & P. 212, Connecticut, Tamarack Swamp.

Fig. 5. *Achnanthes peragalli* var. *fossilis*, (PRV) A-G.C. 44254a, South Carolina, Aiken Co., Upper Three Runs Creek.

Fig. 6 – 7. *Achnanthes peragalli* var. *parvula* comb. nov. A-G.C. 2209, Pennsylvania, Pike Co., Shohola Falls (drawing of Holotype).

Fig. 8 – 9. *Achnanthes chilensis* var. *subaequalis* var. nov. A-G.C. 4451a, Florida, Santa Rosa Co., Escambia River Station 5, left bank, scrapings off *Scirpus* (drawing of Holotype).

Fig. 10 –11. *Achnanthes coarctata* A-H.L.Sm. 6, France, St. Aubert.

Fig. 12 –13. *Achnanthes temperei* A-T. & P. 187, Connecticut, Quinnipiac River, Davis Pit.

Fig. 14. *Achnanthes curvirostrum*, (RV) A-T. & P. 949, Connecticut, Morris Cove.

Fig. 15. *Achnanthes inflata*, (RV) A-Boyer U-1-5, Alabama, Montgomery Co., Montgomery.

Fig. 16. *Achnanthes inflata*, (PRV) A-Boyer A-5-16, Philippine Islands, Luzon, Manila.

Fig. 17. *Achnanthes inflata* var. *elata* A-G.C. 8024, Texas, Jefferson Co., Neches River.

Fig. 18. *Achnanthes inflata* var. *elata* A-G.C. 8524, Texas, Jefferson Co., Neches River.

Fig. 19. *Achnanthes curvirostrum*, (PRV) A-T. & P. 949, Connecticut, Morris Cove.

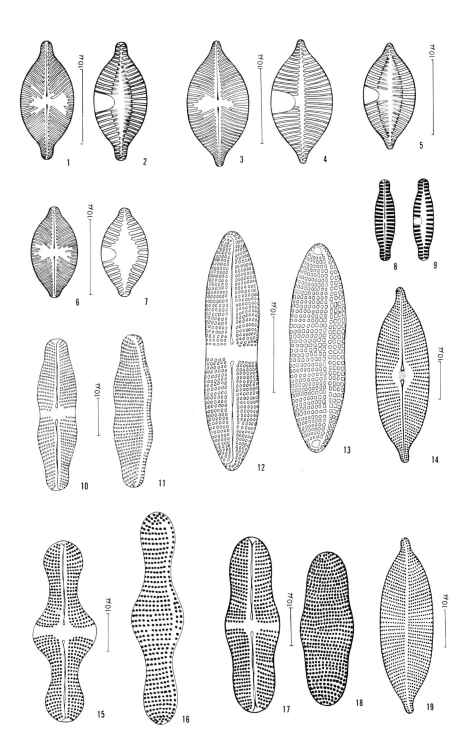

Order **NAVICULALES**

Bessey, Univ. Nebraska Stud., 7:284. 1907.

Structure of the frustules is variable but characterized by having on both valves a well-developed raphe extending from the apices of the valve toward the center. In many genera the two median ends of the raphe are connected by an internal canal. The raphe is not enclosed in a canal and is usually on the surface of the valve and not in a keel. The exception is the Amphiproraceae in which the axial area lies in a keel-like projection. In some genera the raphe lies in or between siliceous ribs.

The surface of the valve is simple in most genera of this order; it may be convex or concave, but does not possess wing-like projections as in the Surirellaceae.

This order contains most of the species found in fresh water.

Type family. — Naviculaceae.

KEY TO THE FAMILIES OF THE NAVICULALES

1. Raphe lying in a keel-like projection of the valve . . . . Amphiproraceae
1. Raphe not in a keel-like projection of the valve 2
   2. Valve symmetrical to the apical and pervalvar axis, and usually to the transverse axis except in those genera with sigmoid shaped valves or sigmoid raphe . . . . Naviculaceae
   2. Valve asymmetrical to the apical or transverse axis 3
3. Valve asymmetrical to the transverse axis, one half of the valve often broader than the other . . . . Gomphonemaceae
3. Valve asymmetrical to the apical axis, symmetrical to the transverse axis
                                              Cymbellaceae

Family **NAVICULACEAE** Kütz.

Kütz., Bacill., p. 88. 1844.

The genera belonging to this family are characterized by having a well-developed raphe on both valves of the frustule. The frustules are typically symmetrical to the apical and perivalvar axis, and they are symmetrical to the transverse axis except in those genera where the shape of the valve is sigmoid and in those genera in which the raphe and axial areas are sigmoid. They may or may not have intercalary bands and internal septa.

This is the largest family of diatoms found in fresh water. Many of the species belonging to this family are also found in brackish and marine water.

Type genus. — *Navicula* Bory.

KEY TO THE GENERA OF NAVICULACEAE

1. Valves with septa 2
1. Valves without septa 3
    2. Septa marginal, not extending across the valve, loculate ... *Mastogloia* (p. 297)
    2. Septa extending across the valve surface, not loculate .... *Diatomella* (p. 296)
3. Valve sigmoid 5
3. Valve not sigmoid 4
    4. Raphe sigmoid, valve with diagonal symmetry .... *Scoliopleura* (p. 643)
    4. Raphe not sigmoid, symmetry of valve not diagonal 6
5. Longitudinal and transverse striae on valve surface perpendicular to each other
                                           Gyrosigma (p. 312)
5. Longitudinal and transverse striae not at a 90 degree angle to each other
                                           Pleurosigma (p. 330)
    6. Valve with two longitudinal canals—one on each side of the axial area
                                       Diploneis (p. 408)
    6. Valve without such canals 7
7. Valve with marginal ridges or furrows, striae distinctly punctate
                                       Neidium (p. 383)
7. Valve otherwise formed 8
    8. Raphe lying in or between two siliceous ribs 9
    8. Raphe not so formed 11
9. Raphe extending the whole length or most of the length of the valve 10
9. Raphe usually very short, and the central area linear; if raphe longer, the central
   area of irregular width .... *Amphipleura* (p. 302)
    10. Terminal nodule rounded or like a pencil point .... *Frustulia* (p. 304)
    10. Terminal nodule not so shaped .... *Frickia* (p. 311)
11. Striae not costa-like or with chambered structure 12
11. Striae costa-like and with a chambered structure 15
    12. Central area a stauros (thickened area) or tigilla present 13
    12. Central area not a stauros 14
13. Tigilla (X shaped thickenings) present .... *Capartogramma* (p. 372)
13. Tigilla absent .... *Stauroneis* (p. 357)
    14. Striae crossed by longitudinal, hyaline, somewhat thickened lines, usually
      the striae are not clearly defined throughout part of their length
                                     Anomoeoneis (p. 373)
    14. Striae usually definitely formed throughout their length, if not so they are
      not crossed by well defined hyaline lines .... *Navicula* (p. 439)
15. Striae apparently crossed by one or more narrow longitudinal bands near the
   margin of the valve .... *Caloneis* (p. 577)
15. Striae not apparently crossed by bands or if so, the bands are fairly broad
                                     Pinnularia (p. 590)
15. Striae divided into segments by one or more siliceous ribs ...... *Oestrapia* (p. 576)

Genus **Diatomella** Grev. nom. cons.

Grev., Ann. Mag. Nat. Hist., Ser. 2, 15:259. 1855.
Disiphonia Ehr., Mikrogeol., pl. 35A(2), fig. 7. 1854.

Frustules forming filaments. Frustules in girdle view rectangular; intercalary bands present. The structure of the septa evident in girdle view by the thickening of the intercalary bands. Each septum with three large holes, one at each end of the valve and one at the center of the valve below the median ends of the raphe. Valve with marginal striae and a large central area. Raphe distinct.

This genus is distinguished by the formation of the septa which are evident in valve or girdle view.

When this genus was described it consisted of a single species, and thus, the generic description is very brief.

Type species. — Diatomella balfouriana (W. Sm.) Grev.

1. **Diatomella balfouriana** Grev. var. **balfouriana**   PL. 20, FIGS. 6-7

> *Diatomella balfouriana* Grev., Ann. Mag. Nat. Hist., Ser. 2, 15:259, pl. 9, figs. 10-13. 1855.
> *Grammatophora?* *Balfouriana* W. Sm., Brit. Diat., vol. 2, p. 43. 1856.

Valve linear or with slightly convex sides and rounded apices. A septum extends the entire length of the valve with three large holes, one at each end of the valve and one at the center of the valve. Axial area and central area forming a broad, linear space. Raphe straight, terminal fissures indistinct. Median ends of the raphe somewhat distant from each other. Striae marginal; parallel in the middle portion of the valve, somewhat radiate toward the apices. Striae, 18-22 in 10μ. Length, 12-55μ. Breadth, 6-8μ.

This taxon is distinguished by the characteristics of the septum and the broad central area.

Type locality. — Not specifically indicated, but title of article in which the genus and species is described is "Report on a collection of Diatomaceae made in the District of Braemar by Prof. Balfour and Mr. George Lawson."

U. S. distribution. — GEOGRAPHICAL: Wyoming. ECOLOGICAL: Often found in mountainous conditions, prefers cool water of low nutrient content.

Genus **Mastogloia** Thwaites *ex* W. Sm.

Thwaites *ex* W. Sm., Syn. British Diat., vol. 2, pp. 63-64. 1856.

Valve elliptical to lanceolate or linear with broad and bluntly rounded to protracted, capitate ends. Axial area narrow. Raphe generally wavy or lateral in some portions of each branch, but may be filiform and straight. Central area generally small; may be expanded on both sides to form an H-configuration. Striae mostly slightly radiate to parallel, coarsely to finely punctate. Transapical ribs between the striae sometimes rather thick, costate. Puncta variously arranged in obliquely decussating, straight, or undulating longitudinal rows.

Distinctive intercalary band with loculi (marginal chambers) present on the inner side of the band. Chambers may be of equal or of varying sizes in a single band.

Most of the species in this genus are marine or brackish-water forms. Only a few taxa are found in strictly fresh water.

Boyer (1927b, p. 327) gives the type for this genus as "*Mastogloia dansei* Thw." Actually *M. danseii* was originally described in 1848 as *Dickieia danseii* by Thwaites and this name should be applied as the type.

Type species. — *Dickieia danseii* Thwaites. 1848. [= *Mastogloia elliptica* var. *danseii* (Thwaites *ex* W. Sm.) Cl.].

KEY TO THE SPECIES OF MASTOGLOIA

1. Valve with central area expanded to produce an H-configuration; central loculi larger than toward ends of intercalary band 2
1. Valve with central area elliptical, circular, or rectangular, but not as above; central loculi about the same size as remaining loculi 3
   2. Raphe filiform, not twisted or lateral; frustules generally small, not exceeding about 40μ in length .... [4] *M. pumila*
   2. Raphe twisted or lateral, not filiform; frustules generally larger, up to about 95μ in length .... [5] *M. braunii*
3. Striae broad, composed of double rows of puncta .... [1] *M. grevillei*
3. Striae narrower, composed of a single row of puncta 4
   4. Raphe essentially filiform with a slight deflection occasionally noted midway between proximal and distal ends; central striae not conspicuously in longer and shorter sequence 5
   4. Raphe with conspicuous lateral portion midway between proximal and distal ends; central striae alternately longer and shorter ..... [3] *M. elliptica* var. *danseii*
5. Central area rectangular, extending to outer border of loculi
                                              [2] *M. smithii* var. *lacustris*
5. Central area more elliptical, not extending to outer border of loculi 6
   6. Valve with protracted, distinctly capitate ends ... [2] *M. smithii* var. *amphicephala*
   6. Valve with short, subrostrate to subcapitate ends .... [2] *M. smithii*

1. **Mastogloia grevillei** W. Sm. var. **grevillei**   PL. 20, FIGS. 8-9

Mastogloia grevillii W. Sm., Syn. British Diat., vol. 2, pp. 65-66, pl. 62, fig. 389. 1856.

Valve linear with cuneate to subrostrate and bluntly rounded ends. Axial area linear, narrowing toward the ends. Raphe becoming quite lateral about midway between the proximal and distal ends. Distal raphe ends curving over the ends of the valve in the same direction. Central area orbicular, rather small. Conspicuous transapical ribs present; radiate, becoming nearly parallel at the ends; between each two ribs are two rows of puncta arranged in diagonal series. Loculi of intercalary band about equal in size; inner margins straight or slightly convex. Striae, 9-10 in 10μ. Puncta, about 20 in 10μ. Loculi, 6-8 in 10μ. Length, 30-60μ. Breadth, 8-12μ.

This species is best distinguished by the double rows of puncta separated by thickened costate ribs.

Type locality. — Uncertain, fresh water. Pentland Hills. . . .

U. S. distribution. — GEOGRAPHICAL: New England States; Indiana, Michigan, Nebraska. ECOLOGICAL: Most often observed as a littoral form in lakes and ponds, occasionally from slow-flowing rivers.

2. **Mastogloia smithii** Thwaites *ex* W. Sm. var. **smithii**

PL. 20, FIGS. 10-11

Mastogloia smithii Thwaites *ex* W. Sm., Syn. British Diat., vol. 2, p. 65, pl. 54, fig. 341. 1856.

Valve elliptical to elliptical-lanceolate with short, protracted, subrostrate to subcapitate ends. Axial area narrow, linear. Raphe filiform, very slightly lateral about midway between the center and the valve ends; distal ends curving in the same direction at extreme ends of the valve. Central area small, elliptical to nearly quadrangular; margins not extending to edge of the chambers. Striae parallel or very slightly radiate; punctate. Loculi of intercalary band about equal in size; inner margin of loculi slightly convex. Striae, 18-19 in 10μ. Puncta, 14-17 in 10μ. Loculi, 6-8 in 10μ. Length, 20-45μ; Hustedt (1930, p. 216) gives length up to 65μ. Breadth, 8-14μ; Hustedt (*loc. cit.*) gives breadth up to 16μ.

This species is usually considered to have a straight, filiform raphe, but a very slight bulge or lateral displacement of the raphe can sometimes be noted about midway on each raphe branch. This feature is characteristic in most species of *Mastogloia*, but is usually much more prominent. The slight broadening in *M. smithii* can be detected by observing the raphe while changing focus. A very small thickening resembling a terminal nodule is apparent at either end of the valve. The distal raphe ends appear to curve to one side of this.

Longer specimens (53μ—Cleve, 1894, p. 52; 65μ—Hustedt, 1930, p. 216) have not been seen from this country.

Type locality. — Uncertain, fresh or brackish water. 'Little Sea,' Dorsetshire . . . [England].

U. S. distribution. — GEOGRAPHICAL: New England States, Gulf Coast States, South Central States, East Central States, Lakes States, Plains States. ECOLOGICAL: Fresh and brackish water. More often reported from freshwater lakes (oligohalobe, indifferent?).

2. **Mastogloia smithii** var. **amphicephala** Grun.   PL. 20, FIGS. 14-15

Mastogloia smithii var. *amphicephala* Grun. *in* V. H., Syn. Diat. Belgique, pl. 4, fig. 27. 1880.

Valve with more protracted, distinctly capitate ends. Other features as in variety *smithii*. Striae, 18-19 in 10μ. Puncta, 14-17 in 10μ. Loculi, 6-8 in 10μ. Length, 30-45μ. Breadth, 10-14μ.

The valve ends in this taxon tend to be more flattened-capitate than rounded-capitate.

In our collections this variety exhibits a very small size range. Illustrations in the literature also fall within this range. If further observations confirm this, the probability that it is only a part of the nominate variety should be considered.

Type locality. — Uncertain, possibly Belgium.

U. S. distribution. — GEOGRAPHICAL: New York, Illinois, Michigan, Kansas, New Mexico. ECOLOGICAL: A fresh-water, lake form. Reported by others from coastal brackish water, but we have no such United States records to date.

2. Mastogloia smithii var. lacustris Grun. PL. 20, FIGS. 12-13

Mastogloia smithii var. *lacustris* Grun. *in* Schneider, Naturw. Beitr. Kenntn. Kaukasusländer, p. 111. 1878.

Striae slightly coarser, 15-16 in 10μ, than in variety *smithii*. Central area larger, more rectangular. Lateral margins of the central area extending to outer border of the loculi. Other features as in variety *smithii*. Striae, 15-16 in 10μ. Puncta, 13-15 in 10μ. Loculi, 6-8 in 10μ. Length, 20-45μ. Breadth, 8-11μ.

Although the shape of this variety does vary somewhat as the nominate variety, it is more generally linear-lanceolate—not elliptical-lanceolate. The striae also tend to be somewhat more radiate than in variety *smithii*.

Type locality. — Kaukasusländer, . . . Süsswasserseen.

U. S. distribution. — GEOGRAPHICAL: New England States, East Central States, Lakes States; Kansas, Montana, Utah. ECOLOGICAL: More commonly found in fresh-water lakes as a shore form; sometimes in springs; reported occasionally from slightly brackish water.

3. Mastogloia elliptica var. danseii (Thwaites) Cl. PL. 20, FIGS. 20-23

Dickieia danseii Thwaites, Ann. Mag. Nat. Hist., Ser. 2, 1:171-172, pl. 12(K), figs. 1-4. 1848.
Mastogloia danseii (Thwaites) W. Sm., Syn. British Diat., vol. 2, p. 64, pl. 62, fig. 388. 1856.
Mastogloia elliptica var. *danseii* (Thwaites) Cl., K. Svenska Vet.-Akad. Handl., Ny Följd, 27(3):152-153. 1895.

Valve linear-elliptical with parallel or slightly convex sides and broad, cuneate extremities. Axial area narrow, linear. Raphe becoming abruptly broad (lateral) about midway between the center and the ends of the valve; distal ends curving in the same direction. Central area orbicular.

Striae radiate throughout; distinctly punctate. Central striae alternately longer and shorter. Loculi of about equal size; inner margins convex. Striae, 16-18 in 10μ. Puncta, about 16 in 10μ. Loculi, 8-10 in 10μ. Length, 20-51μ. Breadth, 11-15μ. Hustedt (1933, p. 502) gives to 80μ.

The nominate variety has been reported from several United States localities, but examination of the material revealed that they were merely somewhat shorter forms of variety *danseii* with slightly convex sides. The variety *elliptica* has markedly convex sides, a lesser length-to-breadth ratio, and less cuneate ends than variety *danseii*.

Type locality. — . . . upon rocks on the tidal shore of the river Tamar. [Devonport ? (Plymouth), England].

U. S. distribution. — Geographical: New York, Virginia, Texas, Michigan, Utah. Ecological: A halophilic to mesohalobic taxon characteristic of coastal areas. Also found in inland lakes with some salinity (high conductivity?).

4. **Mastogloia pumila** (Grun.) Cl. var. **pumila**   PL. 20, FIGS. 16-17

> *Mastogloia braunii* var. *pumila* Grun. *in* V. H., Syn. Diat. Belgique, pl. 4, fig. 23.
> 1880. (text, p. 71. 1885.)
> *Mastogloia pumila* (Grun.) Cl., K. Svenska Vet.-Akad. Handl., Ny Följd, 27(3):
> 157. 1895.

Valve elliptical-lanceolate to linear-lanceolate with slightly protracted, broadly rounded ends. Axial area very narrow. Raphe straight, filiform; distal ends curving in the same direction. Central area contiguous with a narrow, longitudinal clear area on either side forming an H-configuration. Striae parallel to very slightly radiate; finely punctate. Loculi considerably larger in the middle than toward the ends of the band; inner margins convex. Striae, 22-24 in 10μ. Loculi, 3-4 in 10μ in the middle; 6-8 in 10μ on either side. Length, 25-41μ. Breadth, 8-10μ.

This diatom is best distinguished from *Mastogloia braunii* by its smaller size, filiform—not wavy—raphe, and the character of the loculi. In *M. braunii* the chambered portion of the intercalary band extends nearly to the point where the ends differentiate. In *M. pumila* the loculi stop some distance from the ends. The central loculi of *M. pumila* are also larger and less numerous than the central loculi of *M. braunii*. On this basis there seems to be little justification for considering this taxon a variety of *M. braunii* as Grunow has done.

Hustedt (1933, p. 553) records specimens of this taxon as small as 20μ long and 5μ wide. None of the United States specimens seen have been this small. Hustedt also extends the striae range to about 30 in 10μ. Our specimens are coarser and within the range given by Grunow *in* Van Heurck and by P. T. Cleve.

Type locality. — Uncertain, possibly Belgium.

U. S. distribution. — GEOGRAPHICAL: Virginia, Texas. ECOLOGICAL: Brackish water to marine (mesohalob?). Characteristic of bays and estuaries along the east coast and the Gulf of Mexico.

5. **Mastogloia braunii** Grun. var. **braunii**   PL. 20, FIGS. 18-19

Mastogloia braunii Grun., Verh. Zool.-Bot. Ges. Wien, 13:156, pl. 4, fig. 2. 1863.

Valve lanceolate with rounded extremities. Axial area linear, narrowing near the ends. Raphe wavy, having two noticeable twists—one near the proximal ends and one about midway on each raphe branch; distal ends curving slightly in the same direction. Central area contiguous with longitudinal clear areas on each side, forming an H-configuration. Striae slightly radiate; punctate; crossed by a longitudinal "line" on each side. Loculi larger in the middle than toward the ends of the band; inner margins convex. Striae, 15-20 in 10μ. Puncta, about 16-20 in 10μ. Loculi, 4.5-6 in 10μ in the middle, becoming 8-8.5 in 10μ toward the ends. Length, 30-95μ. Breadth, 14-29μ.

The longitudinal "lines" in this diatom appear to be the result of a depression of the valve on either side of the axial area making the midline area of the valve lower than the peripheral portion. These "lines" were probably interpreted by Grunow (*loc. cit.*) and others as an extension of the H-shaped area.

Type locality. — Asia Minor, El Tor, ad litoral maris rubri prope El Tor, ubi legit *Charae crinitae* insidentem.

U. S. distribution. — GEOGRAPHICAL: Maine, California. ECOLOGICAL: Brackish water, estuarine (mesohalob?).

Names of Taxa reported from the U. S. (fresh to brackish water) which could not be verified by a specimen from a public herbarium.

Mastogloia elliptica (Ag.) Cl. (recorded by Elmore and Boyer).

Genus **Amphipleura** Kütz.

Kütz., Bacill., p. 103. 1844.

This genus is distinguished by the structure of the raphe and the siliceous rib which encloses it. It is most closely related to the genus *Frustulia* Grun. *in* Rabh.

Valve fusiform to linear-lanceolate. A thick siliceous rib lies in the apical axis of the valve, bifurcates toward each apex, and ends in a nodule. Raphe situated between bifurcations. Transverse striae very fine, punctate. Puncta arranged so they usually form longitudinal lines, but in some cases such as *Amphipleura rutilans* (Trent.) Cl. they are indistinct.

An excellent discussion of the relationships of this genus is given by Cleve (1894, p. 125). The frustules are free living or enclosed in gelatinous tubes. These species are usually found in fairly hard fresh water or in more or less brackish water.

Type species. — Frustulia pellucida Kütz. [= *Amphipleura pellucida* (Kütz.) Kütz. (type designated by Boyer, 1927)].

1. **Amphipleura lindheimeri** Grun. var. **lindheimeri** PL. 21, FIGS. 1a-b

Amphipleura lindheimeri Grun., Verh. Zool.-Bot. Ges. Wien, 12:469, pl. 13, figs. 11a-b. 1862.
Amphipleura pellucida var. *lindheimeri* (Grun.) Cl., K. Svenska Vet.-Akad. Handl., Ny Följd, 26(2):126. 1894.

Valve broadly fusiform with obtusely rounded ends. Siliceous rib between the ends of the raphe, narrow-linear but wider than in *Amphipleura pellucida* (Kütz.) Kütz., irregularly widened in the middle of the valve. Length of each branch of the raphe varies from one-third to one-sixth the length of the valve. Striae parallel, distinctly punctate; 26-28 in 10μ. Longitudinal lines undulate; 26-28 in 10μ, or sometimes not quite so numerous as the transverse striae. Length, $120-330\mu$. Breadth, $23-27\mu$.

This species is closely related to *A. pellucida* (Kütz.) Kütz. from which it mainly differs by: (1) the variable length of the branches of the raphe and (2) the siliceous rib which connects the two parts of the raphe is usually wider in the middle than at the ends. Hustedt (1937c, p. 725) gives an excellent account of the systematics of this species.

Type locality. — . . . in aquis torrentibus Americae borealis (on rocks in the rapids of Comale Creek leg. cl. Lindheimer 1845) [U.S.A., Texas].

U. S. distribution. — GEOGRAPHICAL: Texas.

2. **Amphipleura pellucida** (Kütz.) Kütz. var. **pellucida** PL. 21, FIGS. 2a-b

Frustulia pellucida Kütz., Linnaea, 8:543, pl. 13, fig. 11. 1833.
Amphipleura pellucida (Kütz.) Kütz., Bacill., p. 103, pl. 3, fig. 52; pl. 30, fig. 84. 1844.

Valve narrow, elongate to linear-lanceolate with rounded, obtuse ends. Branches of the raphe short, $15-20\mu$. Siliceous rib connecting branches of the raphe narrow; definitely not variable in width as in some species. Transverse striae parallel throughout most of the valve, somewhat radiate at the ends; 37-40 in 10μ. Longitudinal lines (formed by the arrangement of the puncta) finer and very difficult to count. Length, $80-140\mu$. Breadth, $7-9\mu$.

This species is characterized by the short branches of the raphe which do not vary much in length, and by the narrow, straight siliceous rib which connects them. The siliceous rib is not variable in width as in some species.

Type locality. — Germany, Weisenfels. (*Lectotype*—A-Kütz. Dec. 9, No. 83, Patrick.)

U. S. distribution. — GEOGRAPHICAL: New England States, Middle Atlantic States, Southeastern States, Gulf Coast States, South Central States, East Central States, West Central States, Lakes States, Plains States; Arizona, Washington. ECOLOGICAL: This species is usually found in fairly hard water, sometimes in slightly brackish water.

3. **Amphipleura rutilans** (Trent.) Cl. var. **rutilans**   PL. 21, FIG. 3

> *Conferva rutilans* Trent. *in* Roth, Catalecta Bot., Fasc. 3:179.   1806.
> *Schizonema dillwynii* Ag., Syst. Alg., p. 10.   1824.
> *Amphipleura rutilans* (Trent.) Cl., K. Svenska Vet.-Akad. Handl., Ny Földj, 26(2): 126.   1894.

Valve linear-lanceolate with rounded ends. Length of each branch of the raphe about one-third the length of the valve. Median ends of the raphe sometimes bent to one side. Striae parallel at the center of the valve, radiate toward the ends. Longitudinal lines indistinct. Transverse striae, 24-28 in 10μ at the center of the valve to 30 in 10μ at the ends. Length, $15-35\mu$. Breadth, $4-6\mu$.

This species is distinguished by its small size and somewhat coarser striae than those found in *Amphipleura pellucida*. It is closely related to *A. micans* Lyngb. which is also a salt-water species and lives in gelatinous tubes.

Type locality. — . . . prope Eckwarden Ducatus Oldenburgiei (in den alten Pütten) observavit clariss . . . [Germany].

U. S. distribution. — GEOGRAPHICAL: New England States, Middle Atlantic States, Gulf Coast States; Washington, California. ECOLOGICAL: Brackish water.

Genus **Frustulia** Rabh. nom. cons., non Agardh 1824

Rabh., Süssw.-Diat., p. 50.   1853.
Vanheurckia Bréb., Ann. Soc. Phytol. Microgr. Belgique, 1(13/14):201-202.   1868.

Frustules living singly or enclosed in a gelatinous tube. Intercalary bands and septa absent. Valve naviculoid in shape. Raphe groove between two siliceous ribs that fuse at the terminal nodule; often appearing as a single rib, so that it appears as if the raphe longitudinally bisects the siliceous rib. The two ends of the raphe not connected at the central nodule. The terminal nodule thickened, the shape of a pencil point. Longitudinal and transverse striae present, through most of the valve at 90 degree angles.

The valves are symmetrical to the apices, transapical and pervalvar axes.

This genus is most closely related to the genus *Amphipleura* from which it differs in the structure of the raphe and the central area.

An excellent discussion of the structure of the frustule of this genus is given by Hustedt (1935b, pp. 246-264).

Agardh did not typify his genus *Frustulia*.

Type species. — Frustulia saxonica Rabh.

KEY TO THE SPECIES OF FRUSTULIA

1. Raphe curved, dividing the valve asymmetrically . . . . [1] *F. asymmetrica*
1. Raphe straight, dividing the valve symmetrically 2
  2. Terminal nodule swollen and then abruptly attenuated, "pencil point" in shape   3
  2. Terminal nodule not so formed, valve linear with rounded ends . . . [2] *F. interposita*
3. Median ends of the raphe turned to one side, surrounded by an asymmetrical central area . . . . [5] *F. weinholdii*
3. Median ends of the raphe straight 4
  4. Striae in the middle of the valve radiate, central area rounded . . . . . [4] *F. vulgaris*
  4. Striae in the middle of the valve perpendicular to the raphe; central area linear, slightly constricted or lanceolate in shape, sometimes elongated
[3] *F. rhomboides* & vars.

1. **Frustulia asymmetrica** (Cl.) Hust. var. **asymmetrica**   PL. 22, FIG. 4

Frustulia vulgaris var. *asymmetrica* Cl., K. Svenska Vet.-Akad. Handl., Ny Följd, 26(2):122, pl. 5, fig. 29. 1894.
Frustulia asymmetrica (Cl.) Hust., Ber. Deutschen Bot. Ges., 67:269. 1954.

Valve asymmetric-elliptical with obtuse ends. Raphe eccentric, more approximate to the less convex side. The raphe at the terminal nodule has two lateral extensions. Terminal nodules at some distance from the ends of the valve. Central area small, asymmetrical. Transverse striae slightly radiate at the center of the valve, parallel at the ends. Striae finely punctate, 22-30 in 10μ. Cleve states the longitudinal lines are 19-23 in 10μ, whereas Hustedt says they are finer than the transverse striae. Length, 50-75μ. Breadth, 14-18μ.

Type locality. — U.S.A., New Jersey.

U. S. distribution. — GEOGRAPHICAL: New Jersey, Georgia. ECOLOGICAL: Found in water of low mineral content, slightly acid. Hustedt (*loc. cit.*) records it as a brackish water form.

2. **Frustulia interposita** (Lewis) Cl. var. **interposita**   PL. 22, FIG. 5

Navicula interposita Lewis, Proc. Acad. Nat. Sci. Philadelphia, for 1865:18, pl. 2, fig. 19. 1865.

Frustulia ? interposita (Lewis) DeT., Syll. Alg., vol. 2, sect. 1, p. 278. 1891.
Frustulia interposita (Lewis) Cl., K. Svenska Vet.-Akad. Handl., Ny Földj, 26(2):123. 1894.

Valve linear-elliptical with broadly rounded ends. The characteristic terminal nodule for the genus *Frustulia* which is a narrow "porte-crayon" is not present, instead the siliceous rib is not attenuated. This is the condition also in *Frustulia interposita* var. *incomperta* (Lewis) Cl. Central area slightly wider than the axial area. Transverse striae parallel, distinct; 20-22 in 10μ. Longitudinal striae parallel, 16-20 in 10μ. Length, 100-130μ. Breadth, 23-27μ.

This taxon differs from *Frustulia interposita* var. *incomperta* by its smaller size and its coarser striae.

Type locality. — Uncertain, South America, Paraiba Harbor.

U. S. distribution. — GEOGRAPHICAL: Southeastern States; New Jersey, California. ECOLOGICAL: Found in water of low mineral content.

3. Frustulia rhomboides (Ehr.) DeT. var. rhomboides   PL. 21, FIG. 5

Navicula rhomboides Ehr., Phys. Abh. Akad. Wiss. Berlin, for 1841:419, pl. 3(1), fig. 15. 1843.
Vanheurckia rhomboides (Ehr.) Bréb., Ann. Soc. Phytol. Microgr. Belgique, 1(13/14):204. 1868.
Frustulia rhomboides (Ehr.) DeT., Syll. Alg., vol. 2, sect. 1, p. 277. 1891.

Valve rhombic-lanceolate, narrowing sharply to the rounded apices. Axial and central areas narrow but distinct. Transverse striae perpendicular to the raphe at the center of the valve, sometimes becoming slightly convergent toward the ends of the valve, but radiate at the apices. Transverse striae, 20-30 in 10μ. Longitudinal striae, 20-30 in 10μ. Length, 70-160μ. Breadth, 15-30μ.

Type locality. — Mexico, Hidalgo Prov., Real del Monte.

U. S. distribution. — GEOGRAPHICAL: New England States, Middle Atlantic States, Southeastern States, Gulf Coast States, South Central States, East Central States, West Central States, Lakes States; Montana, Wyoming, Utah, Washington, Oregon, California. ECOLOGICAL:Commonly found in bogs or lakes in slightly acid water. Recorded in the tropics in pH of 7-8.

3. Frustulia rhomboides var. amphipleuroides (Grun.) Cl.

PL. 21, FIG. 4

Navicula (Vanheurckia) rhomboides var. *amphipleuroides* Grun. *in* Cl. & Grun., K. Svenska Vet.-Akad. Handl., Ny Földj, 17(2):47, pl. 3, fig. 59. 1880.
Frustulia rhomboides var. *amphipleuroides* (Grun.) Cl., K. Svenska Vet.-Akad. Handl., Ny Földj, 26(2):123. 1894.
Vanheurckia rhomboides var. *amphipleuroides* (Grun.) Patr., Farlowia, 2(2):170. 1945.

This variety differs from the nominate variety in that the siliceous ribs enclosing the raphe are slightly eccentric and bent a little; and also the central nodule is elongate. Transverse striae, 22-24 in 10μ. Longitudinal striae, 18-24 in 10μ. Length and breadth as in nominate variety.

Type locality. — Jenissey bei Korepowskoi.

U. S. distribution. — GEOGRAPHICAL: New England States, Middle Atlantic States, Southeastern States, South Central States, West Central States; Montana, Washington. ECOLOGICAL: In slightly acid water of low mineral content.

3. **Frustulia rhomboides** var. **capitata** (A. Mayer) Patr. comb. nov.

PL. 21, FIG. 8

> *Frustulia saxonica* var. *capitata* A. Mayer, Denkschr. Bayer. Bot. Ges. Regensburg, 13 (N.F. 7):30, pl. 3, fig. 7. 1917.
> *Frustulia rhomboides* var. *saxonica* f. *capitata* (A. Mayer) Hust. *in* Pasch., Süssw.-Fl. Mitteleuropas, Heft 10, Aufl. 2, p. 221. 1930.
> *Vanheurckia rhomboides* var. *crassinervia* f. *capitata* (A. Mayer) Patr., Farlowia, 2(2):171. 1945.

Valve linear-lanceolate with distinctly capitate apices. Siliceous ribs enclosing the raphe narrow, widened toward the center of the valve. Ribs constricted at the center of the valve as is characteristic for *Frustulia rhomboides*. Transverse and longitudinal striae, 24-30 in 10μ. Length, 40-60μ. Breadth, 10-13μ.

This variety differs from the nominate variety by its smaller size, distinctly capitate apices, and very fine striae. The longitudinal striae are sometimes slightly undulate at the center of the valve.

Hustedt has made this variety a form of *F. rhomboides* var. *saxonica*. It seems preferable to make it a variety of *F. rhomboides* because if one recognized only one taxon with smaller size and finer striae as a variety, then both varieties *crassinervia* and *capitata* would logically become forms. There is no evidence that they have evolved from *F. rhomboides* var. *saxonica*. It is more probable that these three entities represent separate lines of differentiation. One might consider variety *crassinervia* as an undulate form of variety *capitata* or *vice versa*.

Type locality. — Nördlichen Oberpfalz, Fichtelgebirge, "Karges." [Germany].

U. S. distribution. — GEOGRAPHICAL: Pennsylvania. ECOLOGICAL: Slightly acid water of low mineral content.

3. **Frustulia rhomboides** var. **crassinervia** (Bréb. *ex* W. Sm.) Ross

PL. 22, FIG. 1

> *Navicula crassinervia* Bréb *ex* W. Sm., Syn. British Diat., vol. 1, p. 47, pl. 31, fig. 271. 1853.

Vanheurckia crassinervia (Bréb. *ex* W. Sm.) Bréb., Ann. Soc. Phytol. Microgr. Belgique, 1(13/14):204. 1868.

Vanheurckia rhomboides var. *crassinervia* (Bréb.) V. H., Syn. Diat. Belgique, p. 112. 1885. (*pro parte.*)

Frustulia rhomboides var. *crassinervia* (Bréb. *ex* W. Sm.) Ross, Natl. Mus. Canada Bull., No. 97, pt. 2, pp. 212-213. 1947. (*pro parte.*)

Valve lanceolate to elliptical-lanceolate with attenuated, rostrate apices. Margins of the valve slightly undulate. Axial area narrow; central area not expanded, the same width as the axial area. Striae very fine. Transverse striae, 36-40 in 10μ. Longitudinal striae appear to be a little finer than the transverse striae. Longitudinal striae, probably about 40 in 10μ. Length, 30-50μ. Breadth, 10-15μ.

There has been a great deal of confusion in the literature as to the distinction between this taxon and *Frustulia rhomboides* var. *saxonica*. Some authors have synonymized them; others have regarded them as separate entities. The main differences in the two taxa are that the margins of the valve in variety *saxonica* are smooth, whereas in variety *crassinervia* they are undulate. Also the apices in variety *saxonica* are not attenuate and are slightly rostrate, whereas in variety *crassinervia* they are somewhat attenuated and rostrate.

Rabenhorst (1864, p. 227) considered the two taxa as distinct; however, Brébisson (*loc. cit.*, 1868) synonymizes Rabenhorst's taxon with his. However, one cannot be sure that Brébisson saw Rabenhorst's specimens. Certainly William Smith's illustrations and specimens of Brébisson's taxa which I have seen are different in the shape of the valve from Rabenhorst's specimens. Van Heurck's slide no. 162 which he cites in his description of *Vanheurckia rhomboides* var. *crassinervia* has both taxa on the slide.

Both taxa are very distinct in the United States where I have found them.

Type locality. — Uncertain.

U. S. distribution. — Geographical: Middle Atlantic States, Southeastern States. Ecological: Seems to prefer oligotrophic to somewhat dystrophic water.

3. **Frustulia rhomboides** var. **saxonica** (Rabh.) DeT.   pl. 21, fig. 7

Frustulia saxonica Rabh., Süssw.-Diat., p. 50, pl. 7, fig. 1. 1853. (Bacill. Sachs. No. 42. 1851.)

Frustulia rhomboides var. *saxonica* (Rabh.) DeT., Syll. Alg., vol. 2, sect. 1, p. 277. 1891.

Vanheurckia rhomboides var. *saxonica* (Rabh.) Mills & Phillips., Trans. Hull Sci. Club, 1:173, pl. 18, fig. 26. 1901.

Valve lanceolate to rhombic-lanceolate; apices slightly drawn out and rounded. Transverse and longitudinal striae very fine. Transverse striae, 36 in 10μ. Longitudinal striae, 40 in 10μ. Length, 40-70μ. Breadth, 12-20μ.

This variety is distinguished from the nominate variety mainly by its smaller size and finer striae.

Rabenhorst (1864, p. 227) states that the striae are "32-36 in 0,001″" which is 13-14 in 10μ. However, his authenticated specimens which he states are the same as his specimen of the type are very finely striated.

Many diatomists have synonymized *Navicula crassinervia* Bréb. *ex* W. Sm. with this taxon. Rabenhorst (1876, p. 122) states that "if now Dr. Woodward maintains that *F. saxonica* is identical with *N. crassinervia* we must suppose that he is ignorant of one or the other of them." It is evident that Rabenhorst considered these two taxa distinct from each other.

Type locality. — Uncertain, Saxony.

U. S. distribution. — GEOGRAPHICAL: New England States, Middle Atlantic States, Southeastern States, South Central States, East Central States, West Central States, Plains States.

3. **Frustulia rhomboides** var. **viridula** (Bréb.) Cl.   PL. 21, FIG. 6

> *Colletonema viridulum* Bréb. *ex* Kütz., Sp. Alg., p. 105. 1849.
> *Schizonema viridulum* (Bréb.) Rabh., Fl. Europaea Alg., sect. 1, p. 266. 1864.
> *Vanheurckia viridula* (Bréb.) Bréb., Ann. Soc. Phytol. Microgr. Belgique, 1(13/14): 203. 1868.
> *Frustulia viridula* (Bréb.) DeT., Syll. Alg., vol. 2, sect. 1, p. 278. 1891.
> *Frustulia rhomboides* var. *viridula* (Bréb.) Cl., K. Svenska Vet.-Akad. Handl., Ny Följd, 26(2):123. 1894.

Valve linear-lanceolate; slightly attenuated toward somewhat rostrate, rounded ends. Median ends of the raphe a little more distant from each other than in the nominate taxon. Siliceous ribs enclosing the raphe wider at the central area—not notched as is typical for *Frustulia rhomboides* (Ehr.) DeT. Sometimes the ribs appear wider on one side of the central nodule than on the other. Transverse striae parallel. Longitudinal and transverse striae 26-30 in 10μ. Length, 80-110μ. Breadth, 14-16μ.

I have examined specimens of Brébisson on H. L. Smith Type Slide 88. Smith says that these specimens are part of the original material. The above description is based on these and other specimens.

Type locality. — France, Falaise.

U. S. distribution. — GEOGRAPHICAL: East Central States; Connecticut, Washington. ECOLOGICAL: Usually found in water of low mineral content.

4. **Frustulia vulgaris** (Thwaites) DeT. var. **vulgaris**   PL. 22, FIG. 3

> *Schizonema vulgare* Thwaites, Ann. Mag. Nat. Hist., Ser. 2, 1:170, pl. 12(H), figs. 1-5. 1848.

Vanheurckia vulgaris (Thwaites) V. H., Syn. Diat. Belgique, p. 112. 1885. (as
    Schizonema vulgare; pl. 17, fig. 6. 1880.)
Frustulia vulgaris (Thwaites) DeT., Syll. Alg., vol. 2, sect. 1, p. 280. 1891.
Brebissonia vulgaris (Thwaites) Kuntze, Revisio Gen. Plant., vol. 3, pt. 2, p. 398.
    1898.

Valve lanceolate to linear-lanceolate with subrostrate, rounded ends.
Central area about central nodule rounded. Median ends of the raphe
somewhat distant from each other. Transverse striae slightly radiate at the
center of the valve, sometimes slightly convergent near the ends. Transverse striae, 24 in 10μ at the center of the valve to 34 in 10μ at the ends.
Longitudinal striae, 26-35 in 10μ. Length, 50-70μ. Breadth, 10-13μ.

This species is distinguished by its size, shape, and the striae which
are slightly radiate at the center of the valve and may be slightly convergent at the ends.

Type locality. — England.

U. S. distribution. — GEOGRAPHICAL: New England States, Middle Atlantic States, Southeastern States, Gulf Coast States, South Central States,
East Central States, West Central States, Lakes States, Plains States;
Montana, Wyoming, New Mexico, California. ECOLOGICAL: Usually found
in water of low mineral content which is circumneutral.

5. **Frustulia weinholdii** Hust. var. **weinholdii**   PL. 22, FIG. 2

Frustulia weinholdii Hust. *in* Rabh., Kryptog.-Fl. Deutschland, vol. 7(2), no. 5,
    p. 731, fig. 1101. 1937.

Valve linear-lanceolate with rounded to capitate ends. Terminal nodules
of the raphe somewhat distant from the ends of the valve. Median ends of
the raphe turned to one side and surrounded by a large asymmetrical
central area. Transverse striae parallel or slightly radiate at the center of
the valve, strongly radiate at the ends. Transverse striae, 30-34 in 10μ at
the center of the valve to 40 in 10μ at the ends. Longitudinal striae a little
coarser, slightly undulate. Length, 40-60μ. Breadth, 7-10μ.

This species is most easily distinguished by the asymmetrical central
area and the structure of the median ends of the raphe.

This species was illustrated, but not described in A.S., *Atlas Diat.* (1936,
pl. 406, figs. 7-8). A discussion of the range in structure of this species is
given by Wallace (1960, p. 2).

Type locality. — Germany, near Kassel.

U. S. distribution. — GEOGRAPHICAL: New England States, Middle Atlantic States, Southeastern States, Gulf Coast States, South Central States;
California. ECOLOGICAL: Found in water of low mineral content.

Species Recorded Since 1960

Frustulia rhomboides f. *occidentalis* Sov. (recorded by Sovereign, 1963).

Genus **Frickia** Heid. *in* A. S.

Heid. *in* A. S., Atlas Diat., pl. 264, fig. 1. 1906.

This genus can be recognized easily by the terminal nodule of each end of the raphe being a narrow rib between the ends of the longitudinal ribs which enclose the raphe, the markings on the valve surface extending over longitudinal ribs, and the structure of the central nodule.

This monotypic genus is closely related to *Frustulia;* the valves are linear to linear-lanceolate. The longitudinal ribs which enclose the raphe are expanded as thin lamellae under the raphe into a canal-like space which communicates with the inside of the cell by a somewhat narrowed slit. The raphe is a simple slit or groove. The terminal nodules are in the form of narrow ribs and extend a little further toward the apices of the valves than the longitudinal ribs which enclose the raphe. These ribs are below the surface of the valve and vary in thickness. The central nodule appears as an elongate dark spot surrounded by a bright ring. The apparent "transverse poroid striae" are formed, according to Hustedt, by the intersection of fine longitudinal and transverse ribs. The transverse ribs and, therefore, the "poroid striae" are parallel at the center of the valve and radiate toward the ends of the valve. At the ends of the valve they may be very irregular in structure. The fine longitudinal ribs are irregular and wavy.

An excellent description of the structure of the frustule of this genus is given by Hustedt (1935b, p. 247).

Type species. — Navicula lewisiana Grev. [= *Frickia lewisiana* (Grev.) Heid.].

1. **Frickia lewisiana** (Grev.) Heid. var. **lewisiana**   PL. 22, FIGS. 6a-c

Navicula lewisiana Grev., Trans. Micr. Soc. London, New Ser., 11:15, pl. 1 fig. 7. 1863.
Frustulia lewisiana (Grev.) DeT., Syll. Alg., vol. 2, sect. 1, p. 278. 1891.
Frickea lewisiana (Grev.) Heid. *in* A. S., Atlas Diat., pl. 264, fig. 1. 1906.

Valve linear, a little narrower at the broadly rounded ends. Raphe between two siliceous ribs which are on the inner surface of the valve. Raphe ending in a cylindrical polar nodule which ends at a considerable distance from the apex of the valve. The ends of the siliceous ribs may clasp the cylindrical polar nodule and simulate a "porte-crayon," or they may be almost straight as shown in the illustration. The siliceous ribs are somewhat thicker about the central nodule. Near the central nodule and near the polar nodules they are crossed for a short distance by the punctate striae. For the rest of the length of the valve they are clear. Transverse striae punctate, usually 24-26 in 10μ. Lewis states they are 20-24 in 10μ, whereas Dr. Wallick (according to Greville) states they are 34 in 10μ. Longitudinal striae not visible. Length variable, 225-300μ. Breadth, 40-45μ.

This species is the only one in this genus. It is easily recognized by the structure of the raphe and the two siliceous ribs.

Type locality. — Uncertain, United States.

U. S. distribution. — Geographical: Middle Atlantic States, Southeastern States; Florida. Ecological: Brackish water.

Genus **Gyrosigma** Hass. nom. cons.

Hass., British Freshw. Alg., vol. 1, p. 435. 1845.

Valve elongated, slightly to strongly sigmoid. Intercalary bands lacking. Axial area narrow, sigmoid to undulate. When the axial area and the raphe form an extra curvature near the central area, they are considered as being undulate. When no such recurving is apparent, they are called sigmoid. Raphe mostly inconspicuous except at the ends. Outer proximal raphe ends curved in opposite directions forming a hook, or straight; inner ends straight. Outer distal raphe ends usually indistinct, but often apparent as a hook toward the margin; inner distal raphe ends straight. Central area small, orbicular; (longitudinally) elliptical or irregular and diagonal. Terminal area central or eccentric. Central and terminal nodules present, not always coinciding with axial and terminal areas. Striae punctate. Puncta forming both transverse and longitudinal rows.

One species of this genus, *Gyrosigma eximium*, is known to grow in tubes (*Endosigma* Bréb.); all the others appear to be free living.

Type species. — *Navicula hippocampus* Ehr. [? *Gyrosigma attenuata* (Kütz.) Rabh.].

KEY TO THE SPECIES OF GYROSIGMA

1. Valves with narrow elongate beaks sharply distinguished from valve body; beaks not exceeding 3μ in width 2
1. Valves with broader and shorter beaks or with extremities not sharply distinguished from valve body 4
   2. Transverse striae fine, at least 26 in 10μ; valves large, about 150-270μ long . . . . [19] *G. macrum*
   2. Transverse striae coarser, not exceeding about 22 in 10μ; valves smaller, 60-150μ long 3
3. Transverse striae above and below central area slightly to moderately convergent; axial area and raphe becoming eccentric at juncture of valve body and beaks, fresh-water species . . . . [17] *G. wormleyi*
3. Transverse striae above and below central area parallel; axial area and raphe central at juncture of valve body and beaks, brackish-water species . . . [18] *G. fasciola*

4. Longitudinal striae, 12 in 10μ near axial area, becoming about 20 in 10μ toward margins, valves with very broad bluntly rounded ends . . [16] *G. hummii*

4. Longitudinal striae not, or only slightly, variable in number from axial area to valve margins, valves with narrower rounded or pointed ends 5

5. Valves with scalpelliform extremities (valve margins in terminal 10μ asymmetrically attenuated) 6

5. Valves with other than scalpelliform extremities (valve margins in terminal 10μ symmetrically attenuated) 12

6. Valves 20-32μ wide, longitudinal striae coarse, not exceeding 16 in 10μ 7

6. Valves narrower, not exceeding 15μ in width, longitudinal striae finer, not less than 22 in 10μ 8

7. Valves abruptly attenuated, central area about 10-12μ long . . . . . . [13] *G. balticum*

7. Valves gradually attenuated, central area about 5-7.5μ long
[13] *G. balticum* var. *californicum*

8. Valves with diagonal central area and distant outer proximal raphe ends; longitudinal striae 22-24 in 10μ . . . . [8] *G. nodiferum*

8. Valves with elliptical or orbicular central area; outer proximal raphe ends not distant; longitudinal striae finer, not less than 27 in 10μ 9

9. Raphe strongly sigmoid, approaching or reaching valve margin near extremities, longitudinal striae very fine (near 40 in 10μ) . . . . [11] *G. obscurum*

9. Raphe not strongly sigmoid, not approaching valve margin near extremities; longitudinal striae not exceeding 30-31 in 10μ 10

10. Outer proximal raphe ends in the form of a question mark, axial area and raphe slightly undulate, central except near the ends where they become slightly eccentric . . . . [9] *G. temperei*

10. Outer proximal raphe ends curved in opposite directions or straight, not shaped like a question mark; axial area and raphe sigmoid, diagonal 11

11. Valve extremities broad, bluntly rounded, outer proximal raphe ends curved in opposite directions . . . . [4] *G. eximium*

11. Valve extremities narrow, rounded, usually subtilely constricted, outer proximal raphe ends somewhat "T" shaped . . . . [5] *G. scalproides*

12. Valves large, 150-450μ long, 25-44μ wide 13

12. Valves smaller, 50-160μ long, 6 to about 23μ wide 16

13. Longitudinal striae coarser than transverse striae, becoming indistinct at valve margins . . . . [6] *G. attenuatum*

13. Longitudinal striae same in number or finer than transverse striae, distinct at valve margins 14

14. Longitudinal striae slightly finer than transverse striae, axial area and raphe with short undulation near valve center . . . . [15] *G. strigilis*

14. Longitudinal striae same in number as transverse striae, axial area and raphe with longer undulation 15

15. Valves lanceolate, length not exceeding 300μ (fresh water)
[14] *G. terryanum* f. *fontanum*

15. Valves linear-lanceolate, larger, 340-450μ (brackish water) . . . . . [14] *G. terryanum*

16. Central area diagonal, large 17

16. Central area elliptical or orbicular, smaller 18

17. Valve linear; longitudinal striae, 22-24 in 10μ . . . . [8] *G. nodiferum*

17. Valve linear-lanceolate; longitudinal striae, 17-19 in 10μ . . . . [7] *G. sciotense*

1. **Gyrosigma acuminatum** (Kütz.) Rabh. var. **acuminatum**

PL. 23, FIGS. 1-3

Frustulia acuminata Kütz., Linnaea, 8:555, pl. 14, fig. 36. 1833.
Navicula acuminata Kütz., Bacill., p. 102, pl. 4, fig. 26; pl. 30, fig. 15. 1844.
Gyrosigma acuminatum (Kütz.) Rabh., Süssw.-Diat., p. 47, pl. 5 (*Gyrosigma*), fig. 5a. 1853.
Pleurosigma acuminatum (Kütz.) Grun., Verh. Zool.-Bot. Ges. Wien, 10:561, pl. 6, figs. 6-7. 1860.

Valve moderately sigmoid, lanceolate, gradually tapering to obtusely rounded ends. Axial area and raphe sigmoid, central. Outer proximal raphe ends curved in opposite directions. Central area longitudinally elliptical. Terminal area slightly eccentric. Transverse and longitudinal striae about equally as distinct. Transverse striae on either side of the central area appearing slightly radiate, or sometimes parallel to the axial area. Longitudinal striae curving outward on either side of the central area. Transverse striae, 16-18 in 10μ; longitudinal striae, 17-20 in 10μ. Length, 60 to about 125μ. Breadth, 12-16μ.

This diatom is best distinguished from *Gyrosigma sciotense* by the character of the central and terminal areas (see discussion under *G. sciotense*). One of Kützing's figures for this diatom measures only about 40μ long. Hustedt (1930, p. 222) gives a maximum length of 200μ. Specimens of this taxon observed from the United States are more intermediate in size. No such extremely small or large forms have thus far been seen.

I have seen one specimen of this taxon (A-G.C. 5921) in which the outer proximal raphe ends hook in the same direction. Being a large cell this may represent a post-auxospore anomaly.

Several earlier names have often been included in synonymy for this diatom (Kütz., 1844). None of these (*Bacillaria fusiformis* Ehr., *Navicula fusiformis* Ehr., *Navicula sigmoidea* Ehr., *Navicula flexuosa* Ehr.) are sufficiently described and illustrated to consider for use without having the type specimen for reference. In view of the uncertainties in the descriptions (see Ehr., 1835, p. 259, for a discussion of some of the difficulties) and the lack of Ehrenberg's specimens, these names have to be considered here as *nomina dubia*.

Although this taxon has been reported from many parts of the United States (see below), I have been able to verify records from Ohio, Tennessee, and Nebraska only.

Type locality. — Uncertain.

U. S. distribution. — GEOGRAPHICAL: New England States, Middle Atlantic States, Southeastern States, Gulf Coast States, South Central States, East Central States, West Central States, Lakes States, Plains States; California. ECOLOGICAL: Appears to be eurytopic, fresh-water, alkalibiont.

2. **Gyrosigma spencerii** (Quek.) Griff. & Henfr. var. **spencerii**

PL. 23, FIG. 4

> *Navicula spencerii* Quek., Pract. Treat. Micr., p. 440, pl. 9. 1848.
> *Pleurosigma spencerii* (Quek.) W. Sm., Ann. Mag. Nat. Hist., Ser. 2, 9:12, pl. 2, figs. 15-16. 1852.
> *Gyrosigma spencerii* (Quek.) Griff. & Henfr., Microgr. Dict., 1st ed., p. 303, pl. 11, fig. 17. 1856.
> *Pleurosigma kützingii* Grun., Verh. Zool.-Bot. Ges. Wien, 10:561, pl. 6, fig. 3. 1860.
> *Pleurosigma gracilentum* Rabh., Fl. Europaea Alg., sect. 1, p. 240. 1864.
> *Gyrosigma kützingii* (Grun.) Cl., K. Svenska Vet.-Akad. Handl., Ny Földj, 26(2): 115. 1894.

Valve moderately sigmoid, lanceolate; tapering to narrow, rounded ends. Axial area and raphe very slightly undulate. Terminal area slightly eccentric. Outer proximal raphe ends curved in opposite directions, close (about 1.5µ apart). Central area small, longitudinally elliptical. Transverse and longitudinal striae about equally as conspicuous. Transverse striae, 18-20 in 10µ; longitudinal striae, 22-24 in 10µ. Length, 95-140µ; Cleve gives 220µ. Breadth, 13-15µ.

The epithet "*spencerii*" should be attributed to Quekett (1848, p. 440) and not William Smith (1852, p. 12) as per Cleve (1894, p. 115), Hustedt (1930, p. 225), and Van Heurck (1885, p. 118).

A slide in the Academy diatom herbarium (A-G.C. 3174) labelled: "*Navicula spencerii*, Croton River, N. Y., from Prof. Bailey, original specimen," has ringed specimens which fit the original description of Quekett and which appear identical with Grunow's *P. kuetzingii*. These specimens are also identical with the Van Heurck slide (A-V.H. 187) for *P. kuetzingii* and are in agreement with Grunow's description of that taxon. Grunow himself (1860, p. 562, under *Pleurosigma spencerii*) states "Die vorige Art [*P. kuetzingii*] liesse sich fast als eine grössere form derselben betrachten."

Forms agreeing with the illustration of Hustedt (1930, p. 225, fig. 336) for *G. spencerii* are here referred to variety *curvula* (q.v.).

Type locality. — U.S.A., New York, Croton River(?).

U. S. distribution. — Geographical: New England States, Middle Atlantic States, Southeastern States, Gulf Coast States, South Central States, East Central States, West Central States, Lakes States, Plains States; California. Ecological: Rather common in creeks, rivers, and lakes; alkaliphil; can withstand some salt concentration, oligohalobe (indifferent?).

2. **Gyrosigma spencerii** var. **curvula** (Grun.) Reim. comb. nov.

PL. 23, FIG. 8

Pleurosigma spencerii var. *curvula* Grun. *in* Cl. & Grun., K. Svenska Vet-Akad. Handl., Ny Földj, 17(2):60. 1880.

Valve linear or linear-lanceolate—not lanceolate as the nominate variety; ends more gradually attenuated and broader in relation to the valve width at the center. Striae tend to be a bit more numerous than in variety *spencerii*. Character of the striae, the raphe, the axial area, and the nodules as in the nominate variety. Transverse striae, 20-22 in 10μ; longitudinal striae, 24-25 in 10μ. Length, $70\text{-}120\mu$. Breadth, $9\text{-}11\mu$.

The illustration of Hustedt (1930, p. 225, text fig. 336, as *G. spencerii*) bears a very strong resemblance to variety *curvula* and probably is to be referred here.

The *Navicula curvula* of Ehrenberg (1838, p. 181, pl. 13, fig. 14) and the *Gyrosigma curvula* of Rabenhorst (1853, p. 47, pl. 5, fig. 8) are not possible to categorize from the published data. Whether or not they are to be in any way associated with this taxon remains for future work. The illustrations shown by Ehrenberg and Rabenhorst make their affinity seem doubtful.

Type locality. — Uncertain, Häufig in brackischem Wasser an der Küste der Nordsee, in den Salinen von Schönebeck und Dürrenberg, Nordamerika, etc.

U. S. distribution. — Geographical: Middle Atlantic States, Southeastern States; California. Ecological: Reported from brackish-water areas, but has been found from fresh water on the coastal plain (oligohalobe, "indifferent"?).

3. **Gyrosigma obtusatum** (Sulliv. & Wormley) Boyer var. **obtusatum**

PL. 23, FIG. 5

Pleurosigma obtusatum Sulliv. & Wormley, American Jour. Sci., Ser. 2, 27:251. 1859.

Gyrosigma obtusatum (Sulliv. & Wormley) Boyer, Contr. Biol. Micr. Sect. Acad. Nat. Sci. Philadelphia, 1:7, pl. 2, fig. 11. 1922.

Valve slightly sigmoid, linear-lanceolate, gradually tapering to obtusely rounded ends. Axial area and raphe sigmoid, central. Outer proximal raphe ends terminated as a short "T." Terminal area eccentric. Central area longitudinally elliptical. Transverse striae more conspicuous than longitudinal striae; center striae coarser, usually slightly diagonal and somewhat undulate. Longitudinal striae curving outward on both sides of the central area. Transverse striae, 20 in 10μ at the center; 22-24 in 10μ toward the ends. Longitudinal striae, 26-29 in 10μ. Length, 65-90μ. Breadth, 12-14μ.

Best distinguished from *Gyrosigma scalproides* by its linear-lanceolate shape and the central—not eccentric—axial area and raphe; from *G. spencerii* var. *curvula* by the larger central area and different shape and position of the outer proximal raphe ends.

The characteristics of the raphe ends and the striae in *G. obtusatum* and *G. scalproides* are similar. In my opinion the inclusion of one as a variety of the other still seems unwarranted, principally on the basis of the quite different position of the raphe (central vs. eccentric) on the valve face.

Type locality. — U. S. A., Ohio, Columbus, fresh water.

U. S. distribution.— GEOGRAPHICAL: New England States, Middle Atlantic States, East Central States; South Carolina, Kentucky. ECOLOGICAL: Insufficiently known.

4. **Gyrosigma eximium** (Thwaites) Boyer var. **eximium**   PL. 23, FIG. 6

Schizonema eximium Thwaites, Ann. Mag. Nat. Hist., Ser. 2, 1:169, pl. 12, figs. 1-4. 1848.

Pleurosigma eximium (Thwaites) Cl. & Grun., K. Svenska Vet.-Akad. Handl., Ny Följd, 17(2):61. 1880.

Gyrosigma scalproides var. *eximia* (Thwaites) Cl., K. Svenska Vet.-Akad. Handl., Ny Följd, 26(2):118. 1894.

Gyrosigma eximium (Thwaites) Boyer, Proc. Acad. Nat. Sci. Philadelphia, 79(2), Suppl.:462. 1927.

Valve slightly sigmoid, linear with scalpelliform ends. Axial area and raphe eccentric, diagonal, slightly sigmoid. Outer proximal raphe ends hooked in opposite directions. Central area elongate-elliptical. Terminal area eccentric. Transverse striae more conspicuous than longitudinal striae. Transverse striae, 23-24 in 10μ; longitudinal striae, 28-30 in 10μ. Length, 60-100μ. Breadth, 9-13μ.

This taxon is best distinguished from *Gyrosigma scalproides* by its more linear shape and hooked outer proximal raphe ends. Its manner of growth in tubes is distinctive.

Specimens of this taxon examined show the outer proximal raphe deflection to be in the same direction as the curvature of the corresponding end of the diatom instead of in the opposite direction, which appears to be the case in all the other species of *Gyrosigma*. I am not prepared to assess this characteristic at the present time.

Type locality. — England, Crews' Hole near Bristol, in a rapid stream of fresh water on filaments of *Vaucheria*, roots of grass, etc.

U. S. distribution. — GEOGRAPHICAL: Middle Atlantic States, Southeastern States, Lakes States(?); Illinois(?), Kansas(?). ECOLOGICAL: Appears to be more characteristic of brackish waters (oligohalobe?) but has been reported from fresh water, especially on the coastal plain.

5. **Gyrosigma scalproides** (Rabh.) Cl. var. **scalproides**   PL. 23, FIG. 7

Pleurosigma scalproides Rabh., Fl. Europea Alg., 1:241. 1864.
Gyrosigma scalproides (Rabh.) Cl., K. Svenska Vet.-Akad. Handl., Ny Följd, 26(2): 118. 1894.

Valve slightly sigmoid, linear, more than half the length of diatom; then gradually attenuated to bluntly rounded, often very slightly constricted ends. Axial area and raphe eccentric, diagonal, weakly sigmoid. Ends scalpelliform, but sometimes appearing nearly symmetrical in shape. Outer proximal raphe ends somewhat "T" shaped. Terminal area eccentric. Central area small, longitudinally elliptical or orbicular. Transverse striae more distinct than longitudinal striae, slightly coarser at the center (more widely spaced) than toward the ends. Central transverse striae may be either straight and radiate, slightly curved, or undulate. Longitudinal striae curving outward on both sides of the central area. Transverse striae, 20 in 10μ at the center, then 24 in 10μ; longitudinal striae, 28-31 in 10μ. Length, 50-75μ. Breadth, 8-12μ; Rabenhorst gives 15μ.

This diatom is best distinguished by the subtle knob-like ends, the lateral raphe, and the peculiar "T" shaped outer proximal raphe ends. This latter characteristic effectively separates this taxon from *G. eximium*. Although the character of the more widely spaced striae around the central area varies and is occasionally noted also in *G. eximium*, it seems to be more consistently true of *G. scalproides* than of *G. eximium*.

Hustedt (1930, p. 226) records specimens of this taxon as small as 25μ long and 5.5μ wide. Rabenhorst (1864, p. 241) records specimens as wide as 15μ. Such extreme sizes have not been observed from this country.

This taxon is further discussed under *G. obtusatum*.

Type locality. — Germany, . . . am Elbufer im Gehege bei Dresden.

U. S. distribution. — GEOGRAPHICAL: New England States, Middle Atlantic States, Southeastern States, Gulf Coast States, South Central States, East Central States, West Central States, Lakes States, Plains States; California. ECOLOGICAL: A rather widely distributed taxon more characteristic of flowing water habitats (rheophil?) which are circumneutral or slightly alkaline.

6. **Gyrosigma attenuatum** (Kütz.) Rabh. var. **attenuatum** PL. 24, FIG. 1

Frustulia attenuata Kütz., Linnaea, 8:555, pl. 14, fig. 35.   1833.

Pleurosigma attenuatum (Kütz) W. Sm., Ann. Mag. Nat. Hist., Ser. 2, 9:11, pl. 2, figs. 11-(?)13, 18.   1852.

Gyrosigma attenuata (Kütz) Rabh., Süssw.-Diat., p. 47, pl. 5, fig. 2.   1853.

Valve slightly to moderately sigmoid, rather strongly arched; lanceolate, gradually tapering to obtusely rounded ends. Axial area and raphe slightly undulate. Outer proximal raphe ends hooked in opposite directions. Central area small, elliptical, often irregular. Terminal area eccentric. Longitudinal striae coarser and much more distinct than transverse striae except at the margins where the transverse striae appear distinct due to the valve contour. Transverse striae, 14-16 in 10μ; longitudinal striae, 10-12 in 10μ. Length, 150-225μ. Breadth, 23-27μ.

Ehrenberg's *Navicula hippocampus* is often considered to be a part of this taxon. Ehrenberg, himself (1838, p. 180) placed Kützing's *Navicula attenuata* in synonymy saying that he had seen the Kützing specimens and considered them to be the same even though Kützing reported his specimens from relatively fresh water, and Ehrenberg found his in the North Sea. In the illustrations of Ehrenberg the diatom appears broader at the center and much more sharply (acutely—not attenuately) narrowed toward the ends than in the illustration of Kützing (1833b, p. 555). This suggests the possibility that we might actually be dealing with two taxa.

Boyer (1927b, pp. 455-456) keeps *Gyrosigma attenuatum* (Kütz.) Cl. and *G. hippocampus* (Ehr.) Hass. separate, saying of the latter: "Differs from *G. attenuatum* in its marine habitat."

None of the specimens at the Academy (including Boyer's listed as *N. hippocampus*, *Pleurosigma hippocampus*, or *G. hippocampus*) fit the shape of Ehrenberg's *N. hippocampus*. Until this relationship has been more thoroughly worked out *G. hippocampus* must be considered in questionable synonymy with *G. attenuatum*.

Type locality. — Europe. Ad plantas aquaticas prope Leucopetram.

U. S. distribution. — GEOGRAPHICAL: New England States, Middle Atlantic States, Southeastern States, Gulf Coast States, East Central States, West Central States, Lakes States, Plains States; Washington, California. ECOLOGICAL: Widespread distribution, appears to prefer alkaline waters (alkalibiont?), can withstand slight salt intrusion, current indifferent.

7. Gyrosigma sciotense (Sulliv. & Wormley) Cl. var. sciotense

PL. 24, FIG. 5

Pleurosigma sciotensis Sulliv. & Wormley, American Jour. Sci., Ser. 2, 27:251. 1859.
Gyrosigma sciotense (Sulliv. & Wormley) Cl., K. Svenska Vet.-Akad. Handl., Ny
Följd, 27(3):pl. 1, fig. 5. 1895.

Valve slightly to moderately sigmoid, linear-lanceolate; gradually tapering to obtusely rounded ends. Axial area slightly undulate, curve leading to
the central area slight. Outer proximal raphe ends curved in opposite
directions. Terminal area eccentric, forming narrow cornucopia on one
side of the end. Central area oblique, about 5-6.5μ long. Longitudinal
striae only slightly finer than transverse striae; both about equally as conspicuous. Transverse striae, 16-17 in 10μ; longitudinal striae, 17-19 in 10μ.
Length, 100-160μ. Breadth, 15-18μ.

This diatom is best distinguished from *Gyrosigma acuminatum* by having a diagonal central area, slightly undulate axial area, and a more eccentric
terminal area. The central area of *G. acuminatum* is elliptical; the axial area
is sigmoid, not noticeably recurved near the central area; and the terminal
nodule is expanded more as a "V," not as a narrow cornucopia.

Similarity between this taxon and *G. nodiferum* is discussed under the
latter taxon.

In some respects there seems to be a suggestion of gradation from
G. acuminatum to *G. sciotense* to *G. nodiferum*. At present, however, the
characters used to distinguish these three taxa appear to be constant enough
to warrant their separate consideration.

Type locality. — U. S. A., Ohio, Columbus [Scioto River].

U. S. distribution. — Geographical: New England States, East Central
States, Plains States(?). Ecological: Insufficiently known.

8. Gyrosigma nodiferum (Grun.) G. West, var. nodiferum   PL. 24, FIG. 2

Pleurosigma nodiferum Grun. *in* Cl. & Grun., K. Svenska Vet.-Akad. Handl., Ny
Följd, 17(2):59. 1880.
Gyrosigma spencerii var. *nodifera* (Grun.) Cl., K. Svenska Vet.-Akad. Handl., Ny
Följd, 26(2):117. 1894.
Gyrosigma nodiferum (Grun.) G. West, Jour. Linn. Soc. (Bot.), 38:157. 1907.

Valve slightly sigmoid, linear, gradually tapering to obtusely rounded
nearly symmetrical ends which may sometimes appear slightly scalpelliform. Axial area and raphe sigmoid or very slightly undulate. Outer proximal raphe ends distant, curved in opposite directions. Terminal area large,
eccentric, lateral, forming a cornucopia on one side. Central area oblique,
about 8.5-10μ long. Transverse striae more conspicuous than longitudinal
striae except along axial area where converse is true due to arch of the valve.

Longitudinal striae finer than transverse striae, curving slightly outward on either side of the central area. Transverse striae, 17-20 in 10μ; longitudinal striae, 22-24 in 10μ. Length, 60-150μ. Breadth, 11-14μ.

Best distinguished by the diagonal central area, together with the presence of striae over the ends making a rather large extremely deflected terminal area.

This diatom looks much like *Gyrosigma sciotense*. It is distinguished by its more linear shape and finer striae. The central and terminal areas also are slightly larger. In our specimens the axial area in *G. nodiferum* does not clearly recurve near the central area as is true in *G. sciotense*.

Type locality. — Uncertain, . . . süssen Wassern Europas . . . schwach salzigen Wasser der Elbmündung und der Samoa Inseln?

U. S. distribution. — GEOGRAPHICAL: Middle Atlantic States, Southeastern States, Gulf Coast States, South Central States; California. ECOLOGICAL: Fresh to slightly brackish waters (oligohalobe, indifferent?).

9. **Gyrosigma temperei** Cl. var. **temperei**　　　　PL. 24, FIG. 3

> *Gyrosigma temperei* Cl., Diatomiste, 2(15):55, pl. 3, fig. 3. 1893.
> *Pleurosigma quininpiaceii* M. Perag. *in* Temp. & Perag., Diat. Monde Entier, 2nd ed., p. 101. 1908.
> *Gyrosigma quinnipiacii* (M. Perag. *in* Temp. & Perag.) Boyer, Proc. Acad. Nat. Sci. Philadelphia, 79(2), Suppl.:459. 1927.

Valve very slightly sigmoid, linear with broad, scalpelliform ends. Axial area and raphe slightly undulate, central except near the ends where they are slightly eccentric. Outer proximal raphe ends hooked in opposite directions, hook deflected like a "question mark," inner ends straight. Terminal area eccentric, laterally displaced, expanded as a cornucopia. Central area small, oblong. Transverse striae more conspicuous than longitudinal striae. Transverse striae radiate around the center; becoming parallel (perpendicular to the axial area) towards the ends. Longitudinal striae curving outward on either side of the central area. Transverse striae, 20 in 10μ on either side of the central area; becoming 24-26 in 10μ throughout most of the valve; near the ends in the area just above the terminal nodule, about 28 in 10μ. Longitudinal striae, about 27-30 in 10μ. Length, 100-185μ. Breadth, 13-15μ.

Peragallo distinguishes his *Pleurosigma quininpiaceii* from *P. temperei* on the basis of the coarser striae and the expanded terminal nodules (in *P. quininpiaceii*). Examination of A-T.&P. 187 (isotype for *P. quininpiaceii*); A-T.&P. 826, Newark, New Jersey, with heavy population of *G. temperei* as listed by Tempére and Peragallo; A-Boyer C-5-11, West River, Connecticut, (*G. temperei*); and also A-Boyer 926, Quinnipiac River, Connecticut, (*G. quinnipiacii*); show forms which are indistinguishable from one another. Depending on where the transverse striae are measured on the valve face, the striae range from 20 in 10μ at the center to about 28 in 10μ on one side of the valve just above the terminal nodules. The longitudinal striae all measure somewhat finer, 27-30 in 10μ, than the 24 in 10μ given by Peragallo and later by Boyer. The expanded terminal nodules all have about the same appearance. Cleve's original illustration for *G. temperei* (1893, pl. 3, fig. 3) also indicates expanded terminal nodules. The peculiar "question mark" shape of the outer proximal raphe ends is apparent in both forms.

On these bases it is my opinion that these two names refer to the same taxon. Therefore the older epithet has been retained.

Type locality. — U.S.A., Connecticut, Eaux saumâtres.

U. S. distribution. — GEOGRAPHICAL: Connecticut, New Jersey, Florida. ECOLOGICAL: Appears restricted to brackish-water estuaries (mesohalobe?).

10. **Gyrosigma exile** (Grun.) Reim. comb. nov., var. **exile**

PL. 24, FIG. 4

> *Pleurosigma spencerii* var.? *exilis* Grun. *in* Cl. & Grun., K. Svenska Vet.-Akad. Handl., Ny Földj, 17(2):60. 1880.
> *Gyrosigma spencerii* var. *exilis* (Grun.) Cl., K. Svenska Vet.-Akad. Handl., Ny Földj, 26(2):117. 1894.

Valve slightly sigmoid, linear to lanceolate-linear with obtusely rounded ends. Axial area and raphe sigmoid, becoming slightly eccentric at the valve curvature. Proximal raphe ends curved in opposite directions. Central area longitudinally elliptical. Terminal area slightly eccentric. Transverse striae more conspicuous than longitudinal striae, convergent above and below the central area, becoming parallel toward the ends. Longitudinal striae curving outward on either side of the central area. Transverse striae, 26-29 in 10μ; longitudinal striae, 30-32 in 10μ. Length, 50-85μ. Breadth, 6-10μ.

This diatom is characterized best by its small size, fine longitudinal striae, and nearly linear shape. The convergent transverse striae above and below the central area are characteristic of the specimens I have examined from this country. Whether or not this is really diagnostic for the species remains to be determined.

This taxon has been placed in *Gyrosigma spencerii* as a variety by Cleve (1894, p. 117), but it is so different from that taxon in almost every respect that it has been elevated to a distinct species.

Type locality. — France, Arromanches.

U. S. distribution. — GEOGRAPHICAL: Southeastern States; Kentucky. ECOLOGICAL: Fresh to slightly brackish water (oligohalobe, indifferent?).

11. Gyrosigma obscurum (W. Sm.) Griff. & Henfr. var. obscurum

PL. 24, FIG. 7

Pleurosigma obscurum W. Sm., Ann. Mag. Nat. Hist, Ser. 2, 9:8, pl. 1, fig. 11. 1852.

Gyrosigma obscurum (W. Sm.) Griff. & Henfr., Microgr. Dict., 1st ed., p. 302, pl. 11, fig. 27. 1856.

Valve slightly sigmoid, linear, more than one-half the length of the valve; then attenuated to rather narrowly rounded ends. Surface of the valve strongly arched with slightly elevated axial portion. Axial area and raphe eccentric throughout, sigmoid, close to the margin near the ends. Proximal raphe ends indistinct, but appearing straight. Central area quite small, orbicular or longitudinally elliptical. Terminal area inconspicuous. Transverse striae much more conspicuous than longitudinal striae. Transverse striae appearing undulate due to the contour of the valve surface; considering the contour they are essentially perpendicular to the axial area. Longitudinal striae unresolved except with good optics, essentially parallel to the axial area. Transverse striae, 26-30 in 10μ; longitudinal striae very fine, about 40 in 10μ. Length, 85-150μ. Breadth, 10-15μ.

This species is best distinguished by its somewhat undulate surface and seeming lack of longitudinal striae. These longitudinal striae can be observed only with good optics. When resolved it is noted that, on the relatively flat surface of the valve, fine longitudinal striae are visible; where the valve is depressed, about one-third the distance from axial area to valve margin, "oblique" striae are noted slanting at about a 45 degree angle toward the axial area. On the side of the valve near the sharply convex margin "oblique" striae are again seen, but they are now at a 45 degree angle toward the valve margin. It seems evident that a combination of valve undulation plus curving of the valve gives the appearance of oblique striae being present. The fine puncta are actually arranged so as to form "longitudinal" lines (as seen on the flat face of the valve), but are seen by the eye to form oblique lines where the valve arches. Because of this, Griffith and Henfrey's combination is being accepted, considering the diatom in the genus Gyrosigma instead of Pleurosigma, where many others have placed it.

Type locality. — England. Poole Bay(?), Lewes(?).

U. S. distribution. — GEOGRAPHICAL: New England States, Middle Atlantic States; Florida. ECOLOGICAL: Apparently euryhaline, found in slightly to highly brackish water.

12. **Gyrosigma distortum** (W. Sm.) Griff. & Henfr. var. **distortum**

PL. 24, FIG. 6

Pleurosigma distortum W. Sm., Ann. Mag. Nat. Hist., Ser. 2, 9:7, pl. 1, fig. 10. 1852.

Gyrosigma distortum (W. Sm.) Griff. & Henfr., Microgr. Dict., 1st ed., p. 303, pl. 11, fig. 20. 1856.

Valve distinctly sigmoid, lanceolate with rather short-protracted obtuse ends. One margin forming the ends smoothly rounded, opposite margin somewhat angular. Axial area and raphe sigmoid, becoming eccentric toward the ends. Outer proximal raphe ends indistinct. Terminal area eccentric. Central area very small, orbicular. Longitudinal striae straight or only slightly wavy on either side of the central area; about equally as conspicuous as transverse striae. Transverse striae, 24 in 10μ; longitudinal striae, 26-28 in 10μ. Length, 70-120μ. Breadth, 15-17μ.

In my opinion, the illustration of Hustedt (1930, p. 225, text fig. 334) represents a form other than the *P. distortum* of W. Smith.

Type locality. — England, coast of Sussex.

U. S. distribution. — Geographical: New England States. Ecological: Brackish to marine (mesohalobe?).

13. **Gyrosigma balticum** (Ehr.) Rabh. var. **balticum**

PL. 25, FIG. 1

Navicula baltica Ehr., Phys. Abh. Akad. Wiss. Berlin, for 1833:258. 1835.

Pleurosigma baltica (Ehr.) W. Sm., Ann. Mag. Nat. Hist., Ser. 2, 9:8, pl. 2, figs. 1, 17. 1852.

Gyrosigma baltica (Ehr.) Rabh., Süssw.-Diat., p. 47, pl. 5, fig. 6. 1853.

Valve slightly sigmoid; linear, moderately arched, with bluntly rounded, subconical, or scalpelliform ends. Valve margins straight, slightly incurved or slightly wavy. Axial area and raphe undulate, eccentric. Outer proximal raphe ends curving in opposite directions. Central area elongate (about 10-12μ long), diagonal, elliptical. Terminal area approximately in middle of the ends. Transverse and longitudinal striae about equally as distinct. Longitudinal striae curving outward on either side of the central area, about same in number as the transverse striae. Transverse and longitudinal striae, 11-16 in 10μ. Length, 200-400μ. Breadth, about 20-32μ.

Cleve (1894, p. 118) and Hustedt (1930, p. 224) give the width as 20-40μ. Specimens from this country and those of Van Heurck (A-V.H. 180) from France do not exceed about 32μ in width.

The valve features of *G. balticum*, *G. terryanum*, and *G. strigilis* are very similar and indicate the close affinity of these taxa. These affinities were early recognized by Peragallo (1890, pp. 18, 21). *G. balticum* and var. *californicum* are placed together here as the more linear forms with asymmetrically attenuate ends, as distinguished from the symmetrically attenuate ends of *G. strigilis* and *G. terryanum*. There may be a distinction in the character of the terminal area of *G. balticum*, although I do not want to employ this character in the description at the present time. The different configuration of the terminal area may be associated with the outer distal raphe end which appears to terminate in a small notch and not extend to the valve margin as is more clearly seen in *G. strigilis* and *G. terryanum*.

Meister's *Gyrosigma balticum* var. *incurva* probably belongs here in synonymy.

Type locality. — Europe.

U. S. distribution. — GEOGRAPHICAL: New England States, Middle Atlantic States, Southeastern States, Gulf Coast States; Washington, California. ECOLOGICAL: Brackish-water, coastal species.

13. **Gyrosigma balticum** var. **californicum** Grun. *ex* Cl.   PL. 25, FIG. 2

> *Gyrosigma balticum* var. *californica* Grun. *ex* Cl., K. Svenska Vet.-Akad. Handl., Ny Följd, 26(2):119. 1894.

Valve gradually attenuate (narrower) toward the ends, central area not as elongate (about 5-7.5μ long); otherwise not different from the nominate variety except for more restricted range of dimensions. Striae, 14 in 10μ. Length, 250- > 300μ. Breadth, 24-26μ.

Type locality. — U.S.A., California, Brooklyn.

U. S. distribution. — GEOGRAPHICAL: California. ECOLOGICAL: Insufficiently known; apparently a moderately to highly brackish-water taxon.

14. **Gyrosigma terryanum** (Perag.) Cl. var. **terryanum**   PL. 25, FIG. 3

> *Pleurosigma terryanum* H. Perag. (*balticum* var.?), Diatomiste, 1(4/5) Suppl.:18, pl. 7, fig. 21. 1890-1891.
> *Gyrosigma terryanum* (Perag.) Cl., K. Svenska Vet.-Akad. Handl., Ny Följd, 26(2): 114. 1894.

Valve rather broad, linear-lanceolate with symmetrically attenuate extremities. Axial area and raphe undulate, eccentric. Outer proximal raphe ends curving in opposite directions. Central area diagonal, elliptical or nearly circular. Terminal area slightly eccentric. Transverse and longitudinal striae about equally as distinct. Longitudinal striae curving outward slightly on either side of the central area, about the same in number as the transverse striae. Transverse and longitudinal striae, 14 in 10μ. Length, 340-450μ. Breadth, 36-44μ.

This species is broader and has a more prolonged recurving of the axial area and raphe into the central area than *G. strigilis* to which it is strongly allied. See discussion under *G. balticum* for further interpretation of this taxon.

Type locality. — U.S.A., Connecticut, Marsh, South End.

U. S. distribution. — GEOGRAPHICAL: Connecticut. ECOLOGICAL: Brackish water (salt "indifferent"?), coastal.

14. **Gyrosigma terryanum** f. **fontanum** Reim. f. nov.   PL. 25, FIG. 4

Valvis lanceolatis brevioribus quam illis varietatis nominatae. Striis longitudinalibus et transversis 13-14 in 10μ, longitudine 270-285μ, latitudine 40-42μ.

Valves lanceolate, shorter than the nominate variety; otherwise not different. Longitudinal and transverse striae, 13-14 in 10μ. Length, 270-285μ. Breadth, 40-42μ.

This diatom was originally identified by Mr. F. J. Keeley as *G. strigilis* var. and is listed on the slide as "fresh water" from a spring in Florida. It does not have the fine longitudinal striae of *G. strigilis,* and is also markedly broader. The morphology indicates it is more clearly a part of *G. terryanum.*

It may well be that this form is only a fresh-water ecophene of the species, but, at present, there is not enough evidence for this conclusion.

Type locality. — U.S.A., Florida, Green Spring(?). (*Holotype*—A-G.C. 2861, Reimer.)

U. S. distribution. — GEOGRAPHICAL: Florida. ECOLOGICAL: Insufficiently known (fresh water).

15. **Gyrosigma strigilis** (W. Sm.) Cl. var. **strigilis**   PL. 25, FIG. 5

Pleurosigma strigilis W. Sm., Ann. Mag. Nat. Hist., Ser. 2, 9:8, pl. 2, fig. 4. 1852.
Gyrosigma strigilis (W. Sm.) Cl., K. Svenska Vet.-Akad. Handl., Ny Földj, 26(2): 115. 1894.

Valve moderately sigmoid, linear-lanceolate with gradually attenuated subacute ends. Central axis of the valve slightly elevated or humped. Axial area and raphe slightly undulate and eccentric. Outer proximal raphe ends curved in opposite directions at very edge of the central area, difficult to resolve. Terminal area slightly eccentric. Central area small, diagonal, elliptical to oval. Transverse striae more pronounced than longitudinal striae. Longitudinal striae curving slightly outward on either side of the central area. Transverse striae, 12-14 in 10μ; longitudinal striae, 15-16 in 10μ. Length, 250-380μ. Breadth, 30-39μ. Hustedt (1930, p. 224) gives 27-35μ.

See discussion under *Gyrosigma balticum* and *G. terryanum* for affinities with those taxa.

Type locality. — England, Hull.

U. S. distribution. — GEOGRAPHICAL: New England States, Middle Atlantic States; Nevada. ECOLOGICAL: Records confirmed only from brackish water along the northeast coast of United States. The specimens of Hanna and Grant from Nevada have not been seen.

16. Gyrosigma hummii Hust. var. hummii   PL. 26, FIGS. 1-2

Gyrosigma hummii Hust., Duke Univ. Mar. Stat. Bull., No. 6, pp. 33-34, pl. 10, fig. 2. 1955.

Valve slightly sigmoid; broadly linear-lanceolate with blunt, broad, and obtusely rounded ends. Axial area and raphe sigmoid, slightly eccentric toward the ends. Proximal raphe ends curving slightly in the same direction, indistinct. Terminal area very small, in the middle of the ends. Central area small, orbicular. Longitudinal striae curving outward very slightly on either side of the central area or not at all; coarse near the axial area, finer near the valve margins. Transverse striae, 13-15 in 10μ. Longitudinal striae, about 12 in 10μ near the axial area, becoming about 20 in 10μ near the valve margins. Length, 115-190μ. Breadth, 25-30μ.

Readily distinguished from Gyrosigma balticum by its length-to-breadth ratio (G. hummii—4-6:1; G. balticum—10:1 or greater) and by the sigmoid —not undulate—axial area and raphe.

This diatom was called Gyrosigma simile (Grun.) Boyer by Boyer (1927b, p. 457, A-Boyer 11). Grunow's description of Pleurosigma (balticum var.?) simile, in my opinion, is not satisfactory for Boyer's diatom. Hustedt (loc. cit.) discussed this problem and found it necessary to erect a separate taxon for specimens like Boyer's, indicating that Boyer's illustration was more closely allied to his G. hummii than to G. simile. Boyer's specimen is undoubtedly the same and is included here as G. hummii.

Type locality. — U.S.A., North Carolina, Beaufort (marine littoral) . . . mud from the beach . . . piles in the harbor.

U. S. distribution. — GEOGRAPHICAL: Middle Atlantic States, Southeastern States. ECOLOGICAL: Marine and brackish water, apparently rare in slightly brackish water (mesohalobe?) and probably not to be found at all in fresh water.

17. Gyrosigma wormleyi (Sulliv.) Boyer var. wormleyi   PL. 26, FIG. 3

Pleurosigma wormleyi Sulliv. in Sulliv. & Wormley, Amer. Jour. Sci., Ser. 2, 27:251. 1859.

Pleurosigma parkeri Harrison, Quart. Jour. Micr. Sci., 8:104, text fig. 1860.

Gyrosigma distortum var. parkeri (Harrison) Cl., K. Svenska Vet.-Akad. Handl., Ny Följd, 26(2):116. 1894.

Gyrosigma wormleyi (Sulliv.) Boyer, Contr. Biol. Micr. Sect. Acad. Nat. Sci. Philadelphia, 1:7, pl. 2, fig. 10. 1922.

Valve distinctly sigmoid with long, protracted, narrow ends. Ratio of end width to valve width at the center, 1:4 or more. Axial area and raphe sigmoid, slightly eccentric near the ends. Proximal raphe ends indistinct. Terminal area central or very slightly eccentric. Central area small, elongate-elliptical. Transverse and longitudinal striae about equally as conspicuous.

Transverse striae often slightly curved. Transverse striae, 20-22 in 10μ; longitudinal striae, 23-25 in 10μ. Length, $75\text{-}115\mu$. Breadth, $13\text{-}17\mu$.

The long, narrow ends and the coarser striae of *Gyrosigma wormleyi* set it apart from a closely related species *G. distortum* which has short, blunt ends and somewhat finer striae.

Pleurosigma parkeri Harrison has been considered as a variety of *G. distortum* by Cleve (*loc. cit.*), Hustedt (1930, p. 224) and as a separate species of *Gyrosigma* by Boyer (1927b, p. 460) and others. It appears identical with *G. wormleyi* except for its slightly larger given size (about 96-114μ, Harrison, 1860, p. 104; vs. 76μ, Sullivant, 1859, p. 251). With no other criteria for keeping these two entities separate as Boyer has done, they are here united; the older name is retained.

A single United States record for *G. parkeri* var. *stauroneioides* is given by Boyer (1927b, p. 463). Examination of his material (A-Boyer 783, Schuylkill River) reveals a diatom which appears identical with *G. wormleyi*. Some valves have a "band"-like area weakly expressed which extends across the valve center. This area does not seem to be a stauros thickening, but merely a refraction caused by the change in juxtaposition of the striae in this area. In other valves this is not apparent. In populations of *G. wormleyi* one can see varying degrees of interruption of the longitudinal striae pattern in this area. Boyer's record for variety *stauroneioides* is, thus, included in this interpretation of *G. wormleyi*. It is possible that Grunow's taxon (*Pleurosigma parkeri* var. *stauroneioides*) belongs here in synonymy.

Hustedt considers this a fresh- to brackish-water species and gives a maximum size of 150μ long and 25μ wide with up to 27 longitudinal striae in 10μ. Such large forms have not been seen from this country; also it has only been observed from fresh-water localities.

Type locality. — U. S. A., Ohio, Columbus.

U. S. distribution. — Geographical: New England States, Middle Atlantic States, East Central States, Lakes States; California. Ecological: Insufficiently known, but most probably to be considered a fresh-water species.

18. Gyrosigma fasciola (Ehr.) Griff. & Henfr. var. fasciola PL. 26, FIG. 4

Ceratoneis fasciola Ehr., Phys. Abh. Akad. Wiss. Berlin, for 1839:144, pl. 4, fig. 6. 1841.

Pleurosigma fasciola (Ehr.) W. Sm., Syn. British Diat., vol. 1, p. 67, pl. 21, fig. 211. 1853.

Gyrosigma fasciola (Ehr.) Griff. & Henfr., Microgr. Dict., 1st ed., p. 303, pl. 11, fig. 21. 1856.

Valve distinctly sigmoid; lanceolate to elliptical-lanceolate central portion, narrowing abruptly to long, thin beaks which are bluntly rounded or flattened. Axial area and raphe central, sigmoid, appearing slightly eccentric in the beaks of some valves. Proximal raphe ends indistinct (straight?). Terminal area central or very slightly eccentric. Central area quite small, orbicular or longitudinally elliptical. Transverse and longitudinal striae about equally as distinct. Transverse striae, 20-22 in 10μ; longitudinal striae, 20-24 in 10μ. Length, 60-150μ. Breadth, 12-24μ.

This diatom is distinguished from *Gyrosigma wormleyi* in that the ends are narrower (1.5-2μ) and more sharply set off from the valve body. In *G. wormleyi* the ends taper more gradually from the valve body and have a width of about 3-5.5μ. The axial area of *G. wormleyi* becomes slightly eccentric as it enters the ends; this is not true of *G. fasciola*.

Ehrenberg's distribution record (1856, p. 85) from Iowa is doubtful and is probably to be referred to the fresh-water species *G. wormleyi*.

Type locality. — [Europe], Cuxhaven und Tjörn in der Nordsee und bei Wismar in der Ostsee.

U. S. distribution. — GEOGRAPHICAL: New England States, Middle Atlantic States, Southeastern States; California. ECOLOGICAL: Brackish to marine; appears quite commonly in salinities from about 1000-20,000 p.p.m. (mesohalobe?).

19. **Gyrosigma macrum** (W. Sm.) Griff. & Henfr. var. **macrum**

PL. 26, FIGS. 5a-b

Pleurosigma macrum W. Sm., Syn. British Diat., vol. 1, p. 67, pl. 31, fig. 276. 1853.
Gyrosigma macrum (W. Sm.) Griff. & Henfr., Microgr. Dict., 1st ed., p. 303, pl. 11, fig. 22. 1856.

Valve distinctly sigmoid; narrow, lanceolate central portion, narrowing abruptly to long thin beaks, slightly flattened or bulbous at the ends. Axial area and raphe sigmoid, central. Proximal raphe ends indistinct (straight?). Terminal area also indistinct, but appearing to have a lateral extension. Central area small, (longitudinally) linear-elliptical. Transverse and longitudinal striae both indistinct. Transverse striae, 26-28 in 10μ; longitudinal striae, 30-33 in 10μ. Length, 200-270μ; Peragallo (1891, p. 216) gives length as 150-270μ. Breadth, 10-13μ.

Best distinguished from *Gyrosigma fasciola* by its finer striae, greater length, narrower width at the center, and characteristic linear-elliptical central area.

Peragallo (1891, p. 26) has apparently switched the plate citations of *Pleurosigma macrum* and *P. prolongatum*. These two taxa are very closely allied. W. Smith, however, has distinguished them sufficiently to indicate that they are not the same. *Gyrosigma prolongatum* is smaller, has less pronounced beaks, and has coarser striae according to W. Smith's original descriptions. An examination of W. Smith's material should help clarify their relationship. *G. prolongatum* does not appear to intrude from salt water into brackish water where *G. macrum* seems to be best suited. Although *G. prolongatum* has been recorded from the United States, it has been found only in marine waters and, therefore, has been excluded from consideration at this time.

Type locality. — England, Iford, Sussex.

U. S. distribution. — GEOGRAPHICAL: Middle Atlantic States. ECOLOGICAL: Mesohalobe.

Names of Taxa reported from the U. S. (fresh to brackish water) which could not be verified by a specimen from a public herbarium.

Gyrosigma distortum var. *stauroneioides* (Grun.) Cl. (recorded by Cleve).
Gyrosigma obliquum (Grun.) Boyer (recorded by Boyer).
Gyrosigma parkeri var. *stauroneioides* (Grun.) Boyer (recorded by Boyer).
Gyrosigma scalproides var. *obliqua* (Grun.) Cl. (recorded by Cleve).
Gyrosigma simile (Grun.) Boyer (recorded by Boyer).
Gyrosigma wansbeckii (Donk.) Cl. (recorded by Boyer, Silva).
Navicula scalprum Gaillon *in* Turpin (recorded by Ehrenberg).
Pleurosigma obliquum Grun. *in* Cl. & Grun. (recorded by DeToni).
Pleurosigma parkeri var. *stauroneioides* Grun. (recorded by DeToni).
Pleurosigma spenceri var. *minor* Grun. (recorded by Chase).

Names of taxa reported from the U. S. which are either illegitimate or of uncertain application

Gyrosigma hippocampus (Ehr.) Hass. (recorded by Boyer).
Navicula flexuosa Ehr. (recorded by Ehrenberg).
Navicula hippocampus Ehr. (recorded by Bailey).
Navicula sigma Ehr. (recorded by Ehrenberg).
Pleurosigma hippocampus (Ehr.) W. Sm. (recorded by Curtis).

Genus **Pleurosigma** W. Sm. nom. cons.

W. Sm., Ann. Mag. Nat. Hist., Ser. 2, 9:2. 1852.

Valve elongated, slightly to strongly sigmoid. Intercalary bands lacking. Axial area narrow, sigmoid to undulate as in the genus *Gyrosigma*. Raphe very narrow, generally inconspicuous. Proximal and distal ends indistinct, usually appearing straight or only slightly curved. Central area small, mostly orbicular or somewhat rhombic. Striae punctate. Puncta forming transverse and diagonal rows.

Type species. — *Navicula angulata* Quek. [= *Pleurosigma angulatum* (Quek.) W. Sm.].

KEY TO THE SPECIES OF PLEUROSIGMA

1. **Pleurosigma angulatum** (Quek.) W. Sm. var. **angulatum**

PL. 27, FIGS. 1a-c

Navicula angulata Quek., Pract. Treat. Micr., p. 438, pl. 8, figs. 4-7. 1848.
Pleurosigma angulatum (Quek.) W. Sm., Ann. Mag. Nat. Hist., Ser. 2, 9:7, pl. 1, fig. 7. As: var. β, fig. 8; var. γ, fig. 9. 1852.

Valve slightly sigmoid, rhombic-lanceolate; slightly to distinctly angular in the middle, tapering rather sharply to acutely rounded ends. Valve surface relatively flat. Axial area and raphe sigmoid, becoming eccentric toward the ends. Central area small, rhombic. Transverse and diagonal striae about the same in number, crossing at an angle of from 51 to 60 degrees. Striae pattern near the ends changing from transverse-oblique to transverse-longitudinal. Transverse and diagonal striae, 17-19 in 10μ; Cleve (1894, p. 40) and Hustedt (1930, p. 228) give to 22 in 10μ. Length, 130-360μ. Breadth, 30-60μ.

As pointed out by Quekett (1848, p. 438), individual specimens of this taxon may not show a distinct angle in the margin near the center of the valve. Without this angle they closely resemble the typical shape of variety *aestuarii*. In such cases the rostrate ends, the narrower valve (to 22μ), and the slightly finer striae (to 23 in 10μ) of variety *aestuarii* sufficiently distinguish it from this taxon.

Some specimens of this taxon possibly are less than 100μ in length (thus including Quekett's "var. γ" which is about 80μ long), but such small specimens have not been observed in our collections from this country. Most authors set the lower limits of length at about 150μ.

There is some question as to the correct name for this taxon. Kützing (1844, p. 102) described in general terms a *Navicula thuringica*. His illustration (pl. 4, fig. 27) is quite similar in outline to *Pleurosigma angulatum*. In synonymy he cites *Frustulia attenuata* Kütz. 1833 (ex parte). Examination of his Dec. 9, No. 83 for that taxon shows no forms matching his *N. thuringica*. Rather than change the name of this taxon on quite dubious grounds, it seems best to retain Quekett's well-known epithet, which is more adequately described, unless it can be more definitely shown that *N. thuringica* is really the same taxon as *P. angulatum*.

Type locality. — Uncertain, upon *Conferva* in the Humber at Hull? England?

U. S. distribution. — Geographical: Middle Atlantic States, Southeastern States, Gulf Coast States, East Central States. Ecological: More often reported from brackish water, but may be found inland in waters of high conductivity.

1. Pleurosigma angulatum var. aestuarii (Bréb.) V. H.

PL. 27, FIGS. 3a-c

Navicula (Gyrosigma) aestuarii Bréb. in Kütz., Sp. Alg., p. 890. 1849.
Pleurosigma aestuarii (Bréb. in Kütz.) W. Sm., Syn. British Diat., vol. 1, p. 65, pl. 31, fig. 275. 1853.
Pleurosigma angulatum var. *aestuarii* (Bréb. in Kütz.) V. H., Syn. Diat. Belgique, pl. 18, fig. 8. 1880. (text, p. 115. 1885.)

Valve somewhat shorter than the nominate variety. Ends set off from the valve body; obtusely rounded, substrate to rostrate. Striae slightly finer than in variety *angulatum*. Other features the same. Transverse and diagonal striae, 19-23 in 10μ. Length, 70-132μ. Breadth, 17-22μ.

Wm. Smith (1852, p. 7) placed *Navicula aestuarii* Kütz. in synonymy with *Pleurosigma angulatum*. Cleve (1894, p. 42) notes that *P. aestuarii* is striate like *P. angulatum*, but intimates that he does not consider it a part thereof because of the eccentric nature of the axial area and raphe in contrast to the "central" axial area of *P. angulatum.*

The "off center" nature of the axial area does appear to vary somewhat in both forms. In the smaller forms of *P. angulatum* it is more pronounced and practically identical to that of variety *aestuarii;* in the longer forms of *P. angulatum* it is a bit less conspicuous. A few instances of *P. aestuarii* also show the slightly angular shape in the middle portion of the valve as is common to variety *angulatum.* Finally, the change in striation pattern at the extremities is common to both forms.

All of these features confirm the close relationship of these two diatoms. The rostrate ends, however, are constant and typical for variety *aestuarii.* Retention of this taxon as a variety of *P. angulatum* seems justified with the above characteristic plus the smaller dimensions and slightly finer striae.

Type locality. — [France], In sabulosis marinis Galliae borealis.

U. S. distribution. — GEOGRAPHICAL: Middle Atlantic States. ECOLOGI-CAL: Meso (?)-euhalobe.

2. **Pleurosigma salinarum** Grun. var. **salinarum**   PL. 27, FIGS 2a-c

> *Pleurosigma salinarum* Grun. *in* Cl. & Grun., K. Svenska Vet.-Akad. Handl., Ny Följd, 17(2):54. 1880.
> *Pleurosigma pusillum* Grun. *in* Cl. & Grun., K. Svenska Vet.-Akad. Handl., Ny Följd, 17(2):54. 1880.
> *Pleurosigma salinarum* var. *pusilla* (Grun. *in* Cl. & Grun.) Cl., K. Svenska Vet.-Akad. Handl., Ny Följd, 26(2):39. 1894.

Valve slightly sigmoid, lanceolate or linear-lanceolate with rather strongly attenuated, narrow, rounded obtuse ends, which may sometimes be slightly set off from the valve body. Valve surface relatively flat. Axial area and raphe slightly sigmoid; slightly eccentric towards the ends. Central area small, elongate-elliptical or rhombic. Transverse striae slightly coarser and somewhat more conspicuous than diagonal striae. Diagonal striae crossing at an angle of about 46-53 degrees. Transverse striae, 22-25 in 10μ; diagonal striae, 25-28 in 10μ. Length, 70-130μ. Breadth, 13-17μ.

Best distinguished by the characteristic of the ends and the relatively fine striae.

P. T. Cleve (1894, p. 39) makes *Pleurosigma pusillum* Grun. a variety of *P. salinarum.* I cannot find sufficient difference, except for size, to warrant its separation from *P. salinarum.* The smaller forms (considered by Cleve as variety *pusilla* are much more common in very slightly brackish or even fresh water; the longer forms are more frequent in moderately brackish water, but all size ranges can be found in a single collection. Further study is needed to clarify the exact relationship of these two taxa. Our specimens for *P. salinarum* fit the original description of Grunow and later descriptions well.

I do not know whether or not *P. delicatulum* var. *salinarum* Grun. belongs here in synonymy as Cleve (*loc. cit.*) indicates.

Type locality. — [Europe], In Salinen und salzigen Binnenwässern . . . .

U. S. distribution. — GEOGRAPHICAL: Gulf Coast States. ECOLOGICAL: Euryhaline, nearly fresh to moderately brackish water.

2. **Pleurosigma salinarum** var. **boyeri** (Keeley) Reim. comb. nov.

PL. 27, FIGS. 4 a-c

> *Pleurosigma boyeri* Keeley, Proc. Acad. Nat. Sci. Philadelphia, 77:31-32, text fig. p. 31. 1926.

Valve narrower and with finer oblique striae than the nominate variety. Other valve features the same. Transverse striae, 24-26 in 10μ; diagonal striae, 30-32 in 10μ. Length, 86-100μ. Breadth, 10-11μ.

This variety appears to have too many affinities with *Pleurosigma salinarum* to maintain it as a distinct species. It may be actually a fresh-water ecophene of the nominate variety, but there is not sufficient evidence to substantiate this at the moment.

In the collections from the type locality, the valve appears to be rather weakly silicified.

Type locality. — U.S.A., Florida, DeLeon Spring. (*Lectotype*—A-Boyer M-7-19, Reimer.)

U. S. distribution. — GEOGRAPHICAL: Florida. ECOLOGICAL: Found in a fresh-water spring and a river in Florida.

3. **Pleurosigma elongatum** W. Sm. var. **elongatum**   PL. 28, FIGS. 1a-c

> *Pleurosigma elongatum* W. Sm., Ann. Mag. Nat. Hist., Ser. 2, 9:6, pl. 1, fig. 4. 1852.

Valve slightly sigmoid, narrow, linear-lanceolate; gradually tapering to acutely rounded ends. Valve surface slightly arched. Axial area and raphe central in the main portion of the valve, becoming eccentric near the ends. Central area small, elliptical or rhomboid. Transverse striae slightly finer than diagonal striae, crossing each other at an angle of about 63-68 degrees. Transverse striae, 18-20 in 10μ; diagonal striae, 16-19 in 10μ. Length, (?130) 200-380μ. Breadth, 20-30μ.

Distinguished from *Pleurosigma delicatulum* by the slightly coarser striae, generally larger valves, and the somewhat greater inclination of the oblique striae.

W. Smith in his original description characterizes the axial area as central. Cleve (1894, p. 38), Peragallo (1891, p. 7), Hustedt (1930, p. 228), and others have indicated the same. Our specimens (A-Boyer Z-5-11, A-

Feb. 2672, A-V.H. 173) all show the axial area becoming eccentric near the ends. The Van Heurck (1880, pl. 18, fig. 7), Peragallo (1891, pl. 5, figs. 5, 8), and Hustedt (1930, text fig. 343a) illustrations all show this same off center position of the axial area near the ends. This is not a matter of a canted specimen, for perfectly flat specimens also show such an eccentric axial area.

Type locality. — England, exact location uncertain (Poole Bay, brackish water near Lewes, Hull).

U. S. distribution. — GEOGRAPHICAL: Middle Atlantic States. ECOLOGICAL: Mesohalobe.

4. **Pleurosigma strigosum** W. Sm. var. **strigosum**   PL. 28, FIGS. 2a-c

Pleurosigma strigosum W. Sm., Ann. Mag. Nat. Hist., Ser. 2, 9:7, pl. 1, fig. 6.   1852.
Pleurosigma angulatum var. *strigosum* (W. Sm.) V. H., Syn. Diat. Belgique, p. 115. 1885.

Valve slightly sigmoid, linear-lanceolate to lanceolate, tapering to subacute to obtuse ends. Valve surface slightly arched. Axial area and raphe slightly sigmoid, becoming eccentric toward the ends. Central area small, orbicular or rhombic. Transverse and diagonal striae about the same in number. Diagonal striae crossing each other at an angle of about 70-75 degrees. Transverse and diagonal striae, 15-18 in 10μ. Length, 150-310μ. Breadth, 30-33μ.

Distinguished best from *Pleurosigma angulatum* by the continuation of diagonal striae pattern into the ends and the more distinct appearance of the striae and ribs. In *P. angulatum* the valve appears to be somewhat less silicified. For further discussion, see *P. angulatum*.

The puncta on either side of the central area seem to be modified into dashes. This has been noted in specimens examined in our laboratory, including W. Smith's slide no. 136. Not knowing how constant this feature might be, it has been left out of the diagnosis. If it does prove to be a useful taxonomic feature it would represent another aid in distinguishing this taxon from *P. angulatum*. Finer striate forms (up to 22 in 10μ) as per Cleve (1894, p. 41) have not been noted in our collections.

Cleve (*loc. cit.*) placed *P. strigosum* in *P. angulatum* as a variety. Even though the shape can be quite similar and the striae number and angle are about the same, other features as described, are so different that it seems best to retain this as a separate taxon.

Type locality. — England, exact location uncertain. (Rye, Coast of Sussex, and Hull.)

U. S. distribution. — GEOGRAPHICAL: Middle Atlantic States. ECOLOGICAL: Meso(?)-euhalobe.

5. Pleurosigma australe Grun. var. australe   PL. 28, FIGS. 3a-c

Pleurosigma australe Grun. *in* Reise Novara, Bot., vol. 1, p. 21, pl. 1, fig. 18. 1868 (1870?).

Valve moderately sigmoid, narrow-lanceolate with narrow, rounded, subacute ends. Valve surface highly arched toward the axial area. Axial area and raphe slightly eccentric, more pronounced near the ends. Central area circular or somewhat rhombic. Transverse striae somewhat finer than diagonal striae, which cross each other at an angle of about 60 degrees near the center. Striae and puncta coarse in the middle portion of the valve; becoming finer at the ends, tending to appear in transverse and longitudinal rows only near the ends. Transverse striae, 20-22 in 10μ at the center; becoming 24 in 10μ at the ends. Diagonal striae, 16-17 in 10μ at the center; becoming 19-20 in 10μ near the ends. Length, $50\text{-}110\mu$. Breadth, $15\text{-}17\mu$.

Similar to *Pleurosigma angulatum*, but easily distinguished by its slightly raised axial area, its smaller size, and its larger sized puncta in the middle portion of the valve.

Type locality. — Neuseeland, an der Küste, auf *Ballia callitricha*.

U. S. distribution. — GEOGRAPHICAL: Middle Atlantic States. ECOLOGICAL: Insufficiently known.

6. Pleurosigma delicatulum W. Sm. var. delicatulum

PL. 28, FIGS. 4a-b

Pleurosigma delicatulum W. Sm., Ann. Mag. Nat. Hist., Ser. 2, 9:6, pl. 1, fig. 5. 1852.
Gyrosigma delicatulum (W. Sm.) Elm., Univ. Nebraska Stud., 21(1/4):105, pl. 18, figs. 512-513. 1922.

Valve slightly sigmoid, narrow-lanceolate; gradually tapering to acutely rounded ends. Valve surface relatively flat. Axial area and raphe central in the main portion of the valve, becoming eccentric toward the ends. Central area elliptical. Transverse and diagonal striae about same in number. Diagonal striae crossing each other at an angle of about 55-60 degrees. Transverse and diagonal striae, 20-23(25?) in 10μ. Length, $130\text{-}280\mu$. Breadth, $13\text{-}19\mu$.

Best distinguished from *Pleurosigma salinarum* and varieties by its much more narrow-lanceolate shape and coarser striae.

W. Smith's original description of this diatom gives a striae count of about 20 in 10μ, and a maximum width of 17μ. In his *Synopsis of the British Diatomaceae* (1853, p. 65), he expands the striae count in the description to 25 in 10μ. His illustration, pl. 21, fig. 202, measures about 19μ wide. Cleve (1894, pp. 37-38) gives the width as $20\text{-}30\mu$ and a striae count of 25 in 10μ. The forms observed from the United States are never over 20μ wide (most commonly 14-17μ) and have a striae count (both transverse and diagonal) of 20-23 in 10μ.

It is difficult to know for sure whether we are all dealing with a single variable taxon or whether two or three forms are involved (see discussion under *P. elongatum*). For purposes of this work the general limits of W. Smith's original description are maintained, additionally so, because the populations to which we are applying this name seem to be thusly delimited. Unfortunately, no material of W. Smith could be found for *P. delicatulum* or *P. elongatum* for study. Further study may show *P. elongatum* to be only a variety of this taxon, more suited to highly brackish water.

Type locality. — England, Lewes, Brackish water.

U. S. distribution. — GEOGRAPHICAL: New England States, Middle Atlantic States, Gulf Coast States, East Central States, West Central States, Plains States; Utah, Arizona, California. ECOLOGICAL: More widely distributed in this country in fresh and relatively hard waters although it has been reported from some brackish-water areas. Reports from highly brackish to marine waters may involve other closely related taxa.

Taxa reported from the U. S. (fresh to brackish water) which could not be verified by a specimen from a public herbarium.

Pleurosigma delicatulum var. *americana* Cl. (recorded by Cleve).
Pleurosigma paradoxum Perag. (recorded by Boyer).

Taxa Reported Since 1960

Pleurosigma normani (recorded by Lackey, 1963).

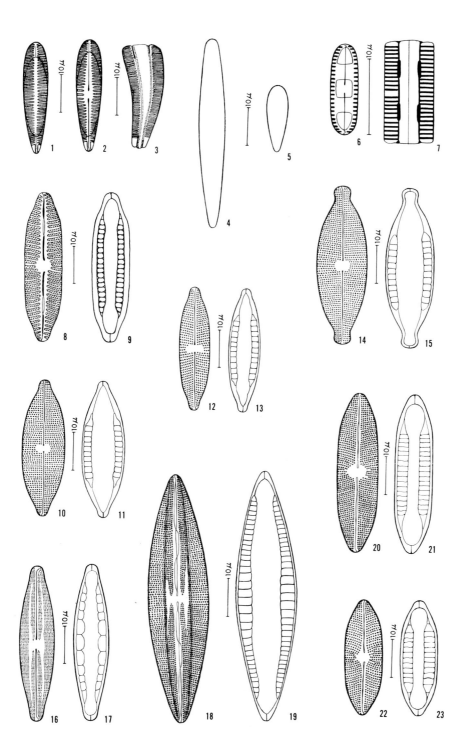

PLATE 21

Fig. 1a–b. *Amphipleura lindheimeri* A-H.L.Sm. 17, West Indies, Cuba.
Fig. 2a–b. *Amphipleura pellucida* A-Kütz. Dec. 9, No. 83, Germany, Weisenfels (drawing of Lectotype).
Fig. 3. *Amphipleura rutilans* A-Boyer W-6-11, Canada, Hudson Bay, Gray Goose Island.
Fig. 4. *Frustulia rhomboides* var. *amphipleuroides* A-G.C. 2356, Missouri, Camden Co., in shallow water Ellis Ford, at confluence of Firey Creek and Little Niangua River.
Fig. 5. *Frustulia rhomboides* A-V.H. 160, England, Aberdeenshire, Bemachie.
Fig. 6. *Frustulia rhomboides* var. *viridula* A-V.H. 163, England.
Fig. 7. *Frustulia rhomboides* var. *saxonica* A-G.C. 2477, Kentucky, Powell Co., Natural Bridge.
Fig. 8. *Frustulia rhomboides* var. *capitata* comb. nov. A-G.C. 2147, Pennsylvania, Monroe Co., Pocono Lake.

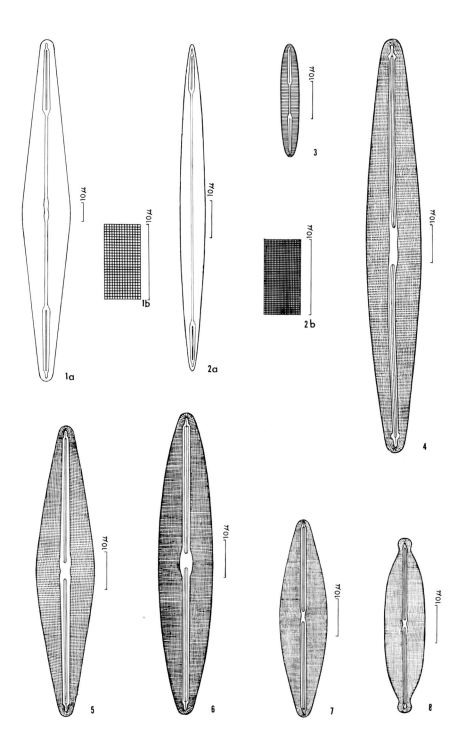

1a

1b

2a

2b

3

4

5

6

7

8

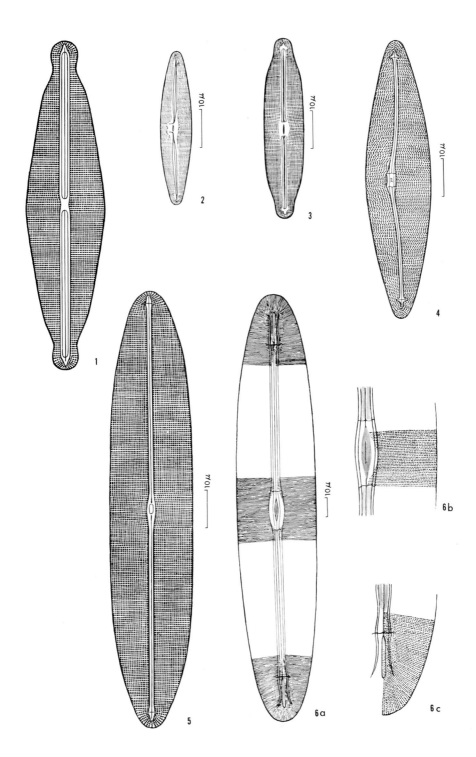

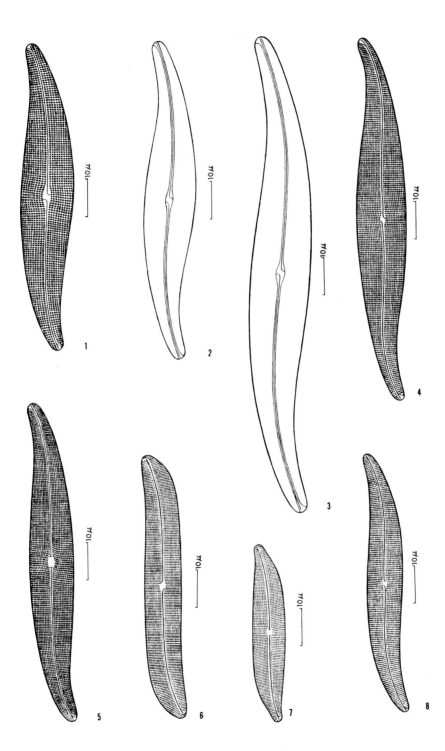

1

2

3

4

5

6

7

PLATE 25

Fig. 1. *Gyrosigma balticum* A-V.H. 180, France, Courceules.
Fig. 2. *Gyrosigma balticum* var. *californicum* A-Cl. & Möll. 246, California, Brooklyn.
Fig. 3. *Gyrosigma terryanum* A-G.C. 2784, Connecticut (?) #2A, Dike #2, South End.
Fig. 4. *Gyrosigma terryanum* f. *fontanum* f. nov. A-G.C. 2861, Florida, Green Spring (drawing of Holotype).
Fig. 5. *Gyrosigma strigilis* A-137, W.Sm. 208, England, Hull.

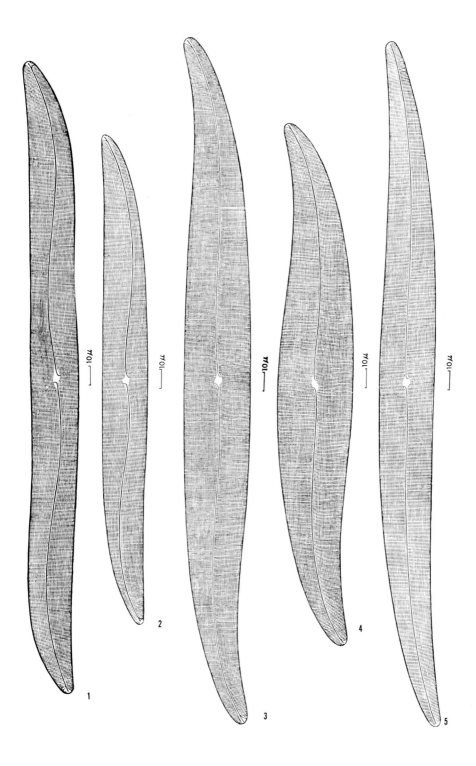

1

2

3

4

5

10μ

10μ

10μ

10μ

10μ

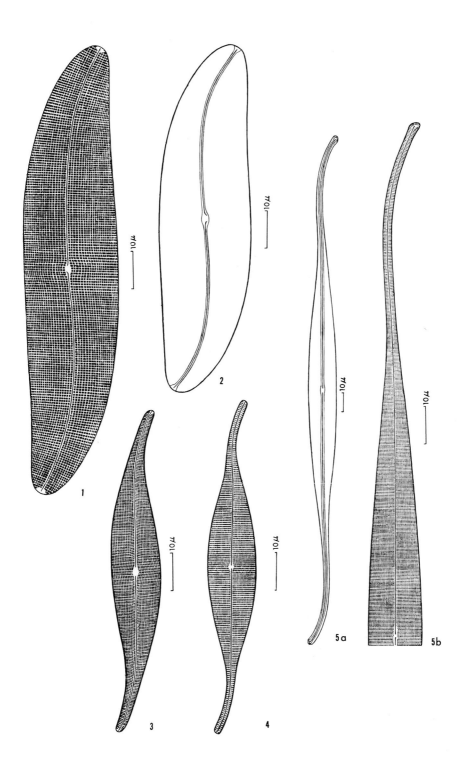

1

2

3

4

5a

5b

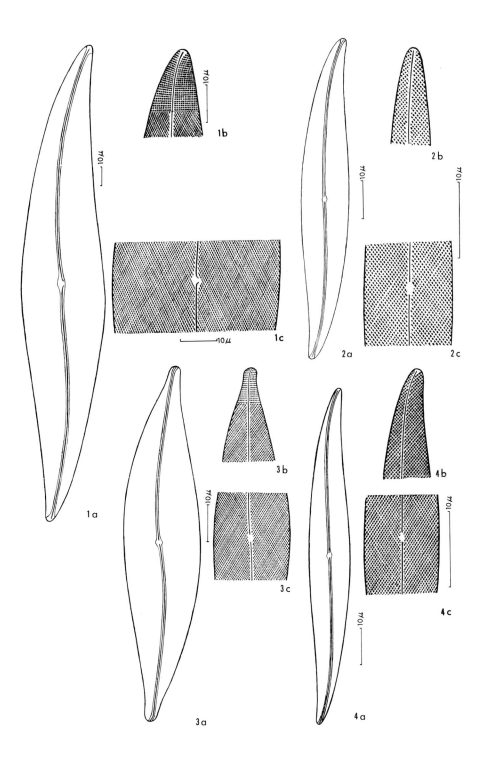

1b

10μ

1c

10μ

10μ

2b

2a

2c

10μ

10μ

3b

3c

3a

4b

4a

4c

10μ

10μ

10μ

1a

10μ

PLATE 28

Fig. 1a–c. *Pleurosigma elongatum* A-V.H. 173, England, Sussex.
Fig. 2a–c. *Pleurosigma strigosum* A-136, W.Sm. 203, England, Sussex.
Fig. 3a–c. *Pleurosigma australe* N.Y.B.G.-Ward B-12-7, Delaware, Wilmington.
Fig. 4a–b. *Pleurosigma delicatulum* A-G.C. 6708a, Arizona, Supai, above Mooney Falls.

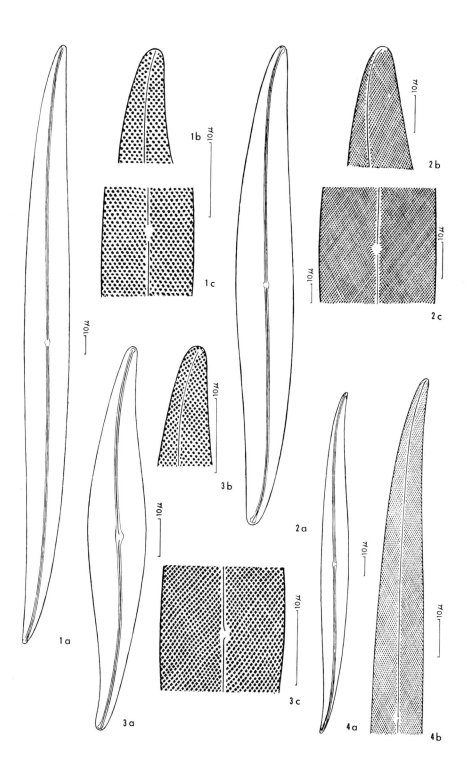

1a

1b   10 μ

1c

2a

2b   10 μ

2c   10 μ

3a

3b   10 μ

3c   10 μ

4a

4b   10 μ

Genus **Stauroneis** Ehr.

Ehr., Ber. Akad. Wiss. Berlin, for 1843:45. 1843.

Valves most generally lanceolate, naviculoid, smaller forms elliptical; symmetrical to the transverse (parapical) and apical (paratransapical— Hustedt, 1956, p. 8) axes. Intercalary bands may be present, but when so are without true septa. Terminal internal valve protrusions (pseudosepta) present in certain species giving, in valve view, much the same appearance as true septa. Central thickening (nodule) present, laterally expanded to the margin, of variable thickness and density. Central area usually corresponding with the stauros, but in some cases it (central area) may not quite reach the valve margins. Striae, where visible, coarsely or finely punctate; mostly radiate to parallel (a very few species show convergent striae near ends).

Some members of this genus are extremely difficult to distinguish, especially those with a shallow fascia. Such diatoms have often been placed in the genus *Navicula*. On the other hand certain taxa which more properly belong in *Navicula* have been placed here by other workers simply because of a lack of striae at the center. There should be some degree of transverse thickening at the center before a diatom is considered further as being a member of *Stauroneis*.

The genus is now being investigated by R. Ross of the British Museum.

Type species. — *Bacillaria phoenicenteron* Nitz. (*pro parte*). [= *Stauroneis phoenicenteron* (Nitz.) Ehr.]

KEY TO THE SPECIES OF STAURONEIS

1. Valves with distinct pseudosepta 2
1. Valves without distinct pseudosepta 9
    2. Valves with broadly rounded ends which are not distinct from valve body, striae distinctly punctate 3
    2. Valves with narrow, rounded, beaked ends which are set off from valve body, striae less distinctly punctate 5
3. Striae coarse, less than 18 in 10μ 4
3. Striae finer, 18 or more in 10μ .... [7] *S. obtusa*
    4. Valves quite large, $130\text{-}380\mu$; axial area broad, $7\text{-}10\mu$
    [12] *S. acuta* var. *terryana*
    4. Valves somewhat smaller, $80\text{-}170\mu$; axial area narrower, $4\text{-}6\mu$ .... [12] *S. acuta*
5. Valve margins parallel or slightly concave 6
5. Valve margins convex, triundulate 7
    6. Striae, 22-25 in 10μ .... [11] *S. ignorata*
    6. Striae 28-30 in 10μ .... [11] *S. ignorata* var. *rupestris*
7. Puncta in longitudinally undulating rows, especially near valve margins
    [8] *S. livingstonii*
7. Puncta indistinct 8

8. Valves conspicuously triundulate ....[10] *S. smithii*

8. Valves with convex, subtilely undulate margins......[10] *S. smithii* var. *incisa*

9. Valves small, less than 15μ long; striae more than 35 in 10μ ....[5] *S. nana*

9. Valves larger, striae coarser 10

   10. Valves with conspicuous longitudinal ribs which are thicker than transverse
       ribs 11

   10. Valves without such ribs 12

11. Longitudinally undulating ribs interrupted at stauros (fascia)......[13] *S. stodderi*

11. Longitudinally undulating ribs not interrupted at stauros (fascia)
                                                   [14] *S. staurolineata*

   12. Valves highly arched; brackish-water species ....[6] *S. amphioxys*

   12. Valves not highly arched; fresh-water species 13

13. Valves small, about 20-23μ long, 4-6μ wide....................[4] *S. kriegeri*

13. Valves larger, (25?) 30-380μ long, (8?) 10-53μ wide 14

   14. Valves with distinctly capitate ends................................. 25

   14. Valves with other than distinctly capitate ends 15

15. Spacing of puncta becoming irregular toward axial area except at the ends 16

15. Spacing of puncta regular 18

   16. Subterminal nodules present ....[15] *S. frickii* var. *angusta*

   16. Subterminal nodules absent 17

17. Valves elliptic-lanceolate with protracted rostrate-capitate ends .....[16] *S. nobilis*

17. Valves linear-lanceolate with attenuate apices, ends not distinctly set off from
       valve body ....[16] *S. nobilis* var. *baconiana*

   18. Valves linear, elongate; ends blunt ....[9]*S. schinzii*

   18. Valves not linear, elongate; ends not bluntly rounded 19

19. Striae, not more than 20 in 10μ; valves generally broad-lanceolate, about 16μ
       broad or more 20

19. Striae, more than 20 in 10μ; valves generally more narrow-linear to lanceolate,
       mostly less than 16μ broad 23

   20. Stauros incomplete, short striae at the margins of stauros
                                 [1] *S. phoenicenteron* var. *brunii*

   20. Stauros complete, occasionally an isolated short stria intruding in stauros,
       but stauros not uniformly interrupted at margins 21

21. Axial area sharply constrictive near central area then abruptly flaring into
       central area ....[2] *S. fluminea*

21. Axial area more or less linear 22

   22. Valves narrow-lanceolate; striae 17-20 in 10μ...[1] *S. phoenicenteron* f. *gracilis*

   22. Valves broad-lanceolate, striae coarser...............[1] *S. phoenicenteron*

23. Fascia bordered by row of coarser puncta, valve ends only slightly produced
                               [3] *S. anceps* var. *americana*

23. Fascia not bordered by row of coarser puncta, valve ends distinctly set off from
       valve body 24

   24. Axial area sharply constrictive near central area, then abruptly flaring into
          central area ....[2] *S. fluminea*

   24. Axial area more or less linear...................................... 25

25. Valves with parallel sides ....[3] *S. anceps* f. *linearis*

25. Valves with convex sides 26

   26. Valve ends narrow-capitate, striae 26 or more in 10μ....[3] *S. anceps* f. *gracilis*

   26. Valve ends more abruptly and broadly capitate, striae 20-25 in 10μ
                                     [3] *S. anceps*

1. Stauroneis phoenicenteron (Nitz.) Ehr. var. phoenicenteron

PL. 29, FIGS. 1-2

Bacillaria phoenicenteron Nitz. (*pro parte*), Neue Schrift. Naturf. Ges. Halle, 3(1):
92-97, pl. 4, figs. 12, 14 (*non* figs. 1-11, 13, 15-22). 1817.

Stauroneis baileyi Ehr., Phys. Abh. Akad. Wiss. Berlin, for 1841:422. 1843.

Stauroneis pteroidea Ehr., Phys. Abh. Akad. Wiss. Berlin, for 1841:423. 1843.

Stauroneis phoenicenteron (Nitz.) Ehr., Phys. Abh. Akad. Wiss. Berlin, for 1841:387,
pl. 2(5), fig. 1; pl. 3(1), fig. 17. 1843.

Stauroneis lanceolata Kütz., Bacill., p. 104, pl. 30, fig. 24. 1844.

Stauroneis phoenicenteron var. *lanceolata* (Kütz.) Brun, Diat. Alpes Jura, p. 89,
pl. 9, fig. 5. 1880.

Stauroneis phoenicenteron var. *genuina* Cl., K. Svenska Vet.-Akad. Handl., Ny Följd,
26(2):149. 1894.

Stauroneis phoenicenteron var. *baileyi* (Ehr.) Cl., K. Svenska Vet.-Akad. Handl.,
Ny Följd, 26(2):149. 1894.

Valve lanceolate with rounded, attenuated extremities which are occasionally slightly protracted. Axial area linear, varying in width from about 4-8μ, but usually broad. Stauros mostly linear, sometimes slightly expanding. Raphe broad, tapering toward the proximal and the distal ends. Striae radiate throughout, distinctly punctate. Striae, 12-17 in 10μ. Puncta variable in number as the striae. Length, 70-380μ. Breadth, 16-53μ.

Easily distinguished from *Stauroneis acuta* by the more lanceolate shape and the lack of pseudosepta.

The striae number of specimens observed from the United States varies from 12 to about 16 or 17 in 10μ. Cleve places the upper limit at 21 in 10μ and Hustedt (1959, p. 768) at 20 in 10μ. Such finely striate forms so far have not been noted here except as form *gracilis*.

Type locality. — Germany, Wittenberg.

U. S. distribution. — GEOGRAPHICAL: New England States, Middle Atlantic States, Southeastern States, Gulf Coast States, South Central States, East Central States, West Central States, Lakes States, Plains States; Wyoming, New Mexico, Washington, Oregon, California. ECOLOGICAL: Oligohalob, pH "indifferent"; apparently has a wide range of ecological tolerance (euryök).

1. Stauroneis phoenicenteron f. gracilis (Ehr.) Hust. PL. 29, FIGS. 3-4

Stauroneis gracilis Ehr. (*pro parte*), Phys. Abh. Akad. Wiss. Berlin, for 1841:423,
pl. 2(1), fig. 17. 1843. [*non* Ehr., pl. 1(2), fig. 14. 1843.]

Stauroneis phoenicenteron var. *amphilepta* (Ehr.) Cl. (*pro parte*), K. Svenska Vet.-
Akad. Handl., Ny Följd, 26(2):149. 1894.

Stauroneis phoenicenteron var. *gracilis* (Ehr.) Dipp., Diat. Rhein-Mainebene, p. 82,
text figs. 174a-c. 1904.

Stauroneis phoenicenteron f. *gracilis* (Ehr.) Hust. *in* Pasch., Süssw.-Fl. Mitteleuropas,
Heft 10, Aufl. 2, p. 255. 1930.

Valve more narrow-lanceolate, striae slightly more numerous, than in variety *phoenicenteron*. Other features the same as the nominate variety. Striae, about 17-20 in 10μ. Length, 80-160μ. Breadth, about 16-21μ.

Ehrenberg described a *Stauroneis amphilepta* (1843, p. 422) and gave two illustrations for it. His description does not agree with his illustrations in that the description states, " . . .apicibus constrictis subcapitatis." Neither illustration has such ends. They are attenuate, but hardly constricted. This epithet of Ehrenberg should be rejected as a *nomen dubium*.

Type locality. — South America, Chile.

U. S. distribution. — GEOGRAPHICAL: New England States, Middle Atlantic States, Southeastern States, Gulf Coast States, East Central States, West Central States, Lakes States; Washington, Oregon. ECOLOGICAL: Euryök as the species; more often found in lakes and ponds, but not restricted to them.

1. Stauroneis phoenicenteron var. brunii (M. Perag. & Hérib.) Voigt
PL. 29, FIG. 5

Stauroneis bruni M. Perag. & Herib. *in* Hérib., Diat. Auvergne, p. 76, pl. 3, fig. 22. 1893.

Stauroneis phoenicenteron var. *brunii* (M. Perag. & Hérib. *in* Hérib.) Voigt, Not. Bot. Chinoise, Mus. Heude [Shanghai], No. 6, p. 4. 1943.

Marginal striae bordering fascia. Length not known to exceed about 160μ. Other features as in variety *phoenicenteron*. Striae, 14-16 in 10μ. Puncta, 12-14 in 10μ. Length, 125-160μ. Breadth, 29-32μ.

Type locality. — France, Puy-de-Dôme; fossil.

U. S. distribution. — GEOGRAPHICAL: Massachusetts, Texas. ECOLOGICAL: Insufficiently known; has not been found in any appreciable numbers.

2. Stauroneis fluminea Patr. & Freese var. fluminea   PL. 29, FIG. 6

Stauroneis fluminea Patr. & Freese, Proc. Acad. Nat. Sci. Philadelphia, 112:184, pl. 1, fig. 9. 1961.

Valve linear with attenuate-rostrate ends. Axial area narrow; constricted about 4μ from the central area, then expanding into the central area. Fascia expanding toward the margins. Raphe filiform; narrowing toward the distal ends; reflexing at the proximal ends. Proximal ends of the raphe rounded, distal ends hooked in same direction. Striae radiate throughout, punctate. Striae, 18-24 in 10μ. Length, 60-90μ. Breadth, 12-18μ.

Best distinguished from *Stauroneis anceps* f. *linearis* by the rostrate—not capitate—ends and the expansion of the axial area near the central area. The variable width of the axial area also distinguishes it from the *S. phoenicenteron* group.

Type locality. – U.S.A., Alaska, Second Judicial Div., pool near Nunivak Lake, Barrow. (*Holotype*–A.G.C. 8193, Patrick & Freese, 1961.)

U. S. distribution. – GEOGRAPHICAL: Wyoming. ECOLOGICAL: So far found in soft, slightly acid to neutral waters only.

3. **Stauroneis anceps** Ehr. var. **anceps** PL. 30, FIG. 1

> *Stauroneis anceps* Ehr., Phys. Abh. Akad. Wiss. Berlin, for 1841:422, pl. 2(1), fig. 18. 1843.
> *Stauroneis anceps* var. *amphicephala* (Kütz.) V. H., Syn. Diat. Belgique, pl. 4, fig. 6. 1880.

Valve elliptical-lanceolate to linear-lanceolate with protracted rostrate to capitate ends. Axial area linear except near the ends where it constricts somewhat. Fascia usually broadening toward the valve margin. Raphe straight, narrowing slightly toward the proximal and the distal ends. Striae radiate throughout; puncta small but distinct. Striae, 20-25 in 10μ. Puncta fine. Length, 24-75μ. Breadth, 9-15μ.

The wider range of dimensions given by Hustedt (1930, p. 256), i.e., length, 20-130μ; breadth, 6-18μ; striae, 20-30 in 10μ, do not apply to those specimens observed so far from the United States.

This quite variable species is generally smaller and more finely striate than *Stauroneis phoenicenteron* and its varieties to which it is allied.

Type locality. – French Guiana, Cayenne [South America].

U. S. distribution. – GEOGRAPHICAL: New England States, Middle Atlantic States, Southeastern States, Gulf Coast States, South Central States, East Central States, West Central States, Lakes States, Plains States; Montana, Wyoming, New Mexico, Arizona, Washington, Oregon, California. ECOLOGICAL: A widespread eurytopic species; pH "indifferent."

3. **Stauroneis anceps** f. **gracilis** Rabh. PL. 30, FIG. 2

> *Stauroneis anceps* f. *gracilis* Rabh., Fl. Europaea Alg., sect. 1, p. 247. 1864.
> *Stauroneis anceps* var. *gracilis* Brun, Diat. Alpes Jura, p. 89, pl. 9, fig. 2. 1880.

Valve elongate, elliptical-lanceolate with extremely narrowed capitate ends; otherwise as variety *anceps*. Striae, usually not coarser than 26 in 10μ. Length, 40-55μ. Breadth, 8-10μ.

Type locality. – [Germany], In einem Graben am Teiche von Hussinetz bei Strehlen . . . (Rabh. #1208).

U. S. distribution. – GEOGRAPHICAL: New England States, Middle Atlantic States, Southeastern States, South Central States, East Central States, Plains States. ECOLOGICAL: Occurs with the nominate variety.

3. Stauroneis anceps f. linearis (Ehr.) Hust.   PL. 30, FIG. 3

Stauroneis linearis Ehr., Phys. Abh. Akad. Wiss. Berlin, for 1841:423, pl. 1(2), fig. 11. 1843.

Stauroneis anceps f. *linearis* (Ehr.) Hust. *in* Pasch., Süssw.-Fl. Mitteleuropas, Heft 10, Aufl. 2, p. 256, text fig. 407. 1930.

Valve with parallel sides and distinctly capitate ends. Other features as in the nominate variety.

Type locality. – Chile.

U. S. distribution. – GEOGRAPHICAL: Middle Atlantic States, Southeastern States, East Central States, Lakes States, Plains States; Wyoming, California. ECOLOGICAL: Occurs with the nominate variety.

3. Stauroneis anceps var. americana Reim.   PL. 30, FIG. 4

Stauroneis anceps var. *americana* Reim., Proc. Acad. Nat. Sci. Philadelphia, 113: 199, pl. 2, fig. 11. 1961.

Valve with protracted attenuate-rostrate ends. Stauros linear and bordered by a row of coarse puncta. Striae, 26-28 in 10μ. Puncta, about 30 in 10μ. Length, 48-50μ. Breadth, 12.5μ.

Type locality. – U.S.A., South Carolina, Aiken County, Upper Three Runs Creek. (*Holotype*–A-G.C. 44254a, Reimer, 1961.)

U. S. distribution. – GEOGRAPHICAL:Known only from the type locality. ECOLOGICAL: Insufficiently known.

4. Stauroneis kriegeri Patr. var. kriegeri   PL. 30, FIG. 5

Stauroneis anceps var. *capitata* M. Perag. *in* Temp. & Perag., Diat. Monde Entier, 2nd ed., p. 57. 1908.

Stauroneis pygmaea Krieg., Beitr. Naturdenkmalpflege, 13:272, pl. 2, fig. 28. 1929. [*non* Castr.]

Stauroneis kriegeri Patr., Farlowia, 2(2):175. 1945.

Valve linear with parallel to slightly convex sides. Ends rostrate to capitate. Axial area narrow. Fascia linear to slightly expanded toward the margins; may appear somewhat broader on one side. Raphe filiform. Striae radiate throughout, finely but distinctly punctate. Striae, 26 in 10μ. Length, 20-23μ. Breadth, 4-6μ.

Best distinguished by the small size, the fine but distinctly punctate striae and the linear or only slightly expanded fascia.

Type locality. – Europe, Germany, Hochmoor, Diebelsee.

U. S. distribution. – GEOGRAPHICAL: New England States, Middle Atlantic States, Southeastern States, West Central States; California. ECOLOGICAL: Appears to be pH "indifferent," oligohalob; more characteristic of headwater areas.

5. Stauroneis nana Hust. var. nana PL. 30, FIG. 6

Stauroneis nana Hust., Abh. Naturw. Ver. Bremen, 34:259, text fig. 3. 1957.

Valve small, transparent, elliptical-lanceolate with slightly protracted, bluntly rounded ends. Axial area narrow, linear. Fascia markedly expanding to the margins. Raphe straight, filiform; proximal ends distant, distal ends indistinct. Striae very fine, indistinct; strongly radiate near the center of the valve, direction undetermined toward the ends. Length, 10-12μ. Breadth, 3-3.5μ.

Best distinguished from other species of *Stauroneis* by the sharply expanding stauros and the very fine striae.

Type locality. — Europe, North Germany, Weser River at Mittelsbüren.

U. S. distribution. — GEOGRAPHICAL: Texas. ECOLOGICAL: Insufficiently known. This diatom was rare in the Texas sample. There seems to be no record of its occurrence in large numbers anywhere.

6. Stauroneis amphioxys Greg. var. amphioxys PL. 30, FIG. 7

Stauroneis amphioxys Greg., Trans. Micr. Soc. London, New Ser. 4:48, pl. 5, fig. 23. 1856. [*non* (Ehr.) Ralfs.]
Stauroneis gregorii Ralfs *in* Pritch., Hist. Infusoria, 4th ed., p. 913. 1861.

Valve elliptical-lanceolate, with attenuated obtusely rounded extremities. Not distinct from the valve body. Valve highly arched. Axial area narrow, becoming wider near the center. Terminal nodules small, but quite conspicuous. Fascia rather narrow, marginally bordered by very short striae which are sometimes difficult to observe, being on the contour side. Raphe filiform, proximal ends quite close; distal ends hooking at about 90 degrees in same direction, then recurving into the ends. Striae slightly radiate at the center to parallel near the ends. Puncta visible but very fine. Striae, 16-17 in 10μ near the center; 19-20 in 10μ toward the ends. Length, 50-70μ. Breadth, 15-18μ.

This diatom is distinguished principally by the highly arched valve and the distal raphe-end hooks.

Type locality. — Scotland, Glenshira sand; fossil.

U. S. distribution. — GEOGRAPHICAL: Connecticut, Georgia. ECOLOGICAL: Euryhaline; slightly brackish to marine waters of the coast.

7. Stauroneis obtusa Lagerst. var. obtusa PL. 30, FIGS. 8-9

Stauroneis obtusa Lagerst., Bih. K. Svenska Vet.-Akad. Handl., 1(14):36, pl. 1, fig. 11. 1873.

Valve linear-elliptical to linear-lanceolate with broadly rounded, subrostrate ends only slightly set off from the main portion of the valve. Pseudosepta conspicuous. Axial area narrow, linear; flaring abruptly at the center. Fascia rather broad, conspicuously expanding toward the margins. Raphe faint, lateral, twisting near the proximal ends where it becomes quite conspicuous; proximal ends curving slightly in same direction, distal ends curving in same direction. Striae radiate throughout, often slightly curved except near the ends where they become straight. Puncta distinct. Striae, 18-20 in 10μ at the center, becoming 24-26 in 10μ at the ends. Length, 32-76μ. Breadth, 5-10μ.

Distinguished from *Stauroneis acuta* by its smaller size, finer striae, and more linear shape.

The more extreme sizes as reported by Hustedt (1959, p. 817), i.e., length, 25-120μ; breadth, to 13μ, ! 20μ, (1930, p. 260); have not been seen so far in this country.

Type locality. — Spitzenbergen, Kobbe B. [Norway].

U. S. distribution. — GEOGRAPHICAL; Middle Atlantic States, Southeastearn States, Lakes States; California. ECOLOGICAL: Found more frequently in running water or otherwise well-aerated habitats; (?)alkaliphilous, (salt) "indifferent" or halophobe.

8. **Stauroneis livingstonii** Reim. var. **livingstonii**   PL. 30, FIG. 10

Stauroneis livingstonii Reim., Proc. Acad. Nat. Sci. Philadelphia, 113:203-204, pl. 2, fig. 4. 1961.

Valve linear-elliptical with slightly triundulate sides and narrow, rostrate ends. Pseudosepta present extending into the valve about the length of the ends. Axial area narrow, linear. Fascia narrow, linear. Margins of the fascia sometimes with very short striae. Raphe filiform; proximal ends close; distal ends indistinct but appearing to curve slightly over the ends. Striae radiate throughout, the relatively strong arch of the valve frequently giving the appearance of curved striae. Striae punctate; puncta towards the margins progressively larger and in longitudinally undulating rows. Striae, 25-26 in 10μ to 28 in 10μ near the ends. Puncta, about 24 in 10μ. Length, 27-33μ. Breadth, 7.5-8μ.

Characterized by the different size puncta· (large near the margins, becoming smaller toward the center), and the narrow fascia.

Type locality. — U. S. A., South Carolina, Aiken County, Upper Three Runs Creek. (*Holotype*—A-G.C. 44272a, Reimer, 1961.)

U. S. distribution. — GEOGRAPHICAL: South Carolina. ECOLOGICAL: To date found only in a small dystrophic tributary of the Savannah River.

9. **Stauroneis schinzii** (Brun) Cl. var. **schinzii**   PL. 30, FIG. 11

Navicula schinzii Brun, Mém. Soc. Phys. Hist. Nat. Genève, 31(2):38, pl. 16, fig.1. 1891.

Stauroneis schinzii (Brun) Cl., K. Svenska Vet.-Akad. Handl., Ny Földj, 26(2): 146. 1894.

Valve linear, slightly gibbous at the center. Ends very broadly rounded, obtuse; about as wide as the gibbous center. Axial area broad, linear; becoming suddenly ovoid at the terminal ends; appearing somewhat thicker as a siliceous rib. Margin of the axial area somewhat irregular. Fascia shallow, relatively small, expanding slightly toward the margins. Raphe broad, narrowing somewhat toward the proximal and the distal ends. Distal raphe ends branched, forming semicircular hooks curving in same direction. Striae radiate at the center, becoming parallel toward the ends, or occasionally convergent. Striae usually somewhat curved. Puncta distinct, regular. Striae, 15-18 in 10μ (Cleve gives 20 in 10μ). Puncta, 15-18 in 10μ. Length, 130-221μ. Breadth, 17-19μ (Cleve gives 11μ).

Distinguished by its relatively large size, linear shape, and quite broadly rounded, obtuse apices.

For a discussion of this taxon see Reimer (1961, pp. 205-206).

Type locality. — Africa, Southwest Africa. Exact locality uncertain: Lacs d'Olukonda et d'Omlica (Afrique sud-ouest), sur Charas.

U. S. distribution. — GEOGRAPHICAL: Alabama (rare). ECOLOGICAL: Insufficiently known.

10. **Stauroneis smithii** Grun. var. **smithii**   PL. 30, FIG. 12

Stauroneis linearis Ehr. *sensu* W. Sm., Syn. British Diat., vol. 1, p. 60, pl. 19, fig. 193. 1853. [*non Stauroneis linearis* Ehr.]
Stauroneis smithii Grun., Verh. Zool.-Bot. Ges. Wien, 10:564, pl. 6, fig. 16. 1860.

Valve elliptical-lanceolate to lanceolate with triundulate margins; the center undulation is the broadest. Ends short, produced, narrow-rostrate. Pseudoseptum present at either end. Axial area very narrow, linear. Fascia narrow, linear; sometimes slightly broader at extreme margins. Raphe narrow, filiform. Striae slightly to moderately radiate throughout, finely punctate. Striae, 26-30 in 10μ. Length, 14-40μ. Breadth, 4-9μ.

Characterized by the deep, narrow fascia; triundulate sides; and apiculate ends.

Type locality. — Europe, Lower Austria. Exact locality uncertain; in Gräben und Tümpeln der Kalksteinformation, an verschiedenen Orten Unterösterreichs.

U. S. distribution. — GEOGRAPHICAL: New England States, Middle Atlantic States, Southeastern States, South Central States, East Central States, West Central States, Lakes States, Plains States; Wyoming. ECOLOGICAL: Alkaliphilous, eurytopic.

10. Stauroneis smithii var. incisa Pant.   pl. 30, fig. 13

> *Stauroneis smithii* var. *incisa* Pant., Resultate Wiss. Erforsch. Balatonsees, vol. 2, pt. 2, sect. 1, p. 27, pl. 2, fig. 45. 1902.

Valves elliptical-lanceolate to rhombic-lanceolate, more subtilely undulate than the nominate variety. Ends only slightly protracted. Other features as in the nominate variety. Striae, 32-33 in 10μ. Length, 22-25μ. Breadth, 5-5.5μ.

Very similar in shape to *Stauroneis ignorata,* but distinguished by its convex—not parallel—sides and finer striae.

Type locality. — Europe, Hungary, Lake Balaton, Seeschlamm; Siofok.

U. S. distribution. — Geographical: Middle Atlantic States; Georgia. Ecological: Insufficiently known.

11. Stauroneis ignorata Hust. var. ignorata   pl. 30, fig. 14

> *Stauroneis parvula* var. *prominula* Grun. *in* Cl., K. Svenska Vet.-Akad. Handl., Ny Följd, 26(2):149. 1894.
>
> *Stauroneis ignorata* Hust., Abh. Naturw. Ver. Bremen, 31:620, text figs. 48-50. 1939.
>
> *Stauroneis prominula* (Grun. *in* Cl.) Hust. *in* Rabh., Kryptog.-Fl. Deutschland, vol. 7(2), no. 6, pp. 805-807. 1959. (*nom. superf.*)

Valve linear with narrow, rostrate ends. Conspicuous pseudoseptum present. Axial area narrow, linear; flaring slightly at the central fascia. Fascia linear, prominent nodular-like thickenings at the margins giving the appearance of a slight constriction. Raphe filiform; proximal ends rather distant; distal ends not visibly differentiated. Striae parallel. Puncta very indistinct. Striae, (?18μ—Hustedt, 1959, p. 805) 22-24 in 10μ. Length, 18-40μ. Breadth, 3-8μ.

Distinguished from other small *Stauroneis* with pseudosepta by the parallel sides; rather coarse, indistinctly punctate, parallel striae; and the rostrate ends.

For a discussion of the taxonomic problems involved see Reimer (1961, pp. 201-202). In this paper Grunow's *prominula* was misspelled as *promulina.*

Type locality. — Finland, Tana Elf.

U. S. distribution. — Geographical: New York, Indiana, Nebraska. Ecological: Prefers slightly alkaline, fresh waters (alkaliphil?); also appears in slightly brackish water, inland lakes and ponds.

11. Stauroneis ignorata var. rupestris (Skv.) Reim.   pl. 30, fig. 15

> *Stauroneis parvula* var. *rupestris* Skv., Bull. Fan Mem. Inst. Biol., Bot. 7(6):221-222, pl. 1, fig. 20. 1937.
>
> *Stauroneis ignorata* var. *rupestris* (Skv.) Reim., Proc. Acad. Nat. Sci. Philadelphia, 113:202-203, pl. 2, fig. 8. 1961.

Ends subrostrate. Striae finer than in the nominate variety. Other features as in variety *ignorata*. Striae, 28-30 in 10μ. Length, 18-20μ. Breadth, 4μ.

Type locality. — China, Hangchow; In rupestris muscosis prope Hangchow.

U. S. distribution. — GEOGRAPHICAL: Indiana, Michigan, Texas. ECOLOGICAL: Insufficiently known.

12. **Stauroneis acuta** W. Sm. var. **acuta**   PL. 31, FIG. 1

Stauroneis acuta W. Sm., Syn. British Diat., vol. 1, pp. 59-60, pl. 19, fig. 187. 1853.
Pleurostauron acutum (W. Sm.) Rabh. *ex* Cramer, Hedwigia, 2(3):17, pl. 1, fig. B. 1859.

Frustules commonly found adherent in chains. Intercalary bands evident in girdle view. Valve rhombic-lanceolate, often slightly gibbous at the center with rather broadly rounded ends. Pseudosepta present, quite conspicuous. Axial area broad, 4-6μ; narrowing slightly near the ends. Central fascia broadening toward the margins. Raphe straight, rather broad and lateral; 1-2μ at widest point, except at the proximal and the distal ends where it becomes filiform. Striae, 12-16 in 10μ. Puncta, about same as the striae. Length, 80-170μ. Breadth, 15-27μ. Hustedt (1959, p. 819) gives to 40μ.

This taxon is best characterized by its conspicuous pseudosepta, coarser striae, and more or less tumid center.

Type locality. — Uncertain, [? New Zealand (Queckett)].

U. S. distribution. — GEOGRAPHICAL: New England States, Middle Atlantic States, East Central States, Lakes States, Plains States; Colorado, Washington. ECOLOGICAL: Alkaliphilous, oligohalob; more often found in alkaline springs, lakes, and upper to middle reaches of streams.

12. **Stauroneis acuta** var. **terryana** Temp. *ex* Cl.   PL. 31, FIG. 5

Stauroneis acuta var. *terryana* Temp. *ex* Cl., K. Svenska Vet.-Akad. Handl., Ny Följd, 26(2):150. 1894.
Stauroneis terryi Ward *ex* Terry, Rhodora, 9:126. 1907.
Stauroneis acuta var. *maxima* M. Perag. *in* Temp. & Perag., Diat. Monde Entier, 2nd ed., p. 87. 1908.
Stauroneis terryi (Ward *ex* Terry) Palm. (*ampl.*), Proc. Acad. Nat. Sci. Philadelphia, 62:457, pl. 34, figs. 1-3. 1910.

Valve larger, axial area and raphe broader, than in variety *acuta*. Axial area, 7-10μ. Raphe, about 4μ. Striae, 11-13 in 10μ. Puncta, 9-12 in 10μ. Length, 130-380μ. Breadth, 32-60μ.

Palmer (1910, p. 456) noted that the original specimens of this taxon were collected by Wm. A. Terry from Fall Mountain, Connecticut. Some of this material was sent by Terry to J. Tempère who in turn forwarded a specimen of the material to P. T. Cleve. Just how Cleve got the designation

"Brackish water" is not known, but it appears almost certain that the specimen in his possession was actually from the fresh-water collection of Terry.

For further discussion of this taxon see: Hustedt (1959, p. 821) and Reimer (1961, pp. 195-198).

Type locality. — U.S.A., Connecticut, Hartford Co., Bristol, Fall Mountain.

U. S. distribution. — Geographical: New England States. Ecological: To date reported only from lakes and streams in New England.

13. Stauroneis stodderi Lewis var. stodderi   PL. 31, FIG. 4

Stauroneis stodderii Lewis, Proc. Acad. Nat. Sci. Philadelphia, 17:13-14, pl. 2, fig. 6. 1865.

Navicula stodderi (Greenl.) Cl., K. Svenska Vet.-Akad. Handl., Ny Följd, 26(2): 110. 1894.

Stauroneis stodderi var. *superbe* Temp. & Perag., Diat. Monde Entier, 2nd ed., p. 201. 1910.

Valve elliptical-lanceolate; narrowing rather abruptly to elongate, rostrate ends. Axial area rather broad, linear. Fascia narrow, linear. Raphe rather broad, narrowing near the center and the ends. Proximal raphe ends close; distal ends forking about 1μ from the valve ends at the terminal nodules. One raphe branch curving into the valve end. Striae radiate, composed of transversely elongate puncta formed by thickened longitudinal ribs. Longitudinal ribs approximately parallel; interrupted at the fascia except for occasional appearance of a single uninterrupted rib on the valve mantle. Striae, 17-22 in 10μ. Longitudinal ribs, 10-13 in 10μ. Length, 75-95μ. Breadth, 17-19μ.

The thickened fascia across the valve face precludes placing this diatom in any genus other than *Stauroneis*.

Forms listed by Cleve (1894, p. 110) as narrow as 14μ are probably to be referred to S. *staurolineata* Reim.

Type locality. — U.S.A., New Hampshire. Exact locality uncertain: Bemis Lake, Wolfboro, Gorham Pond.

U. S. distribution. — Geographical: New England States; Pennsylvania (fossil?). Ecological: So far found only in lakes, lake sediments, and alluvial deposits.

14. Stauroneis staurolineata Reim. var. staurolineata   PL. 31, FIG. 6

Stauroneis staurolineata Reim., Proc. Acad. Nat. Sci. Philadelphia, 113:206-207, pl. 2, fig. 3. 1961.

Valve lanceolate, tapering to narrow-rostrate ends. Axial area linear, broadening at the ends. Fascia narrow, linear, crossed by conspicuous longitudinal hyaline ribs. Raphe linear, slightly broadened between the valve center and the ends. Proximal raphe ends close; distal ends forking about 3 to 4μ from the valve ends at a subterminal nodule. One raphe branch elongate, hooking into the end. Striae radiate except at the ends where they become single puncta due to the thick longitudinal ribs extending into the ends. Longitudinal ribs approximately parallel, not conspicuously undulate and not interrupted at the fascia. Striae, 16-17 in 10μ. Longitudinal ribs, 9-11 in 10μ. Length, 90-115μ. Breadth, 15-17μ.

Best distinguished from *Stauroneis stodderii* by the presence of longitudinal ribs passing through the stauros. For a discussion of these taxa see Reimer (1961, pp. 206-209).

Type locality. — U.S.A., New Hampshire, Carroll County, Wolfboro. (*Holotype*—A-H. L. Sm. 502, Reimer, 1961.)

U. S. distribution. — GEOGRAPHICAL: New England States, Middle Atlantic States. ECOLOGICAL: So far, found only from recent lake sediments and fossil clay.

15. Stauroneis frickii var. angusta Boyer PL. 31, FIGS. 7a-d

Stauroneis frickii var. *angusta* Boyer, Diat. Philadelphia, p. 88, pl. 26, fig. 18. 1916.

Valve lanceolate with broadly rounded, obtuse ends. Axial area rather broad, linear; widening at the ends around the terminal nodules. Subterminal nodules large, conspicuous. Fascia approximately linear with very short striae at the margins. Raphe broad, narrowing toward the proximal and distal ends. Distal raphe end with one shortened and one prolongated branch, the latter proceeding to the valve end; branching originates about 7μ from the valve ends. Striae radiate throughout, continuous over both ends. Puncta small, irregular around the center and on the margins of the axial area. Striae, 15-16 in 10μ throughout. Length, about 175μ. Breadth, 28-29μ.

This taxon differs from variety *frickii* in that it has an approximately linear fascia which has shortened striae at the margins. The variety *frickii* has an expanded fascia and no apparent marginal striae. The thick terminal nodules and distant branching of the distal raphe ends are the primary distinguishing features of this taxon.

Hustedt (1959, p. 821) places *Stauroneis frickii* in synonymy with *S. acuta* indicating that forms like *S. frickii* are often found with *S. acuta* and are the same taxon. Boyer's variety *angusta* is associated with *S. phoenicenteron* f. *gracilis* and is rare in the collection. At present, variety *angusta* is being maintained as a variety until more specimens can be seen. There is, however, a strong possibility that this variety may be associated with auxospore formation in *S. phoenicenteron* f. *gracilis* or possibly *S. acuta*.

Type locality. — U.S.A., Pennsylvania, Delaware County, Newtown Square.

U. S. distribution. — Geographical: Known only from the type locality. Ecological: Insufficiently known.

16. Stauroneis nobilis Schum. var. nobilis   pl. 31, fig. 2

Stauroneis nobilis Schum., Schrift. Phys.-Ökon. Ges. Königsberg, 8:59, pl. 2, fig. 60. 1867.

Stauroneis anceps var.? *nobilis* (Schum.) Cl., K. Svenska Vet.-Akad. Handl., Ny Földj, 26(2):148. 1894.

Stauroneis alabamae var. *angulata* Heid. *in* A. S., Atlas Diat., pl. 242, fig. 5. 1903.

Valve elliptical-lanceolate with narrow, protracted ends and slightly undulate sides. Raphe lateral, narrowing at the proximal and the distal ends. Axial area rather broad except at the ends where it constricts somewhat. Fascia narrow, linear or occasionally becoming smaller towards the margin. Striae radiate throughout, punctate. Puncta arranged in longitudinally undulating rows, spaced rather far apart except at the margins and ends, where they appear closer together. Striae, 14-17 in 10μ. Length, 120-150μ; Hustedt (1959, p. 778) gives $100\text{-}185\mu$. Breadth, $23\text{-}38\mu$.

Best distinguished by the more distant striae on the central parts of the valve surface and its peculiar undulate shape.

Type locality. — Germany, Prussia, (Landgraben) prope Regimontium.

U. S. distribution. — Geographical: New England States, Middle Atlantic States, Southeastern States. Ecological: Seems to prefer dystrophic, soft-water lakes and small streams.

16. Stauroneis nobilis var. baconiana (Stodd.) Reim.   pl. 31, fig. 3

Stauroneis baconiana Stodd., Proc. Boston Soc. Nat. Hist., 7:26, 27. 1859.

Stauroneis nobilis var. *baconiana* (Stodd.) Reim., Proc. Acad. Nat. Sci. Philadelphia, 113:204-205. 1961.

Valve narrow, linear-lanceolate with long, narrow ends. Undulation near the ends much more subtile; striae near the ends somewhat more numerous than in variety *nobilis.* Other features as in the nominate variety. Striae, 16 in 10μ near the center to 20 in 10μ toward the ends. Length, $115\text{-}140\mu$. Breadth, $15\text{-}22\mu$, narrowing to $3\text{-}5\mu$ toward the ends.

For a discussion of this variety see Reimer (1961, pp. 204-205).

Type locality. — U.S.A., Massachusetts, Suffolk County, West Roxbury near Boston; small stream.

U. S. distribution. — Geographical: Massachusetts. Ecological: Insufficiently known.

Taxa reported from the U. S. (fresh water) which could not be verified by a specimen from a public herbarium.

Navicula phyllodes (Ehr.) Ehr. (= *Stauroneis phyllodes* Ehr.) (recorded by Ehrenberg).

Pleurostauron parvulum Grun. (= *Navicula ruttneri* Hust. *fide* Hust.) (recorded by Tempère & Peragallo and Allen).

Stauroneis alabamae Heid. *in* A. S. [= *Stauroneis nobilis* f. *alabamae* (Heid.) Cl.-Eul.] (recorded by Hohn).

Stauroneis americana Heid. (recorded by Boyer).

Stauroneis gallica M. Perag. (recorded by Tempère & Peragallo).

Stauroneis legumen (Ehr.) Kütz. (recorded by Ehrenberg, Elmore and Boyer).

Stauroneis parvula Jan. (= *Navicula ruttneri* Hust. *fide* Hust.) (recorded by Elmore and Neel).

Stauroneis phyllodes Ehr. (recorded by Chase, Tempère & Peragallo and Tiffany & Britton).

Stauroneis producta Grun. (recorded by Chase and Tiffany & Britton). 1952).

Stauroneis sieboldii Ehr. (recorded by Tempère & Peragallo).

Names of taxa reported from the U. S. which are either illegitimate or of uncertain application

Amphiprora constricta Ehr. [*Stauroneis constricta* (Ehr.) W. Sm.] (recorded by J. W. Bailey).

Pleurosiphonia phoenicenteron Ehr. (*nom. nud.*) (recorded by Ehrenberg).

Stauroneis amphilepta Ehr. (recorded by Ehrenberg and Tempère & Peragallo).

Stauroneis anceps var. *birostris* (Ehr.) Cl. (?*Stauroneis anceps* Ehr.) (recorded by Cleve and Tiffany & Britton).

Stauroneis birostris Ehr. (?*Stauroneis anceps* Ehr.) (recorded by Cleve & Möller).

Stauroneis binodis Ehr. (recorded by Ehrenberg).

Stauroneis dicephala Ehr. (recorded by Ehrenberg).

Stauroneis euglypta Ehr. (recorded by Ehrenberg).

Stauroneis eurysoma Ehr. (recorded by Ehrenberg).

Stauroneis fenestra Ehr. (recorded by Ehrenberg).

Stauroneis lineolata Ehr. [?*Stauroneis stodderi* var. *insignis* (Grun.) Mills.] (recorded by Tempère & Peragallo).

Stauroneis macrocephala Kütz. (recorded by Tempère & Peragallo).

Stauroneis platalea Ehr. (recorded by Ehrenberg).

Taxa Recorded Since 1960

Stauroneis norvegica Hust. (recorded by Reimer, 1962).
Stauroneis tenera Hust. (recorded by Hohn & Hellerman, 1963).
Stauroneis triundulatum Borge (recorded by Woodson & Holoman, 1965).

Genus **Capartogramma** Kuff.

Kuff., Expl. Hydrobiol. Lac Tanganyika (1946-1947), Res. Sci., 4(3):27. 1956.

Valve shape symmetrical (generally lanceolate) to lunate, with or without produced ends. Intercalary bands present in some species (i.e., *C. karstenii* (Zanon) Ross, *fide* Ross), lacking in others (i.e., *C. crucicula*). Pseudoseptum present, one in each extremity of the valve. Two narrow struts of silicon (tigilla) connect the central nodule with the valve margin in such a fashion as to form an "X" configuration across the center of the valve. The struts, or tigilla, penetrate rather deeply into the cell cavity. Occasionally an individual tigillum will be bifurcated giving the appearance of three struts on one side. This is the main feature which characterizes the genus (Ross, 1963, p. 50). The peculiar configuration of this central structure is referred to by some as a "bifid stauros" and this term is often employed when the species are considered under the genus *Stauroneis*.

The striae are radiate to parallel or slightly convergent at the ends, and are punctate with a tendency for their being finely punctate.

There is some indication that the morphology of individual puncta in *Capartogramma* (as shown by the electron microscope) may be different than that of *Stauroneis*. This, however, is based only on a few key species in each group and cannot yet be established as a distinguishing feature for the genus.

Only one species has been recorded, so far, from the United States.

Type species. — *Capartogramma jeanii* Kuff. [= *Capartogramma karstenii* (Zanon) Ross].

1. **Capartogramma crucicula** (Grun. *ex* Cl.) Ross var. **crucicula**
PL. 30, FIG. 16

Schizostauron crucicula Grun. *ex*. Cl., K. Svenska Vet.-Akad. Handl., Ny Följd, 18(5):16, pl. 3, fig. 44. 1881.
Stauroneis crucicula (Grun. *ex* Cl.) Boyer, Diat. Philadelphia, p. 89, pl. 27, fig. 10. 1916. [*non* W. Sm. 1853.]
Stauroneis merrimacensis Woodh. & Tweed, Rev. Algol., Nouv. Ser., 5:143, pl, 2, fig. 27. 1960.
Capartogramma crucicula (Grun. *ex* Cl.) Ross, Bull. British Mus. (Nat. Hist.), 3(2):59-64, pl. 1B, 2A, text figs. 1a, 8-11. 1963.

Valve elliptical-lanceolate with produced, rostrate ends. Pseudosepta present at the ends. Axial area narrow, linear. Stauros bifid, forming an "X" across the face of the valve. Raphe straight, filiform; proximal ends close. Striae radiate throughout, indistinctly punctate. Striae, 24 in 10μ. Length, 20-36μ. Breadth, 7.5-9μ.

Distinguished by the peculiar configuration of the stauros.

Type locality. — U.S.A., New England, Merrimac River on *Chara*.

U. S. distribution. — GEOGRAPHICAL: New England States, Middle Atlantic States, Southeastern States, Gulf Coast States, South Central States. ECOLOGICAL: Found in many fresh-water rivers but seems to develop larger populations in brackish-water areas.

Genus **Anomoeoneis** Pfitz.

Pfitz., Bot. Abh. Geb. Morph. Physiol., 1(2):77. 1871.

Valve usually lanceolate; transversely and longitudinally symmetrical in shape; only one or two forms known with a central constriction. Axial area usually narrow, median. Raphe straight; proximal ends straight or curving slightly in same direction, distal ends straight or, on the larger forms, hooking as a sickle in the same direction. Central area symmetrical, asymmetrical unilateral, or uniting with large or small lateral spaces thereby presenting a lyriform appearance. Striae punctate, arranged transversely, and spaced so as to form longitudinal or oblique hyaline lines (ribs) which appear undulate.

As mentioned by Pfitzer, the valves are symmetrical in shape. Considering the wall markings, however, they may be asymmetrical (*e.g.*, *A. sphaerophora*). This may be due either to a unilaterally developed central area or to irregularities of punctation on either side of the axial area. It is, therefore, in this sense of asymmetry that Pfitzer employed the name *Anomoeoneis* from the Greek meaning "asymmetrical" or "unequal" ship.

Type species. — *Navicula sphaerophora* Ehr. [= *Anomoeoneis sphaerophora* (Ehr.) Pfitz.].

KEY TO THE SPECIES OF ANOMOEONEIS

1. Striae pattern between valve margin and axial area interrupted by a large lyriform area which is either devoid of puncta or has puncta widely scattered; striae not exceeding 18 in 10μ 2
1. Lyriform area not present; striae exceeding 18 in 10μ 4
   2. Valve with protracted ends 3
   2. Valve with attenuated—not protracted—ends . . . . [2] *A. costata*
3. Margins of valve regularly convex; valves generally larger, 65-200μ
                                                 [1] *A. sphaerophora* var. *sculpta*
3. Margins of valve less convex and often nearly parallel; valves generally smaller, 30-80μ . . . . [1] *A sphaerophora*

1. **Anomoeoneis sphaerophora** (Ehr.) Pfitz. var. **sphaerophora**

PL. 32, FIG. 1

> *Navicula sphaerophora* Ehr., Phys. Abh. Akad. Wiss. Berlin, for 1841:419, pl. 3 (4), fig. 3. 1843.
>
> *Anomoeoneis sphaerophora* Pfitz., Bot. Abh. Geb. Morph. Physiol., 1(2):77, pl. 3, fig. 10. 1871.

Valve elliptical-lanceolate with rostrate to capitate ends; margins convex, frequently subparallel in the middle portion of the valve. Axial area linear, bordered by a single row of puncta. Distal raphe ends large, sickle-shaped, curved in the same direction. Central area irregularly rounded, usually unilaterally developed, sometimes reaching the margin. Lateral elongate clear areas uniting with the central area to give a lyriform configuration; lateral areas sometimes irregularly and faintly punctate. Striae slightly radiate throughout the valve except at the ends where they may be parallel. Puncta becoming more distant towards the central axis, forming irregular longitudinal lines. Striae, 15-17 in 10µ. Length, 30 to about 80µ. Breadth, 13-22µ.

The epithet *Navicula sphaerophora* has been attributed to Kützing (1844, p. 95), but this epithet was used prior to that time by Ehrenberg (1843, p. 419). Even though Kützing did not make a specific citation to Ehrenberg in his discussion of *Navicula sphaerophora*, it is difficult to imagine that he was not well aware of Ehrenberg's *N. sphaerophora*, for there is hardly a page of his 1844 work which does not carry at least one reference to the Ehrenberg paper where *N. sphaerophora* was described. It would appear equally odd that he would deliberately ignore Ehrenberg's epithet and use it again for another diatom, especially so in the light of his criticism of Ehrenberg on p. 7 for having ignored several of his (Kützing's) original epithets and also those of others.

For these and for several other reasons too lengthy to discuss here, I consider that Kützing actually did base his concept of *N. sphaerophora* on Ehrenberg's description. Even with the paucity of information in these early descriptions and the incomplete nature of the drawings they are so similar that, with the other evidence, I must conclude that they were both referring to the diatom which is rather unanimously accepted today as *A. sphaerophora*.

From this standpoint one would have further to conclude that Pfitzer's combination is a *de facto* transferral of Ehrenberg's (not Kützing's) type to the genus *Anomoeoneis*.

As pointed out by Ross (private communication), the transfer of *Navicula rostrata* Ehr. (1840, p. 213) to *Anomoeoneis* as the earliest available specific epithet, is prevented by the existence of *A. rostrata* (O. Müll.) Freng. (1934, p. 355).

Type locality. — Mexico, Atotonilco el Grande.

U. S. distribution. — GEOGRAPHICAL: New England States, Middle Atlantic States, East Central States, West Central States, Lakes States, Plains States; Kentucky, Texas, Arizona, Montana. ECOLOGICAL: Appears to have strong preference for hard waters (alkalibiont?). Found in streams, ponds, lakes and intermittent pools. Although a fresh-water taxon, it is often found in inland areas with some salt concentration (halophil).

1. **Anomoeoneis sphaerophora** var. **sculpta** O. Müll.   PL. 32, FIG. 2

Navicula rostrata Ehr., Ber. Akad. Wiss. Berlin, for 1840:213.   1840.
Navicula tumens W. Sm., Syn. British Diat., vol. 1, p. 52, pl. 17, fig. 150.   1853.
Navicula sculpta Ehr., Mikrogeol., pl. 10(1), figs. 5a-b; pl. 10(2), fig. 3.   1854.
    [*nom. superf.*]
Anomoeoneis sculpta (Ehr.) Cl., K. Svenska Vet.-Akad. Handl., Ny Följd, 27(3):6.
    1895.
Anomoeoneis sphaerophora var. *sculpta* O. Müll., Hedwigia, 38:303.   1900.

Valve elliptical-lanceolate with protracted, substrate to rostrate-apiculate ends; margins regularly convex throughout the main portion of the valve. Axial area narrow, linear, bordered by a single row of puncta. Central area united with elongate lateral areas forming lyrate area; sometimes with median expansion on one side which extends to the margin. Striae slightly radiate throughout the valve except at the ends where they are often parallel. Puncta arranged in longitudinally undulating rows. Individual puncta more dispersed near lateral clear areas than at the valve margins. Striae, 11-16 in 10μ. Length, 65-200μ. Breadth, 25-36μ.

This is best distinguished from variety *sphaerophora* by its larger size and quite convex, arc-like sides.

Forms as broad as 60μ as reported by Hustedt (1959, p. 741) have not been observed in our collections.

Type locality. — Italy, Fossilis in Hetruria ad Santafioram.

U. S. distribution. — Geographical: New York, Nebraska, Utah, California. Ecological: As the species.

2. Anomoeoneis costata (Kütz.) Hust. var. costata   PL. 32, FIGS. 3, 8

Navicula costata Kütz., Bacill., p. 93, pl. 3, fig. 56. 1844.
Navicula bohemica Ehr., Mikrogeol., pl. 10(1), fig. 4. 1854.
Anomoeoneis polygramma (Ehr.) Cl., K. Svenska Vet.-Akad. Handl., Ny Följd,
    27(3):6. 1895. [*non Stauroneis polygramma* Ehr. 1843.]
Anomoeoneis sphaerophora var. *polygramma* (Ehr.) O. Müll., Hedwigia, 38:301.
    1900.
Anomoeoneis costata (Kütz.) Hust. *in* Rabh., Kryptog.-Fl. Deutschland, vol. 7(2),
    no. 6, pp. 744-747, fig. 1111. 1959.

Valve elliptical to elliptical-lanceolate with obtuse—not protracted—extremities. Larger forms may be slightly gibbous at the center. Axial area broad, tapering gradually toward the valve ends, slightly narrowed at the central area. Raphe rather broad, linear. Distal raphe ends curved in same direction. Central area large, unequally expanded transversely, one side reaching the margin. Striae slightly radiate except at the ends where they become parallel or slightly convergent. Puncta becoming somewhat more distant toward the central axis, forming irregular longitudinal lines. Striae, 13-16 in 10μ. Length, 50-175μ. Breadth, 20-42μ.

The obtuse, non-protracted ends and the dissection of the large lyriform area on the valve face into distinct longitudinal ribs best distinguish this taxon from *Anomoeoneis sphaerophora*.

Part of Elmore's (1922, pl. 11, figs. 390-392) concept of *Navicula sculpta* Ehr. undoubtedly belongs here.

Type locality. — [Italy], Im Bergmehl von St. Fiore.

U. S. distribution. — Geographical: Plains States; Utah. Ecological: [Mesohalob?] Found in inland waters with moderate to high salt concentration.

3. Anomoeoneis follis (Ehr.) Cl. var. follis   PL. 32, FIG. 4

Navicula follis Ehr., Infusionsthierchen, p. 179. 1838.
Navicula serians var. *follis* (Ehr.) Cl., & Möll., Diatoms, pt. 5, p. 8, No. 275. 1879.
A.? [*Anomoeoneis*] *follis* (Ehr.) Cl., K. Svenska Vet.-Akad. Handl., Ny Följd,
    27(3):7. 1895.

Valve rhombic with extremely gibbous middle portion. Ends long, rostrate. Axial area very narrow. Raphe straight, filiform. Central area small, elliptical. Striae radiate in the gibbous portion, parallel toward either end; distinctly punctate; a few shorter striae interposed on either side of the central area. Puncta forming irregular longitudinal lines. Striae, 22-26 in 10μ. Length, 12-54μ. Breadth, 12-19μ.

Kützing described a *Frustulia inflata* (1833, p. 545) which resembles this taxon in some respects. His illustrations (Taf. 13, fig. 14) give the impression, however, that the valve is elevated at the center. This is not true of *A. follis*. Until the identity of *Frustulia inflata* can be determined, it seems best to continue use of the well-established name of Ehrenberg for this taxon.

Type locality. — [Italy], Im Bergmehl von Santafiora in Toscana, fossil.

U. S. distribution. — Geographical: New England States; Illinois, Michigan, California (?). Ecological: Fresh water; more characteristic of lakes. Frequently found in fossil deposits.

3. **Anomoeoneis follis** var. **hannae** Reim.   PL. 32, FIGS. 5-6

> *Anomoeoneis follis* var. *hannae* Reim., Proc. Acad. Nat. Sci. Philadelphia, 113:188-189, pl. 1, figs. 5A-5B. 1961.

Valve with long-connate extremities; striae not becoming as fine as in the nominate variety. Other features not different. Striae, 19-22 in 10μ. Length, 25-73μ. Breadth, 13-21μ.

The distinctive shape of the extremities makes the center of the valve appear less gibbous even though the actual width measurements are about the same as in variety *follis*. The striae are rather constant (as given) in 10μ, whereas in variety *follis* they may be as fine as 24-26 in 10μ. For further discussion of this taxon see Reimer (*loc. cit.*).

Type locality. — U.S.A., New Jersey, Ocean Co., Toms River. (*Holotype*—A-Boyer 818, Reimer, 1961.)

U. S. distribution. — Geographical: New Jersey, Florida (fossil). Ecological: Insufficiently known.

3. **Anomoeoneis follis** var. **fossilis** Reim.   PL. 32, FIG. 7

> *Anomoeoneis follis* var. *fossilis* Reim., Proc. Acad. Nat. Sci. Philadelphia, 113:187-188, pl. 1, fig. 9. 1961.

Ends long, protracted, subcapitate to capitate—not rostrate as in variety *follis*. This variety is also somewhat larger and with coarser striae than the nominate variety. Striae, 19-20 in 10μ. Length, 50-80μ. Breadth, 13-18μ.

The long, subcapitate to capitate ends best distinguish this variety from variety *follis*.

Type locality. — U.S.A., Florida, Santa Rosa Co., one and one-half miles northeast of Milton. Fossil (Pleistocene?), recent? (*Holotype*—A-G.C. 45101, Reimer, 1961.)

U. S. distribution. — GEOGRAPHICAL: Recorded from the above locality only. ECOLOGICAL: Not known.

4. Anomoeoneis serians (Bréb. *ex* Kütz.) Cl. var. serians   PL. 33, FIG. 1

Navicula lineolata Ehr., Phys. Abh. Akad. Wiss. Berlin, for 1841:418, pl. 1(3), fig. 4a; pl. 2(6), fig. 27; pl. 4(1), fig. 6. 1843. [*non* Ehr. 1838.]
Navicula serians Bréb. *ex* Kütz., Bacill., p. 92, pl. 28, fig. 43c, pl. 30, fig. 23. 1844.
A.? [*Anomoeoneis*] *serians* (Bréb. *ex* Kütz.) Cl., K. Svenska Vet.-Akad. Handl., Ny Földj, 27(3):7. 1895.

Valve rhombic-lanceolate with convex sides and acute extremities. Axial area narrow, linear-lanceolate. Raphe straight, filiform. Central area symmetrical, ovoid to somewhat elliptical. Striae slightly radiate, crossed by longitudinal undulating lines, 9-12 in 10μ, forming puncta. Striae, 19-21 in 10μ. Length, 50-100μ. Breadth, 12-18μ.

This diatom is characterized by its smoothly tapering sharp-pointed ends.

Forms with striae as fine as 24 in 10μ as reported by Hustedt (1959, p. 747) have not been noted from this country.

The name *Navicula lineolata* was first used by Ehrenberg in 1838 (pp. 188-189, pl. 14, fig. 4). This illustration of Ehrenberg's is unquestionably a *Surirella* and not a *Navicula*. Later Ehrenberg used the same epithet (*N. lineolata*) for a quite different diatom. It is this later designation that Kützing (1844, p. 92) cites in synonymy with Brébisson's *Navicula serians*. The name *N. lineolata* cannot apply here, then, because of its prior use in 1838 for a *Surirella*.

Type locality. — Uncertain, Peru, Guiana angl., Martinique I., Cuba I., New-York, Bridgwater, Mass., Neufundland, Labrador.

U. S. distribution. — GEOGRAPHICAL: New England States, Middle Atlantic States, Southeastern States, Gulf Coast States, East Central States, West Central States, Lakes States; Wyoming. ECOLOGICAL: More often found in lakes and swamps, occasionally in rivers draining such areas, acidophil or acidobiont(?).

4. Anomoeoneis serians var. acuta Hust.   PL. 33, FIG. 2

Anomoeoneis serians var. *acuta* Hust., Arch. Hydrobiol. Suppl., 15(2):218, pl. 15, figs. 23-24. 1937.

Differs from variety *serians* by having prolonged narrow ends. Valve margin forming the ends is concave—not straight or convex as in variety *serians*. Striae, 24-26 in 10μ. Length, 40-50μ. Breadth, 8-8.5μ.

Hustedt gives the striae count as "etwa 27 in 10μ" for this taxon.

Type locality. — Uncertain, Westjava: Bach und Teichabfluss im botanischen Garten in Buitenzorg . . . Mittelsumatra: Häufig im grossen Wasserfall in der Harau-Kloof . . . Nordsumatra: Tobasee . . . .

U. S. distribution. — GEOGRAPHICAL: Florida. ECOLOGICAL: Apparently an acid water form (acidophil?-acidobiont?).

4. **Anomoeoneis serians** var. **apiculata** Boyer   PL. 33, FIGS. 3-6

> *Navicula serians* var. a (apiculate) Lewis, Proc. Acad. Nat. Sci. Philadelphia, 17:8-9,
> pl. 2, fig. 5a. 1865. [*non N. serians* Bréb. *ex* Kütz. 1844.]
>
> *Anomoeoneis serians* var. *apiculata* Boyer, Proc. Acad. Nat. Sci. Philadelphia, 79(2),
> Suppl.:325. 1927.

Differs principally in shape from the nominate variety. Valve with slightly undulate margins and subcapitate to capitate ends. Striae, 21-24 in 10μ. Length, 50-80μ. Breadth, 12.5-20μ.

The shape of this variety is similar to that of *Anomoeoneis vitrea*. It is easily distinguished, however, by having coarser striae (*A. vitrea* has over 30 in 10μ) and a slightly triundulate margin.

Type locality. — U.S.A., New Hampshire, Carroll Co., Bemis Lake.

U. S. distribution. — GEOGRAPHICAL: New England States. ECOLOGICAL: Insufficiently known. Principally in lakes and lake sediments.

4. **Anomoeoneis serians** var. **brachysira** (Bréb. *ex* Kütz.) Hust.

PL. 33, FIGS. 7-11

> *Navicula aponina* var. *brachysira* Bréb. *ex* Kütz., Sp. Alg., p. 69. 1849.
> *Navicula brachysira* Bréb. *ex* Rabh., Süssw.-Diat., p. 39, pl. 5 (*Navicula*), figs.
> 11c-e. 1853.
> *Navicula serians* var. *minor* Grun. *in* V. H., Syn. Diat. Belgique, pl. 12, fig. 8. 1880.
> *Navicula serians* var. *minima* Grun. *in* V. H., Syn. Diat. Belgique, pl. 12, fig. 9.
> 1880.
> *A.?* [*Anomoeoneis*] *brachysira* (Bréb. *ex* Rabh.) Grun. *ex* Cl., K. Svenska Vet.-Akad.
> Handl., Ny Följd, 27(3):7. 1895.
> *Anomoeoneis serians* f. *minor* Boyer, Diat. Philadelphia, p. 80, pl. 17, fig. 13. 1916.
> *Anomoeoneis serians* var. *brachysira* (Bréb. *ex* Kütz.) Hust. *in* Pasch., Süssw.-Fl.
> Mitteleuropas, Heft 10, Aufl. 2, p. 264, text fig. 427. 1930.

Valve smaller with more variable ends (sub-acute to bluntly rounded) and with finer striae than the nominate variety. Other features as in variety *serians*. Striae, 24 in 10μ to about 28-30 in 10μ at the ends. Length, 12-50μ. Breadth, 4-10μ.

There are some peculiar variations in the striae count in this taxon. In some frustules of variety *brachysira* the striae count on one valve is coarser than on the opposite valve. Occasionally, some specimens are found with a striae count of 24-26 in 10μ throughout the valve instead of the usual number given in the description. Such a curious condition is also to be found in some members of the genus *Gomphonema*. I do not know what mechanism is involved here, but am of the opinion that this represents but a single variable feature within this taxon. In those populations where such variation occurs, the valve shape remains about the same and numerous forms can be found with striae intermediate between the two conditions discussed.

This variety is smaller and has finer striae than the nominate variety. It is sometimes confused with *Anomoeoneis vitrea*, but can be separated from that taxon by its rounded—not protracted—ends and slightly coarser striae, not exceeding 30 in 10μ.

I am still uncertain about the interpretation of the Kützing (1833) exsiccata material (A-Kütz., Dec. No. 16) for *Brachysira aponina* and, therefore, cannot state at this time just what its relationship is to *A. serians* var. *brachysira*.

Type locality. — Uncertain, In aquis calidis thermarum Euganeorum (Euganean Hills, Italy); prope Falaise inter alias Diatomeas legit amic. DeBrébisson (France).

U. S. distribution. — Geographical: New Jersey, Georgia, Florida, Wyoming. Ecological: Fresh to brackish water, in lakes and rivers.

5. **Anomoeoneis vitrea** (Grun.) Ross comb. nov., var. **vitrea**

pl. 33, figs. 12-13

> *Gomphonema* ? *vitreum* Grun. *in* Schneider, Naturw. Beitr. Kenntn. Kaukasus-länder, p. 110. 1878.
> *Navicula exilis* Grun. *in* V. H., Syn. Diat. Belgique, pl. 12, figs. 11-12, 1880. [*non N. exilis* Kütz. 1844.]
> *Anomoeoneis* ? *exilis* (Kütz.) Cl., K. Svenska Vet.-Akad. Handl., Ny Följd, 27(3):8. 1895. [*non N. exilis* Kütz. 1844.]
> *Navicula variabilis* Ross, Natl. Mus. Canada Bull., No. 97, p. 197. 1947. [*nom. superf.*]
> *Anomoeoneis variabilis* (Ross) Reim., Proc. Acad. Nat. Sci. Philadelphia, 113:194-195, pl. 1, figs. 7-8. 1961.

Valve lanceolate to narrow-lanceolate with protracted, rostrate to capitate ends. Axial area narrow. Raphe straight, filiform. Central area small, ovoid. Both areas often indistinct. Striae radiate, finely punctate. Striae, 30-35 in 10μ. Length, 14-35μ. Breadth, 4-6μ.

This taxon varies in shape from a longer, capitate form to a shorter, rostrate form. The slightly broader form resembles *A. serians* var. *thermalis* Grun., but is differentiated by the finer striae. Cleve (1895, p. 8) gives 27 striae in 10μ for variety *thermalis*, whereas, in *A. exilis*, the striae are commonly 32-35 in 10μ, apparently not being less numerous than 30 in 10μ.

Information regarding the above new combination has been supplied by R. Ross of the British Museum (Nat. Hist.), who kindly transmitted it to the authors in private communications. The following is a quotation from Ross:

"When this species is placed in the genus *Anomoeoneis* . . . its correct name is *A. vitrea*, for this includes the earliest available epithet. *A. exilis* (Kütz.) Cleve is based on *Navicula exilis* Kütz. and therefore cannot be applied to this species [Ross, *op. cit.*]. A combination under *Anomoeoneis* based on *Navicula microcephala* Grunow cannot be made because of *A. microcephalum* A. Berg, described by Berg as a new species.

"Reimer (*loc. cit.*), accepting that this species could not be called *Anomoeoneis exilis*, made for it the new combination *A. variabilis*, based on *N. variabilis*, which in its turn is based on *Gomphonema vitreum* Grun., the epithet of which was available for transfer into *Anomoeoneis*. Since his name has a legitimate basionym, it is not technically illegitimate but it can never be used, since it has the same type as *A. vitrea*, which is both legitimate and incorporates an earlier epithet."

The synonymy presented above does not include all of the names proposed by Ross, but only those names which were used in reports of diatoms from the U. S. The other epithets which Ross considers in synonymy with *A. vitrea* are as follows: *Achnanthidium microcephalum* sensu W. Smith, Syn. Brit. Diat. 2: 31, t. 61 fig. 380. 1856 [*non* Kützing]; *Navicula exilis* sensu Grunow, Verh. Zool.—Bot. Ges. Wien 10: 553, t. 4 fig. 11-12. 1880 [*non* Kützing]; *Colletonema exile* Grunow, Verh. Zool.-Bot. Ges. Wien 10: 571. 1860.; *Navicula microcephala* Grunow in Fenzl, Reise Österr. Fregatte "Novara," Bot. 1: 19. 1868.; *Navicula gomphonemacea* Grunow *in* V. H., Syn. Diat. Belgique: t. 12 fig. 13. 1800 [*nom. superf.*]; *Anomoeoneis spectabilis* Manguin, Trav. Algol.: 135, t.2 fig. 29. 1942.; *Anomoeoneis microcephala* A. Berg, Ark. Bot. 32A(1): 12, t.3 fig. 125. 1945.; *Anomoeoneis brachysira* var. *lanceolata* (A. Mayer) Cleve-Euler, K. Svenska Vet.-Akad. Handl., ser. 4,4(5): 199, fig. 919 e-f. 1953 (citations as given by Ross).

Type locality. — [Austria] . . . im Erlafsee bei Mariazell.

U. S. distribution. — GEOGRAPHICAL: New England States, Middle Atlantic States, Southeastern States, Gulf Coast States, East Central States, West Central States, Lakes States; Arizona, Oregon. ECOLOGICAL: Adapted to wide range of ecological conditions, but seems to prefer alkaline waters (alkaliphil?).

6. Anomoeoneis zellensis (Grun.) Cl. var. **zellensis**   PL. 33, FIG. 14

Navicula zellensis Grun., Verh. Zool.-Bot. Ges. Wien, 10:521, pl. 3, figs. 34a-d. 1860.

A.? [*Anomoeoneis*] *zellensis* (Grun.) Cl., K. Svenska Vet.-Akad. Handl., Ny Följd, 27(3):7. 1895.

Valve linear, somewhat triundulate. Ends subrostrate, broad and obtuse. Axial area very narrow. Central area rather large, elliptical-subrectangular. Striae fine, slightly radiate; crossed by longitudinal undulating lines. Striae, 28-30 in 10μ. Length, 15-35μ. Breadth, 4-6μ.

Very small specimens of this diatom (V.H. 129) seem to have less produced, slightly more cuneate ends.

Best distinguished as a small linear form with undulate sides and broad, subrostrate ends.

Type locality. — Habitat in lacu "Erlaf-See" dicto prope Mariazell [Styria, Austria], praesertim in fasciculis mucosis Encyonematis et Gomphonematis.

U. S. distribution. — Geographical: New York, Michigan. Ecological: Insufficiently known.

7. **Anomoeoneis styriaca** (Grun.) Hust. var. **styriaca**   pl. 33, fig. 15

Navicula styriaca Grun. *in* V. H., Syn. Diat. Belgique, pl. 17, figs. 7-8. 1880.
Anomoeoneis styriaca (Grun.) Hust. *in* Pasch., Süssw.-Fl. Mitteleuropas, Heft 10, Aufl. 2, p. 265, text fig. 432. 1930.

Valve rhombic-lanceolate. Ends varying from bluntly rounded to subacute and somewhat pointed. Axial area narrow. Raphe straight, filiform. Proximal raphe ends distant; distal ends straight. Central area elongate, often slightly narrower at the center. Striae radiate throughout, punctate; interrupted by longitudinally undulating hyaline spaces. Striae, 20-22 in 10μ at the center; becoming 27-28 in 10μ toward the ends. Length, 20-35μ. Breadth, 5-8μ.

This diatom is readily identified by the elongate central area and the distant proximal raphe ends.

Type locality. — Uncertain, Belgium? eastern Alps?

U. S. distribution. — Geographical: New Jersey. Ecological: Found once in slightly brackish water but probably more characteristic of fresh water. Hustedt considers it characteristic of alkaline lakes, etc.

Names of Taxa reported from the U. S. (fresh water) which
could not be verified by a specimen from a public herbarium.

Anomoeoneis exilis var. *thermalis* (Grun.) Cl. [= *Anomoeoneis serians* var. *brachysira* f. *thermalis* (Grun.) Hust.] (recorded by Sovereign).

Anomoeoneis sculpta var. *major* Cl. (= *Anomoeoneis sphaerophora* var. *sculpta* O. Müll.) (recorded by Cleve).

Names of Taxa reported from the U. S. which are either
illegitimate or of uncertain application

Navicula inflata Kütz. [?*Anomoeoneis follis* (Ehr.) Cl. var. *follis*] (recorded by Gratacap & Woodward, Schultze and Curtis).

Navicula bipunctata Grun. *in* V.H. [?*Anomoeoneis bipunctata* (Grun.) Cl.] (recorded by Tempère & Peragallo).

Taxa Recorded Since 1960

Anomoeoneis polygramma var. *platensis* Freng. (recorded by Castenholz, 1960).

Anomoeoneis sphaerophora var. *guentheri* O. Müll. (recorded by Castenholz, 1960).

Genus **Neidium** Pfitz.

Pfitz., Bot. Abh. Geb. Morph. Physiol., 1(2):39. 1871.

Valves linear, lanceolate to elliptical. Intercalary bands present (according to Hustedt). Septa absent. Sides for the most part convex; a few entities have parallel or concave margins. Axial area essentially linear; usually narrowing near the central area and the ends; straight or somewhat diagonal. Central area elliptical, ovate, or somewhat quadrangular; transverse or diagonal. In a few cases the central area may become fascia-like (*Neidium kozlowii* Meresch.) Raphe straight or somewhat diagonally displaced. Proximal ends of the raphe (Reimer, 1959a, p. 4) generally curved in opposite directions; in a few cases they are straight and abruptly terminated. Distal ends of the raphe commonly bifurcate, often not well resolved and thus difficult to define. Raphe usually becoming narrower near the proximal and the distal ends. Terminal nodules present, sometimes quite pronounced.

Striae punctate. Orientation of the striae quite variable. The striae are commonly described as being oblique. This is the most common appearance of much of the striation on the valve face, but in a single diatom valve the striae direction may vary from radiate to parallel, oblique, and/or convergent.

Two to several longitudinally oriented ribs ("lines"), more distinct than the network of ribs forming the puncta; visible on the valve surface. Any two ribs plus the enclosed space is referred to as a "band." Three kinds of bands are recognized: (1) *axial band* (*N. hitchcockii*)—the thicker axial area and the central nodule form one margin of the band; (2) *primary longitudinal band*—the first band between the axial area (or axial band) and the valve margin, frequently appearing just at the margin;

(3) *secondary longitudinal bands*—narrower bands lying, if present, between the primary band and the valve margin (Reimer, 1959a, p. 3).

The so-called "defaut regulier" discussed by Voigt (1943, p. 2) is present in most members of this genus. This refers to the gap along the axial area formed either by a shortened stria or a bending of the end of the stria. In *Neidium* these appear on one side of the valve only; there is a single one in both the upper and lower third of the valve.

Some forms of this genus are rather similar to *Anomoeoneis*, to *Navicula,* and in some cases to *Stauroneis. Neidium* is distinguished from these by the characteristic longitudinal bands as described above. When present, the hooked proximal raphe ends further aid in distinguishing the genus *Neidium* from the other three genera.

Many members of this genus are morphologically very similar. Cleve (1894, p. 67) has suggested that they might all be variants of the same species. The morphological differences, however, are distinct enough to separate many of the species without difficulty. Variation within some species presents somewhat of a problem. Variation in shape is a criterion often used to separate varieties and forms. In cases where variations appear constant the separation is warranted. So often, however, only a few specimens appear in a collection, giving very little clue as to the amount of variation. Until the actual amplitude of variation in form between entities can be established, it will be necessary to rely on more subjective opinion in separating or uniting the species of *Neidium* similar in appearance. Published evidence of population studies and of cytological and genetic experiments will be a most welcome addition to our knowledge of this genus. Only then can such terms as "genotype" and "phenotype" (Cholnoky, 1962, pp. 92-93) be used with any meaning.

Type species. — Navicula affinis Ehr. [Designated by Boyer, 1927.] [= *Neidium affine* (Ehr.) Pfitz.].

KEY TO THE SPECIES OF NEIDIUM

1. Proximal ends of the raphe straight, not curved in opposite directions   2
1. Proximal ends of the raphe curved in opposite directions   6
   2. Valves slightly to moderately constricted at the center   3
   2. Valves with parallel or convex sides, not constricted at the center   4
3. Primary longitudinal band marginal, indistinct; striae, 22-28 in 10μ
[17] N. binode

3. Primary longitudinal band submarginal, distinct; striae, 18-20 in 10μ
[18] N. dubium f. constrictum

   4. Valve ends hardly distinguished from valve body, quite short, apiculate; striae, 24-28 in 10μ . . . . [19] *N. ladogense* var. *densestriatum*
   4. Valve ends more distinct, substrate to subcapitate; striae, 20 in 10μ or less   5

5. Ratio of valve width at the center to width at the ends greater than 3:1; striae slightly radiate to parallel ....[18] *N. dubium*
5. Ratio of valve width at the center to width at the ends 2:1-2.5:1; striae more strongly radiate at the center becoming convergent at the ends .... [20] *N. temperei*
    6. Primary longitudinal band present only in the upper and lower third of the valve ....[21] *N. rudimentarum*
    6. Primary longitudinal band present along both sides of the valve face, not interrupted 7
7. Valve width, 60-75μ at the center ....[2] *N. tumescens*
7. Valve width, 4 to about 40μ at the center 8
    8. Valves with apiculate ends 9
    8. Valves without apiculate ends; ends either not set off from the valve body (*i.e.*, rounded to cuneate extremities) or subrostrate to capitate 13
9. Valve constricted at the center ....[8] *N. apiculatum* var. *constrictum*
9. Valve not constricted in center 10
    10. Valves triundulate, a longitudinal band (axial band) present along both sides of axial area ....[7] *N. hitchcockii*
    10. Valves not triundulate, no such area present 11
11. Striae coarse, about 16 in 10μ; puncta varying in size and number from 18 in 10μ along axial area to 12-14 in 10μ near longitudinal band ....[15] *N. sacoense*
11. Striae finer, about 20-22 in 10μ; puncta about same size and number throughout the valve, 22-26 in 10μ 12
    12. Ends very short, apiculate (cuspidate); puncta, 24-26 in 10μ
                                     [8] *N. apiculatum*
    12. Ends longer, broadly apiculate to rostrate; puncta coarser, about 22 in 10μ
                           [4] *N. affine* var. *humerus*
13. A longitudinal band (axial band) along both sides of the axial area
                           [7] *N. hitchcockii*
13. No such area present 14
    14. Primary longitudinal band constricted at the valve center......[14] *N. boyeri*
    14. Primary longitudinal band not constricted at the valve center 15
15. Striae, coarse, less than 20 in 10μ 16
15. Striae finer, more than 20 in 10μ 22
    16. Valves with long protracted, subcapitate to capitate ends ....[3] *N. productum*
    16. Valves with broadly rounded or cuneate extremities or ends, not long protracted 17
17. Valves large, 50 to about 200μ long; 16 to about 40μ wide 18
17. Valves smaller, 35-47μ long; 9-12μ wide...........[16] *N. kozlowii* var. *parvum*
    18. Primary longitudinal band broad, marginal, and with quite irregularly placed puncta along the band ....[13] *N. maximum*
    18. Primary longitudinal band narrower, submarginal, and with more regularly placed puncta 19
19. Valve extremities cuneate 20
19. Valve extremities obtusely rounded, not cuneate 21
    20. Valves slightly tumid at the center ....[1] *N. iridis* var. *subundulatum*
    20. Valves with parallel sides, not tumid at the center
                          [1] *N. iridis* var. *amphigomphus*
21. Ends subtilely distinguished from main part of the valve; valve margin becoming slightly concave a short distance from the valve apices... [1] *N. iridis* var. *ampliatum*

21. Ends not distinguished from main part of the valve; valve margin convex to
    apices of the valve . . . .[1] *N. iridis*
    22. Valves linear; ends not set off from the valve body 23
    22. Valves linear to lanceolate or elliptical-lanceolate with protracted sub-
        rostrate to capitate ends 28
23. Striae. 21-24 in 10μ . . . .[9] *N. bisulcatum* var. *baicalense*
23. Striae, 25-30 in 10μ 24
23. Striae, over 30 in 10μ 25
    24. Valves with slightly undulate sides . . . . . [9] *N. bisulcatum* var. *subundulatum*
    24. Valves, linear, sides not undulate 26
25. Striae oblique throughout valve; very fine, 36 in 10μ or more . . . . . .[12] *N. alpinum*
25. Striae not oblique throughout valve; fine, 30-34 in 10μ . . . .[11] *N. herrmannii*
    26. Axial area and raphe slightly diagonal; striae strongly oblique
                                                            [10] *N. hercynicum*
    26. Axial area and raphe straight; striae not strongly oblique, usually radiate
        around central part of the valve 27
27. Extremities cuneate . . . .[9] *N. bisculatum* var. *nipponicum*
27. Extremities broadly rounded, not cuneate . . . .[9] *N. bisulcatum*
    28. Valves with triundulate sides 29
    28. Valves with other than triundulate sides 32
29. Ends broad; ratio of valve width at center to width at ends, about 2:1 30
29. Ends narrower; ratio of valve width at center to width at ends, 2.5:1-3:1 31
    30. Striae, 20-21 in 10μ; ends flattened . . . .[4] *N. affine* var. *undulatum*
    30. Striae, 24 in 10μ; ends rounded . . . .[4] *N. affine* var. *hankense*
31. Striae strongly oblique throughout central part of the valve; raphe and axial
    area perpendicular to paratransapical axis . . . .[5] *N. gracile* f. *aequale*
31. Striae not strongly oblique throughout central part of the valve, mostly radiate;
    raphe and axial area often slightly diagonal to paratransapical axis
                                                            [6] *N. floridanum*
    32. Axial area and raphe slightly diagonal; striae strongly oblique throughout,
        26-30 in 10μ . . . .[10] *N. hercynicum* f. *subrostratum*
    32. Axial area and raphe straight, striae slightly to moderately oblique in part
        of the valve only, 20-24 in 10μ 33
33. Valves 95-110μ long; puncta, about 20 in 10μ . . . .[4] *N. affine* var. *ceylonicum*
33. Valves shorter, not exceeding 70-80μ; puncta, 22-24 in 10μ 34
    34. Ends broad, mostly subrostrate; ratio of valve width at center to width at ends,
        about 2:1 or less . . . .[4] *N. affine*
    34. Ends narrower, rostrate, capitate or apiculate; ratio of valve width at center to
        width at ends greater than 2:1 35
35. Ratio of valve width at center to width of end 2.5:1 or less, valves generally less
    than 9μ wide at center . . . .[4] *N. affine* var. *longiceps*
35. Above ratio about 3:1 or greater, valves generally wider at center (9-22μ) 36
    36. Valves, 14-22μ wide; ends broadly apiculate . . . .[4] *N. affine* var. *humerus*
    36. Valves narrower; ends rostrate to capitate . . .[4] *N. affine* var. *amphirhynchus*

1. **Neidium iridis** (Ehr.) Cl. var. **iridis**   PL. 34, FIG. 1

Navicula iridis Ehr., Phys. Abh. Akad. Wiss. Berlin, for 1841:418, pl. 4(1), fig. 2.
    1843.
Navicula firma Kütz., Bacill., p. 92, pl. 21, fig. 10. 1844.

Pinnularia iridis (Ehr.) Rabh., Süssw.-Diat., p. 42, pl. 6, fig. 1. 1853.

Neidium firmum (Kütz.) Pfitz., Bot. Abh. Geb. Morph. Physiol., 1(2):39. 1871.

Neidium iridis (Ehr.) Cl., K. Svenska Vet.-Akad. Handl., Ny Följd, 26(2):69. 1894.

Navicula iridis var. *firma* (Kütz.) V. H., Treat. Diat., p. 221. 1896.

Valve elongate, linear-elliptical. Sides convex, tapering smoothly to obtusely rounded extremities. Axial area narrowing near the center and the ends. Raphe straight, narrowing at the proximal and the distal ends. Proximal ends curving in opposite directions, distal ends bifurcate. Central area diagonally to transversely elliptical. Primary longitudinal band submarginal; two to several secondary bands visible in the valve view. Striae punctate; oblique to radiate in the middle portion of the valve, becoming parallel to convergent at the ends. Striae, 14-18 in 10μ. Puncta, 13-18 in 10μ. Length, about 50-190μ. Breadth, 16 to about 40μ.

This species is quite variable in form and structure. Where no clear series of intergrades is apparent, the forms and varieties are retained. The nominate variety is often confused with variety *amphigomphus* which has cuneate ends.

Type locality. — U.S.A., New York, West Point.

U. S. distribution. — GEOGRAPHICAL: New England States, Middle Atlantic States, Southeastern States, Gulf Coast States, South Central States, East Central States, West Central States, Lakes States, Plains States; Wyoming, Washington, Oregon, California. ECOLOGICAL: Appears to prefer standing or only slightly moving water (rheophobe?), lakes, ponds, bogs; occasionally in rivers; pH "indifferent," probably oligosaprobic.

1. **Neidium iridis** var. **amphigomphus** (Ehr.) A. Mayer   PL. 34, FIG. 2

Navicula amphigomphus Ehr., Phys. Abh. Akad. Wiss. Berlin, for 1841:417, pl. 3(1), fig. 8. 1843.

Pinnularia disphenia Ehr., Phys. Abh. Akad. Wiss. Berlin, for 1841:420, pl. 3(7), fig. 21. 1843.

Pinnularia amphigomphus Ehr., Phys. Abh. Akad. Wiss. Berlin, for 1841, pl. 2(1), fig. 27. 1843.

Navicula disphenia (Ehr.) Kütz., Bacill., p. 93, pl. 28, fig. 54. 1844.

Neidium amphigomphus (Ehr.) Pfitz., Bot. Abh. Geb. Morph. Physiol., 1(2):39. 1871.

Navicula iridis var. *amphigomphus* (Ehr.) V. H., Syn. Diat. Belgique, pl. 13, fig. 2. 1880. (text, p. 104. 1885.)

Neidium iridis var. *amphigomphus* (Ehr.) A. Mayer, Denkschr. Bayer. Bot. Ges. Regensburg, 13(N.F. 7):30. 1917.

Valve broadly linear with cuneate extremities. This variety usually does not attain as great a size as the species. Other characteristics vary as the species. Striae, 15-16 in 10μ. Puncta, 15-18 in 10μ. Length, 65-150μ. Breadth, 16-40μ.

Type, locality. — Uncertain, Real del monte Mexico, New York, Stratford, Conn., Andower, Mass., Boston et Bridgwater, Mass., Maine [U.S.A.].

U. S. distribution. — GEOGRAPHICAL: New England States, Middle Atlantic States, Southeastern States, Gulf Coast States, East Central States, Lakes States, Plains States; Arizona, Washington, Oregon, California. ECOLOGICAL: Same as the nominate variety.

1. **Neidium iridis** var. **ampliatum** (Ehr.) Cl.   PL. 34, FIG. 5

Navicula ampliata Ehr., Mikrogeol., pl. 15A, figs. 32, 35?.   1854.
Neidium iridis var. *ampliata* (Ehr.) Cl., K. Svenska Vet.-Akad. Handl., Ny Följd, 26(2):69.   1894.
Navicula iridis var. *ampliata* (Ehr.) Dipp., Diat. Rhein-Mainebene, p. 65, fig. 139. 1904.

Valve with broad, subrostrate to rostrate, very slightly set-off ends. Sides slightly to moderately convex. Striae and puncta, 16-19 in 10μ. Length, 60 to about 100μ. Breadth, 17-24μ.

This variety is best distinguished from variety *iridis* by the slight incurving of the valve margins to form broad but indistinct ends.

In 1842 (p. 337) Ehrenberg used the name "*Navicula ampliata* n. sp." but did not include a description or illustration. The valid publication date, then, must be 1854 when illustrations were supplied.

Type locality. — Kieselguhre von Down, Mourne Mountains, Irland.

U. S. distribution. — GEOGRAPHICAL: New England States, Middle Atlantic States, Gulf Coast States, West Central States, Lakes States; Tennessee, Arizona, Washington, Oregon. ECOLOGICAL: More commonly a lake and bog form, but occasionally found in streams; pH-"indifferent."

1. **Neidium iridis** var. **subundulatum** (Cl.-Eul.) Reim.   PL. 34, FIG. 3

Neidium iridis var. *intermedia* f. *subundulata* Cl.-Eul., K. Svenska Vet.-Akad. Handl., Tredje Ser., 11(2):127, fig. 354.   1932.
Neidium iridis var. *firmum* f. *subundulata* (Cl.-Eul.) Cl.-Eul., K. Svenska Vet.-Akad. Handl., Fjärde Ser., 5(4):120-121, fig. 1774k.   1955.
Neidium iridis var. *subundulata* (Cl.-Eul.) Reim., Proc. Acad. Nat. Sci. Philadelphia, 111:26, pl. 3, fig. 1.   1959.

Valve linear, generally with slightly gibbous center; extremities attenuated, obtusely rounded, cuneate. Axial area straight, narrowing near the central area and the ends. Raphe straight, narrowing toward the proximal and the distal ends. Proximal raphe ends curved in opposite directions; distal ends bifurcate. Central area elliptical, slightly diagonal. Primary longitudinal band submarginal. Striae oblique, becoming convergent toward the ends. Striae, 16-17 in 10μ. Puncta, 16-18 in 10μ. Length, 75-150μ. Breadth, 25-29μ.

Type locality. – [Sweden], Långören am 6/9 (Pr. 152) Fossil, Tåkernsee.

U. S. distribution. – GEOGRAPHICAL: New England States, Middle Atlantic States; Iowa. ECOLOGICAL: To date reported only from lakes and springs.

2. **Neidium tumescens** (Grun.) Cl. var. **tumescens**   PL. 34, FIG. 4

Navicula (firma var.) *tumescens* Grun. *in* A. S., Atlas Diat., pl. 49, fig. 10. 1877.
Neidium tumescens (Grun. *in* A. S.) Cl., K. Svenska Vet.-Akad. Handl., Ny Följd, 26(2):70. 1894.

Valve broadly lanceolate with attenuated or apiculate ends. Sides convex or sometimes parallel for a short distance above and below the middle part of the valve. Axial area narrowing at the ends and also at the central area; about 4-6μ wide at the widest point. Raphe straight, twisting just above and below the central area, rather broad. Proximal raphe ends curved in opposite directions; distal ends bifurcate. Central area ovate. Primary longitudinal band about 8-12μ from the margin at the center. Several secondary bands present between the primary longitudinal band and the margin. Striae very slightly radiate at the center, becoming slightly convergent at the ends; usually curved or even sigmoid. Striae, 14-16 in 10μ. Puncta, 16-18 in 10μ except toward the margins where they are coarser. Length, 150-225μ. Breadth, 60-75μ.

Type locality. – U.S.A., Maine, Cherryfield (fossil).

U. S. distribution. – GEOGRAPHICAL: New England States; New Jersey, Florida. ECOLOGICAL: Appears to be a lake form; more frequently found in sediments.

3. **Neidium productum** (W. Sm.) Cl. var. **productum**   PL. 35, FIG. 1

Navicula producta W. Sm., Syn. British Diat., vol. 1, p. 51, pl. 17, fig. 144. 1853.
Navicula iridis var. *producta* (W. Sm.) V. H., Syn. Diat. Belgique, p. 104. 1885.
Neidium productum (W. Sm.) Cl., K. Svenska Vet.-Akad. Handl., Ny Följd, 26(2):69. 1894.

Valve broadly linear to linear-elliptical. Ends long, protracted, rostrate to capitate; about one-third the width of the valve at the center. Axial area straight, narrower near the central area and also near the ends. Terminal nodules quite evident. Raphe straight, narrowing near the proximal and the distal ends. Proximal ends curved in opposite directions; distal ends bifurcate. Central area small, diagonally elliptical. Primary longitudinal band present, submarginal. Striae punctate; more or less oblique except at the ends where they become parallel to convergent. Striae, 16-18 in 10μ. Puncta, 17-20 in 10μ. Length, 60-100μ. Breadth, 20-30μ.

This diatom is similar to *Neidium affine* var. *amphirhynchus*. It is distinguished mainly, however, by the coarser striae and the more protracted ends.

Type locality. — [England], Exact locality uncertain, fresh water. Lewes, Oct. 1851, W. Sm. East Shalford, Mr. Capron.

U. S. distribution. — Geographical: New England States, Middle Atlantic States, East Central States, Lake States; Oregon. Ecological: Lakes and streams; pH "indifferent"(?).

4. Neidium affine (Ehr.) Pfitz. var. affine   pl. 35, fig. 2

Navicula affinis Ehr., Phys. Abh. Akad. Wiss. Berlin, for 1841:417, pl. 2(2), fig. 7. 1843.

Neidium affine (Ehr.) Pfitz., Bot. Abh. Geb. Morph. Physiol., 1(2):39. 1871.

Neidium affine var. *genuina* Cl., K. Svenska Vet.-Akad. Handl., Ny Földj, 26(2):68. 1894.

Neidium affine var. *genuina* f. *minor* Cl., K. Svenska Vet.-Akad. Handl., Ny Földj, 26(2):68. 1894. [*pro parte.*]

Neidium affine var. *genuinum* f. *minor* subf. *subrostratum* A. Mayer, Ber. Naturw. Ver. Regensburg, 17:54, pl. 1, fig. 4. 1925.

Neidium affine var. *genuinum* f. *media* A. Mayer, Ber. Naturw. Ver. Regensburg, 17:54, pl. 1, figs. 5, 21. 1925. [*non* Cleve 1894.]

Valve linear-lanceolate with narrowed, obtusely rounded, subrostrate to rostrate ends. Sides parallel or slightly convex. Axial area straight, narrowing near the central area and the ends of the valve. Raphe straight, slightly narrower near the proximal and the distal ends. Proximal ends of the raphe curving in opposite directions. Distal ends abruptly bifurcate. Central area transversely or diagonally elliptical. Longitudinal band present along both sides of the valve; submarginal. Striae parallel or oblique, becoming convergent at one or both ends. Striae, 22-24 in 10μ. Puncta, about 24 in 10μ. Length, 30-65μ (80μ?). Breadth, 8-13μ. Ratio of valve width at center to width at end, 2:1 or less.

The amplitude of this quite variable taxon is not yet known. Based on our present knowledge, the segments found in this country which appear distinct are given below. For a discussion of some of the problems in this taxon see Reimer (1959a, pp. 8-9), Cholnoky (1962, pp. 92-93).

Type locality. — Uncertain, Surinam, Guiana angl., Caraccas, Guadeloupe I., St. Domingo I., San Miguel Mexico; Puente de Dios Mex., New-York, Bridgwater, Mass., Labrador, Neufundland, Kotzebue's Sund.?

U. S. distribution. — Geographical: New England States, Middle Atlantic States, Southeastern States, Gulf Coast States, South Central States, West Central States, Lakes States, Plains States; New Mexico, California. Ecological: Fresh water, most common in quiet water areas; pH "indifferent." Has not been observed in large numbers from any collection.

4. Neidium affine var. amphirhynchus (Ehr.) Cl.   PL. 35, FIG. 3

Navicula amphirhynchus Ehr., Phys. Abh. Akad. Wiss. Berlin, for 1841:417, pl. 3(1),
    fig. 10. 1843.

Neidium amphirhynchus (Ehr.) Pfitz., Bot. Abh. Geb. Morph. Physiol., 1(2):186,
    pl. 4, fig. 1. 1871.

Neidium affine var. *amphirhynchus* (Ehr.) Cl., K. Svenska Vet.-Akad. Handl., Ny
    Följd, 26(2):68. 1894. [*pro parte.*]

Neidium iridis var. *amphirhynchus* (Ehr.) A. Mayer, Denkschr. Bayer. Bot. Ges.
    Regensburg, 13(N.F. 7):29, pl. 2, fig. 34. 1917. [*non* (Ehr.) V. H.]

Ends protracted, rostrate to capitate, slightly narrower than in variety *affine*. Other characters as the species. Striae, 22-24 in 10μ. Length, $30\text{-}45\mu$. Breadth, $9\text{-}12\mu$. Ratio of valve width at center to width of end, 3:1-4:1.

Specimens which exceed 50μ in length and show a center-width to end-width ratio of about 2:1, as illustrated by Hust. (1930, p. 242, fig. 377) for var. *amphirhynchus*, have not been observed from this country. Van Heurck's illustration (1880, pl. 13, fig. 5) may possibly be referred to *N. productum* (W. Sm.) Cl.

Type locality. — Uncertain, Real del Monte Mex., Atotonilco el Gr. Mex., Montezuma Fl., Mexico.

U. S. distribution. — GEOGRAPHICAL: New England States, Middle Atlantic States, Southeastern States, Gulf Coast States, South Central States, East Central States, West Central States, Lakes States, Plains States; New Mexico, Washington, Oregon, California. ECOLOGICAL: Eurytopic, alkaliphilic ("indifferent"?); apparently a bottom and littoral form of lakes, also found in small numbers in rivers and streams.

4. Neidium affine var. ceylonicum (Skv.) Reim.   PL. 35, FIG. 6

Neidium affine var. *genuina* f. *ceylonica* Skv., Ann. Roy. Bot. Gard. Peradeniya,
    11(3) [Ceylon Jour. Sci., Sec. A. Bot.]:254, pl. 32, fig. 24. 1930.

Neidium affine var. *ceylonica* (Skv.) Reim., Proc. Acad. Nat. Sci. Philadelphia,
    111:11, pl. 1, fig. 7. 1959.

Valve larger than in the nominate variety and variety *amphirhynchus*. Ends protracted, attenuate, not rounded and truncate as in variety *affine*. Striae, 20-22 in 10μ. Puncta, about 20 in 10μ. Length, $95\text{-}110\mu$. Breadth, $19\text{-}23\mu$.

Type locality. — [Ceylon], Mud from paddy field Udagama near Peradeniya.

U. S. distribution. — GEOGRAPHICAL: Connecticut. ECOLOGICAL: Insufficiently known.

4. Neidium affine var. hankense (Skv.) Reim.   PL. 35, FIG. 9

> Neidium affine var. undulata f. hankensis Skv., Mem. S. Ussuri Br. State Russian
> Geogr. Soc., 3:44, pl. 2, fig. 13. 1929.
> Neidium affine var. amphirhynchus f. major, triundulata Cl.-Eul., K. Svenska Vet.-
> Akad. Handl., Tredje Ser., 11(2):123, text fig. 341. 1932. [nom. illegit.]
> Neidium longiceps var. undulatum (A. Mayer) Cl.-Eul., K. Svenska Vet.-Akad.
> Handl., Fjärde Ser., 5(4):112, fig. 1163f. 1955.
> Neidium affine var. hankensis (Skv.) Reim., Proc. Acad. Nat. Sci. Philadelphia,
> 111:11-12, pl. 1, fig. 4. 1959.

Valve triundulate, ends rostrate to capitate. Other characters as in variety *affine*.

This diatom is not considered a part of *Neidium affine* var. *undulatum* for reasons stated in the discussion of that variety.

A. Mayer (1925, pl. 1, figs. 16-17) described a *N. affine* (E) *undulatum* (Grun.), and A. Cleve-Euler (1955, figs. 1164c-e) described a *N. affine* (β) *undulatum* (V. H.) Cl., both of which fit this taxon and not variety *undulatum* (Grun.) Hust.

Type locality. — [Asia], Siberia, Hanka Lake near Vladivostok. U.S.A., Pennsylvania, Chester Co., Ridley Creek near U. S. Rt. 3.

U. S. distribution. — Geographical: Pennsylvania, Missouri. Ecological: Insufficiently known.

4. Neidium affine var. humerus Reim. var. nov.   PL. 35, FIG. 5

Valvae lineari-ellipticalibus. Apicibus anguste, apiculatis. Striis, 20-22 in 10μ. Punctae, ca. 22 in 10μ. Longitudine, 41-78μ. Latitudine, 14-22μ.

Valve linear-elliptical or occasionally linear. Ends narrow, produced, apiculate; formed by an abrupt narrowing of the margins. Striae, 20-22 in 10μ. Puncta, about 22 in 10μ. Length, 41-78μ. Breadth, 14-22μ.

Since this is a new variety and not a new name as originally indicated (Reimer, 1959a, p. 12), a Latin diagnosis is included here to validate the taxon.

Distinguished from the nominate variety by the apiculate ends, the "shoulders" subtending the ends, and the generally broader valve.

Several faint lines, appearing as extensions of the striae into the central area, are often but not always present. This is of doubtful taxonomic significance, as the same thing has been observed occasionally in other species of *Neidium*.

A. Schmidt (1877, pl. 49, fig. 32) illustrated a diatom which is probably the same as this taxon, but he called it *Navicula amphigomphus* Ehr. His figure 31, of the same plate, appears also to be the same. I do not consider these two illustrations of A. Schmidt as part of *amphigomphus*.

The entity seems to be more properly a part of the *affine* group in which it is placed as a new variety.

Type locality. — U.S.A., Maryland, Montgomery County, Potomac River. (*Holotype*—A-G.C. 44285a, Reimer.)

U. S. distribution. — GEOGRAPHICAL: Maryland, Tennessee. ECOLOGICAL: To date recorded only from rather large rivers (Potomac and Tennessee Rivers). We have two unconfirmed reports of its occurrence in the upper Delaware River (New Jersey) and the lower San Joaquin River (California).

4. **Neidium affine** var. **longiceps** (Greg.) Cl.   PL. 35, FIG. 4

> *Navicula longiceps* Greg., Quart. Jour. Micr. Sci., 4:8, pl. 1, fig. 27. 1856.
> *Neidium affine* var. *longiceps* (Greg.) Cl., K. Svenska Vet.-Akad. Handl., Ny Följd, 26(2):68. 1894.

Valve narrower and sides more nearly parallel than in variety *amphirhynchus.* Other characters as in variety *amphirhynchus.* Striae, 24-26 in 10μ. Puncta, 24-26 in 10μ. Length, 25-38μ. Breadth, 6-9μ. Ratio of valve width at center to width of end, 2:1-2.5:1.

This taxon is considered by some to be identical with variety *amphirhynchus* and even with the nominate variety. Although very similar in general appearance, intergrades have never been observed or demonstrated. The smaller dimensions and parallel sides appear constant. Therefore, it is being maintained here as a variety. This variety does not occur commonly with the species.

Type locality. — Scotland, Banffshire. (*Lectotype*—B.M.-47646, Reimer, 1959.)

U. S. distribution. — GEOGRAPHICAL: Middle Atlantic States, Southeastern States, South Central States. ECOLOGICAL: Lakes and rivers, acidophil.

4. **Neidium affine** var. **undulatum** (Grun.) Cl.   PL. 35, FIGS. 7-8

> *Navicula affinis* var. *undulata* Grun., Verh. Zool.-Bot. Ges. Wien, 10:544, pl. 5, fig. 6. 1860.
> *Neidium affine* var. *undulata* (Grun.) Cl., K. Svenska Vet.-Akad. Handl., Ny Följd, 26(2):68. 1894.
> *Neidium amphirhynchus* var. *undulatum* (Grun.) Meist., Beitr. Kryptog.-Fl. Schweiz, 4(1), p. 107, pl. 14, fig. 18. 1912.
> *Neidium affine* f. *undulatum* (Grun.) Hust. *in* Pasch., Süssw.-Fl. Mitteleuropas, Heft 10, Aufl. 2, p. 243. 1930.

Valve with triundulate margins; broad subrostrate to capitate ends. Striae generally coarser than in variety *affine.* Striae, 20-22 in 10μ. Puncta, 20 in 10μ. Length, 55-80μ. Breadth, 14-17μ.

This variety is slightly larger and has coarser striae and puncta than the nominate variety. The triundulate margins best distinguish it from variety *affine*. The bluntly rounded ends, slightly coarser striae, and somewhat stronger undulations separate it best from variety *hankense*. For further discussion of this taxon see Reimer (1959a, pp. 14-15).

Type locality. — [Austria].

U. S. distribution. — Geographical: Wyoming. Ecological: The few distribution data available indicate it is principally a lake form.

5. **Neidium gracile f. aequale** Hust.   PL. 35, FIG. 10

> *Neidium gracile* f. *aequalis* Hust., Arch. Hydrobiol. Suppl., 15(3):406, pl. 16, fig. 10. 1938.

Valve triundulate with protracted, subrostrate to rostrate ends; undulations of approximately equal size. Axial area narrow, width diminishing near the central area and also near the ends. Raphe straight, narrower near the central area and the ends. Proximal ends of the raphe curved in opposite directions; distal ends bifurcate. Central area diagonally elliptical. Primary longitudinal band submarginal, extending into the convex portion of the undulations. Striae oblique, becoming convergent at the ends. Striae, 22-24 in 10μ. Puncta, 22-24 in 10μ. Length, 35-55μ. Breadth, 8-12μ.

This variety is separated from the nominate variety by Hustedt on the basis of the undulations. In the variety *gracile*, the middle undulation is longer and does not extend as far out as the upper and lower undulations, thus making the widest part of the valve at the upper and lower undulations and not at the center. Such forms have not been observed so far in the United States.

Type locality. — [Asia], Mittelsumatra; im Grundschlamm aus dem Singkaraksee.

U. S. distribution. — Geographical: Georgia. Ecological: Found primarily in lakes and swampy areas.

6. **Neidium floridanum** Reim. var. **floridanum**   PL. 36, FIG. 1

> *Neidium floridanum* Reim., Proc. Acad. Nat. Sci. Philadelphia, 111:22, pl. 2, fig. 9. 1959.

Valve triundulate with protracted, distinctly rostrate ends. Undulations short, abrupt, making the greater part of the valve margin concave. Axial area narrow, width diminishing further near the central area and the ends. Raphe straight or slightly diagonal, narrower near the central area and the ends. Proximal ends of the raphe curved in opposite directions; distal ends bifurcate. Central area diagonally elliptical to transversely elliptical. Primary longitudinal band submarginal. Striae radiate, becoming convergent or oblique at the ends. Striae, 24 in 10μ. Puncta, 20-22 in 10μ. Length, 50-57μ. Breadth at the center undulation, 12-14μ.

This diatom is very similar to *Neidium gracile* Hust., but differs mainly in that the striae are radiate around the center and not oblique as they are in *N. gracile*. Also the primary longitudinal band does not follow the exact contour of the valve margins. Finally, the undulations are short and abrupt, forming distinct "shoulders" below each end, and a short gibbous center making the greater part of the valve margin concave. Valve ends considerably more narrow and evenly—not bluntly—rounded as in *N. affine* var. *undulatum*. For further discussion of this taxon see Reimer (1959a, pp. 22-23).

Type locality. — U.S.A., Florida, Taylor-Lafayette county line. Drainage ditch on *Utricularia*. (*Holotype*—A-G.C. 44155b, Reimer, 1959.)

U. S. distribution. — GEOGRAPHICAL: South Carolina, Florida. ECOLOGICAL: Insufficiently known.

7. **Neidium hitchcockii** (Ehr.) Cl. var. **hitchcockii**   PL. 36, FIG. 2

Navicula hitchcockii Ehr., Phys. Abh. Akad. Wiss. Berlin, for 1841:418. 1843.
Neidium hitchcockii (Ehr.) Cl., K. Svenska Vet.-Akad. Handl., Ny Följd, 26(2):69. 1894.

Valve linear with triundulate sides; ends apiculate, narrowing sharply. Axial area narrow. Raphe straight, filiform. Proximal ends curved in opposite directions; terminal ends bifurcate. Central and terminal thickenings rather prominent. Central area small, transversely elliptical. Axial and central areas bordered on either side by an indistinct longitudinal band (axial band) into which the striae extend but become quite indistinct. The outer margin of this band appears as a longitudinal line down either side, parallel to the axial area. Primary longitudinal band at or near both margins; edge of the band forming a longitudinal line parallel to the margin. Striae punctate, slightly radiate throughout most of the valve, becoming parallel to convergent at the ends. Striae, about 20 in 10μ. Puncta, 20 in 10μ. Length, 35 to about 100μ. Breadth, about 8-15μ.

The presence of axial bands distinguishes this diatom quite clearly from other triundulate forms. Although the ends approach a narrow-rostrate shape in isolated cases, I prefer to consider them all as apiculate.

Type locality. — U.S.A., Bridgwater, Mass.

U. S. distribution. — GEOGRAPHICAL: New England States, Middle Atlantic States, East Central States, Lakes States; South Carolina, Washington, California. ECOLOGICAL: Appears to be characteristically a lake form; sometimes found in rivers draining lakes as an allochthonous form.

8. **Neidium apiculatum** Reim. var. **apiculatum**   PL. 36, FIG. 3

Neidium apiculatum Reim., Proc. Acad. Nat. Sci. Philadelphia, 111:16, pl. 3, fig. 6.
1959.

Valve elliptical with apiculate ends. Axial area narrowing near the central area and the ends. Raphe straight, rather broad throughout. Proximal raphe ends short; much thinner than main axis of the raphe; curved in opposite directions. Distal ends bifurcate, also thinner than main axis of the raphe. Central area transversely elliptical or somewhat rectangular, often irregular in outline. Primary longitudinal band prominent along both sides, submarginal. Striae radiate throughout most of the valve, becoming parallel or convergent near the ends; usually curved, the arch of the curve away from the ends. Striae, 20 in 10μ. Puncta, 24-26 in 10μ. Length, 30-48μ. Breadth, 15-20μ.

This diatom resembles *Neidium ladogense* in shape and general appearance. Proximal raphe hooks are apparent, however, and are absent in *N. ladogense*. Also the striae become parallel to convergent at the ends in *N. apiculatum*, whereas in *N. ladogense* the striae are radiate throughout. The figure of A. Schmidt (1877, pl. 49, fig. 6), identified as N[*avicula*] *dilatata* Ehr., is also very closely related to this diatom. It does not appear to be a part of Ehrenberg's *N. dilatata* and thus is in need of proper description. It may well belong here as a separate variety. I have not seen any record of this diatom from the United States. For further discussion of this taxon see Reimer (*loc. cit.*).

Type locality. — U.S.A., South Carolina, Aiken County, Upper Three Runs Creek. (*Holotype*—A-G.C. 44266c, Reimer, 1959.)

U. S. distribution. — GEOGRAPHICAL: Southeastern States. ECOLOGICAL: Not enough known to record ecological preference, but, to date, found only in small, slightly dystrophic streams.

8. **Neidium apiculatum** var. **constrictum** Reim.   PL. 36, FIG. 4

Neidium apiculatum var. *constrictum* Reim., Proc. Acad. Nat. Sci. Philadelphia, 111:17, pl. 3, fig. 7.   1959.

Valve smaller, more rectangular, with central constriction and with slightly finer striae than the nominate variety. Other features as described for variety *apiculatum*. Striae, 24 in 10μ. Puncta, 24-26 in 10μ. Length, 22-25μ. Breadth, 9-10μ.

Type locality. — U.S.A., South Carolina, Aiken County: Upper Three Runs Creek. (*Holotype*—A-G.C. 44266b, Reimer, 1959.)

U. S. distribution. — GEOGRAPHICAL: Southeastern States. ECOLOGICAL: Same as the species.

9. **Neidium bisulcatum** (Lagerst.) Cl. var. **bisulcatum** PL. 36, FIG. 5

> *Navicula bisulcata* Lagerst., Bih. K. Svenska Vet.-Akad. Handl., 1(14):31, pl. 1, fig. 8. 1873.
> *Neidium bisulcatum* (Lagerst.) Cl., K. Svenska Vet.-Akad. Handl., Ny Följd, 26(2):68. 1894.

Valve linear with parallel or slightly concave sides; ends broadly rounded, not distinct from the main part of the valve. Axial area straight, narrowing near the central area and the ends. Raphe straight, narrowing slightly near the proximal and the distal ends. Proximal ends curved in opposite directions; distal ends bifurcate. Central area transversely or somewhat diagonally elliptical. Primary longitudinal band marginal. Striae parallel on either side of the central area, radiate above and below the central area, convergent at the ends. Striae, 26-30 in 10μ. Puncta, 24-28 in 10μ. Length, 35-75μ. Breadth, 7-12μ.

Characterized by its linear shape, broadly rounded ends, and relatively fine striae.

Type locality. — Uncertain, Spetsbergen (?), Beer. Eil. (?).

U. S. distribution. — GEOGRAPHICAL: New England States, Middle Atlantic States, Southeastern States; Tennessee, Indiana, Nebraska. ECOLOGICAL: Frequently listed from lakes but also common in rivers. Schroeder (1939, p. 69) lists it from the Funda River as a β-mesosaprobe showing a winter maximum. Has not been noted in large numbers from the United States.

9. **Neidium bisulcatum** var. **baicalense** (Skv. & Meyer) Reim.

PL. 36, FIG. 6

> *Neidium bisulcatum* f. *baicalensis* Skv. & Meyer, Proc. Sungaree Riv. Biol. Stat. [Harbin], 1(5):14, pl. 1, fig. 50. 1928.
> *Neidium bisulcatum* var. *baicalensis* (Skv. & Meyer) Reim., Proc. Acad. Nat. Sci. Philadelphia, 111:18-19, pl. 2, fig. 2. 1959.

Valve with more convex sides (linear-elliptical) and with coarser striae and puncta than in the nominate variety. Other features as in variety *bisulcatum*. Striae, 22-24 in 10μ. Puncta, about 22 in 10μ. Length, 29-50μ. Breadth, 9-13.5μ.

The coarser striae of this variety readily distinguish it from the nominate variety.

Type locality. — [Asia], Lake Baikal.

U. S. distribution. — GEOGRAPHICAL: New England States, Middle Atlantic States; Indiana, New Mexico. ECOLOGICAL: Insufficiently known; probably pH "indifferent."

9. **Neidium bisulcatum** var. **nipponicum** Skv.   PL. 36, FIG. 13

> *Neidium bisulcatum* var. *nipponicum* Skv., Philippine Jour. Sci., 61(1):29, pl. 3, fig. 1. [*non* pl. 4, fig. 8]. 1936.

Differs from variety *bisulcatum* in that it has attenuated, cuneate ends; it is also slightly smaller. Other features as in the nominate variety. Striae, 26-30 in 10μ. Puncta, 24-28 in 10μ. Length, 18-26μ. Breadth, 5-6μ.

See remarks under *Neidium alpinum* for distinguishing features.

Type locality. — [Japan], Honshu Island, Shinano Province, Kizaki Lake.

U. S. distribution. — GEOGRAPHICAL: Virginia. ECOLOGICAL: Insufficiently known.

9. **Neidium bisulcatum** var. **subundulatum** (Grun.) Reim. comb. nov.
PL. 36, FIGS. 7-8

> *Navicula firma* var. *subundulatum* Grun. *in* A. S., Atlas Diat., pl. 49, fig. 16.   1877.
> *Navicula subundulata* (Grun.) DeT., Syll. Alg., vol. 2, sect. 1, p. 159.   1891.
> *Neidium bisulcatum* var. *undulata* O. Müll., Forschungsber. Biol. Stat. Plön, 6:62.
> 1898.
> *Neidium bisulcatum* f. *inflata* A. Mayer, Ber. Naturw. Ver. Regensburg, 14:108, pl. 28, fig. 13.   1913.
> *Neidium bisulcatum* f. *undulata* (O. Müll.) Hust *in* Pasch., Süssw.-Fl. Mitteleuropas, Heft 10, Aufl. 2, p. 242, fig. 375.   1930.
> *Neidium bisulcatum* f. *major* Cl.-Eul., Comm. Biol. Soc. Sci. Fennica, 4(14):22, pl. 6, fig. 153.   1934.

Valve somewhat larger and with slightly triundulate margins, rounded to subcuneate ends. Puncta surrounding the central area somewhat enlarged. Striae may become slightly less numerous than variety *bisulcatum*. Otherwise not different from the nominate variety. Striae, 25-28 in 10μ. Length, 70-100μ. Breadth, 13-19μ.

Fossil specimens from Sing Sing (N.Y.B.G.-Ward C-4-12) are slightly larger (90-100μ long, 16-19μ broad) than extant specimens from Pennsylvania and New York (70-80μ long, 12-15μ broad); they also have slightly more rounded ends. Such differences do not seem great enough to warrant separate classification as inferred by O. Müller (*op. cit.*).

Type locality. — U.S.A., New York, Hudson River, Sing Sing.

U. S. distribution. — GEOGRAPHICAL: New York, Pennsylvania. ECOLOGICAL: Probably to be considered as oligotrophic. More commonly found in streams, ditches, ponds, etc.

10. **Neidium hercynicum** A. Mayer var. **hercynicum**   PL. 36, FIGS. 9-10

> *Neidium hercynicum* A. Mayer, Denksch. Bayer. Bot. Ges. Regensburg, 13(N.F. 7): 30, pl. 3, figs. 2-4.   1917.

Valve elongate-elliptical with attenuate extremities; slightly sigmoid in girdle view. Axial area slightly diagonal, becoming somewhat narrower near the central area and the ends. Raphe appearing slightly diagonal in the valve view; more distinct near the central area and the ends. Proximal ends of the raphe curved in opposite directions, thinner than the middle portion of the raphe; distal ends extending over the end of the valve, also thinner than the main portion of the raphe. Central area diagonal, elliptical to diamond-shaped. Longitudinal ribs and longitudinal band present on either side of the valve; usually marginal, occasionally submarginal. Striae oblique, curved, sometimes nearly parallel at one end of the valve. Striae, 26-28 in 10μ. Puncta, 26-30 in 10μ. Length, 25-50μ (to 75μ, A. Mayer). Breadth, 5-8μ (to 13μ, A. Mayer).

For a discussion of taxonomic problems see Reimer (1959a, pp. 23-24).

Type locality. — Uncertain, Fichtelgebirge . . . (?) Kösseine, Karges, Ebnath, Fuchsmühl, Wiesau, Fichtelsee.

U. S. distribution. — GEOGRAPHICAL: Connecticut, Pennsylvania. ECO-LOGICAL: Small dystrophic streams and swamps.

10. **Neidium hercynicum** f. **subrostratum** Wallace   PL. 36, FIGS. 11-12

Neidium hercynicum f. *subrostratum* Wallace *in* Reim., Proc. Acad. Nat. Sci. Philadelphia, 111:24-25, pl. 2, fig. 7. 1959.

Differs from the species in that it has broadly rounded, subrostrate ends. Measurements as in the nominate variety.

Type locality. — U.S.A., South Carolina, Aiken Co., Upper Three Runs Creek. (*Holotype*—A-G.C. 3984a, Reimer, 1959.)

U. S. distribution. — GEOGRAPHICAL: Middle Atlantic States, Southeastern States; Kentucky. ECOLOGICAL: Found more commonly in small, fast-flowing, slightly acid streams draining swampy lowlands.

11. **Neidium herrmannii** Hust. var. **herrmannii**   PL. 36, FIG. 14

Neidium herrmanni Hust., Arch. Hydrobiol. Suppl., 15(3):408-409, pl. 16, fig. 11. 1938.

Valve linear with gradually attenuate, obtusely rounded extremities. Axial area narrow, linear. Raphe straight, filiform. Proximal raphe ends long, curved in opposite directions, extending nearly to the edge of the central area; distal ends slightly bifurcate, difficult to resolve. Central area diagonally elliptical, somewhat irregular in shape. Primary longitudinal band marginal. Striae slightly radiate around the central area, oblique above and below the central area, becoming convergent near the ends. Striae,

30-34 in 10μ. Puncta very fine, Hustedt gives 40 in 10μ. Length, 28-30μ. Breadth, 4.5-6μ.

The diatom is somewhat similar in outline to *Neidium alpinum*, but is easily distinguished by the coarser striae, which converge near the ends, and the longer proximal raphe ends. The finer striae and puncta, together with the long proximal raphe hooks, exclude this diatom from consideration under *N. bisulcatum*.

As pointed out by Cholnoky (1960, p. 89), Hustedt's *N. inconspicuum* is quite similar to *N. herrmannii*. I have not seen the type for *N. inconspicum*, but another specimen of Hustedt's which I did examine appeared to have much finer transverse striae (about 38 in 10μ) resolved with much more difficulty than *N. hermannii*. On this basis I hesitate to synonymize these two diatoms until the problem can be studied further.

Type locality. — [Sumatra], Wasserfall bei Panjingahan, im Aufprall des Wassers . . . pH 8.3. (*Holotype*—U.B.-Hust. Ne-84, Reimer, 1959.)

U. S. distribution. — GEOGRAPHICAL: Pennsylvania, South Carolina. ECOLOGICAL: In small, fast-flowing headwater streams.

12. **Neidium alpinum** Hust. var. **alpinum**   PL. 36, FIG. 15

Neidium alpinum Hust., Internat. Rev. Ges. Hydrobiol., 43:189, text fig. 48.   1943.
Neidium perminutum Cl.-Eul., K. Svenska Vet-Akad. Handl., Fjärde Ser., 5(4):110, fig. 1158.   1955.

Valve linear to linear-lanceolate with parallel or slightly convex sides, ends subcuneate to cuneate. Axial area narrow, about the same width throughout. Raphe straight, filiform. Proximal ends of the raphe curved in opposite directions, short; distal ends indistinct. Central area transversely elliptical to subrectangular. Primary longitudinal band marginal. Striae oblique throughout the entire valve. Striae, 36 in 10μ; Hustedt gives 36-40 in 10μ. Puncta, about 35 in 10μ (difficult to resolve). Length, 16-22μ. Breadth, 4.5-5μ.

Differences between this taxon and *Neidium herrmannii* are discussed under the latter. Distinguished readily from *N. bisulcatum* var. *nipponicum*, which has the same shape, by the finer striae and oblique striae throughout the valve.

Type locality. — [Switzerland], Schweizer Alpen, Landschaft Davos; an Fadenalgen im unteren Grialetschsee.

U. S. distribution. — GEOGRAPHICAL: Pennsylvania. ECOLOGICAL: Lakes and small headwater streams.

13. **Neidium maximum** (Cl.) Meist. var. **maximum**   PL. 37, FIG. 1

Neidium affine var. *genuina* f. *maxima* Cl., K. Svenska Vet.-Akad. Handl., Ny Följd, 26(2):69.   1894.

Neidium affine f. *maxima genuina* O. Müll., Forschungsber. Biol. Stat. Plön, 6(1):63.
    1898.
Navicula iridis var. *maxima* Temp. & Perag., Diat. Monde Entier, 2nd ed., p. 119.
    1909. [*nom. nud.*]
Neidium maximum (Cl.) Meist., Beitr. Kryptog.-Fl. Schweiz, 4(1), p. 109. 1912.
Neidium iridis var. *maxima* (Cl) Hust., Arch. Hydrobiol., 10:137. 1914.
Neidium schmidtii Reim., Proc. Acad. Nat. Sci. Philadelphia, 111:30-32, pl. 4,
    fig. 1. 1959. [*nom. superf.*]

Valve large, linear-elongate with parallel or very slightly undulate sides. Ends broadly rounded, subcuneate to cuneate. Axial area straight, broad, narrowing near the central area and the ends. Raphe straight, broad (2-2.5μ), narrowing sharply near the proximal and the distal ends. Proximal ends of the raphe curved in opposite directions; distal ends bifurcate. Central area ovoid to elliptical, transverse or slightly diagonal. Primary longitudinal band broad, marginal. Striae oblique, becoming convergent toward the ends. Striae, 12 in 10μ; Cleve (*loc. cit.*) gives 12-17 in 10μ. Puncta, 12-13 in 10μ, quite irregular at margins; Cleve (*loc. cit.*) gives 12-15 in 10μ. Length, 175-325μ. Breadth, 33-40μ.

Best distinguished by its large size and broad marginal primary longitudinal band. The collection of Tempère and Peragallo (A.-T.&P. 36) has some forms which are slightly undulate mixed in with those having parallel sides. It is quite possible that Grunow's *Navicula firma* var. *subampliata* (A. Schmidt, 1877, pl. 49, fig. 19) is only a shorter form of this taxon.

On the basis that the description and illustration of *Neidium maximum* (Cl.) Meist. did not fit the type of *N. affine* var. *genuina* f. *maxima* Cl., Reimer (*loc. cit.*) erected a new name for this taxon. Since Meister included Cleve's type in his description synonymy, Meister's name must be used at the specific level whether or not his diatom was the same as Cleve's. The name *N. schmidtii* is thus superfluous according to the International Botanical Code.

It is possible that the specimens of Meister are within the range of variation of Cleve's diatom, but until better comparative material is at hand and more is known about the variation of the primary longitudinal band, Meister's specimens will remain as suspect for another taxon (Reimer, *loc cit.*).

P. T. Cleve (1894, p. 69) gives the striae up to 17 in 10μ and the puncta as fine as 15 in 10μ. Such finely striate and punctate specimens have not been seen in any of our collections.

Type locality. — U.S.A., New York, Monticello. New York, Sullivan Co.

U. S. distribution. — GEOGRAPHICAL: New England States. ECOLOGICAL: Appears to be restricted to lakes, ponds, and other open water.

14. Neidium boyeri Reim. var. boyeri   PL. 37, FIGS. 2a-b

Neidium boyeri Reim., Proc. Acad. Nat. Sci. Philadelphia, 111:20, pl. 2, fig. 1.
1959.

Valve lanceolate with slightly convex sides. Ends gradually attenuate, obtusely rounded, subrostrate to rostrate. Axial area straight, very slightly narrower near the central area and the ends. Raphe straight, narrowing near the proximal ends. Near the distal ends the raphe is also slightly narrower than the main portion of the raphe, but not so noticeably as at the proximal ends. Proximal ends of raphe curved in opposite directions, short; distal ends bifurcate over the end of valve. Central area transversely elliptical. Cutting across the longitudinal ribs on the valve surface are indistinct chambers, similar to those found in *Pinnularia,* which taper toward the axial area. The chambers appear to have outer "puncta" which decrease in size from the valve margin to the axial area. On either side of the central area these openings tend to be slightly larger. The inner side of the chambers give the appearance of a sieve or network of very fine puncta which are especially easy to see along the longitudinal band. Primary longitudinal band present; submarginal (constricted) at the central part of the valve, becoming marginal toward either end. Striae slightly radiate in the center, becoming parallel to slightly convergent near the ends. Striae, 12-14 in 10μ. Puncta, 9-14 in 10μ. Length, 84-90μ. Breadth, 20-22μ.

This diatom is best distinguished by the chamber-like, tapering striae. The structure of the chamber openings is similar to that observed under the electron microscope by Kolbe and Gölz (1943, p. 94, pl. 2, figs. 7a, 7b) for *Neidium iridis* but in *N. boyeri* the chambers are apparently larger and/or morphologically different. No such structure has been seen on specimens of *N. iridis* using the light microscope.

Type locality. — U.S.A., New Hampshire, Sullivan Co., near Sunapee, Perkins Pond. (*Holotype*—A-Boyer 778, Reimer, 1959.)

U. S. distribution. — GEOGRAPHICAL: New England States. ECOLOGICAL: To date found only in lakes and ponds.

15. Neidium sacoense Reim. sp. nov.   PL. 37, FIG. 3

Valvae late lineares, apicibus apiculatis. Area centralis elliptica, leviter obliqua. Apices raphi proximales in directionibus oppositis curvatis, apicibus distalibus bifidis. Striae ad centrum parallelae vel paulum radiatae, ad apices convenientes. Vitta longitudinalis marginalis, lata, inaequaliter et crassissime punctatis. Striae, 15-16 in 10μ. Puncta, 18 in 10μ in ambo lateris areae axialis, 12-14 in 10μ prope vittam longitudinalem. Longitudine, 60-80μ. Latitudine, 19-25μ.

Valve broadly linear with abruptly narrowing, acutely rounded and apiculate ends. Axial area straight, narrowing toward the center and the ends of the valve. Raphe straight, narrowing at the proximal and the distal ends. Proximal ends curving in opposite directions; distal ends bifurcate. Central area small, orbicular. Primary longitudinal band marginal, quite wide and with very coarse, elongate puncta which are irregularly placed. Striae generally parallel or somewhat radiate at the center, becoming convergent at the ends; oblique at least on some part of the valve. Striae, 15-16 in 10μ. Puncta, 18 in 10μ on either side of the axial area; 12-14 in 10μ near the longitudinal band. Length, 60-80μ. Breadth, 19-25μ.

Distinguished best by the quite narrow, apiculate ends and large, elongate puncta in the primary longitudinal band.

Reimer (1959, pp. 29-30) indicated that *N. sacoense* was a new combination. Ross (personal communication) kindly pointed out that, in fact, this is a new species. The validation date for this taxon, then, becomes the publication date of this work. A. Schmidt's illustration (1877, pl. 49, figs. 33-34) labelled "*N[avicula] amphigomphus* E." appears identical to this taxon.

Type locality. — U.S.A., Maine, York Co. (?), Saco Pond. (*Holotype*—A-Shulze 367, Reimer.)

U. S. distribution. — GEOGRAPHICAL: New England States, Middle Atlantic States. ECOLOGICAL: Found more commonly in lakes and ponds.

16. **Neidium kozlowii** var. **parvum** Mereschk.   PL. 37, FIG. 4

Neidium kozlowi var. *parva* Mereschk., Arb. d. Exped. d. Kais. Russischen Geog. Ges. 1899-1901, vol. 8, p. 16, text fig. 7. 1906.

Valve elliptical-lanceolate with broad, bluntly rounded, subrostrate to rostrate ends. Axial area straight, narrower near the central area and the ends. Raphe straight, narrowing slightly near the proximal and the distal ends. Proximal ends curved in opposite directions, thinner than the raphe axis; distal ends bifurcate, also thinner than the raphe axis. Central area diagonally elliptical. Primary longitudinal band submarginal. Striae oblique throughout, occasionally becoming parallel at the very end. Puncta distinct. Striae, 15-18 in 10μ. Puncta, 14-18 in 10μ. Length, 35-47μ. Breadth, 9-12μ.

Our specimens have somewhat finer striae than the number usually given for variety *parvum*, but are otherwise identical with the descriptions and illustrations of variety *parvum* and are, therefore, considered well within the range of variation for this taxon. Best distinguished from the nominate variety by the elliptical central area and finer striae. The variety *kozlowii* has a central fascia and striae, about 10-12 in 10μ.

The exact taxonomic position of this diatom is uncertain. It does not show clearly the thickened central fascia characteristic of *N. kozlowii* and, in many respects, is closely related in valve features to the *N. iridis* complex. Our specimens agree with Mereschkowsky's description and illustration, however, and are considered under this taxon until further studies indicate otherwise.

Type locality. — Tibet.

U. S. distribution. — GEOGRAPHICAL: New York, Tennessee, Iowa. ECO-LOGICAL: More characteristic of impounded waters.

17. **Neidium binode** (Ehr.) Hust. var. **binode**   PL. 37, FIG. 6

Navicula binodis Ehr., Ber. Akad. Wiss. Berlin, for 1840:212.   1840.
Neidium binodis (Ehr.) Hust., Arch. Hydrobiol., 40:933, 934.   1945.

Valve linear-elliptical with central constriction. Ends narrow, sharply protracted, obtusely rounded, rostrate. Axial area narrow. Raphe straight, about the same width throughout. Proximal ends of the raphe straight, blunt, not bent in opposite directions. Distal ends in the axial area narrow, linear, distinct, apparently straight. Central area small, transversely ellip-tical to nearly quadrangular. Longitudinal band indistinct, present at the margin and best visible when the valve is partly canted. Striae radiate throughout. Puncta arranged in undulating longitudinal rows; difficult to resolve for counting. Striae, 22-24 in 10μ to 26-28 in 10μ at the ends. Puncta, 22-24 in 10μ. Length, 15-30μ. Breadth, 6-9μ.

Best distinguished from *Neidium dubium* f. *constrictum* by the char-acteristic marginal longitudinal band and finer striae.

In valve view the striae appear punctate only about two-thirds the distance from the axial area to the valve margin. Near the valve margin the striae appear nonpunctate. This is due to the marked contour of the valve near the margins (Hustedt, 1945, p. 933).

Type locality. — [Italy]. Fossilis ad Santafioram Italiae nuper reperta.

U. S. distribution. — GEOGRAPHICAL: Pennsylvania, Tennessee, Indiana, Michigan, Utah. ECOLOGICAL: Has not been seen in large numbers; appar-ently pH "indifferent," oligosaprobic.

18. **Neidium dubium** (Ehr.) Cl. var. **dubium**   PL. 37, FIG. 5

Navicula dubia Ehr., Phys. Abh. Akad. Wiss Berlin, for 1841:418, pl. 2(2), fig. 8.   1843.
Neidium dubium (Ehr.) Cl., K. Svenska Vet.-Akad. Handl., Ny Földj, 26(2):70.   1894.

Valve broadly linear with mostly convex, occasionally parallel, sides and abruptly tapering rostrate ends. Ends vary from long rostrate to very short, abrupt rostrate. Axial area narrow, linear. Raphe straight, approximately the same width throughout. Proximal ends of the raphe straight, not curved in opposing directions; distal ends indistinct, probably straight. Central area small, transversely elliptical or nearly quadrangular. Striae slightly radiate to nearly parallel throughout. Puncta distinguished as individual, but often difficult to see clearly. Striae, 18-20 in 10μ. Puncta, about 20 in 10μ. Length, 30-50μ. Breadth, 10-16μ.

This diatom is best distinguished by the straight—not hooked—proximal raphe ends, shallow puncta, and slightly radiate to parallel striae. Hustedt (1930, p. 246) gives striae as fine, 24 in 10μ. Striae in our specimens do not exceed 20 in 10μ.

Van Heurck describes a *Navicula iridis* var. *dubia* (Ehr.) and shows a specimen (1885, pl. B, fig. 32) with somewhat hooked proximal raphe ends. The slide he indicates (No. 79) has specimens which agree in all details except the character of the proximal raphe ends, which are straight. Straight proximal raphe ends are also seen in the Cleve & Möller (A-Cl. & Möll. 78) specimens for *Navicula dubia*. Van Heurck's illustration is excluded from this concept of *Neidium dubium;* his specimens, on the contrary, (A-V.H. 79) do belong here. Van Heurck was either in error with his illustration or he was observing a diatom quite close, if not identical, to *Neidium affine* var. *humerus.*

Type locality. — [South America], Surinam (Dutch Guiana).

U. S. distribution. — GEOGRAPHICAL: New England States, Middle Atlantic States, Southeastern States, East Central States, West Central States, Lakes States, Plains States; Oregon, California. ECOLOGICAL: Found in lakes and streams; pH "indifferent." Has not been found in large numbers.

18. **Neidium dubium** f. **constrictum** Hust.   PL. 37, FIG. 8

Neidium affine var. *rhodana* Brun, Diatomiste, 2, pl. 14, figs. 8-10.   1895.
Navicula mucronata Elm., Univ. Nebraska Stud., 21:85, pl. 10, fig. 387.   1922.
Neidium dubium f. *constricta* Hust. *in* Pasch., Süssw.-Fl. Mitteleuropas, Heft 10,
    Aufl. 2, p. 246, fig. 384b.   1930.

Valve slightly constricted at the center. Otherwise as the species.

A form with margins slightly flattened midway between the center and the ends occurs occasionally. At present it is being considered as a part of this taxon (Reimer, 1959a, pp. 21-22).

Type locality. — Uncertain, Central Europe.

U. S. distribution. — GEOGRAPHICAL: New York, Maryland, Iowa, Michigan, New Mexico. ECOLOGICAL: Appears mostly as a lake form, but sometimes found in rivers.

19. **Neidium ladogense** var. **densestriatum** (Østr.) Foged   PL. 37, FIG. 7

Caloneis ladogensis var. *densestriata* Østr., Danske Diat., p. 12, pl. 1, fig. 4. 1910.
Neidium ladogensis var. *densestriata* (Østr.) Foged, Bot. Not., for 1952 (2):165. 1952.

Valve broadly elliptical to elliptical-lanceolate with small apiculate ends. Axial area straight, narrowing near the center and the ends of the valve. Raphe straight, about the same width throughout or slightly narrower toward the distal ends. Proximal ends straight—not curved in opposite directions; distal ends bifurcate. Central area irregularly quadrangular. Primary longitudinal band submarginal. Striae radiate throughout; in the upper and lower one-fourth of the valve the striae are curved-radiate, the curve bending away from the ends. Striae and puncta, 24-28 in 10μ. Length, 20-35μ. Breadth, 12-15μ.

Differences between this variety and *Neidium apiculatum* are discussed under *N. apiculatum*.

Type locality. — Uncertain, Jylland, Krog Sø Ld., Madum Sø A. F., Raabjerg Mile E. W., Skagen E. W., Thorsø E. W., Utofte Bs. Alt Ferskv [Denmark].

U. S. distribution. — Geographical: New Jersey, North Carolina. Ecological: Most characteristic of smaller, dystrophic streams.

20. **Neidium temperei** Reim. var. **temperei**   PL. 37, FIG. 9

Neidium temperei Reim., Proc. Acad. Nat. Sci. Philadelphia, 111:33-34, pl. 4, fig. 2. 1959.

Valve lanceolate-elliptical with convex sides and broadly rounded, flattened subcapitate ends. Axial area straight, slightly narrower near the central area and the ends. Raphe straight, about same width throughout. Proximal ends of the raphe straight, rounded, slightly enlarged; distal ends sharply bifurcate at about a 90 degree angle. Central area transversely dilated; a flattened ellipse, nearly quadrangular. Primary longitudinal band present on both sides of the valve, submarginal. Striae radiate at the center, becoming convergent at the ends. Striae, 16-17 in 10μ. Puncta, 16-18 in 10μ. Length, 60-75μ. Breadth, 18-20μ.

This diatom is best distinguished from *Neidium dubium* in that the striae are radiate at the center to sightly convergent at the ends. In *N. dubium* the striae are parallel or slightly radiate throughout. The valve on *N. temperei* also appears more heavily silicified, with sharper valve features than *N. dubium*.

Type locality. — U.S.A., Connecticut, Bristol (Hartford Co.), Tamarack Swamp. (*Holotype*—A-T.&P. 211, Reimer, 1959.)

U. S. distribution. — Geographical: New England States. Ecological: Appears to be an open-water, lake form.

21. **Neidium rudimentarum** Reim. var. **rudimentarum** PL. 37, FIG.. 10

Neidium rudimentarum Reim., Proc. Acad. Nat. Sci. Philadelphia, 111:28-29, pl. 3, fig. 3. 1959.

Valve linear to linear-elliptical with convex margins. Ends broad, three-fifths to two-thirds the width of the valve at the center; obtusely rounded, often subcuneate. Axial area in the larger forms rather broad throughout; in the smaller forms narrowing toward the center and the ends of the valve. Raphe straight; narrowing near the proximal and the distal ends; more sharply defined near the center of the valve. Proximal ends curved in opposing directions, short; distal ends bifurcate. Central area transversely elliptical or diamond-shaped; on either side transversely elongate puncta are present. Primary longitudinal band present near the margins in the upper and lower third only of the valve, submarginal. Striae radiate, becoming convergent at the ends; punctate. Puncta at the margins more or less transversely elongate in irregular longitudinal rows interrupted by longitudinal spaces. Striae, 16-18 in 10μ on either side of the central area; 20-21 in 10μ above and below the central area; about 23 in 10μ at the ends. Length, $60-110\mu$. Breadth, $15-20\mu$.

This species is best distinguished by the "interrupted" longitudinal bands.

Type locality. — U.S.A., New Jersey, Winslow, Blue Hole, Inskip River. (*Holotype*—A-Boyer W-6-23, Reimer, 1959.)

U. S. distribution. — GEOGRAPHICAL: Known only from the type locality. ECOLOGICAL: Insufficiently known.

Names of Taxa reported from the U. S. which could not be verified by a specimen in a public herbarium

Neidium iridis var. *vernalis* Reich. (recorded by Patrick and Hohn).
Neidium kozlowii Meresch. (recorded by Silva).

Names of taxa reported from the U. S. which are either illegitimate or of uncertain application

Navicula affinis f. *maxima* (Ehr.) Temp. & Perag. (recorded by Tempère & Peragallo).
Navicula amphilepta Ehr. (*nom. nud.*) (recorded by Ehrenberg).
Navicula columnaris Ehr. (recorded by Temp. & Perag.).
Navicula dilatata Ehr. (recorded by Ehrenberg and Tempère & Peragallo).
Navicula firma var. *dilatata* Cl. & Möll. (*nom. nud.*) (recorded by Cleve & Möller).

Navicula iridis var. *affinis* (Ehr.) V.H. (recorded by Chase).

Navicula iridis var. *amphirhynchus* (Ehr.) V.H. (recorded by Briggs in Thomas & Chase and Chase).

Neidium dilatatum (Ehr.) Cl. (recorded by Cleve, Boyer, H. L. Smith and Hohn).

Pleurosiphonia affinis Ehr. (recorded by Ehrenberg).

Taxa Recorded Since 1960

Neidium affine var. *tenuirostris* A. Mayer (recorded by Stoermer, 1963).

Neidium decens (Pant.) Stoermer (recorded by Stoermer, 1963).

Neidium distincte-punctatum Hust. (recorded by Stoermer, 1963).

Neidium hankensis Skv. (recorded by Stoermer, 1963).

Neidium hankensis var. *elongata* Skv. (recorded by Stoermer, 1963).

Neidium hitchcockii f. *teres* Sov. (recorded by Sovereign, 1963).

Neidium inconstans Sov. (recorded by Sovereign, 1963).

Neidium iridis f. *vernalis* Reich. (recorded by Reimer, 1962; Shobe, Stoermer, & Dodd, 1963).

Neidium iridis var. *conspicua* A. Mayer (recorded by Reimer, 1962).

Neidium knuthii var. *heilprinensis* Foged (recorded by Dodd & Stoermer, 1962).

Neidium kozlowi var. *baicalensis* f. *robusta* Stoermer (recorded by Stoermer, 1963).

Neidium kozlowi var. *undulata* Stoermer (recorded by Stoermer, 1963).

Genus **Diploneis** Ehr.

Ehr., Ber. Akad. Wiss. Berlin, for 1844:84. 1844.

Cl., K. Svenska Vet.-Akad. Handl., Ny Följd, 26(2):76. 1894. [gives the first complete description of this species.]

The frustules lack intercalary bands and septa. Shape of the valve linear-elliptical, elliptical or more or less constricted in the middle portion of the valve. The valves are characterized by the siliceous wall being thickened at the central nodule. A more or less broad siliceous rib lies in the apical axis which is bisected by the branches of the raphe and which fuses together at the central nodule to form a thickened structure which has an H shape. On the outer sides of the arms of the "H" lies a longitudinal canal of varying breadth on each side of the valve. These canals may be crossed by the costae or more often have poroids or spots arranged in various patterns. Transverse costae are present throughout the valve on the marginal side of the longitudinal canal. They may be almost parallel or more or less radiate. Between the costae are alveoli or single or double rows of pores. The costae may be crossed by longitudinal ribs. The alveoli may be so arranged as to form longitudinal lines.

The species of this genus vary greatly in size and in the distinctness, size, and shape of the longitudinal canals, alveoli, etc. (Fig. 10).

Type species. — *Navicula* (*Pinnularia*) *didyma* Ehr., (designated by Boyer [1927]). [= *Diploneis didyma* (Ehr.) Cl.]

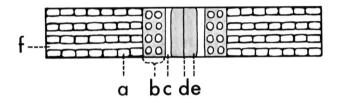

FIGURE 10.

Cross section of valve of Diploneis. a, alveolus; b, longitudinal canal; c, axial area, d, raphe; e, siliceous rib; f, costa.

KEY TO THE SPECIES OF DIPLONEIS

1. Costae separated by a double row of alveoli 2
1. Costae separated by a single row of alveoli 6
   2. Fresh-water species 3
   2. Brackish-water species 4
3. The extensions of the thickened central area distinct but narrow; longitudinal canals one-third to one-fourth the breadth of the valve .... [1] *D. finnica*
3. The extensions of the thickened central area and the central area forming a large lanceolate area; longitudinal canals narrow .... [2] *D. smithii* var. *dilatata*
   4. Longitudinal canals very narrow, with a single row of puncta 5
   4. Longitudinal canals, narrow, having several irregular rows of puncta
                                        [2] *D. smithii* and vars.
5. Costae, 8-12 in 10μ, central area large .... [3] *D. pseudovalis*
5. Costae, 12-18 in 10μ, central area small .... [2] *D. smithii* var. *pumila*
   6. Markings on the longitudinal canals similar to the alveoli between the costae, or indistinct 7
   6. Markings on longitudinal canals of different structure than the alveoli between the costae 10
7. Markings indistinct on longitudinal canals 8
7. Markings on longitudinal canals very similar to the alveoli between the costae; canals narrow 9
   8. Costae, about 20 in 10μ, parallel to slightly radiate ...... [5] *D. marginestriata*
   8. Costae, more than 20 in 10μ, slightly radiate or parallel .... [4] *D. oculata*
9. Central area large, elliptical in shape .... [6] *D. oblongella*
9. Central area not large, longer than broad .... [7] *D. puella*
   10. Valve more or less constricted 11
   10. Valve not constricted 13
11. Costae absent in the middle portion of the valve .... [10] *D. interrupta*
11. Costae present throughout entire length of the valve 12

12. Valve strongly constricted ....[11] *D. bombus*
12. Valve slightly constricted ....[12] *D. didyma*
13. Alveoli very large in size; costae, 7 or less in 10μ ....[9] *D. ostracodarum*
13. Alveoli medium to small in size; costae, 8 or more in 10μ ....[8] *D. elliptica*

1. Diploneis finnica (Ehr.) Cl. var. finnica   PL. 38, FIG. 1

Cocconeis? finnica Ehr., Infusionsthierchen, p. 194. 1838.
Diploneis finnica (Ehr.) Cl., Acta Soc. Fauna Fl. Fennica, 8(2):43, pl. 2, fig. 11.
    1891.
Navicula antinitescens M. Perag. *in* Temp. & Perag., Diat. Monde Entier, 2nd ed.,
    p. 59. 1908.

Valve elliptical. Siliceous rib enclosing the raphe well developed and
fairly broad. Central area elliptical in shape; extensions of central area
distinct, but narrow. Median ends of the raphe fairly far apart. Longitudinal canals broad, forming a lanceolate structure about one-third the
breadth of the valve. Outer surface with single or double rows of sometimes indistinct pores. Costae, 7-8 in 10μ. Between the costae double rows
of alveoli which are about 12 in 10μ. Length, 35-85μ. Breadth, 25-45μ.

This species is related to *Diploneis smithii* (Bréb.) Cl. from which it
differs mainly in the structure of the axial area.

Type locality. — Im finnischen Bergmehl von Kymmene Gård [Finland].

U. S. distribution. — GEOGRAPHICAL: Connecticut, Washington, Oregon.
ECOLOGICAL: Fresh water, particularly standing water; indifferent to small
amounts of salt.

2. Diploneis smithii (Bréb. *ex* W. Sm.) Cl. var. smithii   PL. 38, FIG. 2

Navicula smithii Bréb. *ex* W. Sm., Syn. British Diat., vol. 2, p. 92. 1856.
Diploneis smithii (Bréb. *ex* W. Sm.) Cl., K. Svenska Vet.-Akad. Handl., Ny Följd,
    26(2):96. 1894.

Valve linear-elliptical to elliptical. Central area small or enlarged into
a rounded quadrate or an elliptical area. Longitudinal canals forming a
linear-lanceolate area occupying one-fourth to one-third the breadth of the
valve. Longitudinal canals crossed by transverse, shallow costae of similar
number to those on the main body of the valve; fine, irregularly placed
pores present. Costae radiate, 5-12 in 10μ. Between the costae is a double
row of alveoli. Length, 25-200μ. Breadth, 15-75μ.

This species is distinguished by the shape of the longitudinal canals,
the double rows of alveoli, and the absence of distinct longitudinal lines.

The systematic relationships of this species have been excellently discussed by Hustedt (1937c, p. 648). J. W. Bailey (1842, p. 101, pl. 2, fig. 34)
thought this species belonged to the genus *Cocconeis.*

Type locality. — Seaford, Sussex, Aug. 1851 [England].

U. S. distribution. — GEOGRAPHICAL: New England States, Middle Atlantic States, Southeastern States, Gulf Coast States, Plains States; Utah, Washington, California. ECOLOGICAL: In slightly brackish to brackish water.

2. **Diploneis smithii** var. **dilatata** (M. Perag.) Boyer   PL. 38, FIG. 3

> *Navicula smithii* var. *dilatata* M. Perag. *in* Temp. & Perag., Diat. Monde Entier, 2nd ed., p. 56. 1908.
> *Diploneis smithii* var. *dilatata* (M. Perag.) Boyer, Proc. Acad. Nat. Sci. Philadelphia, 79(2), Suppl.:355. 1927.

Valve broadly elliptical. Central area and extensions of the central area forming a broad lanceolate space. Longitudinal canals narrow, on the surface irregularly placed pores. Siliceous rib enclosing raphe broad. Costae radiate, 5-9 in 10μ. A double row of alveoli between the costae. Length, 40-75μ. Length-to-breadth ratio, about 1:5.

This variety differs from the nominate variety in that the central area with its horns forms a broad lanceolate space and the longitudinal canals are narrow. Also it has been found in fresh water. It might be well to consider this taxon a separate species.

Type locality. — U.S.A., Connecticut, Bristol, Fall Mountain.

U. S. distribution. — GEOGRAPHICAL: Known only from the type locality. ECOLOGICAL: Springs and creek, 800 ft. altitude.

2. **Diploneis smithii** var. **pumila** (Grun.) Hust.   PL. 38, FIG. 4

> *Navicula ovalis* var. *pumila* Grun., *in* Beitr. Palaeont. Österreich-Ungarns, Band 2, p. 150. 1882.
> *Diploneis smithii* var. *pumila* (Grun.) Hust. *in* Rabh., Kryptog.-Fl. Deutschland, vol. 7(2), no. 5, p. 650, text figs. 1052 d-e. 1937.

Valve elliptical. Siliceous rib enclosing the raphe gradually widening toward the central area. Longitudinal canals narrow, linear to linear-lanceolate, only slightly wider at the central area. Central area small, slightly elliptical in shape. As in the nominate variety, a double row of alveoli between the costae. Costae, 12-18 in 10μ. Length, 13-25μ. Breadth, 8-14μ.

This variety differs from the nominate variety by its smaller size, finer structure, and narrow, linear, longitudinal canals. It differs from *Diploneis pseudovalis* Hust. by its finer costae, shape of the longitudinal canals and central area. Its relationship to *D. smithii* is shown by the presence of a double row of alveoli between the costae, and the fact it is a brackish-water species.

This variety has been well characterized by Hustedt (*op. cit.*).

Type locality. — Im Schiefer von Tallya [N.E. Hungary].

U. S. distribution. — Geographical: Middle Atlantic States; Florida. Ecological: In brackish water.

3. Diploneis pseudovalis Hust. var. pseudovalis   pl. 38, fig. 5

Diploneis pseudovalis Hust. *in* Pasch., Süssw.-Fl. Mitteleuropas, Heft 10, Aufl. 2, p. 253, fig. 403. 1930.

Valve linear-elliptical with rounded ends. Central area large. Longitudinal canals narrow, distinct; suddenly swollen around the central area. Outer surface of the longitudinal canals marked with a single row of pores. Costae radiate, 8-12 in 10μ. Between the costae a double row of fine alveoli. Length, $16-31\mu$. Breadth, $9-14\mu$.

This species is closely related to the fresh-water species *Diploneis subovalis* which is usually larger. It is also closely related to *D. smithii* var. *pumila* (Grun.) Hust. which is described above.

Type locality. — Brackwasserform (?), . . . in den Salzgewässern bei Oldesloe in Holstein [Germany].

U. S. distribution. — Geographical: Middle Atlantic States; South Carolina, Kentucky, Nebraska, Utah. Ecological: In slightly to definitely brackish water.

4. Diploneis oculata (Bréb.) Cl. var. oculata   pl. 38, fig. 6

Navicula oculata Bréb., Jour. Quekett Micr. Club., 2:38, fig. 5. 1870.
Diploneis oculata (Bréb.) Cl., K. Svenska Vet.-Akad. Handl., Ny Földj, 26(2):92. 1894.

Valve linear-elliptical. Longitudinal canals narrow, indistinct. Central area rectangular; extensions of central area parallel, narrow. Costae parallel to slightly radiate, 20-28 in 10μ. Alveoli between costae indistinct. Length, $10-20\mu$. Breadth, $6-8\mu$.

This species is similar in many characteristics to *Diploneis marginestriata* Hust. It differs mainly in its narrower longitudinal canals and usually finer striae which are typically parallel.

This species was named "*Navicula oculata* Bréb. in litt." by J. B. H. J. Desmazières "Plantes Cryptogames du Nord de la France," no 110, 1854, but was not described.

Type locality. — . . . near Lagnyi in the environs of Paris [France].

U. S. distribution. — Geographical: Middle Atlantic States, Southeastern States, East Central States; California. Ecological: Fresh water of variable mineral content.

5. Diploneis marginestriata Hust. var. marginestriata PL. 38, FIG. 7

Diploneis marginestriata Hust., Internat. Rev. Ges. Hydrobiol., 10:236, pl. 3, fig. 5. 1922.

Valve linear-elliptical with rounded ends. Central nodule small. Longitudinal canals broad, about one-third to two-thirds the breadth of the valve; sometimes faintly crossed by costae, the ends of which are clearly seen on inner edge of the longitudinal canals, otherwise without markings on the outer surface. Costae parallel or slightly radiate, 18-24 in 10μ. A single row of alveoli between costae. Length, 12-35μ. Breadth, 5-13μ.

This species is distinguished by the broad, smooth, longitudinal canals.

Type locality. — Nieder-Österreich, Lunzes Seengebiet, Untersee.

U. S. distribution. — GEOGRAPHICAL: Middle Atlantic States, Southeastern States; Connecticut. ECOLOGICAL: Fresh water.

6. Diploneis oblongella (Naeg. *ex* Kütz.) Ross var. oblongella

PL. 38, FIG. 8

Navicula oblongella Naeg. *ex* Kütz., Sp. Alg., p. 890. 1849.
Pinnularia ovalis Hilse, Jahres-Ber. Schlesischen Ges. Vaterl. Kult., 36:82. 1860. [Rabh., Alg. Europa's, No. 1025.]
Diploneis (*ovalis* var.?) *oblongella* (Naeg.) Cl., Acta Soc. Fauna Fl. Fennica, 8(2): 44. 1891.
Diploneis ovalis (Hilse) Cl., Acta. Soc. Fauna Fl. Fennica, 8(2):44, pl. 2, fig. 13. 1891.
Diploneis oblongella (Naeg. *ex* Kütz.) Ross, Natl. Mus. Canada Bull., No. 97, p. 212. 1947.

Valve linear-elliptical to broadly elliptical with rounded ends. Central area rounded, sometimes one-third to one-fourth the breadth of the valve. Longitudinal canals narrow, sometimes a little broader about the central area. A single row of pores present; the pores usually so placed as to appear as a continuation of the alveoli. Transverse costae radiate throughout the valve. A single row of alveoli between the costae. Costae, 10-19 in 10μ. Pores, 13-20 in 10μ. Length, 10-100μ. Breadth, 6-35μ.

This species closely resembles *Diploneis parma* Cl. and *D. subovalis* Cl. in many of its characteristics. It differs in the presence of a single row of alveoli between the costae rather than the double row which is characteristic of these two taxa. One should be careful always to examine the outer surfaces of the valves of these species because *D. parma* and *D. subovalis*, when viewed from the inside of the valve, may show only a single row of pores. *D. subovalis* also has a very distinct geographical distribution from that of *D. oblongella*.

The only difference between the taxa *D. ovalis* and *D. oblongella* is their size. Since the size seems to intergrade, the two species have been considered synonyms. Hustedt (1937c, p. 673) points out the difficulties encountered in distinguishing them.

The elliptical specimens of this taxon are often called *Diploneis ovalis* (Hilse) Cl. However, the name *D. oblongella* is the oldest one for this taxon.

Type locality. — In Helvetia [Switzerland].

U. S. distribution. — Geographical: New England States, Middle Atlantic States, Southeastern States, Gulf Coast States, South Central States, East Central States, West Central States, Plains States; Wyoming, Utah, Washington, California. Ecological: Fresh to slightly brackish water; sometimes in damp places (aerophil).

7. **Diploneis puella** (Schum.) Cl. var. **puella**   PL. 38, FIG. 9

> *Navicula puella* Schum., Schrift. Phys.-Ökon. Ges. Königsberg, 8:56, pl. 2, fig. 39. 1867.
>
> *Navicula elliptica* var. *minutissima* Grun. *in* V. H., Syn. Diat. Belgique, pl. 10, fig. 11. 1880.
>
> *Diploneis puella* (Schum.) Cl., K. Svenska Vet.-Akad. Handl., Ny Földj, 26(2):92. 1894.

Valve elliptical. Siliceous rib enclosing the raphe linear, narrow, and distinct. Central area longer than broad, rounded. Longitudinal canals narrow, linear, curved about the central area. Costae radiate, 14-18 in 10μ. Between the costae a row of alveoli. Length, $13\text{-}27\mu$. Breadth, $6\text{-}14\mu$.

Since this taxon is closely related to the smaller forms of *Diploneis elliptica*, it could be considered a variety of this species. It mainly differs from the smaller forms of *D. elliptica* by its finer costae.

Van Heurck (1896, p. 201, pl. 4, fig. 158) states that *Navicula elliptica* var. *minutissima* Grun. is the same as *N. puella* Cl.

Type locality. — Uncertain.

U. S. distribution. — Geographical: New England States, Middle Atlantic States, Southeastern States, Gulf Coast States, South Central States, East Central States, Plains States; Michigan, Utah, Arizona, California. Ecological: Fresh, usually hard, water to slightly salt water.

8. **Diploneis elliptica** (Kütz.) Cl. var. **elliptica**   PL. 38, FIG. 10

> *Navicula elliptica* Kütz., Bacill., p. 98, pl. 30, fig. 55. 1844.
>
> *Diploneis elliptica* (Kütz.) Cl., Acta Soc. Fauna Fl. Fennica, 8(2):42. 1891.
>
> *Diploneis elliptica* var. *grandis* (Grun.) Cl., K. Svenska Vet.-Akad. Handl., Ny Földj, 26(2):92. 1894.

Valve broadly elliptical to linear-elliptical with rounded ends. Central area large, rounded, the extensions of the central area become narrower toward the ends of the valve. Longitudinal canals narrow, generally about the same width throughout the valve, but sometimes a little wider about the central area. A single row of pores on the surface of each longitudinal canal. Costae radiate, 8-14 in 10μ; a single row of alveoli between the costae crossed by longitudinal ribs. The alveoli are usually 12-14 in 10μ in the middle of the valve. Length, $20\text{-}130\mu$. Breadth, $10\text{-}60\mu$.

Some specimens of this species approach *Diploneis oblongella* but usually differ in shape and in the fact that the alveoli are irregularly placed and not as fine. Hustedt has given an account of the variability of this species (1937c, p. 692). The alveoli of Kützing's specimens are as illustrated by Van Heurck (1880, pl. 10, fig. 10) and not as shown in Hustedt's illustration (1930, p. 251, text fig. 395).

I hereby designate the British Museum slide no. 18739 of the Kützing Collection as the lectotype of this species.

Type locality. — Unter verschiedenen Diatomeen bei Falaise: Lenormand! (Herb. Binder) [France]. (*Lectotype*—B. M. 18739, Patrick.)

U. S. distribution. — GEOGRAPHICAL: New England States, Middle Atlantic States, Gulf Coast States, East Central States, Lakes States, Plains States; North Carolina, Montana, Wyoming, Colorado, Washington, Oregon, California. ECOLOGICAL: Fresh water to slightly brackish water; found in bogs, lakes, and springs.

9. **Diploneis ostracodarum** (Pant.) Jur. var. **ostracodarum**

PL. 38, FIG. 11

Navicula ostracodarum Pant., Beitr. Foss. Bacill. Ungarns, Thiel 3, pl. 9, fig. 145. 1892. (text, Thiel 3, p. 76. 1905.)

Diploneis elliptica var. *ostracodarum* (Pant.) Cl., K. Svenska Vet.-Akad. Handl., Ny Följd, 26(2):92. 1894.

Diploneis ostracodarum (Pant.) Jur., Jugoslavenska Akad. Znan. Umjet., Prirod. Istraž., 26:124, fig. 24a. 1954.

Valve elliptical to rhomboid-elliptical in shape. Median ends of the raphe somewhat distant from each other. Central area lanceolate-elliptical in shape. A row of large puncta on the longitudinal canals. Alveoli coarse. Costae, 4.5-7 in 10μ. Length, $30\text{-}55\mu$. Breadth, $20\text{-}40\mu$.

This species is distinguished from *Diploneis elliptica* by its coarser striae and much larger alveoli which compose the striae.

Type locality. — In stratis tertiariis aquae dulcis ad Köpecz in Transilvania.

U. S. distribution. — GEOGRAPHICAL: Oregon.

10. **Diploneis interrupta** (Kütz.) Cl. var. **interrupta**   pl. 38, fig. 12

    Navicula interrupta Kütz., Bacill., p. 100, pl. 29, fig. 93. 1844.
    Diploneis interrupta (Kütz.) Cl., K. Svenska Vet.-Akad. Handl., Ny Följd, 26(2):84.
      1894.

    Valve strongly constricted at the center, dividing the valve into two broadly elliptical portions; ends rounded. Central area quadrate to rectangular in shape. Siliceous rib enclosing the raphe, which is an extension of the central area, distinct and sides almost parallel. Longitudinal canals narrow, almost parallel, with a single row of pores. Costae distinct; convergent near the center of the valve to radiate toward the ends; absent at the center. Alveoli between the costae indistinct, appearing to form a single chamber. Costae, 8-12 in 10μ. Length, $29\text{-}80\mu$. Breadth at the widest part, $12\text{-}27\mu$; at the center, $7\text{-}15\mu$.

    A discussion of the systematic relationship of the nominate variety to various other varieties and closely related species is given by Hustedt (1937c, p. 604).

    This taxon was first described, but not named, by J. W. Bailey (1842, p. 98, pl. 2, fig. 18).

    Type locality. — Uncertain, in der Ostsee an der jutlandischen Küste; in Salzsümpfen bei Stonington, Connecticut [U.S.A.].

    U. S. distribution. — Geographical: Middle Atlantic States; Connecticut, Utah. Ecological: Brackish water.

11. **Diploneis bombus** Ehr. var. **bombus**   pl. 38, fig. 13

    Diploneis bombus Ehr., Ber. Akad. Wiss. Berlin, for 1844:84. 1844. [as *Pinnularia* (*Diploneis*) *bombus*.]
    Navicula densistriata (A. S.) Hanna & Grant, Proc. California Acad. Sci., Ser. 4,
      15:150, pl. 17, figs. 8-10. 1926. [*non* Hust. 1922.]

    Valve strongly constricted at the center, ends elliptical. Siliceous rib enclosing the raphe broad, constricted or narrowed toward the apices of the valve. Longitudinal canals slightly curved, one-third to one-half the breadth of the valve, constricted at the central nodule. The costae are faintly evident on the surface of the longitudinal canals, between them are distinct pores. Central nodule distinct, extensions of the central area broad near base, narrowing toward apices. Costae, 6-8 in 10μ; Hustedt (1937c, p. 705) states rarely 9 in 10μ. The costae are crossed by irregular longitudinal ribs, 2-5 in 10μ. Alveoli large. Length, $30\text{-}150\mu$. Breadth at the widest part, $15\text{-}47\mu$; at the center, $6\text{-}25\mu$.

    This species is related to *Diploneis adonis* (Brun) Cl. from which it mainly differs by the lack of a clear marginal zone, and the structure of the alveoli. It is also closely related to *D. pseudobombiformis* Hust. (1937c, p. 708).

The name *Navicula densistriata* (A. S.) Hanna & Grant was illegitimate when published because it had been used by Hustedt for another taxon in 1922.

Type locality. — [Greece, Island of] Aegina.

U. S. distribution. — GEOGRAPHICAL: Middle Atlantic States, Gulf Coast States; South Carolina, California. ECOLOGICAL: Brackish water.

12. **Diploneis didyma** (Ehr.) Ehr. var. **didyma**   PL. 38, FIG. 14

> *Navicula (Pinnularia) didyma* Ehr., Phys. Abh. Akad. Wiss. Berlin, for 1839:155, 1841.
> *Diploneis didyma?* (Ehr.) Ehr., Mikrogeol., pl. 18, fig. 69. 1854.

Valve linear-elliptical, slightly constricted at the center; ends broadly rounded. Central nodule rectangular or quadrate, sometimes rounded on the outer margins. Longitudinal canals narrow, slightly wider at the center of the valve. Faint markings, the same number as the costae, crossing the longitudinal canals between which is a row of pores. Costae radiate, 8-10 in 10μ, crossed by longitudinal undulating ribs. Between the costae is a row of alveoli. Length, $30\text{-}90\mu$. Breadth, $15\text{-}36\mu$.

Type locality. — Fossil im Kreidemergel von Caltanisetta [Sicily].

U. S. distribution. — GEOGRAPHICAL: Florida, California. ECOLOGICAL: Brackish water, euryhaline.

Taxon for which we could not find specimens

Diploneis fusca var. *delicata* (A.S.) Cl.

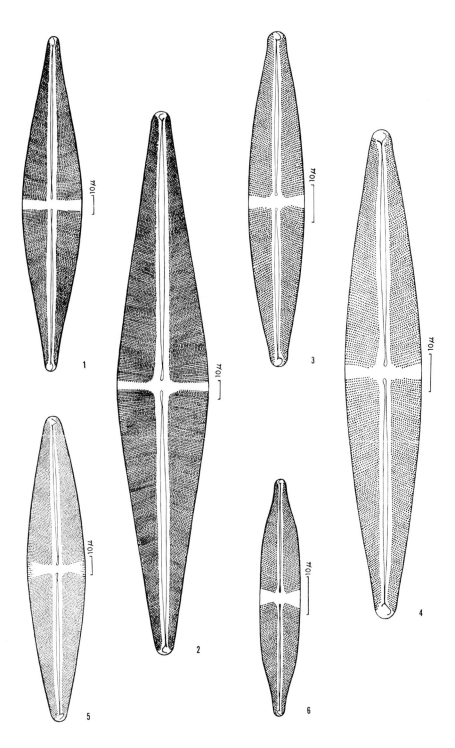

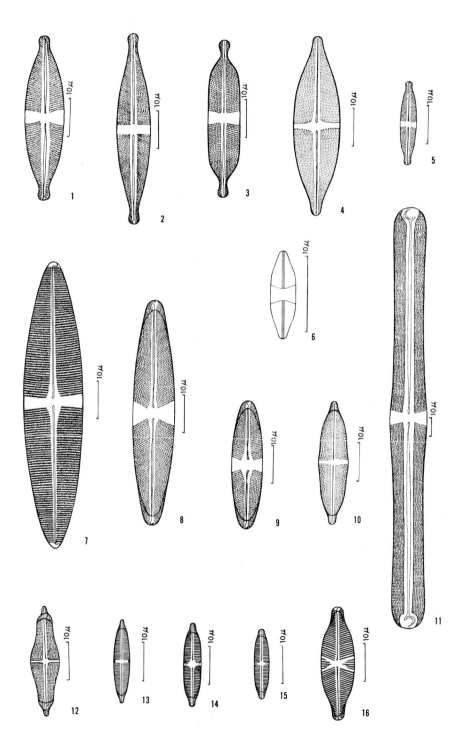

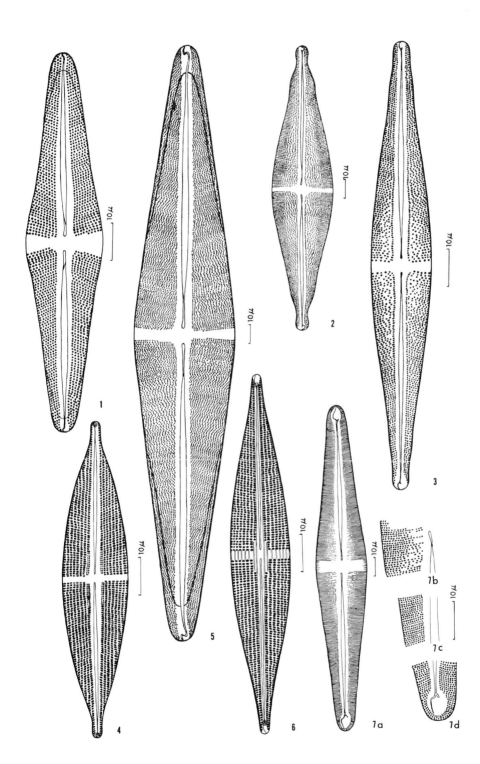

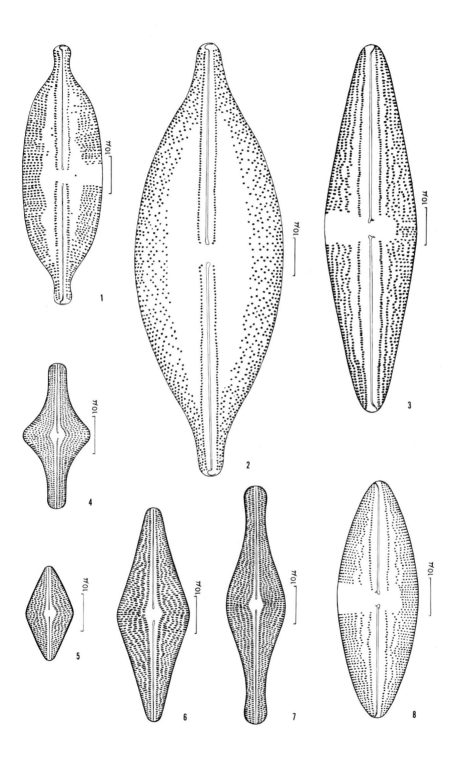

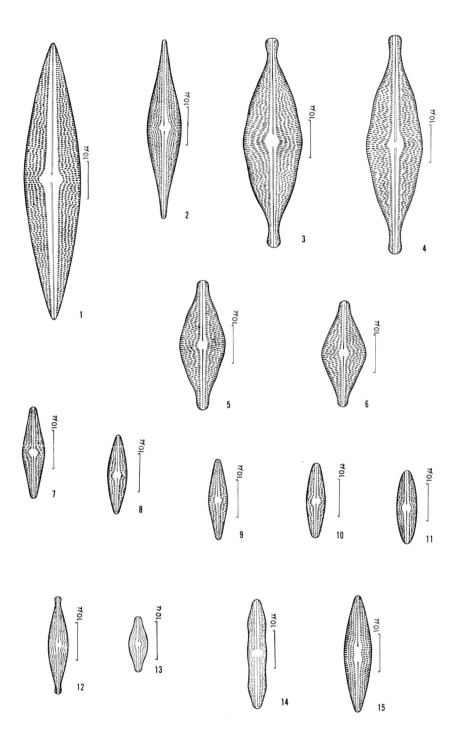

Fig. 1. *Neidium iridis* A-G.C. 5132, Wyoming, Trail's Divide Lake, attached to moss submerged in the water.

Fig. 2. *Neidium iridis* var. *amphigomphus* A-V.H. 67, England, Haverfordwest.

Fig. 3. *Neidium iridis* var. *subundulatum* A-G.C. 1252, Pennsylvania, Delaware Co.

Fig. 4. *Neidium tumescens* A-Boyer W-6-23, New Jersey, Winslow, Blue Hole, Inskip River.

Fig. 5. *Neidium iridis* var. *ampliatum* A-Boyer 762, Virginia, James River Valley Canal Basin.

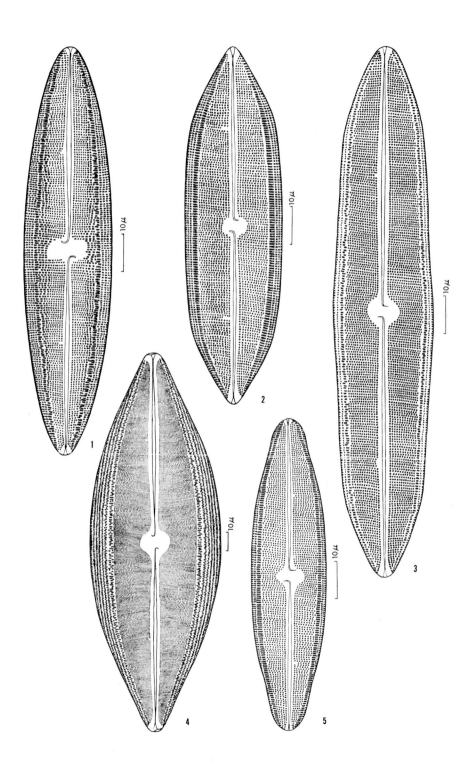

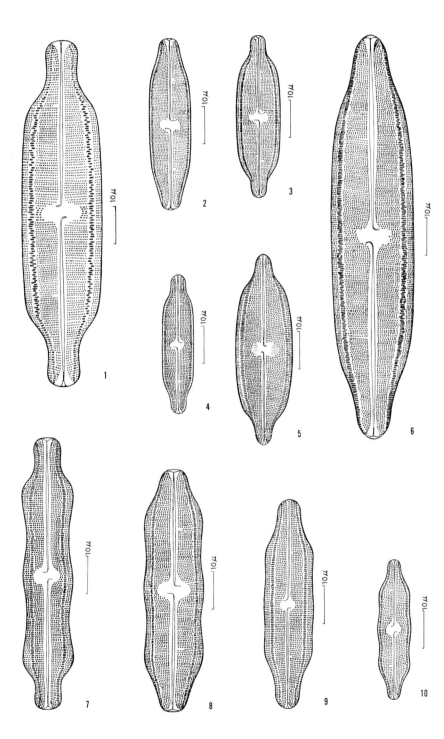

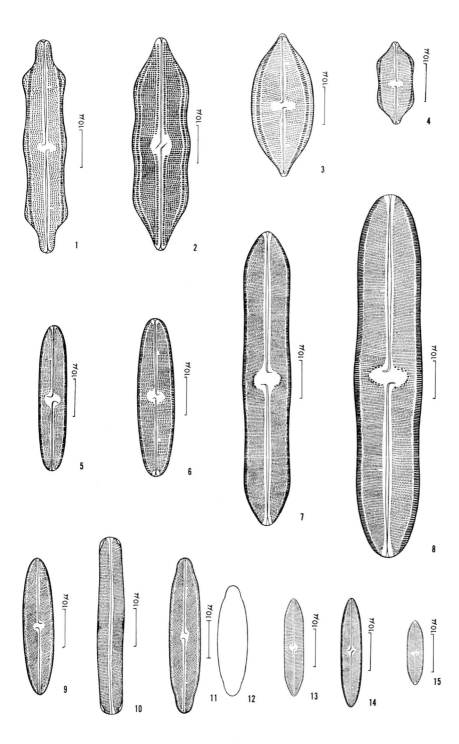

PLATE 37

Fig. 1.   *Neidium maximum* A-G.C. 3194, New York, Sullivan Co.

Fig. 2.   *Neidium boyeri* A-Boyer 778, New Hampshire, near Sunapee, Perkins Pond (drawing of Holotype).

Fig. 3.   *Neidium sacoense* sp. nov. A-Shulze 367, Maine, Saco Pond, York Co. (?) (drawing of Holotype).

Fig. 4.   *Neidium kozlowii* var. *parvum* A-G.C. 43715, Tennessee, Overton Co.

Fig. 5.   *Neidium dubium* A-V.H. 79, Belgium, La Hulpe.

Fig. 6.   *Neidium binode* A-G.C. 6676a, Utah, Cache Co., Stream Mill Creek headwater.

Fig. 7.   *Neidium ladogense* var. *densestriatum* A-G.C. 44413, New Jersey, Burlington Co.

Fig. 8.   *Neidium dubium* f. *constrictum* A-V.H. 79, Belgium, La Hulpe.

Fig. 9.   *Neidium temperei* A-T. & P. 211, Connecticut, Hartford Co., Bristol, Tamarack Swamp (drawing of Holotype).

Fig. 10.   *Neidium rudimentarum* A-Boyer W-6-23, New Jersey, Winslow, Blue Hole, Inskip River (drawing of Holotype).

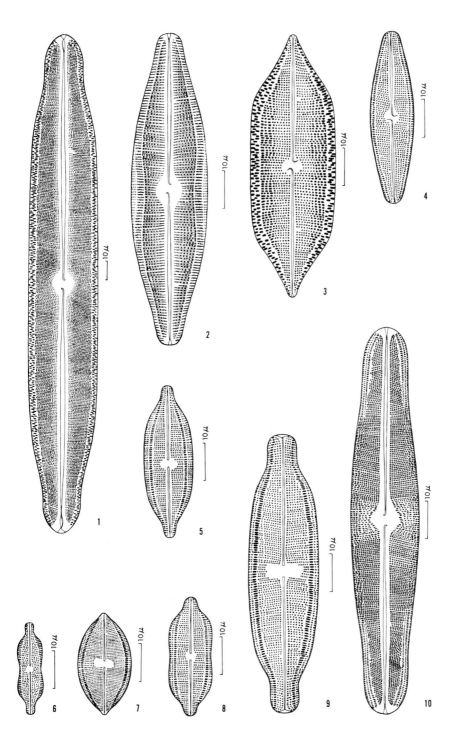

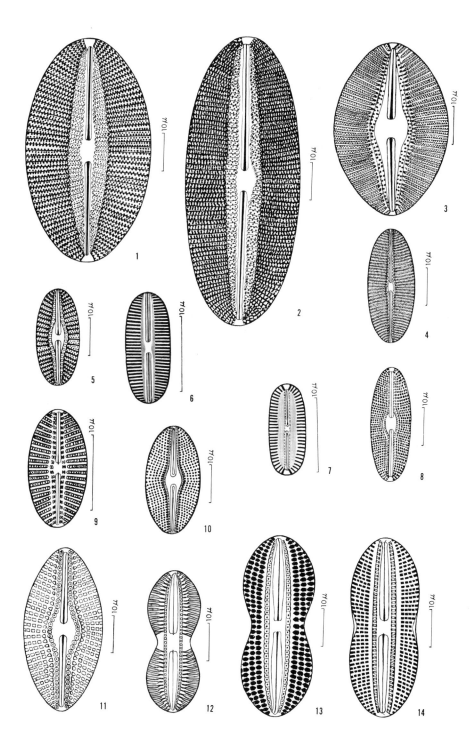

Genus **Navicula** Bory

Bory, Encyclop. Method., p. 562. 1824.

Frustules usually without intercalary bands. Some taxa have internal plates but they are not true septa which are attached to the intercalary bands. Valves linear, lanceolate to elliptical in shape. A simple raphe is present on both valves in the axial area and extends the length of the valve. The striae are typically composed of distinct or indistinct puncta except in the subgenus *Laevistriata* in which they are "costa-like."

Usually there are two large chloroplasts in each frustule, but in a few there is only one, and Hustedt (1961, p. 2) states there are a few species with many small plate-like chloroplasts.

Patrick (1959, and in press) has discussed the various subdivisions of the genus *Navicula* which earlier workers have used. Hustedt (1961) has divided the genus *Navicula* into a number of sections which presumably he regards as belonging to a single subgenus. His sections rarely conform in definition to the grouping of species which has been developed by diatomists over the years. He has redefined them so that many of them are difficult to use in systematically classifying the species of this genus.

In this work we will only consider in the key those subgenera to which species belong that are included in this book. The definition of subgenera described by Patrick (1959) will be used except that a restudy of the subgenera *Lyra* and *Hennedyea* has shown that they should be united. The correct name of the subgenus is *Navicula* subgenus *Lyraneis* Freng.

Type species. — Navicula tripunctata (Müll.) Bory.

KEY TO THE SUBGENERA OF NAVICULA

1. Valve with a lyre-shaped hyaline area on each side of the central area or with a broad hyaline area; one or more short rows of puncta on one or both sides of the axial area 2
1. Valve without these types of hyaline areas and rows of puncta on one or both sides of the axial area 3
    2. Valve with a single row of puncta on one or both sides of the axial area
                                Navicula subg. *Auricula* (p. 440)
    2. Valve with several puncta forming a short row of striae on each side of the axial area ....*Navicula* subg. *Lyraneis* (p. 442)
3. Raphe between two thickened siliceous ribs ...*Navicula* subg. *Pseudofrickia* (p. 498)
3. Raphe otherwise formed 4
    4. Raphe usually in a siliceous thickening of the wall, terminal nodules thickened, often laterally expanded ....*Navicula* subg. *Bacillum* (p. 493)
    4. Structure of the valve not so formed 5
5. Striae distinctly punctate 6
5. Striae not distinctly punctate 12

Navicula subgenus AURICULA Patr.

Navicula subgenus *Auricula* Patr., Not. Nat. Acad. Nat. Sci. Philadelphia, No. 324, p. 3.
   1959.

Valve with row of coarse puncta on one or both sides of the raphe.
The striae are marginal, and the coarse puncta are arranged to form a
longitudinal line. A clear area is present between the striae and the row
of puncta on one or both sides of the raphe.

This subgenus is related to the subgenus *Lyraneis* Freng., but differs in
that the puncta composing the striae and the rows beside the raphe are

coarse—not fine. Also the areas between the marginal striae and the puncta along the raphe are smooth and clear in the specimens I have seen.

Type species. — *Nàvicula auriculata* Hust.

1. Navicula auriculata Hust. var. auriculata   PL. 39, FIG. 1

Navicula auriculata Hust., Ber. Deutschen Bot. Ges., 61(5):273, fig. 4. 1944.

Valve elliptical with rounded ends. Axial area narrow; bordered by coarse puncta that form a complete row on one side but only an incomplete row on the other. Median ends of the raphe somewhat distant; terminal fissures turned in the same direction. Central area joining with smooth lateral areas to form a rather broad clear area. Striae marginal, composed of coarse puncta. Puncta arranged to form a longitudinal line near the margins of the valve. Striae radiate throughout the valve. Striae, 16-20 in 10μ. Length, 13-16μ. Breadth, 5-6μ.

This species is distinguished by the clear area on each side of the raphe and the two rows of puncta bordering the axial area, one of which is complete and the other incomplete. Hustedt states that this species is closely related to *Navicula dissipata* Hust.

Type locality. — West Coast of Africa, Kamerun-Lagune.

U. S. distribution. — GEOGRAPHICAL: Middle Atlantic States, Gulf Coast States, South Central States.

2. Navicula tenera Hust. var. tenera   PL. 39, FIG. 2

Navicula tenera Hust., Arch. Hydrobiol. Suppl., 15(2):259, pl. 18, figs. 11-12. 1937.

Valve elliptical with a broad, clear area in the middle portion of the valve. The middle nodule in this area sometimes appears more opaque than the rest of the area. Axial area delimited on one side by a row of distinct puncta. Median ends of the raphe somewhat distant from each other; terminal fissures not distinct. Striae marginal; composed of distinct puncta. Puncta arranged to form usually two clear longitudinal lines on each side of the valve. Striae, 16-18 in 10μ. Length, 11-14μ. Breadth, 5-7μ.

This species is distinguished from the other species of this subgenus by its shape and coarse striae. This species was first invalidly published as *Navicula uniseriata* Hust. (1934a, pl. 392, figs. 24-27). It was also a later homonym. Therefore, the type locality of *N. tenera* is the type locality of *N. uniseriata.*

Type locality. — . . . von *Najas falciculata* am No-Ufer des Ranu Klindungan (Ostjava) . . . .

U. S. distribution. — GEOGRAPHICAL: Middle Atlantic States, Southeastern States, South Central States; Texas, California.

3. **Navicula circumtexta** Meist. *ex* Hust. var. **circumtexta**

PL. 39, FIG. 3

Navicula circumtexta Meist. *ex* Hust. *in* A. S., Atlas Diat., pl. 394, figs. 33-35.   1934.

Valve lanceolate, narrowed toward rounded ends. A single row of puncta delimiting the axial area on one side. Hyaline lateral areas "H"-shaped. Striae slightly radiate at the center of the valve, convergent or parallel at the ends; distinctly punctate. Striae, 16-18 in 10μ. Length, 26-27μ. Breadth, 6-7μ.

Type locality. — East Asia, Kiang Wau.

U. S. distribution. — GEOGRAPHICAL: Virginia, Texas, Ohio, California. ECOLOGICAL: Hard water.

Navicula subgenus LYRANEIS Freng.

Navicula subgenus *Lyraneis* Freng., Bol. Acad. Nac. Cienc. Cordoba, 27:54.   1923.
Navicula subgenus *Lyra* Patr., Not. Nat. Acad. Nat. Sci. Philadelphia, No. 324, p. 7. 1959.
Navicula subgenus *Hennedyea* Patr., Not. Nat. Acad. Nat. Sci. Philadelphia, No. 324, pp. 6-7.   1959.

Valves with distinctly punctate striae. On each side of the axial area a hyaline area which may be broad or lyre shaped. These hyaline areas are separated from the axial area by rows of short striae. The striae are radiate to parallel at the apices of the valve.

This subgenus is distinguished by the presence of these lateral areas.

This subgenus includes the species of the group *Hennedyees* V.H. and the group *Lyrae* Cl. & Grun. and the *Lyraes* described by Van Heurck.

Type species. — *Navicula pygmaea* Kütz.

1. **Navicula pygmaea** Kütz. var. **pygmaea**   PL. 39, FIG. 4

Navicula pygmaea Kütz., Sp. Alg., p. 77.   1849.

Valve elliptical with broadly rounded ends. Axial area narrow. Lateral areas curved, narrowing toward the raphe at the center of the valve and at the apices. Central area transverse, merging with two narrow lateral areas. Striae radiate; more widely spaced in the middle portion of the valve. Striae, 24-26 in 10μ at the center of the valve to 34 in 10μ at the ends. Length, 16-45μ. Breadth, 8-24μ.

The shape of the lateral areas and the distinctly radiate striae are easily recognized characteristics of this taxon.

Type locality. — [France], In ostrearis Calvadosii . . . .

U. S. distribution. — GEOGRAPHICAL: New England States, Middle Atlantic States, Southeastern States, Gulf Coast States, South Central States, East Central States, West Central States, Plains States; California. ECOLOGICAL: Fresh water of high mineral content and brackish water; sometimes in polluted water.

2. Navicula lyra Ehr. var. lyra PL. 39, FIGS. 5-6

Navicula lyra Ehr., Phys. Abh. Akad. Wiss. Berlin, for 1841:419, pl. 1(1), fig. 9a. 1843.

Valve elliptical to elliptical-lanceolate with slightly constricted, rounded ends. Axial area narrow. Central area transverse; joining two linear, lateral areas which are slightly constricted at the center of the valve. Lateral areas gradually narrowed toward the ends of the valve. Striae radiate throughout most of the valve, parallel in the center and at the ends; distinctly punctate. Striae, 6-14 in 10μ. Puncta, 7-18 in 10μ. Length, 50-180μ Hustedt (1364, p. 500) states to 210μ. Breadth, 26-80μ.

Type locality. — Maluinen-oder Falklands—Inseln.

U. S. distribution. — GEOGRAPHICAL: New England States, Middle Atlantic States, Southeastern States, Gulf Coast States; California. ECOLOGICAL: Brackish to marine water.

Navicula subgenus PUNCTULATA (Grun.) Patr.

Navicula group *Punctulatae* Grun., Verh. Zool.-Bot. Ges. Wien, 10:536. 1860.
Navicula subgenus *Punctulata* Patr., Not. Nat. Acad. Nat. Sci. Philadelphia, No. 324, pp. 9-10. 1959.

Valve with distinctly punctate striae, more or less radiate at ends of the valve. Lateral area and distinct longitudinal lines absent.

This subgenus is distinguished by its clearly punctate striae, which are more or less radiate at the ends but not convergent. The puncta sometimes form undulate longitudinal lines. Longitudinal ribs or clear lines or lateral areas absent. The central or axial areas are variously formed.

This subgenus includes those species formerly included under the groups *Heterostichae* Cl. and *Punctata* Cl. Hustedt (1957, p. 229) was the first to unite these groups. The subgenus is related to the subgenus *Expansa*, but differs in that the terminal striae are radiate to parallel, not convergent.

Type species. — *Navicula maculata* (Bail.) Cl.

KEY TO THE SPECIES OF THE SUBGENUS PUNCTULATA

1. Valve not orbicular or elliptical-orbicular in shape 2
1. Valve orbicular in shape 21
    2. Stigma or isolated punctum not present in the central area 3
    2. Stigma or isolated punctum present 23
3. Central area irregular in shape 4
3. Central area if distinct of definite shape 9
    4. Striae slightly radiate, 11-16 in 10μ .... [6] *N. lacustris*
    4. Striae strongly radiate 5
5. Terminal fissures turned in opposite directions .... [5] *N. insignita*
5. Terminal fissures turned in the same direction 6
    6. Striae, 7-10 in 10μ .... [1] *N. amphibola*
    6. Striae, 18 or more in 10μ 7

7. Apices of the valve rostrate or somewhat capitate 8
7. Apices of the valve rounded; striae, 18-24 in 10μ in center of valve to 30 in 10μ
    at the ends of the valve ....[7] *N. variostriata*
    8. Striae, 18-21 in 10μ ....[2] *N. texana*
    8. Striae, 24-26 in 10μ ....[9] *N. grimmei*
9. Central area transverse, striae typically not irregular in length about the central
    area 10
9. Central area not distinct or elliptical to orbicular in shape 11
    10. Valve large; striae, less than 10 in 10μ ....[10] *N. maculata*
    10. Valve, less than 25μ in length; striae, 20-22 in 10μ ....[4] *N. savannahiana*
11. Striae less distinctly and more finely punctate toward the margins of the valve
    [11] *N. punctulata*
11. Striae with puncta of about equal size throughout their length 12
    12. Central area formed by regular shortening of the striae; striae, 18-20 in 10μ
    [3] *N. orangiana*
    12. Central area formed by striae being of irregular length about the central area 13
13. Valve elliptical-lanceolate to elliptical in shape 14
13. Valve lanceolate 20
    14. Apices of the valve slightly substrate to rostrate or slightly apiculate 15
    14. Apices of the valve rounded, not differentiated from the main body of the
    valve 19
15. Apices of valve distinctly rostrate ....[17] *N. pusilla*
15. Apices of valve somewhat protracted; slightly substrate or somewhat apiculate 16
    16. Striae, 25-30 in 10μ ....[15] *N. cocconeiformis*
    16. Striae, 20 or less in 10μ 17
17. Valve usually more than 40μ long 18
17. Valve usually less than 40μ long ....[16] *N. sovereignae*
    18. Valve elliptical-lanceolate, striae often forming undulate longitudinal lines
    [19] *N. delawarensis*
    18. Valve lanceolate, striae not forming longitudinal lines
    [17] *N. pusilla* var. *jamalinensis*
19. Striae, more than 15 in 10μ ....[12] *N. scutiformis*
19. Striae, less than 15 in 10μ ....[18] *N. latissima*
    20. Valve linear-lanceolate with slightly attenuated, broadly rounded ends
    [8] *N. disputans*
    20. Valve broadly lanceolate, with somewhat protracted, truncate ends
    [17] *N. pusilla* var. *jamalinensis*
21. Apices not differentiated from the main body of the valve, less than 50μ in
    length 22
21. Apices somewhat attenuated, rostrate; valve, greater than 50μ in length
    [10] *N. maculata* var. *orbiculata*
    22. Striae, 7-14 in 10μ ....[13] *N. scutelloides*
    22. Striae, more than 20 in 10μ ....[14] *N. pseudoscutiformis*
23. Valve with a distinct stigma on one side of the valve 25
23. Valve without a distinct stigma, but distinct isolated punctum or puncta present 24
    24. An isolated punctum in the central area ....[20] *N. mutica* and vars.
    24. Several isolated puncta present in the central area ....[23] *N. demerara*
25. Isolated punctum also present ....[22] *N. mobiliensis*
25. Isolated punctum not also present 26

26. Stigma extending to the margin of the valve; striae, 28-30 in 10μ.

[21] *N. muticoides*

26. Stigma not reaching the margin of the valve; striae, less than 25 in 10μ 27

27. Valve lanceolate to elliptical-lanceolate with protracted ends

[20] *N. mutica* var. *tropica*

27. Valve with rostrate apices .... [20] *N. mutica* var. *stigma*

1. **Navicula amphibola** Cl. var. **amphibola**   PL. 39, FIGS. 7-8

Navicula punctata var. *asymmetrica* Lagerst., Bih. K. Svenska Vet.-Akad. Handl.,
  1(14):29, pl. 2, fig. 7a. 1873.
Navicula gastrum var. *styriaca* Grun., *in* Beitr. Palaeont. Österreich-Ungarns, Band
  2, p. 144, pl. 30, fig. 50. 1882.
Navicula amphibola Cl., Acta Soc. Fauna Fl. Fennica, 8(2):33. 1891.

Valve linear-lanceolate to elliptical-lanceolate, sometimes slightly asymmetrical; ends rostrate. Axial area distinct, becoming wider toward the central area. Central area transversely widened, irregularly rectangular in shape. Striae radiate; distinctly punctate; irregular in length about the central area. Striae, 7-10 in 10μ. Puncta, 12-16 in 10μ. Length, 37-70μ. Breadth, 19-28μ.

Type locality. — Beeren Eiland (jord och mossa).

U. S. distribution. — GEOGRAPHICAL: Connecticut, Nebraska, Wyoming, Washington, Oregon, California. ECOLOGICAL: Circumneutral pH; oligohalobe to indifferent.

2. **Navicula texana** Patr. var. **texana**   PL. 39, FIG. 9

Navicula texana Patr., Proc. Acad. Nat. Sci. Philadelphia, 111:98, pl. 8, fig. 5.
  1959.

Margins of the valve parallel; ends narrowed, distinctly rostrate. Axial area narrow. Central area transverse, formed by the irregular shortening of the striae on each side of the central nodule. Striae radiate throughout most of the valve, parallel at the ends; distinctly punctate. Striae, 18-21 in 10μ. Length, 18-22μ. Breadth, 5-7μ.

This species differs from *Navicula ancisa* Hust. (1953, p. 150, fig. 9) in that the striae are parallel at the ends of the valve. It is related to *N. thienemannii* Hust. (1937b, p. 235, pl. 17, figs. 16-17), but differs in the shape of the valve and of the axial and central areas. The striae at the ends of the valve are parallel and not radiate as in *N. thienemannii*.

Type locality. — U.S.A., Texas, Guadalupe County, near Seguin, on filamentous green algae. (*Holotype*—A-G. C. 6587a, Patrick, 1959.)

U. S. distribution. — GEOGRAPHICAL: Known only from the type locality. ECOLOGICAL: Fresh water with high mineral content; hard water.

3. **Navicula orangiana** Patr. var. **orangiana**　　　PL. 40, FIG. 1

> *Navicula orangiana* Patr., Proc. Acad. Nat. Sci. Philadelphia, 111:97, pl. 8, fig. 4. 1959.

Valve linear-lanceolate with narrow, rounded, rostrate ends. Axial area narrow, widening toward the center of the valve. Central area rounded. Striae radiate throughout the valve; distinctly punctate; shortened at the center of the valve to form the more or less rounded central area. Striae, 18-20 in 10μ at the center of the valve to 26 in 10μ at the ends. Length, 17-22μ. Breadth, 5-7μ.

The distinguishing characteristic of this species is the axial area that gradually widens toward the rounded central area. The shape of the valve is also distinctive.

Navicula orangiana, N. savannahiana, and *N. texana* are smaller than most species in the subgenus *Punctulata*, but their clearly punctate, radiate striae and the characteristics of the axial and central areas place them in this group.

This species is most closely related to *N. texana* described above. It is somewhat similar to *N. grimmei* Krasske and *N. thienemannii* Hust.

Type locality. — U.S.A., Texas, Orange County, Sabine River near the mouth of Cow Bayou; diatometer slide. (*Holotype*—A-G. C. 6535a, Patrick, 1959.)

U. S. distribution. — Geographical: Known only from the type locality. Ecological: Brackish water.

4. **Navicula savannahiana** Patr. var. **savannahiana**　　　PL. 40, FIG. 2

> *Navicula savannahiana* Patr., Proc. Acad. Nat. Sci. Philadelphia, 111:97, pl. 8, fig. 7. 1959.

Valve linear with distinctly capitate ends. Axial area narrow. Median ends of the raphe may be slightly turned in the same direction. Central area transverse, not reaching the margins of the valve. Striae radiate; distinctly punctate. Striae, 20-22 in 10μ. Length, 17-22μ. Breadth, 4-5μ.

This species is characterized by the distinctly capitate ends of the valve and the transverse, angularly shaped central area. It is somewhat similar to *Navicula grimmei* Krasske, but differs in that the shape of the valve is linear rather than elliptical-lanceolate and the ends are distinctly capitate.

Type locality. — U.S.A., South Carolina, Aiken County, Savannah River at Mile 134 from the mouth, near Allendale Bridge. (*Holotype*—A-G. C. 4737a, Patrick, 1959.)

U. S. distribution. — Geographical: Southeastern States; Maryland, Kentucky. Ecological: Fresh water of low mineral content.

5. **Navicula insignita** Hust. var. **insignita**   PL. 40, FIG. 3

Navicula insignita Hust., Internat. Rev. Ges. Hydrobiol., 42:73, figs. 126, 139-141. 1942.

Valve broadly lanceolate, narrowed toward rounded ends. Ends sometimes slightly constricted below the apices. Axial area narrow, distinct. Terminal fissures of the raphe turned in opposite directions. Central area orbicular to rhomboid, formed by the irregular shortening of the central striae. Striae radiate throughout the valve; finely punctate. Striae, 9-10 in 10μ at the center of the valve to 11-13 in 10μ at the ends. Length, 31-60μ. Breadth, 12-19μ.

This species is distinguished by the terminal fissures of the raphe being turned in opposite directions.

Type locality. — Luzon: Laguna de Bay (ziemlich häufig) . . . [Philippine Islands].

U. S. distribution. — GEOGRAPHICAL: Florida.

6. **Navicula lacustris** Greg. var. **lacustris**   PL. 40, FIGS. 4-5

Navicula lacustris Greg., Quart. Jour. Micr. Sci., 4:6, pl. 1, fig. 23. 1856.

Valve lanceolate with almost rounded, subacute to subrostrate ends. Axial area indistinct. Central area irregular in outline, more or less rounded or rectangular in shape, terminal fissures of raphe turned in opposite directions. Striae slightly radiate at the center of the valve, becoming more radiate toward the apices; clearly punctate, sometimes punctae on axial area more pronounced than others, irregular in length about the central area. Striae, 11-16 in 10μ. Length, 30-62μ. Breadth, 12-20μ.

This species is distinguished by the shape of the valve, the shape of the central area, and the angle of the striae.

The lectotype of this species (B.M. 643) has been examined.

Type locality. — Scotland, Lochleven. (*Lectotype*—B.M. 643, Patrick.)

U. S. distribution. — GEOGRAPHICAL: Middle Atlantic States; New York, Michigan, North Dakota. ECOLOGICAL: Seems to prefer cool fresh water.

7. **Navicula variostriata** Krasske var. **variostriata**   PL. 40, FIG. 6

Navicula variostriata Krasske, Bot. Arch., 3:197, fig. 12. 1923.

Valve linear-elliptical with rounded ends. Axial area narrow, distinct. Central area distinct, rounded, transverse. Striae radiate throughout the valve; punctate; alternately longer and shorter at the central area. Hustedt (1930, p. 274) says the shorter striae may be lacking. Striae, 18-24 in 10μ at the center of the valve to 28-30 in 10μ at the ends. Length, 22-44μ. Breadth, 6-10μ.

Type locality. — Christteich am Stelberg (Söhre) [Germany].

U. S. distribution. — Geographical: Pennsylvania. Ecological: In swamps, especially with *Sphagnum*; often found in dystrophic water.

8. Navicula disputans Patr. var. disputans   pl. 40, fig. 7

> *Navicula disputans* Patr., Proc. Acad. Nat. Sci. Philadelphia, 111:95-96, pl. 8, fig. 1. 1959.

Valve linear-lanceolate with slightly attenuated, broadly rounded ends. Axial area narrow, widening toward the central area which is orbicularly rhomboid. Striae radiate throughout the valve; distinctly punctate; irregularly shortened about the central area; appearing slightly curved in the middle portion of the valve. Striae, 14 in 10μ. Puncta, 18 in 10μ. Length, 35-53μ. Breadth, 14.5-15.5μ.

This is a very distinctive species and difficult to relate to others. The central area appears regular in outline and resembles *Navicula maculata* (Bail.) Cl. var. *maculata* in shape. However, in *N. maculata* the striae are regularly shortened about the central area, whereas in this species they are irregularly shortened.

Type locality. — U.S.A., South Carolina, Aiken County, Savannah River between Mile 174.8 and 175.1 from the mouth. (*Holotype*—A-G.C. 44496, Patrick, 1959.)

U. S. distribution. — Geographical: Known only from the type locality. Ecological: Water of low mineral content.

9. Navicula grimmei Krasske var. grimmei   pl. 40, fig. 8

> *Navicula grimmei* Krasske, Abh. Ber. Ver. Naturk. Cassel, 56:45, pl. 1, fig. 14. 1925.

Valve elliptical-lanceolate with somewhat capitate or rostrate ends. Axial area narrow. Structure of the terminal fissures of the raphe indistinct. Central area somewhat rectangular, not reaching the margins of the valve. Striae radiate throughout most of the valve, slightly radiate at the ends; unequal in length at the central area thus giving the central area an irregular shape. Striae, 24-26 in 10μ. Puncta composing striae, 27-32 in 10μ. Length, 18-21μ. Breadth, 6μ.

The central area in our specimens is transverse, but not as square in appearance as shown in Krasske's original illustration.

Type locality. — Zerstreut zwischen Kalkmoosen bei Neurode . . . [Germany].

U. S. distribution. — Geographical:Texas, Kansas. Ecological: Widely distributed in temperate and tropic zones; oligohalobe, alkalibiont, mesooxybiont; supralittoral zone on moss; pH 7 or more.

10. Navicula maculata (J. W. Bail.) Cl. var. maculata

PL. 40, FIGS. 9-10

Stauroneis maculata J. W. Bail., Smithsonian Contr. Knowl., 2(8):40, pl. 2, fig. 32. 1851.
Navicula fischeri A. S., Atlas Diat., pl. 6, fig. 38. 1875.
Navicula maculata (J. W. Bail.) Cl., K. Svenska Vet.-Akad. Handl., Ny Följd, 27(3):46. 1895.

Valve lanceolate with subrostrate ends. Axial area linear, distinct. Central area large, transversely widened. Striae radiate; distinctly punctate; regularly shortened about the central area. Striae, 6-7 in 10μ. Puncta, 5-7 in 10μ. Length, 90-120μ. Breadth, 35-45μ.

This species is distinguished by its large size, the shape of the central area, and the coarsely punctate striae.

Type locality. — U.S.A., Florida, Enterprise, common in Lake Monroe.

U. S. distribution. — GEOGRAPHICAL: New England States, Middle Atlantic States; Florida. ECOLOGICAL: Brackish water.

10. Navicula maculata var. orbiculata Patr. var. nov.   PL. 40, FIG. 11

Valva ellipticali ad orbicularem apicibus rostratis attenuatis aliquantulum. Area media transversa, biloba. Striis radiatis, punctatis distincte, saepe inaequalibus in longitudine circum aream mediam. Striis, 5-8 in 10μ. Punctis, 5-6 in 10μ. Longitudo, 57-63μ. Latitudo, 34-41μ.

Valve elliptical to orbicular with somewhat attenuated, rostrate ends. Central area transverse, bilobed. Striae radiate; distinctly punctate; often irregular in length about the central area. Striae, 5-8 in 10μ. Puncta, 5-6 in 10μ. Length, 57-65μ. Breadth, 34-41μ.

This variety is distinguished from the typical specimens of the species by the shape of the valve, the smaller length-to-breadth ratio, and the irregular length of the striae about the central area. In general, I would not describe a variety based on only two specimens. However, these specimens are so distinctly different from the nominate variety and yet so definitely belong to this species that I believe a description is justified.

Type locality. — U.S.A., Alabama, Mobile. (*Holotype*—N.Y.B.G.-Ward, B-36-16, Patrick.)

U. S. distribution. — GEOGRAPHICAL: Known only from the type locality.

11. Navicula punctulata W. Sm. var. punctulata   PL. 41, FIG. 1

Navicula punctulata W. Sm., Syn. British Diat., vol. 1, p. 52, pl. 16, fig. 151. 1853. [non *N. punctulata* Ehr.]
Navicula marina Ralfs *in* Pritch., Hist. Infusoria, 4th ed., p. 903. 1861.

Valve elliptical-lanceolate with poorly developed ends. Valve surface curved toward the margins of the valve. Axial area narrow, distinct. Central area orbicular, a little less than one-third the breadth of the valve in width. Striae radiate; distinctly punctate; often irregular in length about the central area. Puncta appear to be finer and less distinct toward the margins of the valve. This is a variable characteristic and is probably due to the curvature of the valve. Striae, 10-13 in 10μ at the center of the valve to 14 in 10μ at the ends. Puncta variable, 8-12 in 10μ near the center of the valve to 16-18 in 10μ at the margins and at the ends. Length, 39-65μ. Breadth, 25-30μ.

As Hendey (1953, p. 157) points out, the specimens of Wm. Smith from Seaford, Sussex, England, are typical forms of this species. A taxon listed as *Navicula punctulata* by Ehrenberg in 1842 (p. 337), but not characterized until 1854 [pl. 16(1), fig. 1] is not the same taxon as *N. punctulata* W. Sm. Ehrenberg's name is, therefore, a later homonym and is consequently invalid.

Type locality. — England, Sussex, Poole Bay and Seaford; marine. (*Lectotype*—B.M. 23507, Patrick.)

U. S. distribution. — GEOGRAPHICAL: Middle Atlantic States; Massachusetts, Florida, California. ECOLOGICAL: This is a brackish-water species.

12. **Navicula scutiformis** Grun. *ex* A. S. var. **scutiformis**   PL. 41, FIG. 2

Navicula scutiformis Grun. *ex* A. S., Atlas Diat., pl. 70, fig. 62.   1881.

Valve elliptical. Axial area narrow, distinct. Median ends of the raphe somewhat distant from each other. Central area circular to elliptical in shape. Striae radiate throughout the valve; distinctly punctate. Striae irregular in length at the center of the valve; sometimes many of the striae are shorter than the rest, at other times only a few are shorter. Striae, 18-22 in 10μ at the center of the valve; may be 28-30 in 10μ at the ends. Length, 24-40μ. Breadth, 17-24μ.

Type locality. — Norway, Stavanger.

U. S. distribution. — GEOGRAPHICAL: Middle Atlantic States; South Carolina. ECOLOGICAL: Fresh water, especially in northern and alpine regions.

13. **Navicula scutelloides** W. Sm. *ex* Greg. var. **scutelloides**   PL. 41, FIG. 3

Navicula scutelloides W. Sm. *ex* Greg., Quart. Jour. Micr. Sci., 4:4, pl. 1, fig. 15.   1856.

Navicula scutelloides var. *minutissima* Cl., Öfv. K. [Svenska] Vet.-Akad. Förh., 38(10):12, pl. 16, fig. 10.   1882.

Valve orbicular; ends not differentiated from the body of the valve. Axial and central areas indistinct. Striae strongly radiate; punctate; irregular in length about the central area. Striae, 7-14 in 10μ. Puncta, 10-16 in 10μ. Length, 10-30μ. Breadth, 8-20μ.

Type locality. — Uncertain. Norfolk [England], Lochleven.

U. S. distribution. — GEOGRAPHICAL: New England States, Southeastern States, East Central States, Lakes States. ECOLOGICAL: Widely distributed in fresh water.

14. **Navicula pseudoscutiformis** Hust. var. **pseudoscutiformis**

PL. 41, FIG. 4

Navicula pseudoscutiformis Hust. *in* Pasch., Süssw.-Fl. Mitteleuropas, Heft 10, Aufl. 2, p. 291, fig. 495. 1930.

Valve elliptical (almost circular) with broadly rounded ends. Axial area gradually widening toward the center of the valve. No distinct central area. Striae radiate; finely punctate; alternately longer and shorter in the middle portion of the valve. Striae, usually about 26 in 10μ. Cleve-Euler (1953b, p. 195) says the striae may vary from about 18 to 35 in 10μ. Length, 8-25μ. Breadth, 7-17μ.

Type locality. — Zerstreut im Grundschlamm holsteinischer Seen, z.B. Plussee . . . [Germany.]

U. S. distribution. — GEOGRAPHICAL: New England States, Middle Atlantic States, Southeastern States; Wyoming, Utah. ECOLOGICAL: Oligohalobe to indifferent, sometimes found in water of high mineral content; seems to prefer cool water.

15. **Navicula cocconeiformis** Greg. *ex* Grev. var. **cocconeiformis**

PL. 41, FIG. 5

Navicula cocconeiformis Greg. *ex* Grev., Ann. Mag. Nat. Hist., Ser. 2, 15:256, pl. 9, fig. 6. 1855.

Valve rhombic-elliptical to elliptical-lanceolate with slightly protracted, sub-rostrate, broadly rounded ends. Axial area narrow, distinct, slightly wider at the central area. Median ends of the raphe distant from each other. No distinct central area. Striae radiate throughout the valve except at the center where they are almost parallel; very finely punctate; alternately longer and shorter at the center of the valve. Striae, 25-30 in 10μ. Length, 12-40μ. Breadth, 7-15μ.

Our specimens are often more elliptical in shape than the one illustrated by this figure.

Type locality. — [Scotland], . . . Elchies . . . in Banffshire . . . .

U. S. distribution. — GEOGRAPHICAL: New England States, Middle Atlantic States; South Carolina, Florida, Tennessee, Nebraska, Oregon. ECOLOGICAL: Indifferent to halophobe, prefers some iron.

16. **Navicula sovereignae** Hust. var. **sovereignae**   PL. 41, FIG. 6

Navicula sovereignae Hust., Duke Univ. Mar. Stat. Bull., No. 6, p. 25, pl. 8, figs. 18-19. 1955.

Valve elliptical; sides slightly different in outline making the valve somewhat asymmetrical about the longitudinal axis; ends apiculate, subrostrate. Axial area narrow, linear. Raphe filiform. Median ends of the raphe each divided into a straight and a curved portion, the curved portions turning in opposite directions; the median ends appear to be enclosed on either side by a short nodular thickening. Terminal ends of the raphe likewise divided into a straight and curved portion, the latter bending in opposite directions. Central area subquadrangular, about one-fourth the width of the valve. Striae radiate; distinctly punctate; alternately or irregularly longer and shorter at the center of the valve. Striae, 15-20 in 10μ. Puncta, 20-22 in 10μ at the center of the valve to 24 in 10μ toward the ends. Length, 20-40μ. Breadth, 14-18μ.

This species is easily recognized, being distinguished by the slightly asymmetrical shape and the nodular thickenings present at the median raphe ends. Although the asymmetrical character is not specifically mentioned by Hustedt, his illustrations do show the two margins slightly different in shape as is the case with our specimens.

Type locality. — U.S.A., North Carolina, Beaufort; marine littoral mud.

U. S. distribution. — GEOGRAPHICAL: Middle Atlantic States; North Carolina. ECOLOGICAL: Slightly brackish to truly brackish water.

17. **Navicula pusilla** W. Sm. var. pusilla   PL. 41, FIG. 7

Navicula pusilla W. Sm., Syn. British Diat., vol. 1, p. 52, pl. 17, fig. 145. 1853.
Navicula pusilla var. *subcapitata* Boyer, Diat. Philadelphia, p. 91, pl. 25, fig. 8. 1916.

Valve elliptical-lanceolate to oval with produced, rostrate ends. Axial area linear; gradually widening toward the center of the valve into a large, elliptical to rounded central area. Striae strongly radiate; punctate; irregular in length about the central area. Striae, 10-14 in 10μ at the center of the valve to 18-20 in 10μ at the ends. Puncta, 16-20 in 10μ. Length, 25-50μ. Breadth, 12-25μ.

In W. Smith's original drawing the striae at the center of the valve are more widely spaced, but not definitely irregular in length. The slide from which our specimen was drawn is one of W. Smith's from South Wales. The specimens on this slide have striae of irregular length about the central area. The same observation has been made by Cleve (1895, p. 41) and Hustedt (1930, p. 311).

Boyer separates the variety from the species on the basis of the shape of the ends of the valve and the shape of the central area. He evidently did not closely observe W. Smith's illustration which shows the ends to be distinctly rostrate-capitate. As to the central area, its shape may be variable.

The lectotype of this species (W. Sm. 145—B.M. 23508) has been examined.

Type locality. — [England], Brackish water. Lewes, Oct. 1850, W. Sm.

U. S. distribution. — GEOGRAPHICAL: Middle Atlantic States; New York, Georgia, California. ECOLOGICAL: Seems to prefer fresh water of high mineral content or slightly brackish water; aerophil; often found in cool temperate areas.

17. **Navicula pusilla** var. **jamalinensis** Grun. PL. 41, FIG. 8

Navicula pusilla var. *jamalinensis* Grun. *in* Cl. & Grun., K. Svenska Vet.-Akad. Handl., Ny Följd, 17(2):40; pl. 2, fig. 48. 1880.

Valve broadly lanceolate with somewhat protracted, truncate ends. Axial area gradually widening toward the center of the valve. Central area elliptical. Striae strongly radiate throughout the valve; punctate; slightly irregular in length at the center of the valve, but not as irregular as in the typical specimens of the species. Striae, 10-13 in 10μ at the center of the valve to 16 in 10μ at the ends. Puncta, 12-14 in 10μ. Length, 40-65μ. Breadth, 16-23μ.

Our specimens are more lanceolate than the one illustrated by Grunow.

Type locality. — No locality is given with the original description. Cleve (1895, p. 41) gives the Kara Sea.

U. S. distribution. — GEOGRAPHICAL: Texas. ECOLOGICAL: Brackish water in the Neches River. It is hard to believe that this species, known previously only from the Kara Sea, should be found in the warm water of Texas.

18. **Navicula latissima** Greg. var. **latissima** PL. 41, FIG. 9

Navicula latissima Greg., Trans. Micr. Soc. London, 4:40, pl. 5, fig. 4. 1856.

Valve broadly elliptical: the larger forms sometimes having the margins of the valve almost parallel in the middle portion; the shorter forms nearly orbicular in shape. The ends of the valve may be very obtusely acuminate; they may be slightly constricted below the apices, or they may be rounded. Axial area distinct; widening toward the center of the valve into a large, rounded area. Raphe linear; median ends of the raphe enlarged, somewhat conical in shape. Striae strongly radiate; punctate; irregular in length about the central area—often alternately longer and shorter. Striae, 8-13 in 10μ; usually 7-8 in 10μ at the center of the valve to 10 in 10μ at the ends. Puncta, 11-12 in 10μ. Length, 50-150μ. Breadth, 44-65μ.

Type locality. — Post-tertiary diatomaceous sand of Glenshira [Glen Shira, arm of Loch Fyne, Scotland.]

U. S. distribution. — GEOGRAPHICAL: Massachusetts, Delaware, Ohio.

19. Navicula delawarensis Grun. ex Cl. var. delawarensis   PL. 42, FIG. 1

Navicula delawarensis Grun. *ex* Cl., Diatomiste, 2(13):13-14, pl. 1, figs. 7-8.   1893.

Valve elliptical-lanceolate, constricted toward subrostrate ends. Axial area narrow, distinct; widening toward the center of the valve. Raphe filamentous; median ends large, distinct. Central area elliptical. Striae radiate; distinctly punctate; often forming undulate longitudinal lines; irregular in length and often alternately longer and shorter in the middle portion of the valve. Striae, 10-15 in 10µ at the center of the valve to 16 or more in 10µ toward the ends. Puncta, 11-14 in 10µ. Length, 60-100µ. Breadth, 31-44µ.

Type locality. — . . . *Connecticut* (*Tempère*), Embouchure du Delaware [U.S.A.].

U. S. distribution. — Geographical: Middle Atlantic States; Connecticut. Ecological: Slightly brackish to brackish water.

20. Navicula mutica Kütz. var. mutica   PL. 42, FIG. 2

Navicula mutica Kütz., Bacill., p. 93, pl. 3, fig. 32.   1844.
Stauroneis goeppertiana Bleisch *ex* Rabh., Fl. Europaea Alg., sect. 1, p. 248.   1864.
Navicula mutica var. *goeppertiana* (Bleisch *ex* Rabh.) Grun. *in* Cl. & Grun., K. Svenska Vet.-Akad. Handl., Ny Följd, 17(2):41.   1880.

Valve lanceolate with rounded, sometimes slightly protracted ends. Axial area narrow, sometimes widened toward the central area. Median ends of the raphe slightly turned in the same direction. Central area large, transverse; a distinct isolated punctum present. Striae radiate; distinctly punctate; irregularly shortened at the central area. Striae, 14-20 in 10µ, coarser about central nodule. Length, 10-40µ. Breadth, 7-12µ.

Hustedt has given a very good discussion of this species (1937b, pp. 230-233).

Type locality. — [North Sea, E. Frisian Islands], In mit Seewasser vermischten Regenpfützen auf Wangerooge!

U. S. distribution. — Geographical: New England States, Middle Atlantic States, Southeastern States, Gulf Coast States, South Central States, East Central States, West Central States, Lakes States, Plains States; Wyoming, New Mexico, California. Ecological: Found in fresh, brackish, and alkaline water; often an aerophil.

20. Navicula mutica var. cohnii (Hilse) Grun.   PL. 42, FIG. 3

Stauroneis cohnii Hilse, Jahres-Ber. Schlesischen Ges. Vaterl. Kult., 38:83.   1860.
Navicula mutica var. *cohnii* (Hilse) Grun. *in* V. H., Syn. Diat. Belgique, pl. 10, fig. 17.   1880.

Valve elliptical. Axial area linear, distinct. Central area large, rectangular; a distinct, isolated punctum present on one side. Striae distinctly punctate, somewhat more coarsely punctate than in the type variety. Puncta tending to form irregular, longitudinal lines. Length-to-breadth ratio less than in the type form, otherwise the size range is similar. Striae, 15-20 in 10μ.

Type locality. — [Strzelin, Poland], Im März 1860 gesammelt in verlassenen Steinbrüchen am Galgenberge bei Strehlen.

U. S. distribution. — GEOGRAPHICAL: Middle Atlantic States, Southeastern States, West Central States; Tennessee, Ohio, Missouri, California. ECOLOGICAL: Fresh, brackish, and alkaline water.

20. **Navicula mutica** var. **stigma** Patr.   PL. 42, FIG. 5

Navicula mutica var. *stigma* Patr., Proc. Acad. Nat. Sci. Philadelphia, 111:96, pl. 8, fig. 3. 1959.

Valve broadly lanceolate with broad, elongate, rostrate ends. Axial area narrow. Central area transverse; a distinct stigma present on one side. Striae radiate throughout the valve. Striae, 16-19 in 10μ at the center of the valve to 24 in 10μ at the ends. Length, $21\text{-}36\mu$. Breadth, $7\text{-}11\mu$.

The valve of this variety is more tumid in outline than that of the nominate variety. It is distinguished by the presence of a distinct stigma on one side of the central area instead of a punctum as in variety *mutica*.

This diatom has most of the characteristics of *Navicula mutica* var. *tropica* Hust. (1936a, pl. 405, figs. 39-42), including the distinctive stigma in the central area. It is distinguished from variety *tropica* by the tumid center and rather elongate, rostrate ends.

This taxon also closely resembles the illustration of *N. mutica* var. *rhombica* Skv. (1938, p. 270, pl. 2, figs. 16-17), but the presence of a pronounced stigma and the finer striae (Skvortzov gives 15 in 10μ for his taxon) exclude it from variety *rhombica*.

Navicula lagerheimii var. *intermedia* Hust. (1937b, p. 234, pl. 17, fig. 12) is also similar to this variety, but it apparently lacks the distinct stigma which is characteristic of variety *stigma* and variety *tropica*.

Type locality. — U.S.A., South Carolina, Barnwell County, Savannah River about 35 miles upstream from U. S. Highway 301 Bridge; on mud flats. (*Holotype*—A-G.C. 3568a, Patrick, 1959.)

U. S. distribution. — GEOGRAPHICAL: Southeastern States; Pennsylvania. ECOLOGICAL: Seems to prefer water of moderate temperature.

20. **Navicula mutica** var. **tropica** Hust.   PL. 42, FIG. 4

Navicula mutica var. *tropica* Hust., Arch. Hydrobiol. Suppl., 15(2):233, pl. 17, fig. 6. 1937.

Valve lanceolate to elliptical-lanceolate with ends not protracted. Median ends of the raphe turned in the same direction. Central area large, almost reaching the margins of the valve; a large stigma present on one side.

Striae radiate throughout the valve; distinctly punctate. Striae, 20-22 in 10μ. Puncta, about 20 in 10μ. Length, 23-35μ. Breadth, 8-10μ.

This variety is characterized by the distinct stigma in the central area. This characteristic is not possessed by other varieties of this species except *Navicula mutica* var. *stigma* Patr. The presence of the stigma shows the relationship of this variety to *N. mobiliensis* Boyer, though the stigma is not as well developed as in the latter species.

Type locality. — Uncertain, East Java, West Java, South Sumatra.

U. S. distribution. — GEOGRAPHICAL: Middle Atlantic States, Southeastern States, South Central States; California. ECOLOGICAL: Fresh circumneutral water.

20. **Navicula mutica** var. **undulata** (Hilse) Grun.

PL. 42, FIGS. 6-9

Stauroneis undulata Hilse *in* Rabh., Alg. Sachsens resp. Mitteleuropas, No. 963, 1860.
Navicula mutica var. *undulata* (Hilse) Grun. *in* Cl. & Grun., K. Svenska Vet.-Akad. Handl., Ny Följd, 17(2):41. 1880.

Valve lanceolate with undulate margins. Axial area narrow, widening toward the center of the valve. Median ends of the raphe turned in the same direction. Central area a transverse fascia which does not reach the margins of the valve; one or more isolated puncta present, striae radiate throughout the valve except opposite the central area where they are almost parallel. The striae number seems to be variable. In isotype material (Hilse *in* Rabenhorst, *loc. cit.*) there seems to be two forms of this variety. One has the striae 16-20 in 10μ. The other has the striae 21-24 in 10μ. Our specimens have the striae varying from 20-21 in 10μ at the center of the valve to 24 in 10μ at the ends. Length, 15-35μ. Breadth, 5-11μ.

Navicula mutica var. *undulata* (Hilse) Grun. and *N. mutica* var. *nivalis* (Ehr.) Hust. are closely related and may intergrade. The latter is distinctly triundulate, and the margins of the valve are almost parallel, whereas in *N. mutica* var. *undulata* the valve margin is not distinctly triundulate but wavy in appearance, and the valve is more or less lanceolate in general shape. Figure 9 is of isotype material of *Stauroneis undulata* and figures 6-8 are characteristic of some of the specimens found in the United States. Reimer (1959) discusses under *N. mutica* var. *nivalis* (Ehr.) Hust. specimens which I believe belong to this taxon.

Type locality. — [Germany], Im März 1860 in alten Steinbrücken am Galgenberge bei Strehlen . . . .

U. S. distribution. — GEOGRAPHICAL: Maryland, Ohio, California. ECOLOGICAL: Slightly brackish or hard water, rich in nutrient salts.

21. **Navicula muticoides** Hust. var. **muticoides**   PL. 42, FIG. 10

> *Navicula muticoides* Hust., *in* Explor. Parc Natl. Albert, Mission H. Damas (1935-1936), Fasc. 8:82, pl. 4, figs. 33-36.   1949.

Valve elliptical to broadly lanceolate, sometimes with slightly stumpy ends. Axial area distinct; fairly broad, between one-sixth and one-seventh the breadth of the valve, gradually widening toward the central area. Median ends and terminal fissures of the raphe turned in the same direction. Central area a transverse fascia which may or may not reach the margin of the valve. On one side of the area is a distinct stigma which extends from the margin of the valve about one-third of the distance to the central nodule. Striae radiate; distinctly punctate. Puncta on the margins of the valve large, becoming smaller as they approach the raphe. Striae, 28-30 in 10μ. Puncta, 24-28 in 10μ. Length, 10-23μ. Breadth, 6-9μ.

Type locality. — [Belgian Congo], Ziemlich häufig im Berasee (Kivu-see) . . . .

U. S. distribution. — GEOGRAPHICAL: Middle Atlantic States; South Carolina, Florida, Tennessee, California.

22. **Navicula mobiliensis** Boyer var. **mobiliensis**   PL. 42, FIG. 11

> *Navicula mobiliensis* Boyer, Contr. Biol. Micr. Sect. Acad. Nat. Sci. Philadelphia, No. 1, p. 8, pl. 2, fig. 5.   1922.

Valve linear-lanceolate with subcuneate ends. Axial area distinct. Raphe broad; terminal fissures turned in the same direction. Central area transverse, irregular in outline; one to three large puncta present on one side, a large characteristic stigma present on the other side of the valve. Striae radiate throughout most of the valve, almost parallel at the center; curved; finely punctate. Striae, 10-12 in 10μ at the center of the valve to 16 in 10μ at the ends. Puncta, 14-16 in 10μ. Length, 70-95μ. Breadth, 20-25μ.

Boyer in his original description of this species states that one to three coarser puncta occur in the transverse area on each side of the central nodule. Unfortunately, Boyer's original illustration is a photograph and the structure of these puncta is not clear. However, careful examination of his specimens shows that one of the so-called puncta is in fact a stigma as shown in our illustration.

Frenguelli (1953, p. 78, pl. 1, figs. 20-21) describes *Navicula dapaloides* which is very similar to this species except that the central area extends almost to the margins of the valve, and the isolated puncta are absent.

Type locality. — U.S.A., Alabama, Mobile County, Mobile.

U. S. distribution. — GEOGRAPHICAL: Southeastern States, Gulf Coast States.

22. **Navicula mobiliensis** var. **minor** Patr.   pl. 42, fig. 12

> *Navicula mobiliensis* var. *minor* Patr., Proc. Acad. Nat. Sci. Philadelphia, 111:96, pl. 8, fig. 2.   1959.

Valve linear to linear-lanceolate with wedge-shaped ends. Axial area distinct. Central area transverse; a distinct stigma present on one side; on the other side there are several puncta that are isolated from the ends of the striae. Striae radiate through the valve. Striae, 16-20 in 10μ at the center of the valve to 24 in 10μ at the ends. Puncta, usually 20-22 in 10μ. Length, 34-43μ. Breadth, 10-12μ.

In the shape of the valve and in the general characteristics of the axial and central areas, this taxon is similar to the nominate variety. It is distinguished from the nominate variety by its smaller size, its finer striae, and the presence of several isolated puncta near the ends of the striae on the side of the central area opposite to that bearing the stigma.

Type locality. — U.S.A., Pennsylvania, Chester County, Ridley Creek near Garret Mill Road, approximately one-fourth mile upstream from West Chester Pike. (*Holotype*—A·G·C. 44497, Patrick, 1959.)

U. S. distribution. — Geographical: Known only from the type locality.

23. **Navicula demerara** Grun. *ex* Cl. var. **demerara**   pl. 42, fig. 13

> *Navicula demerara* Grun. *ex* Cl., Diatomiste, 2(13):14, pl. 1, fig. 9.   1893.

Valve broadly lanceolate with attenuated or subobtuse ends. Axial area narrow, sometimes indistinct. Terminal fissures of the raphe turned in opposite directions. Central area large, irregular; one or more large puncta present on each side of the central nodule. Striae radiate throughout most of the valve, parallel at the center and the extreme ends; distinctly punctate; irregular in length at the center of the valve. Striae, 14-17 in 10μ at the center of the valve; sometimes a little more numerous toward the ends. Puncta, 14-19 in 10μ. Length, 46-95μ. Breadth, 17-34μ.

Type locality. — Eau douce, Demerara River, Surinam (Coll. Kinker). [British Guiana?]

U. S. distribution. — Geographical: Delaware, Oregon. Ecological: Fresh water.

Navicula subgenus EXPANSA Patr.

> *Navicula* subgenus *Expansa* Patr., Not. Nat. Acad. Nat. Sci. Philadelphia, No. 324, p. 5. 1959.

Valve with punctate striae typically convergent at the ends of the valve, rarely parallel or rarely apparently radiate. Central area distinct, and may be orbicular or laterally expanded.

The most characteristic features of this subgenus are the terminal punctate striae which are convergent or rarely parallel or rarely appearing slightly radiate due to valve shape. The axial areas in the specimens I have seen are narrow. The central area is distinct and may be orbicular or laterally expanded. This subgenus is closely related to the subgenus *Punctulata*, but differs in that the striae at the ends of the valve are typically convergent.

Type species. — Navicula expansa Hagelst.

KEY TO THE SPECIES OF THE SUBGENUS EXPANSA

1. Central area with markings arranged in a pattern .... [1] *N. expansa*
1. Central area without such markings 2
    2. Striae about the central area ending in puncta which are somewhat isolated from the ends of the striae .... [2] *N. semen*
    2. Striae about central area not ending in isolated puncta 3
3. Striae about central area very irregular in length, valve less than 40μ long
                                                 [3] *N. mournei*
3. Striae about central area regularly shortened, central area asymmetrical
                                        [4] *N. creuzburgensis*

1. **Navicula expansa** Hagelst. var. **expansa**   PL. 43, FIGS. 1-3

Navicula expansa Hagelst., New York Acad. Sci., Sci. Surv. Porto Rico & Virgin Isl., 8(3):384, pl. 6, fig. 10. 1939.
Navicula wohlenbergii Brockm., Abh. Senckenbergischen Naturf. Ges., No. 478, p. 16, pl. 4, figs. 4-6. 1950.
Navicula apposita Hust., Ber. Deutschen Bot. Ges., 67:272, fig. 16. 1954.

Valve lanceolate with obtuse or slightly rostrate ends. Axial area narrow, distinct. Area about the central nodule bound by a distinct row of puncta from which, at a lower plane in the valve, striae seem to extend. Raphe with enlarged median ends and strong terminal fissures. Central area rectangular, not reaching the margins of the valve. Striae radiate throughout most of the valve, usually more or less convergent at the ends, but may be (rarely) parallel or slightly radiate; distinctly punctate. Striae, 14-18 in 10μ at the center of the valve to 24 in 10μ at the ends. Length, 45-110μ. Breadth, 18-29μ.

This species is characterized by the peculiar structure of the central area and the distinctly punctate striae which at the very ends of the valve are typically parallel or slightly convergent.

Hustedt has examined the type material of *Navicula wohlenbergii* Brockm. and *N. apposita* Hust. and found that in both taxa the striae near the ends of the valve are usually slightly convergent, though occasionally they are perpendicular or slightly radiate. He found that the direction of the striae near the ends may vary on a single valve and believes this variability is caused by the rather high valve flange. He definitely states (personal communication) that these three species are the same.

I have examined the type material of Hagelstein from the New York
Botanical Gardens. The terminal striae are parallel or slightly convergent
and not radiate as Hagelstein indicates. The valve is somewhat convex. I
agree with Hustedt that these entities all belong to the same taxon.

Type locality. — Porto Rico, Canal de Martin Peña. Marine.

U. S. distribution. — Geographical: Middle Atlantic States, Gulf Coast
States. Ecological: Brackish water.

2. **Navicula semen** Ehr. emend. Donk. var. **semen**   Pl. 43, Fig. 4

> *Navicula semen* Ehr., Phys. Abh. Akad. Wiss. Berlin, for 1841:419, pl. 1(2), fig.
> 17a; pl. 4(2), fig. 8. 1843. (questionable.)
> *Amphiprora navicularis* Ehr., Phys. Abh. Akad. Wiss. Berlin, for 1841:410. 1843.
> *Pinnularia semen* Ehr., Mikrogeol., pl. 6(2), fig. 10. 1854. (questionable.)
> *Navicula semen* Ehr. *emend.* Donk., Nat. Hist. British Diat., p. 21, pl. 3, fig. 8.
> 1870-1873.

Valve oblong-elliptical to elliptical-lanceolate with slightly constricted,
broadly flattened ends. Axial area distinct. Raphe broad; filamentous midway between the terminal and central nodules, somewhat twisted. Central
area orbicular. Striae radiate throughout most of the valve, parallel or convergent at the ends. Striae in the middle portion of the valve distant from
each other and ending in a large distinct punctum which is somewhat isolated from the rest of the stria. Striae near the margins distinctly punctate;
in the center of the valve indistinctly punctate; ends near the raphe composed of a double row of decussating puncta (also seen in specimens,
A-V.H. 97). Striae, 6-8 in 10μ at the center of the valve to 12-14 in 10μ at
the ends. Length, $50\text{-}120\mu$. Breadth, $20\text{-}30\mu$.

Donkin and others have pointed out the difficulty of being sure just
what taxon Ehrenberg has described under the names *Navicula semen* and
Pinnularia semen. Donkin states that he has adopted *semen* as described by
William Smith (1853, p. 50, pl. 16, fig. 141) as the genuine form. However,
as Cleve states (1894, p. 139), William Smith's illustration is not very
good. Therefore, I, as Boyer, have cited Donkin as the authority to emend
the description.

This species is mainly distinguished from others of this subgenus by
the formation of the central area, and the type of striae.

Type locality. — Okak auf Labrador.

U. S. distribution. — Geographical: New England States, Middle Atlantic States, Southeastern States, Gulf Coast States, South Central States,
East Central States, West Central States, Lakes States, Plains States; New
Mexico. Ecological: Seems to prefer cool water of low mineral content;
sometimes an aerophil.

3. **Navicula mournei** Patr. var. **mournei**　　　　PL. 43, FIG. 5

Navicula inflata Donk., Nat. Hist. British Diat., p. 21, pl. 3, fig. 9.　1870-1873.
Navicula mournei Patr.; Proc. Acad. Nat. Sci. Philadelphia, 111:94, pl. 7, fig. 16.
　1959.

Valve lanceolate with convex sides and subcapitate to capitate ends. Axial area narrow, widening very slightly near the center and at the ends. Raphe filiform; median ends broadening at the central area; terminal fissures curving in the same direction. Central area small, orbicular or longitudinally elliptical; one side often slightly more pronounced than the other. Striae radiate, becoming convergent at the ends; punctate. Central three of four striae quite widely spaced, usually of unequal length. Striae, 17-21 in 10μ, considerably less at the central area. Puncta, 25-30 in 10μ. Length, $20\text{-}30\mu$. Breadth, $5\text{-}9\mu$.

The species name *inflata* was first used by Kützing for *Navicula inflata* (Kutz.) Kutz. (1844, p. 99, pl. 3, fig. 36). Kützing states that this taxon is the same as *Frustulia inflata* Kütz. (1833b, p. 545, pl. 13, fig. 14) and *N. follis* Ehr. (1838, p. 179) which we recognize today as *Anomoeoneis follis* (Ehr.) Cl. Whether *N. inflata* (Kütz.) Kütz. is the same as *A. follis* (Ehr.) Cl. needs further study. However, it is certain that *N. inflata* (Kütz.) Kütz. and *N. inflata* Donk. are not the same taxon.

Type locality. — Ireland, Lough Mourne.

U. S. distribution. — GEOGRAPHICAL: Massachusetts, Maryland, Texas. ECOLOGICAL: Fresh water, sometimes found in slightly brackish water.

4. **Navicula creuzburgensis** var. **multistriata** Patr.　　　　PL. 43, FIG. 6

Navicula creuzburgensis var. *multistriata* Patr , Proc. Acad. Nat. Sci. Philadelphia,
　111:93, pl. 7, fig. 12.　1959.

Valve linear-lanceolate with slightly rostrate ends. Axial area distinct. Raphe filamentous, terminal nodule at a little distance from the apices of the valve. Central area well developed, more rounded on one side than on the other. Striae moderately radiate except at the ends where they are convergent; finely but distinctly punctate. Striae, 22-26 in 10μ at the center of the valve to 28-30 in 10μ at the ends. Length, $22\text{-}34\mu$. Breadth, $6\text{-}8\mu$.

This variety differs from the nominate variety in that the striae are more numerous, the central area is larger, and the ends are slightly rostrate.

The characteristics of the raphe and of the axial and terminal areas of both the species and the variety closely resemble those of the genus *Frustulia*. They differ from *Frustulia* in that the raphe is not enclosed in siliceous ribs, and the arrangement of the puncta does not form longitudinal and transverse lines. For these reasons they seem to belong to the genus

Navicula. Hustedt (1957, p. 256) has placed this species in the genus *Frustulia.*

Type locality. — U.S.A., Texas, Orange County, a short distance above the mouth of the Sabine River, common on logs in intertidal zone. (*Holotype*—A-G.C. 6679a, Patrick, 1959.)

U. S. distribution. — GEOGRAPHICAL: Gulf Coast States. ECOLOGICAL: Alkaphil to slightly brackish water.

Navicula subgenus DECUSSATA (Grun.) Patr.

Navicula group *Decussatae* Grun., Verh. Zool.-Bot. Ges. Wien, 10:539. 1860.
Navicula subgenus *Decussata* (Grun.) Patr., Not. Nat. Acad. Nat. Sci. Philadelphia, No. 324, pp. 4-5. 1959.

Valve with striae in decussating rows. The valve is elongate, elliptical, or lanceolate. It is symmetrical—not sigmoid. The puncta, sometimes indistinct, form decussating rows.

This subgenus includes the species of the group *Decussatae* of Grunow. However, since *Navicula decussata* (Kütz.) Petit is a very rare species and I have never seen it, it seemed well to typify this subgenus by a well-known species rather than use the older species.

Type species. — *Navicula placenta* Ehr.

1. **Navicula placenta** Ehr. var. **placenta**   PL. 43, FIG. 8

Navicula (*Ceratoneis*) *placenta* Ehr., Mikrogeol., pl. 33(12), fig. 23. 1854.
Navicula elegantissima M. Perag. *in* Temp. & Perag., Diat. Monde Entier, 2nd ed., p. 56. 1908.

Valve elliptical with apiculate-rostrate to apiculate-capitate ends. Axial area narrow. Central area circular, distinct. Median ends of the raphe distant from each other. Puncta arranged so that they form transverse striae and striae crossing each other at about an 80 degree angle. Transverse striae parallel or slightly radiate. Striae, 22-27 in 10μ. Length, $35\text{-}44\mu$. Breadth, $14\text{-}17\mu$.

Type locality. — Brakischer Tripel vom Columbia-River. Oregon. Nord-Amerika. [U.S.A.]

U. S. distribution. — GEOGRAPHICAL: New England States, Middle Atlantic States, Southeastern States, South Central States. ECOLOGICAL: Fresh water, often associated with moss as an aerophil.

Navicula subgenus SCOLIOPLEUROIDES Patr.

Navicula subgenus *Scoliopleuroides* Patr., Not. Nat. Acad. Nat. Sci. Philadelphia, No. 324, p. 10. 1959.

Valve linear to lanceolate with narrow axial area. Striae usually parallel, more or less distinctly punctate, often in irregular longitudinal rows.

Central area small, rounded—not transversely widened. Valves often weakly silicified.

These species are usually found in brackish water. The usually clearly punctate striae seem to relate this subgenus to the *Punctulata*. However, the almost parallel striae show some relation to the subgenus *Decipientes*. This subgenus includes species of the group *Microstigmaticae* Cl. emend Hust.

Type species. — Navicula scoliopleuroides (Quint.) Hust.

1. **Navicula secreta** var. **apiculata** Patr. PL. 43, FIG. 7

Navicula secreta var. *apiculata* Patr., Proc. Acad. Nat. Sci. Philadelphia, 111:107, pl. 8, fig. 6. 1959.

Valve lanceolate with protracted, rostrate ends. Axial area narrow. Central area transverse, smoothly or irregularly rounded, not reaching the margins of the valve. Striae almost parallel, slightly radiate at the center of the valve and slightly convergent at the ends. Striae, 15-17 in 10μ. Length, $28\text{-}31\mu$. Breadth, $6\text{-}9\mu$.

This taxon differs from the nominate variety in that the ends are protracted-rostrate—not protracted-capitate. The striae are almost parallel and 15-17 in 10μ. In the nominate variety they are radiate toward the center of the valve and almost parallel at the ends.

Type locality. — U.S.A., Texas, Victoria County, Guadalupe River, near Victoria. (*Holotype—*A-G.C. 6604a, Patrick, 1959.)

U. S. distribution. — GEOGRAPHICAL: Middle Atlantic States; Texas, Tennessee, Ohio. ECOLOGICAL: Fresh water of high mineral content.

Navicula subgenus CUSPIDATA (Grun.) Patr.

Navicula group *Cuspidatae* Grun., Verh. Zool.-Bot. Ges. Wien, 10:528. 1860.
Navicula subgenus *Cuspidata* (Grun.) Patr., Not. Nat. Acad. Nat. Sci. Philadelphia, No. 324, p. 4. 1959.

Valve with longitudinal and transverse striae which are perpendicular to each other.

This subgenus is characterized by the longitudinal and transverse striae which are at right angles to each other. The axial and central areas are small or indistinct. The central nodule is small or somewhat elongated, sometimes transversely dilated into a stauros. The terminal fissures of the raphe are small or indistinct, and the ends of the raphe at the central nodule are approximate. This subgenus is related to the subgenera *Fusiformes* and *Halophila*, and includes the species which have been placed under the group *Orthostichae* Cl.

Type species. — Navicula cuspidata (Kütz.) Kütz.

1. Navicula cuspidata (Kütz.) Kütz. var. cuspidata   PL. 43, FIGS. 9-10

Bacillaria fulva Nitz., Neue Schrift. Naturf. Ges. Halle, 3(1):87, pl. 3, figs. 15, 19. 1817. (questionable.)

Frustulia cuspidata Kütz., Linnaea, 8:549, pl. 14, fig. 26. 1833.

Navicula cuspidata (Kütz.) Kütz., Bacill., p. 94, pl. 3, figs. 24, 37. 1844.

Navicula cuspidata var. *ambigua* (Ehr.?) Cl., K. Svenska Vet.-Akad. Handl., Ny Földj, 26(2):110. 1894.

Navicula helvetica Brun, Diatomiste, 2, pl. 14, figs. 1-2. 1895. (questionable.)

Valve lanceolate, gradually tapering toward acute, sometimes slightly attenuated ends, or ends distinctly rostrate. Axial area linear, distinct. Central area usually not differentiated from the axial area though sometimes it may be slightly wider. An inner septum with irregular openings sometimes present. Striae composed of puncta forming transverse and longitudinal lines. Transverse striae parallel; usually 16-22 in 10μ, may be 14-24 in 10μ. Longitudinal lines, 22-26 in 10μ. Length, 30-120μ. Breadth, 15-25μ.

Nitzsch in 1817 gave the name of *Bacillaria fulva* to what he thought was a single taxon. As Kützing (1844, *loc. cit.*) points out, this species of Nitzsch's actually was composed of several species of diatoms. Furthermore, Nitzsch's description and figures were not sufficiently detailed to assign his species name definitely to any present day species.

Kützing (1833, *loc. cit.*) figures *Frustulia cuspidata* with the ends more attenuated than those which are most commonly found in the United States. They are more attenuated than the specimen illustrated by Hustedt (1930, p. 269).

Kützing (1844, *loc. cit.*) illustrates specimens for *Navicula cuspidata*, some of which are the same as those he figured for *Frustulia cuspidata* and some of which belong to the taxon we now recognize as *N. cuspidata* var. *ambigua.*

Mr. Ross of the British Museum has examined type material in the Kützing collection and found all the specimens to have rostrate ends. Likewise, specimens which we have from Brébisson's collection labeled *Frustulia cuspidata* Kütz. (A-G.C. 12453) and *Navicula cuspidata* Kütz. (A-G.C. 12543) definitely have rostrate ends. Kützing (1844) states that he has seen *Frustulia cuspidata* from Brébisson.

It therefore appears that the original taxon had both attenuated and rostrate apices. The specimens illustrated in 1833 were attenuated; those illustrated in 1844 were both attenuated and rostrate.

Type locality. — Uncertain, Germany.

U. S. distribution. — GEOGRAPHICAL: New England States, Middle Atlantic States, Southeastern States, Gulf Coast States, South Central States, East Central States, West Central States, Lakes States, Plains States; Montana, Wyoming, Colorado, Arizona, Washington, Oregon. ECOLOGICAL: Tolerant of a wide range of fresh-water conditions.

1. **Navicula cuspidata** var. **major** Meist.   PL. 44, FIG. 1

Navicula cuspidata var. *major* Meist., Beitr. Kryptog.-Fl. Schweiz., 4(1), p. 134, pl. 20, fig. 10.   1912.

Valve broadly lanceolate, narrowing toward the attenuated, more or less rostrate apices. Axial area distinct, narrow. Central area not differentiated from the axial area. Transverse striae, 11-12 in 10μ. Longitudinal striae not very distinct due to the distance between the transverse striae, about 18 in 10μ. Length, $140\text{-}250\mu$. Breadth, $32\text{-}44\mu$.

Type locality. — Uncertain.

U. S. distribution. — GEOGRAPHICAL: Ohio.

1. **Navicula cuspidata** var. **obtusa** Patr. var. nov.   PL. 44, FIG. 2

Valva lineari-lanceolata, leniter fastigiata ad apices angusta, rotundata. Area axili angusta, distincta. Area media non clare dissimili area axiali. Striis parallelis per valvam, punctatis, punctis facientibus lineas longitudinales et transversas. Lineis transversis 14-17 in 10μ. Lineis longitudinalibus, 24-28 in 10μ. Longitudo, $127\text{-}146\mu$. Latitudo, $23\text{-}29\mu$.

Valve linear-lanceolate, gradually tapering to acute, rounded ends. Axial area narrow, distinct. Central area not clearly differentiated from the axial area. Striae parallel throughout the valve; punctate, the puncta forming longitudinal and transverse lines. Transverse lines, 15 in 10μ. Longitudinal lines, 24-28 in 10μ. Length, $127\text{-}146\mu$. Breadth, $23\text{-}29\mu$.

This variety is very similar to *Navicula halophila* var. *maior* Hérib. (1903, p. 89, pl. 12, fig. 2), but differs in the presence of clearly visible longitudinal lines which makes this taxon a variety of *N. cuspidata.* It differs from *N. cuspidata* var. *kendallii* f. *parallela* L. W. Bail. (1922, p. 164, pl. 2, fig. 4) in having finer transverse striae. Also the illustration of *N. cuspidata* var. *kendallii* f. *parallela* shows indistinct longitudinal lines. These are not mentioned in the description. L. W. Bailey's taxon is a little larger, $142\text{-}184\mu$ long. It differs from the preceding taxon in its finer striae, smaller size, and shape of the valve.

Type locality. — U.S.A., Colorado, Radford Peak. (*Holotype*—A-Boyer, A-6-15, Patrick.)

U. S. distribution. — GEOGRAPHICAL: Known only from the type locality.

2. **Navicula guatemalensis** Cl. & Grove var. **guatemalensis**

PL. 44, FIG. 3a-b

Navicula guatemalensis Cl. & Grove, Diatomiste, 2(19):144, pl. 9, fig. 2.   1894.

Valve linear-lanceolate with rounded ends. Axial area narrow near the ends, gradually widening toward the center of the valve. Terminal nodules transversely widened. Terminal fissures of the raphe distinct and turned in the same direction. Central area not differentiated from the axial area, but a little wider than the axial area. Striae punctate, the puncta forming longitudinal and transverse lines. Around the central nodule the striae break up into irregularly placed puncta. Transverse lines parallel, 11 in 10μ. Longitudinal lines, 23 in 10μ. Length, 115-170μ (Elmore states to 211μ). Breadth, 18-38μ.

A distinctive characteristic of some of our specimens is the irregular placement of the puncta forming the striae about the central nodule. This characteristic is not shown in the original description.

Type locality. — Guatemala; fossil in fresh water.

U. S. distribution. — GEOGRAPHICAL: Nebraska, Washington. ECOLOGI-CAL: Fresh water.

Navicula subgenus HALOPHILA Patr.

Navicula subgenus *Halophila* Patr., Not. Nat. Acad. Nat. Sci. Philadelphia, No. 324, p. 6. 1959.

Valve with striae indistinctly punctate and parallel or almost parallel throughout most of the valve. Longitudinal lines, if present, indistinct.

This subgenus is closely related to the subgenus *Cuspidata*, but differs in that the longitudinal lines are indistinct. The axial and central areas are small. The ends of the raphe at the central nodule are sometimes close together, but may be somewhat distant. Striae indistinctly punctate.

I have placed *Navicula gregaria* Donk. and *Navicula halophila* (Grun.) Cl. in this group because of their almost parallel striae, their narrow axial and central areas, and because the puncta of the striae do not form longitudinal lines or at least they are not present in the specimens I have seen.

These two species are often put in the group *Orthostichae*. One of the distinguishing characteristics of that group is the presence under the light microscope of longitudinal lines formed by the puncta of the striae. The absence of this character excludes these two species from this group (subgenus *Cuspidata*).

Type species. — *Navicula halophila* (Grun.) Cl.

KEY TO THE SPECIES OF THE SUBGENUS HALOPHILA

1. Striae in center of valve 26 or more in 10μ, axial area distinct........[4] N. biconica
1. Striae in center of valve less than 26 in 10μ 2
    2. Median ends of raphe somewhat distant from each other 3
    2. Median ends of raphe close together ....[1] N. halophila
3. Central area no wider than axial area ....[3] N. accomoda
3. Central area wider than axial area or a transverse fascia 4
    4. Central area a little wider than axial area, lanceolate to somewhat elliptical
        in shape ....[2] N. gregaria
        4. Central area transverse fascia, bounded by thickened striae ....[5] N. spicula

1. **Navicula halophila** (Grun.) Cl. var. **halophila**   PL. 44, FIG. 4

>*Navicula cuspidata* var. *halophila* Grun. *in* V. H., Syn. Diat. Belgique, p. 100, Suppl. pl. B, fig. 30. 1885.
>
>*Navicula halophila* (Grun.) Cl., K. Svenska Vet.-Akad. Handl., Ny Följd, 26(2):109. 1894.
>
>*Navicula halophila* var. *minuta* R. d'Aub. *in* Hérib., Ann. Biol. Lacustre, 10:75, pl. 4, fig. 65. 1920.
>
>*Navicula halophila* f. *minor* Kolbe, Pflanzenforschung, 7:67, pl. 1, fig. 4. 1927. [Hustedt in 1927 published this same name for this taxon (Arch. Hydrobiol., 18:244, pl. 7, fig. 26).]

Valve rhombic to linear-lanceolate with acute, sometimes attenuated, rounded ends. Axial area narrow, distinct. Central area usually not differentiated from the axial area, though it may sometimes be slightly wider. Striae parallel throughout most of the valve, slightly convergent at the ends; sometimes slightly radiate about the central area. Transverse striae, 16-20 in 10μ. Longitudinal lines very fine, often not observable; when seen indistinct. Length, $20\text{-}50\mu$. Breadth, $6\text{-}12\mu$. Hustedt (1961) has recorded larger specimens.

Type locality. — Belgium, Blankenberghe; brackish water.

U. S. distribution. — GEOGRAPHICAL: Middle Atlantic States; South Carolina, Ohio, Texas, Wyoming. ECOLOGICAL: Water of high mineral content, or brackish water.

1. **Navicula halophila** f. **tenuirostris** Hust.   PL. 44, FIG. 5

>*Navicula halophila* f. *tenuirostris* Hust., Internat. Rev. Ges. Hydrobiol., 42(1):52, fig. 76. 1942.

Valve lanceolate with very narrow, attenuated, capitate ends. Axial area narrow, distinct. Central area not differentiated from the axial area. Transverse striae parallel throughout the valve. Striae, 20-22 in 10μ. Longitudinal striae not visible. Length, $42\text{-}50\mu$. Breadth, $9\text{-}10\mu$.

This species is differentiated from the nominate variety mainly by the shape of the ends of the valve.

Type locality.—Luzon: Sehr selten in einem Teich beim Bureau of Science.

U. S. distribution. — GEOGRAPHICAL: Ohio. ECOLOGICAL: In hard water.

2. **Navicula gregaria** Donk. var. **gregaria**   PL. 44, FIG. 6

>*Navicula gregaria* Donk., Quart. Jour. Micr. Sci., New Ser., 1:10-11, pl. 1, fig. 10. 1861.

Valve lanceolate with rostrate to capitate ends. Axial area narrow. Central area small, often only slightly wider than the axial area. Striae parallel or only very slightly radiate in the middle portion of the valve, sometimes slightly convergent at the ends. Transverse striae, 16-22 in 10μ. Length, 15-35μ. Breadth, 5-9μ.

The occurrence of the parallel striae is a clear characteristic of this species. I have been unable to detect any longitudinal striae. In his description, Donkin says only that striae are "obscure."

I have examined a specimen from the Donkin herbarium (B.M. 11927) which I have designated as a lectotype. The transverse striae on this specimen are very faint and the longitudinal striae are not apparent. Van Heuck's specimens on slide no. 94 belong to the same taxon.

Type locality. — Uncertain. Since more than one locality is cited, the following lectotype has been chosen from one of these: England, Northumberland. Chibburn mouth, intertidal zone. (*Lectotype*—B.M. 11927, Patrick.)

U. S. distribution. — GEOGRAPHICAL: New England States, Southeastern States, Gulf Coast States, Plains States. ECOLOGICAL: Prefers brackish water and fresh water with high mineral content.

3. Navicula accomoda Hust. var. accomoda   PL. 44, FIG. 7

Navicula accomoda Hust., Arch. Hydrobiol., 43:446, pl. 39, figs. 17-18. 1950.

Valve lanceolate to elliptical-lanceolate with narrow, rostrate ends. Axial area narrow, slightly widened at the central area. Central area not distinct. Median ends of the raphe distant from each other; terminal fissures indistinct. Striae almost parallel. Striae, 20-25 in 10μ at the center of the valve to 32 in 10μ at the ends. Length, 19-35μ. Breadth, 7-10μ.

This species is similar to *Navicula halophila* (Grun.) Cl. but differs from it in that the striae are more distant in the middle portion of the valve.

This species is distinguished by the median ends of the raphe being distant from each other and by the shape of the valve.

Hustedt (1961, p. 64) states that there are very fine longitudinal ribs, hardly visible by the light microscope. They are not visible on our specimen. In Hustedt's original description of the species they are not mentioned. Hustedt (1957, 1961) changed the spelling to "accommoda."

Type locality. — Charemsee [Germany.]

U. S. distribution. — GEOGRAPHICAL: Middle Atlantic States, Southeastern States, South Central States, East Central States, West Central States, Plains States; Texas. ECOLOGICAL: Grows well in the presence of organic pollution.

4. Navicula biconica Patr. var. biconica PL. 44, FIG. 8

Navicula biconica Patr., Proc. Acad. Nat. Sci. Philadelphia, 111:94, pl. 8, fig. 9. 1959.

Valve lanceolate with broadly rounded ends. Axial area distinct. Median ends of the raphe distant from each other. Central area indistinct, no wider than the axial area. Striae parallel; indistinctly punctate. Striae, 26-28 in 10μ at the center of the valve to 40 in 10μ at the ends. Length, 12-14μ. Breadth, 4-5μ.

This species is similar to *Navicula consentanea* Hust. (1939, p. 625, figs. 98-100) in shape and in the indistinct axial and central areas. It differs in that the striae are finer and the median ends of the raphe are farther apart.

It is difficult to place this species in any of the various subgenera of *Navicula*. In the indistinct axial and central areas it is similar to the *Fusiformes* which are marine and brackish-water species. It differs from them in that the median ends of the raphe are far apart. It is somewhat similar to the *Cuspidata* which include fresh-water species, but it lacks the longitudinal lines characteristic of this group. The fact that the median ends of the raphe are somewhat distant from each other suggests a relationship to the *Entoleia*. However, the striae are parallel—not radiate—and the characteristic lanceolate space formed by the axial and central areas is lacking.

Type locality. — U.S.A., South Carolina, Aiken County, Savannah River between Miles 174.8 and 175.1 from the mouth. (*Holotype*—A-G.C. 44492, Patrick, 1959.)

U. S. distribution.—GEOGRAPHICAL: Middle Atlantic States; Tennessee, Missouri. ECOLOGICAL: Soft, circumneutral water.

5. Navicula spicula (Hickie) Cl. var. spicula PL. 44, FIG. 9

Stauroneis spicula Hickie, Monthly Micr. Jour., 12:290. 1874.
Navicula spicula (Hickie) Cl., K. Svenska Vet.-Akad. Handl., Ny Följd, 26(2):110. 1894.

Valve narrow-lanceolate with acute, rounded ends. Axial area very narrow. Central area a narrow, transverse fascia reaching the margins of the valve. Puncta fine, forming indistinct longitudinal lines. Striae transverse, parallel; 25-30 in 10μ. Length, 50-130μ. Breadth, 4-13μ.

This species is most easily distinguished by the very narrow, transverse central area which is bounded by thickened striae.

This species is intermediate between the subgenus *Halophila* and the subgenus *Fusiformes*. Its general shape and the structure of the terminal

ends of the raphe would place it in the *Fusiformes*. The absence of longitudinal striae would place it in the subgenus *Halophila*.

Type locality. — None given. Van Heurck (1885, p. 68) gives Anvers,
Belgium. Van Heurck's specimens (A-V.H. 9) are typical for the species.

U. S. distribution. — GEOGRAPHICAL: Massachusetts, Virginia, Florida.
ECOLOGICAL: Marine to brackish water.

Navicula subgenus DECIPIENTES (Grun. *in* Cl.) Patr.

Navicula group *Decipientes* (Grun.) Cl., K. Svenska Vet.-Akad. Handl., Ny Földj, 26(2):
    138. 1894.
Navicula subgenus *Decipientes* (Grun. *in* Cl.) Patr., Not. Nat. Acad. Nat. Sci. Phila-
    delphia, No. 324, p. 4. 1959.

Striae at the center of the valve further apart than in the rest of the
valve. This gives a distinctive appearance to the median portion of the
valve. Striae radiate or parallel—not convergent.

The most distinguishing characteristics of this subgenus are the striae
which are much further apart in the middle portion of the valve than in
the rest of the valve. This produces a distinctive appearance of the median
portion of the valve. The striae may be radiate or parallel. They may be
distinctly or indistinctly punctate. The valves are lanceolate to linear with
the ends formed in various ways. The axial area is narrow and often indistinct. The clear area about the central nodule is often not differentiated
from the axial area. Sometimes it is transversely dilated.

Type species. — *Navicula crucicula* (W. Sm.) Donk.

KEY TO THE SPECIES OF THE SUBGENUS DECIPIENTES

1. Valve with diaphragms 2
1. Valve without diaphragms 3
    2. Valve with margins undulate toward the ends of the valve ......[6] *N. integra*
    2. Valve with margins that are not undulate as above ....[7] *N. sanctaecrucis*
3. Length of valve, over 100μ; valve lanceolate ....[1] *N. bergenensis*
3. Length of valve, less than 100μ, striae in middle of the valve not of irregular
    length 4
    4. Striae 10 or less in 10μ in center of valve ....[2] *N. crucicula*
    4. Striae 12 or more in 10μ at center of valve 5
5. An isolated punctum at the end of one striae opposite the central nodule
                                                              [5] *N. aikenensis*
5. Isolated punctum absent 6
    6. Ends of the valve rostrate truncate; length of the valve, 17-55μ ..[3] *N. protracta*
    6. Ends of the valve rounded; length of the valve, less than 20μ.....[4]*N. sabiniana*

1. **Navicula bergenensis** Hohn var. **bergenensis**   PL. 45, FIGS. 1a-b

Navicula bergeni Hohn, Trans. American Micr. Soc., 71:270, fig. 1. 1952.

Valve lanceolate; tapering to rounded, somewhat protracted ends. Axial area narrow. Terminal and central nodules distinct. Striae radiate throughout most of the valve except in the middle portion where they are almost parallel. Striae distinctly punctate, the puncta forming transverse and more or less distinct longitudinal lines. Transverse striae, 7-9 in 10μ at the center of the valve to 11-12 in 10μ at the ends. Puncta, 21-24 in 10μ. Length, about 200μ. Breadth, $30\text{-}33\mu$.

This species is characterized by its shape, large size, and coarse striation.

This species is named after the swamp in which it was found.

Type locality. — U.S.A., New York, Genesee County, Bergen Swamp.

U. S. distribution. — GEOGRAPHICAL: Known only from the type locality.

2. **Navicula crucicula** (W. Sm.) Donk. var. **crucicula**   PL. 45, FIG. 2

Stauroneis crucicula W. Sm., Syn. British Diat., vol. 1, p. 60, pl. 19, fig. 192. 1853.
Navicula crucicula (W. Sm.) Donk., Nat. Hist. British Diat., p. 44, pl. 6, fig. 14. 1870-1873.

Valve lanceolate to elliptical-lanceolate, narrowing to slightly protracted, obtuse ends. The breadth of the ends varies so that in some specimens they appear more protracted than in others. Axial area narrow. Central area very small. Striae slightly radiate throughout the valve; coarser and more distant from each other in the middle portion; finely punctate. Striae, 9-10 in 10μ at the center of the valve to 16-19 in 10μ at the ends. Length, $45\text{-}70\mu$; Hustedt (1962, p. 318) states to 92μ. Breadth, $14\text{-}19\mu$; Hustedt (*loc. cit.*) $10\text{-}23\mu$.

The ends of the specimen illustrated are more like those of the specimens illustrated by William Smith than like those illustrated in some of the more recent works. However, this specimen is not as broadly lanceolate as that of William Smith. The angle and number of striae in 10μ, and the shape of the valve distinguishes this species from other species in this group.

Type locality. — Ireland, Belfast Bay; marine.

U. S. distribution. — GEOGRAPHICAL: New England States, Middle Atlantic States, Southeastern States, Gulf Coast States, South Central States; Nebraska. ECOLOGICAL: Brackish to fresh water, euryhaline.

3. **Navicula protracta** Grun. var. **protracta**   PL. 45, FIG. 3

Navicula (*crucicula* var.?) *protracta* Grun. *in* Cl. & Grun., K. Svenska Vet.-Akad. Handl., Ny Följd, 17(2):35, pl. 2, fig. 38. 1880.
Navicula crucicula var. *protracta* (Grun. *in* Cl. & Grun.) V. H., Syn. Diat. Belgique, p. 96, suppl. pl. B, fig. 27. 1885.

Valve linear-lanceolate with rostrate, truncate ends. Axial area narrow. Central area small. Striae radiate throughout most of the valve, radiate or parallel at the ends. In the middle portion of the valve the striae are much more distant from each other than in other parts of the valve. Sometimes short marginal striae are found between the longer striae about the central area. Puncta composing striae fine but distinct. Striae, 12 in 10μ at the center of the valve to 24 in 10μ at the ends. Length, 17-55μ. Breadth, 5-10μ.

The usually smaller size, the finely but distinctly punctate striae, and the characteristics of the central area distinguish this species from *Navicula crucicula* (W. Sm.) Donk.

Type locality. — Arctic; inland brackish and marine water.

U. S. distribution. — GEOGRAPHICAL: New England States, Middle Atlantic States; South Carolina, Illinois, Michigan. ECOLOGICAL: Seems to prefer fresh water with high mineral content or slightly brackish water; often found in polluted water.

4. Navicula sabiniana Patr. var. sabiniana   PL. 45, FIG. 4

Navicula sabiniana Patr., Proc. Acad. Nat. Sci. Philadelphia, 111:91, pl. 7, fig. 15. 1959.

Valve lanceolate with broad, rounded ends. Axial area narrow. Median ends of the raphe slightly turned in the same direction. Central area rounded, not much wider than the axial area. Striae slightly radiate throughout the valve; more distant from each other around the central area. Striae, 16-17 in 10μ except at the center of the valve where they may be 12 in 10μ. Length, 11-16μ. Breadth, 4-6μ.

This species is characterized by its shape and the fact that the striae are farther apart at the center of the valve than at the ends. The central area is larger than that often found in the smaller species of this subgenus.

It is quite similar in shape to *Navicula perparva* Hust. (1937b, p. 246, pl. 20, figs. 16-18). However, the striae are much finer in *N. perparva* than in our taxon. Hustedt places his taxon in the *Minusculae,* thus indicating that the striae are not placed about the central area as in this subgenus. He states, however, that the striae are 20 in 10μ at the center of the valve, becoming finer toward the poles, about 30 in 10μ.

Type locality. – U.S.A., Texas, Orange County, Sabine River near mouth. (*Holotype*—A-G.C. 8030, Patrick, 1959.)

U. S. distribution. — GEOGRAPHICAL: Texas, Tennessee. ECOLOGICAL: Slightly brackish water.

5. **Navicula aikenenses** Patr. var. **aikenenses**   PL. 45, FIG. 5

> *Navicula aikenenses* Patr., Proc. Acad. Nat. Sci. Philadelphia, 111:92, pl. 7, fig. 6.
> 1959.

Valve lanceolate with somewhat rostrate, broadly rounded ends. Axial area narrow. Central area small, transverse. Striae radiate throughout the valve; indistinctly punctate; sometimes slightly curved near the ends of the valve. Striae at the central area farther apart than in the rest of the valve. The median striae on one or both sides of the central area shortened; an isolated punctum at the end of the median stria on one side of the valve. Striae, 17-19 in 10μ toward the ends of the valve. Length, 20-23μ. Breadth, 6-8μ.

This species is similar to *Navicula subdecussis* Hust. and *N. declivis* Hust. in size, the presence of an isolated punctum in the central area, the striae being farther apart in the center of the valve, the narrow axial area, and the small central area.

It differs from *N. subdecussis* Hust. in that the ends are broadly rostrate instead of strongly capitate. The striae of this taxon are slightly radiate in the middle portion of the valve and more strongly radiate at the ends. In *N. subdecussis* Hust. the striae are slightly radiate at the center of the valve and convergent at the ends.

It differs from *N. declivis* Hust. in that the striae are radiate—not parallel—at the ends of the valve. Also, the shape of the valve is more linear-lanceolate and is more broadly rostrate at the ends.

Type locality. — U.S.A., South Carolina, Aiken County, Savannah River at Mile 135 from the mouth of the river. (*Holotype*—A-G.C. 4737a, Patrick, 1959.)

U. S. distribution. — GEOGRAPHICAL: Known only from the type locality. ECOLOGICAL: Found in water of low mineral content.

6. **Navicula integra** (W. Sm.) Ralfs var. **integra**   PL. 45, FIG. 6

> *Pinnularia integra* W. Sm., Syn. British Diat., vol. 2, p. 96.   1856.
> *Navicula integra* (W. Sm.) Ralfs *in* Pritch., Hist. Infusoria, 4th ed., p. 895.   1861.

Valve lanceolate to elliptical-lanceolate with undulate margins; ends apiculate, rostrate. Diaphragm or pseudoseptum present at each end of the valve. Axial area narrow. Central area small. Striae slightly radiate throughout most of the valve, almost parallel at the ends. Striae distinctly separated from each other in the middle portion of the valve, much finer toward the ends. Striae, 12 in 10μ at the center of the valve to 23 in 10μ near the ends. Length, 25-45μ. Breadth, 8-10μ.

This species is distinguished by its undulate margins and apiculate, rostrate ends with diaphragms.

Gregory (1856a, p. 4, pl. 1, fig. 14) calls this taxon *Navicula rostrata* W. Sm. This name is invalid as it is a later homonym. William Smith (*loc. cit.*) states incorrectly that Gregory called this taxon *Pinnularia rostrata* and cites the above references. He states that in order to avoid confusion with *Navicula rostrata* (Ehr.) Kütz., he is giving this species the name of *Pinnularia integra.*

I have examined specimens of this taxon sent to W. Smith by Dr. Arnott, July 1854 (B. M. 23605) with which our specimens agree.

Type locality. — Scotland, Haddington, Lochleven. (*Lectotype*–B.M. 23605, Patrick.)

U. S. distribution. — Geographical: Middle Atlantic States; New York, Ohio, Michigan, Nebraska. Ecological: Seems to prefer waters with high mineral content; often found in polluted waters.

7. Navicula sanctaecrucis Østr. var. sanctaecrucis   PL. 45, FIG. 7

Navicula sanctae crucis Østr., Dansk Bot. Ark., 1(1):31, pl. 1, fig. 24. 1913.

Valve linear-elliptical with protracted, smoothly rounded, rostrate to subcapitate ends. Pseudoseptum or diaphragm present at each end of the valve, sometimes indistinct. Axial area narrow, widening somewhat toward the center. Raphe narrow; broadening toward the central area where the median ends are close together; terminal fissures turned in the same direction. Central area variable; small, orbicular, or lacking. Striae usually radiate throughout the valve, sometimes almost parallel at the ends; finely lineate. Central striae more distant from each other, sometimes slightly curved. Striae, 15-16 in 10μ at the center of the valve to 19-20 in 10μ at the ends. Length, $25\text{-}30\mu$. Breadth, $8.5\text{-}9.5\mu$.

The taxonomic and morphological problems concerning this species are discussed by Reimer (1959b, p. 87).

Type locality. — West Indies, St. Croix.

U. S. distribution. — Geographical: Gulf Coast States; Kentucky. Ecological: Slightly brackish water or fresh water with very high mineral content.

Navicula subgenus ENTOLEIA (Cl.) Patr.

Navicula group *Entoleiae* Cl., K. Svenska Vet.-Akad. Handl., Ny Följd, 26(2):131. 1894.

Navicula subgenus *Entoleia* (Cl.) Patr., Not. Nat. Acad. Nat. Sci. Philadelphia, No. 324, p. 5. 1959.

Axial and central areas forming a lanceolate clear space. Ends of the raphe at the central nodule often somewhat distant. Striae radiate at the ends of the valve.

This subgenus is most easily distinguished by the more or less broad, lanceolate space formed by the axial and central areas. The ends of the raphe at the central nodule are often somewhat distant from each other. The striae are fine, more or less distinctly punctate, and radiate at the ends. Some of the species of this subgenus grow in filaments. The frustules are usually small, as in the *Minusculae*.

Type species. — Navicula entoleia Cl.

KEY TO THE SPECIES OF THE SUBGENUS ENTOLEIA

1. Length of the valve, greater than 40μ . . . . [1] *N. monmouthiana-stodderi*
1. Length of the valve, less than 40μ 2
   2. Valve not concave in the middle portion of the valve 3
   2. Valve concave in the middle portion of the valve 11
3. Axial area narrow, linear-lanceolate or lanceolate, dilated into a large lanceolate the central nodule 4
3. Axial area narrow, linear-lanceolate or lanceolate, dilated into a large lanceolate or rounded area in the middle portion of the valve 6
   4. Striae, less than 20 in 10μ; parallel or slightly convergent at the apices
                                                                [4] *N. convergens*
   4. Striae, more than 20 in 10μ; radiate throughout the valve 5
5. Frustules forming filaments; striae, less than 25 in 10μ . . . [2]*N. confervacea* and vars.
5. Frustules usually not forming filaments; striae, more than 25 in 10μ . . [3] *N. keeleyi*
   6. Central area granular . . . . [10] *N. duomedia*
   6. Central area not granular 7
7. Striae, more than 20 in 10μ 8
7. Striae, less than 20 in 10μ 9
   8. Valve suddenly swollen in the middle, frustule often forming filaments
                                                                [6] *N. perpusilla*
   8. Valve linear lanceolate, frustules not forming filaments . . . . [7] *N. poconoensis*
9. Valve suddenly swollen in the middle portion of the valve . . . . [8] *N. gibbosa*
9. Valve not suddenly swollen in the middle portion 10
   10. Valve linear-elliptical with rounded ends . . . . [5] *N. elmorei*
   10. Valve linear-lanceolate with rostrate, somewhat capitate ends . . . [9] *N. hassiaca*
11. Valve with rostrate ends; striae, less than 30 in 10μ . . . . [12] *N. concava*
11. Valve with rounded ends; striae, more than 30 in 10μ . . . [11] *N. contenta* var. *biceps*

1. **Navicula monmouthiana-stodderi** Yerm. var. **monmouthiana-stodderi**
PL. 45, FIG. 8

Navicula monmouthiana-stodderi Yerm., Jour. Quekett Micr. Club, Ser. 2, 13:418, 422, pl. 27, figs. 3-4. 1918.

Valve fusiform, sometimes slightly asymmetrical; ends sometimes slightly subrostrate. Axial area broad; widening toward the center of the valve to form, together with the central area, a lanceolate space. Central nodule distinct. Median ends of the raphe turned in the same direction;

terminal fissures "comma" shaped. Striae radiate throughout the valve except at the central nodule where they are almost parallel; finely punctate. Striae, 16 in 10μ at the center of the valve to 21 in 10μ at the ends. Length, 48-70μ. Breadth, 7.5-10μ.

This species is characterized by its fusiform, slightly asymmetrical shape, and the broad, linear-lanceolate axial and central areas.

Type locality. — U.S.A., New York, Mohawk River (a small mountain stream in the Adirondack Mountains near Herkimer).

U. S. distribution. — GEOGRAPHICAL: New England States.

2. **Navicula confervacea** (Kütz.) Grun. var. **confervacea**   PL. 45, FIG. 9.

> *Diadesmis confervacea* Kütz., Bacill., p. 109, pl. 30, fig. 8.   1844.
> *Navicula confervacea* (Kütz.) Grun. *in* V. H., Syn. Diat. Belgique, pl. 14, fig. 36. 1880.

Valve lanceolate; ends usually rostrate but sometimes obtuse. Axial area near ends of the valve narrow; widening into a broad, lanceloate area which extends over most of the valve. Median ends of the raphe somewhat distant from each other. Central area not distinguished from the axial area. Striae radiate throughout the valve; indistinctly punctate. Striae, 20-24 in 10μ. Length, 13-25μ. Breadth, 4-7μ.

This species is distinguished by its filamentous growth and the broad, clear, lanceolate area which covers most of the valve.

Type locality. — Unter Conferven aus dem "River Maraval" der Insel Trinidad: Krüger.

U. S. distribution. — GEOGRAPHICAL: Middle Atlantic States, Southeastern States, Gulf Coast States, South Central States, East Central States, West Central States, Lakes States; Arizona, California. ECOLOGICAL: Often an aerophil or in very shallow water; seems to prefer soft, warm water.

2. **Navicula confervacea** var. **peregrina** (W. Sm.) Grun.   PL. 45, FIG. 10

> *Diadesmis peregrina* W. Sm., Ann. Mag. Nat. Hist., Ser. 2, 19:12.   1857.
> *Navicula confervacea* var. *peregrina* (W. Sm.) Grun. *in* V. H., Syn. Diat. Belgique, pl. 14, fig. 37.   1880.
> *Navicula confervacea* var. *hungarica* Grun. *in* V. H., Syn. Diat. Belgique, pl. 14, fig. 38.   1880.

Valve broadly lanceolate to elliptical with rounded or slightly rostrate ends. Axial area narrow at the ends, expanding toward the center of the valve into a broad lanceolate central area. Median ends of the raphe somewhat distant from each other. Striae radiate; finely punctate. Striae, 20-24 in 10μ. Length, 12-20μ. Breadth, 5-8μ.

This taxon differs from the nominate variety by its more elliptical shape and the absence of distinctly rostrate ends. This variety may be found to intergrade with the nominate variety when more populations are studied. As in the nominate variety, this taxon typically forms filaments.

Type locality. — England, Kew Gardens; from water tanks.

U. S. distribution. — GEOGRAPHICAL: Virginia, Florida, Indiana, Kansas, Arizona. ECOLOGICAL: Found in same type of habitat as the nominate variety.

3. Navicula keeleyi Patr. var. keeleyi   PL. 45, FIG. 11

Navicula keeleyi Patr., Farlowia, 2(2):183, pl. 2, fig. 7.   1945.

Valve lanceolate with rostrate to capitate ends. Axial and central areas merging to form a lanceolate space. Striae slightly radiate. Frustules forming filaments. Striae, 29-32 in 10μ. Length, $19-30\mu$. Breadth, $4-5\mu$.

This species is distinguished from other filament-forming species of this subgenus by the shape of the valve and, particularly, the rostrate to capitate ends.

Type locality. — U.S.A., Pennsylvania, Pike County, Shohola Falls. (*Holotype*—A-G.C. 2197, Patrick, 1945.)

U. S. distribution. — GEOGRAPHICAL: Pennsylvania. ECOLOGICAL: An aerophil, living on wet moss.

4. Navicula convergens Patr. var. convergens   PL. 45, FIG. 12

Navicula convergens Patr., Proc. Acad. Nat. Sci. Philadelphia, 111:93, pl. 7, fig. 14. 1959.

Valve swollen in the middle portion; ends rounded. Axial area broad, uniting with the central area to form a lanceolate space. Striae radiate at the center of the valve, parallel or slightly convergent at the ends; finely punctate. Striae, 16 in 10μ at the center of the valve to 24 in 10μ at the ends. Length, $11-13\mu$. Breadth, $3-4\mu$.

This species is similar to *Navicula disparata* Hust. (1942d, p. 61, fig. 109), but differs from it in that it has fewer striae in 10μ at the center of the valve and the striae near the ends of the valve are parallel or convergent. Also, the shape of the valve is more linear in this species than in *N. disparata.* The frustules of *N. convergens* do not form filaments, a type of growth typical of some of the related species.

Type locality. — U.S.A., South Carolina, Aiken County, Savannah River between Miles 174.8 and 175.1 from the mouth. (*Holotype*—A-G.C. 3954a, Patrick, 1959.)

U. S. distribution. — GEOGRAPHICAL: Known only from the type locality. ECOLOGICAL: Soft, circumneutral water.

5. **Navicula elmorei** Patr. sp. nov.   PL. 45, FIG. 13

Valva lineari-ellipticali apicibus rotundis. Area axiali et area media facientibus spatium lanceolatum quod est aliquantulum rotundum et latius circum nodulcm mediam. Striis puntatis subtiliter, parallelis in media parte valvae, radiatis leniter ad apices valvae. Striis, 15-18 in 10μ. Longitudo, 30-33μ. Latitudo, 9-11μ.

Valve linear-elliptical with rounded ends. Axial and central areas forming a lanceolate space which is somewhat rounded and broader around the central nodule. Striae finely punctate; parallel in the middle portion of the valve, slightly radiate at the ends. Striae, 15-18 in 10μ. Length, 30-33μ. Breadth, 9-11μ.

Elmore misidentified this diatom as *Navicula scutum* Schum. (1863, p. 188, pl. 9, fig. 45) which has a very narrow axial area and an indistinct central area. This species is closely related to *N. confervacea* var. *peregrina* (W. Sm.) Cl. (1894, p. 133). It differs in that the striae are coarser, the frustules do not form filaments, and the lanceolate area formed by the axial and central areas is not quite as broad.

Type locality. — U.S.A., Nebraska, pool one mile west of Fremont. (*Holotype*—N.Y.B.G.-Elm. 704, Patrick.)

U. S. distribution. — GEOGRAPHICAL: Nebraska.

6. **Navicula perpusilla** (Kütz.) Grun. var. **perpusilla**   PL. 45, FIG. 14

Synedra perpusilla Kütz., Bacill., p. 63, pl. 3, fig. 31.   1844.
Navicula perpusilla (Kütz.) Grun., Verh. Zool.-Bot. Ges. Wien, 10:552, pl. 4, figs. 7 a-g.   1860.
Navicula flotowii Grun. *in* V. H., Syn. Diat. Belgique, pl. 14, fig. 41.   1880.   (text, p. 109.   1885.)
Navicula perpusilla var. *flotowii* (Grun.) Peters., *in* Bot. Iceland, vol. 2, pt. 2, p. 396. 1928.

Valve linear, swollen in the middle portion; ends broad, rounded. Axial area variable in width, usually one-third to one-fourth the breadth of the valve; becoming wider toward the center of the valve, where it unites with the central area to form a broad elliptical space. Raphe straight; median ends of the raphe small, somewhat distant; terminal fissures indistinct. Striae radiate; very finely punctate. Striae, 30-36 in 10μ. Length, 6-20μ. Breadth, 2.5-3μ.

This species is characterized by the shape of the central and axial areas. The axial area is somewhat variable in breadth as seen by the figures. Some authors have recognized a variety of *flotowii*. However, since all characteristics of the valve seem to intergrade, they do not appear to be separate taxa. It is true that those specimens formerly called variety *flotowii* usually occur in filaments. Specimens of Van Heurck on slide no. 148 (*N. flotoviana* Grun.) are the same taxon as the illustrated specimen.

Type locality. — [Italy], In Salzsümpfen des botanischen Gartens zu Venedig.

U. S. distribution. — GEOGRAPHICAL: Middle Atlantic States, Southeastern States. ECOLOGICAL: Aerophil (often associated with moss), oligohalob (indifferent), pH-indifferent, saproxen.

7. Navicula poconoensis Patr. var. poconoensis PL. 45, FIG. 15

Navicula poconoensis Patr., Farlowia, 2(2):183, pl. 2, fig. 5. 1945.

Valve linear-lanceolate with broad, rostrate ends; margins sometimes slightly concave about the central area. Axial area narrow at the ends and widening toward the center of the valve. Median ends of the raphe somewhat distant; terminal fissures not distinct. Central area orbicular. Striae parallel at the ends of the valve, slightly radiate at the center. Striae, 30-32 in 10μ. Length, $26\text{-}27\mu$. Breadth, $4\text{-}5\mu$.

This species is most closely related to *Navicula perpusilla* (Kütz.) Grun., but differs in its usually greater length-to-breadth ratio, the shape of the ends, and the fact that it does not seem to form filaments.

Type locality. — U.S.A., Pennsylvania, Pike County, Greeley. (*Holotype* —A-G.C. 2188, Patrick, 1945.)

U. S. distribution. — GEOGRAPHICAL: Pennsylvania. ECOLOGICAL: In a swamp.

8. Navicula gibbosa Hust. var. gibbosa PL. 45, FIG. 16

Navicula gibbosa Hust., Arch. Hydrobiol. Suppl., 15(2):253, pl. 18, fig. 10. 1937.

Valve linear, strongly swollen in the middle; ends rounded—not protracted. Axial area narrow, slightly widened toward the center of the valve. Median ends of the raphe distant; terminal fissures indistinct. Central area large, rounded. Striae slightly radiate, usually parallel at the ends. Striae, 15-16 in 10μ. Length, $19\text{-}21\mu$. Breadth, $4\text{-}5\mu$ at the center of the valve, $2\text{-}3\mu$ at the ends.

This species is distinguished by the shape of the valve and of the central area.

Type locality. — Nordsumatra: Selten in zwei Proben aus der breitesten Stelle der Inundationszone des Tobasees.

U. S. distribution. — GEOGRAPHICAL: Southeastern States; New Jersey. ECOLOGICAL: Fresh water, low mineral content, aerophil.

9. **Navicula hassiaca** Krasske var. **hassiaca**   PL. 45, FIG. 17

> *Navicula hassiaca* Krasske, Abh. Ber. Ver. Naturk. Cassel, 56:47, pl. 2, fig. 26.
> 1925.

Valve linear-lanceolate with rostrate, somewhat capitate ends. Axial area narrow at the ends, widening toward the central area. Median ends of the raphe somewhat distant. Central area broad, rounded. Striae slightly radiate at the center of the valve, parallel at the ends. Striae, 16-18 in 10μ. Length, $12\text{-}15\mu$. Breadth, $3\text{-}4\mu$.

Krasske states that this species belongs in the *Minusculae*. However, he also describes and illustrates this species as having a broad area composed of the axial and central areas. This characteristic would place this species in the *Entoleiae* rather than in the *Minusculae*.

Type locality. — Germany, lower Hesse at Vockerode.

U. S. distribution. — GEOGRAPHICAL: South Carolina. ECOLOGICAL: Among *Sphagnum;* prefers slightly acid water; aerophilous.

10. **Navicula duomedia** Patr. var. **duomedia**   PL. 45, FIG. 18

> *Navicula duomedia* Patr., Proc. Acad. Nat. Sci. Philadelphia, 111:92, pl. 7, fig. 13.
> 1959.

Valve linear, swollen in the middle portion; ends rounded. Axial area narrow; widening into, but clearly differentiated from, the central area. Central area forming a large lanceolate space that is granular in appearance. Striae radiate throughout the valve. Striae, 22-24 in 10μ at the center of the valve to 28 in 10μ at the ends. Length, $16\text{-}22\mu$. Breadth, $4.5\text{-}5\mu$.

This species is quite similar in shape to *Navicula flotowii* Grun., but differs in that the striae are coarser and the lanceolate central area has a granular appearance.

Type locality. — U.S.A., South Carolina, Aiken County, slough of Savannah River at Mile 135 from the mouth, near Allendale Bridge. (*Holotype*—A-G.C. 4426a, Patrick, 1959.)

U. S. distribution. — GEOGRAPHICAL: Known only from the type locality. ECOLOGICAL: Water of low salt content, mesotrophic to eutrophic.

11. **Navicula contenta** var. **biceps** (Arn.) V.H.   PL. 45, FIG. 19

> *Navicula trinodis* var. *biceps* Grun. *in* V. H., Syn. Diat. Belgique, pl. 14, fig. 31B.
> 1880.
> *Navicula contenta* var. *biceps* (Arn.) V.H., Syn. Diat. Belgique, p. 109.   1885.

Valve linear, concave in the middle portion; ends broadly rounded. Axial area narrow. Median ends of the raphe somewhat distant. Central area rounded; fairly small or reaching almost to the margins of the valve. Striae usually parallel throughout the valve, sometimes very slightly radiate around the central area. Frustules usually in filaments. Striae, 32-36 in 10μ. Length, 7-15μ. Breadth, 2-3μ.

Van Heurck (1880, pl. 14, fig. 31B, legend) says his taxon is the same as *Diadesmis biceps* Arn. We have not been able to find Arnott's description in a publication. *Diadesmis biceps* (B.M. 3615) is the same taxon as our specimens. Ross (personal communication) states that it is probably from the same collection as the original specimen of Arnott.

Type locality. — Belgium, Groenendael.

U. S. distribution. — GEOGRAPHICAL: New England States, Middle Atlantic States, Southeastern States, South Central States, East Central States, West Central States; Texas. ECOLOGICAL: Often associated with moss; oligohalobe (indifferent), alkaliphil, aerophil; acid to circumneutral water.

12. Navicula pennsylvanica Patr. nom. nov., var. pennsylvanica

PL. 45, FIG. 20

Navicula concava Patr., Farlowia, 2(2):182, pl. 2, fig. 6. 1945. [*non* Harting, Verh. K. Nederl. Inst. Wet., 1 Kl., Ser. 3, 5:118, pl. 3, fig. 15. 1852.]

Valve linear, concave in the middle portion; ends rostrate. Axial area broad, widening toward the center of the valve. Median ends of the raphe fairly distant from each other. Central area large, rounded. Striae radiate at the center of the valve, parallel or only slightly radiate at the ends. Frustules not in filaments. Striae, 26-29 in 10μ. Length, 20-23μ. Breadth at the central nodule, 4-5μ.

The distinguishing characteristics of this species are the concave margins, the shape of the central area, and the striae number.

Type locality. — U.S.A., Pennsylvania, Pike County, Greeley. (*Holotype* —A.G.C. 2188, Patrick, 1945.)

U. S. distribution. — GEOGRAPHICAL: Pennsylvania. ECOLOGICAL: With *Sphagnum* in swamps.

Navicula subgenus MINUSCULA (Cl.) Patr.

Navicula group *Minusculae* Cl., K. Svenska Vet.-Akad. Handl., Ny Földj, 27(3):3. 1895.
Navicula subgenus *Minuscula* (Cl.) Patr., Not. Nat. Acad. Nat. Sci. Philadelphia, No. 324, p. 8. 1959.

Frustules small. The connecting zone is not complex.

The valves are linear to elliptical in shape. The axial area is narrow and often indistinct. The central area may be very small, may be large and quadrate, or may form a transverse fascia. The striae are fine and indistinctly punctate, and are more or less radiate.

The species of this subgenus are, on the one hand, somewhat similar to the *Decipientes* and on the other to the *Navicula*. This subgenus unites the groups *Minusculae* and *Mesolieae* of Cleve. Hustedt (1957) united under the group *Minusculae*, the *Mesolieae*, the *Entolieae*, and the *Minusculae*. I agree that the *Minusculae* and *Mesolieae* should be united, but think the *Entolieae* should be kept separate.

Type species. — *Navicula minuscula* Grun.

KEY TO THE SPECIES OF THE SUBGENUS MINUSCULA

1. Segments of striae near the margin of the valve of distinctly different appearance than those near the center of valve 2
1. Striae not so formed 3
    2. Middle portion of the valve at distinctly different focal plane than the margins of the valve .... [6] *N. festiva*
    2. Striae thickened near the axial area .... [7] *N. latelongitudinalis*
3. Axial and central areas thicker than the rest of the valve, often appearing as a thickened rib; central area very small; striae even in the middle part of the valve, more than 35 in 10μ 4
3. Axial area not distinctly thicker than the rest of the valve 8
    4. Valve linear-elliptical with broadly rounded ends .... [4] *N. pelliculosa*
    4. Valve narrowed toward the ends, usually rostrate or somewhat capitate ... 5
5. Valve very narrow; linear .... [3] *N. subtilissima*
5. Valve lanceolate 6
    6. Ends of the valve only slightly rostrate .... [5] *N. paucivisitata*
    6. Ends of the valve distinctly rostrate or flattened-capitate 7
7. Central area rounded .... [1] *N. arvensis*
7. Central area indistinct .... [2] *N. gysingensis*
    8. Valves elliptical to linear-elliptical or linear with broadly rounded ends ... 9
    8. Valve lanceolate or swollen in the middle portion of the valve 18
9. Central area transversely widened or orbicular in shape 10
9. Central area indistinct 14
    10. Ends of the raphe turned in opposite directions 11
    10. Ends of the raphe not turned in opposite directions 12
11. Central area transversely widened, apices rounded .... [18] *N. vanheurckii*
11. Central area rounded, apices rostrate .... [11] *N. lateropunctata*
    12. Central area orbicular in shape .... [19] *N. orbiculata*
    12. Central area transverse, variable in size 13
13. Striae 18-22 in 10μ .... [16] *N. seminulum* var. *hustedtii*
13. Striae 26 or more in 10μ .... [15] *N. minima*
    14. Striae irregularly shortened at the central nodule .... [8] *N. jaernefeltii*
    14. Striae not irregularly shortened at the central nodule 15
15. Striae strongly radiate .... [14] *N. atomus*
15. Striae slightly radiate 16
    16. Striae more than 30 in 10μ 17
    16. Striae less than 25 in 10μ .... [20] *N. luzonensis*
17. Valve elliptical .... [13] *N. muralis*
17. Valve elliptical-lanceolate with somewhat rostrate ends .... [12] *N. minuscula*
    18. Ends of valve rounded 19
    18. Ends of the valve rostrate to rostrate-capitate 20
19. Striae, more than 30 in 10μ .... [17] *N. secura*
19. Striae, 18-20 in 10μ .... [16] *N. seminulum*

20. Axial area widening toward the transverse, somewhat rhomboidal central
area ....[10] *N. ventralis* var. *chilensis*
20. Axial area linear, central area small ....[9] *N. simula*

1. **Navicula arvensis** Hust. var. **arvensis**   PL. 46, FIGS. 1-2

Navicula arvensis Hust., Arch. Hydrobiol. Suppl., 15(2):249, pl. 20, figs. 19-20. 1937.

Frustules lightly silicified, often making the outline of the valve difficult to see. Shape of the valve variable: larger specimens linear with stumpy, capitate ends; smaller ones linear-elliptical or broadly lanceolate with somewhat rostrate ends. Axial area narrow. Raphe straight, filiform; apparently more heavily silicified than the rest of the frustule. Median ends of the raphe close, sometimes slightly turned in the same direction; terminal fissures indistinct. Central area small. Striae unresolved. Length, 5-13μ. Breadth, 2-5μ.

Although this taxon typically has rostrate ends, we have found specimens in which the rostrate ends almost disappear (Reimer, 1959b, p. 83, pl. 6, fig. 3).

This species resembles *Navicula pseudoarvensis* Hust. (1942a, p. 195, figs. 8-10). It differs from it in that the axial area is straight—not curved as in *N. pseudoarvensis*—and the ends are relatively narrower as well as less distinctly rostrate.

Type locality. — Mittelsumatra, haufig (!) in einer Sawah bei Singkarak.

U. S. distribution. — GEOGRAPHICAL: Middle Atlantic States, Southeastern States, Gulf Coast States, South Central States, East Central States. ECOLOGICAL: Seems to prefer warm water.

2. **Navicula gysingensis** Foged var. **gysingensis**   PL. 46, FIG. 3

Navicula gysingensis Foged, Bot. Not., for 1952:167, fig. 2(7). 1952.

Valve elliptical-lanceolate with protracted, somewhat flattened-capitate ends. Axial area narrow, linear. Raphe straight, filiform. Central area indistinct or lacking. Striae unresolved. Length, 12-17μ. Breadth, 4-5μ.

This diatom is thinly silicified and thus easy to overlook in a collection.

Type locality. — Sweden, the Dalalv at Gysinge, N. W. of Uppsala.

U. S. distribution. — GEOGRAPHICAL: Southeastern States. ECOLOGICAL: In acid soft water.

3. **Navicula subtilissima** Cl. var. **subtillissima**   PL. 46, FIG. 4

Navicula subtilissima Cl., Acta Soc. Fauna Fl. Fennica, 8(2):37, pl. 2, fig. 15. 1891.

Valve linear with capitate apices. Axial area narrow, distinct, appears to be more heavily silicified than the rest of the valve. Central area small, rounded. Striae very fine and hardly visible with the light microscope; a little coarser around the central area where they are of irregular length. The electron microscope shows the striae slightly radiate; about the central area they seem to be more strongly radiate, near the apices they are convergent. Striae, approximately 40-45 in 10µ as seen in the electron microscope. Length, 19-32µ. Breadth, 3.5-5µ.

This species is distinguished by the shape of the valve and the very fine striae.

Type locality. — From a dry rivulet at the shore of Imandia at the foot of Chibinä, collected 1885 by V. F. Brotherus.

U. S. distribution. — Geographical: New England States, Middle Atlantic States, Southeastern States, Gulf Coast States, South Central States.

4. **Navicula pelliculosa** (Bréb. *ex* Kütz.) Hilse var. **pelliculosa**

PL. 46, FIG. 5

Synedra minutissima var. *pelliculosa* Bréb. *ex* Kütz., Sp. Alg., p. 40. 1849.
Navicula pelliculosa (Bréb. *ex* Kütz.) Hilse, Schlesische Ges. Vaterl. Kult (Breslau), Abh. 2, Heft 2, p. 68. 1863.

Valve linear-elliptical with rounded ends. Axial area linear, slightly constricted at the central nodule; strongly silicified. Striae usually too fine to be resolved by the light microscope. Length, 6-11µ. Breadth, 4-5µ.

This diatom is most easily recognized by the lightly silicified valve with its strongly silicified, linear axial area.

Kützing (*loc. cit*) states that *Synedra minutissima β pelliculosa* is the same as *Frustulia pelliculosa* Bréb. *in litt.* This is the earliest published reference we have found attributing this taxon to Brébisson.

Type locality. — France.

U. S. distribution. — Geographical: Middle Atlantic States, Southeastern States, Gulf Coast States, South Central States, East Central States, Plains States; Oregon, California. Ecological: Widely distributed in fresh water; seems to prefer water of high mineral content.

5. **Navicula paucivisitata** Patr. var. **paucivisitata**   PL. 46, FIG. 6

Navicula paucivisitata Patr., Proc. Acad. Nat. Sci. Philadelphia, 111:99, pl. 8, fig. 10. 1959.

Valve lanceolate with somewhat rostrate, rounded ends. Axial area narrow. Central area small, rounded. Striae parallel; more than 35 in 10µ at the center of the valve, too fine to count at the ends. Length, 11-12µ. Breadth, 3-4µ.

This taxon is closely related to *Navicula indifferens* Hust. (1942c, p. 67, figs. 27-30) from which it differs in being larger and more linear-lanceolate in shape. The median ends of the raphe are also closer together than in *N. indifferens.*

Hustedt (1962, p. 254) has synonymized this species with *N. minuscula* Grun. This is not correct because the structure of the central nodule is completely different, and the striae at the center of the valve are always more than 35 in 10μ. Hustedt has not seen the type of this species.

Type locality. — U.S.A., South Carolina, Aiken County, at Mile 149.5 from the mouth of the Savannah River, near Allendale Bridge. (*Holotype*— A-G.C. 44274, Patrick, 1959.)

U. S. distribution. — GEOGRAPHICAL: Known only from the type locality.

6. Navicula festiva Krasske var. festiva PL. 46, FIG. 7

Navicula festiva Krasske, Abh. Ber. Ver. Naturk. Cassel, 56:47, pl. 1, fig. 16. 1925. *Navicula vitrea* (Østr.) Hust. *in* Pasch., Süssw.-Fl. Mitteleuropas, Heft 10, Aufl. 2, p. 289, fig. 489. 1930. (non *N. vitrea* (Cl.) Cl., 1894.)

Valve linear-lanceolate to linear-elliptical with attenuated, rostrate ends. Central portion of the valve in a different focal plane than the margins, producing the appearance of a longitudinal line crossing the striae near each margin. Axial area narrow, distinct; slightly widened at the center of the valve. Striae radiate; 24 in 10μ at the center of the valve to 36 in 10μ at the ends. Length, 20-25μ. Breadth, 5-7μ.

This species is distinguished by the apparent line across the striae near the margins of the valve which is caused by the contour of the valve surface.

Type locality. — [Germany], Zwischen Moosen bei Küchen und Schnellrode.

U. S. distribution. — GEOGRAPHICAL: Middle Atlantic States; Connecticut, South Carolina. ECOLOGICAL: Fresh water, usually of low mineral content.

7. Navicula latelongitudinalis Patr. var. latelongitudinalis

PL. 46, FIG. 8

Navicula latelongitudinalis Patr., Proc. Acad. Nat. Sci. Philadelphia, 111:98, pl. 8, fig. 14. 1959.

Valve linear with rounded ends. Axial area narrow. Central area not differentiated from the axial area. Striae parallel; very fine and difficult to resolve; thickened near the axial area, producing an apparent band on each side of the axial area. Striae, 29-33 in 10μ. Length, 24-31μ. Breadth, 5-6μ.

This is a very distinctive small species. It is easily characterized by the broad band on the striae near the axial area. *Navicula obsita* Hust. (1945,

p. 921, pl. 41, fig. 2) has a similar band. However, it is smaller and more coarsely striated than our taxon.

Type locality. — U.S.A., South Carolina, Aiken County, in a slough of the Savannah River at Mile 134 from the mouth near Allendale Bridge. (*Holotype*—A·G.C. 44258a, Patrick, 1959.)

U. S. distribution. — Geographical: Known only from the type locality. Ecological: Circumneutral water with low mineral content.

8. **Navicula jaernefeltii** Hust. var. **jaernefeltii**   PL. 46, FIG. 9

> *Navicula jaernefeltii* Hust., Arch. Hydrobiol., 39:111. 1942. (A. S., Atlas Diat., pl. 404, figs. 6-13. 1936.)

Valve broadly elliptical with rounded ends. Axial area narrow, linear. Raphe straight; median ends of raphe distant from each other. Central area not, or only slightly, wider than the axial area. Striae radiate; finely punctate; irregularly shortened around the central area. Striae, 25-30 in 10μ at the center of the valve to 32-34 in 10μ at the ends. Length, 8-20μ. Breadth, 6-11μ.

This species is distinguished by the lack of a central area and the finely punctate striae which are of irregular length about the central area.

Type locality. — Finland, Abiskojokk.

U. S. distribution. — Geographical: South Carolina, Ohio.

9. **Navicula simula** Patr. var. **simula**   PL. 46, FIG. 10

> *Navicula simula* Patr., Proc. Acad. Nat. Sci. Philadelphia, 111:101, pl. 8, fig. 8. 1959.

Valve lanceolate with rostrate ends. Axial area narrow, distinct; slightly widened toward the small central area. Striae radiate throughout the valve; coarser at the center than in the rest of the valve. Striae, 28-32 in 10μ at the center of the valve to 37-40 in 10μ at the ends. Length, 10-18μ. Breadth, 3-4μ.

This species is distinguished by the shape of the valve and the shape of the axial and central areas.

Type locality. — U.S.A., South Carolina, Aiken County, Savannah River between Mile 174.8-175.1 from the mouth. (*Holotype*—A·G.C. 44259a, Patrick, 1959.)

U. S. distribution. — Geographical: Known only from the type locality. Ecological: Water of low mineral content.

10. **Navicula ventralis** var. **chilensis** Krasske   PL. 46, FIG. 11

> *Navicula ventralis* var. *chilensis* Krasske, Arch. Hydrobiol., 35:383, pl. 11, fig. 45. 1939.

Valve linear-lanceolate with broad, rostrate to capitate ends. Axial area distinct, becoming wider toward the central area. Central area transverse, somewhat rhomboidal, not reaching the margins of the valve. Striae radiate at the center of the valve, parallel at the ends; very finely punctate. Striae, 20 in 10μ at the center of the valve to 25 in 10μ at the ends. Length, 18-20μ. Breadth, 5-6μ.

This taxon differs from the nominate variety by its slightly coarser striae, broader axial area, and shape of the central area.

Type locality. — Wenige Stücke im Abfluss des Ententeichs bei La Vega [South America] Chile.

U. S. distribution. — GEOGRAPHICAL: Pennsylvania, South Carolina, Florida. ECOLOGICAL: Fresh water of low mineral content.

11. **Navicula lateropunctata** Wallace var. **lateropunctata**

PL. 46, FIGS. 12-13

Navicula lateropunctata Wallace, Not. Nat. Acad. Nat. Sci. Philadelphia, No. 331, p. 4, pl. 2, figs. 3A-B. 1960.

Valve elliptical to lanceolate with rostrate apices. Axial area narrow, distinct. Terminal fissures of the raphe turned in opposite directions. Central area rounded, with an isolated punctum on one side. Striae radiate near the apices of the valve; almost parallel in the middle portion of the valve. Striae a little coarser about the central area. Striae, 19-24 in 10μ. Length, 17-22μ. Breadth, about 8μ.

This species is distinguished by the isolated punctum at the central area and the angle and number of the striae. It is related to *Navicula bremeyeri* f. *rostrata* Hust. from which it mainly differs by the number and angle of the striae.

Type locality. — U.S.A., South Carolina, Aiken County, Upper Three Runs. Coll. J. H. Wallace, May, 1952. (*Type*—A-G.C. 4072a, Wallace, 1952.)

U. S. distribution. — GEOGRAPHICAL: Southeastern States, Gulf Coast States.

12. **Navicula minuscula** Grun. var. **minuscula**

PL. 46, FIG. 14

Navicula minuscula Grun. *in* V. H., Syn. Diat. Belgique, pl. 14, fig. 3. 1880.

Valve elliptical-lanceolate, narrowed toward somewhat rostrate ends. Axial area narrow, distinct. Central area not differentiated from the axial area. Striae radiate except near the center of the valve where they may be parallel. Striae, 30-34 in 10μ. Length, 10-15μ. Breadth, 3-5μ.

Type locality. — Belgium, ditch at Kiel, near Antwerp (Van Heurck, *A Treatise on the Diatomaceae*, p. 228, 1896).

U. S. distribution. — Geographical: Middle Atlantic States; South Carolina, Tennessee, Ohio, Iowa, Michigan, Utah, California. Ecological: Widely distributed in fresh water.

13. **Navicula muralis** Grun. var. **muralis**   PL. 46, FIG. 15

Navicula muralis Grun. *in* V. H., Syn. Diat. Belgique, pl. 14, fig. 27. 1880.

Valve elliptical with rounded ends. Axial area narrow, distinct; slightly wider at the center of the valve than at the ends. Central area not differentiated from the axial area. Striae slightly radiate, 30-36 in 10μ. Length, 5-12μ. Breadth, 4-5μ.

This species differs from *Navicula atomus* Grun. in the somewhat coarser, less radiate striae.

Type locality. — Uncertain, Belgium.

U. S. distribution. — Geographical: New England States; Pennsylvania, North Carolina, Tennessee. Ecological: Fresh water, often an aerophil.

14. **Navicula atomus** (Kütz.) Grun. var. **atomus**   PL. 46, FIG. 16

Amphora ? atomus Kütz., Bacill., p. 108, pl. 30, fig. 70. 1844.
Navicula. atomus (Kütz.) Grun., Verh. Zool.-Bot. Ges. Wien, 10:552, pl. 4, figs. 6a-g. 1860.

Valve linear-elliptical to elliptical with rounded ends. Valve lightly silicified, with axial area often appearing somewhat thicker. Axial area narrow, slightly widened toward the center of the valve. Central area slightly wider than the axial area. Striae strongly radiate, about 30 in 10μ; according to Grunow, more than 25 in 10μ. Length, 4-17μ. Breadth, 2.5-5μ.

Cleve (1895, p. 4) and others have attributed this species to Naegeli. Kützing (1849, p. 40) gives *Synedra atomus* Naeg. *in litt.* = *Amphora? atomus* Kütz. Since I cannot locate any publication of *Synedra atomus* by Naegeli prior to 1844, Kützing should be regarded as the correct author of this name.

Type locality. — [Germany], In süssem Wasser bei Nordhausen.

U. S. distribution. — Geographical: Middle Atlantic States, Southeastern States; Connecticut, Tennessee, Ohio, California. Ecological: Widely distributed, circumneutral pH, often in water with fairly high nutrient level.

15. **Navicula minima** Grun. var. **minima**   PL. 46, FIGS. 17-18

Navicula minima Grun. *in* V. H., Syn. Diat. Belgique, pl. 14, fig. 15. 1880.
Navicula atomoides Grun. *in* V. H., Syn. Diat. Belgique, pl. 14, fig. 12. 1880. (text, p. 107. 1885.)

Navicula minima var. *atomoides* (Grun. *in* V. H.) Cl., K. Svenska Vet.-Akad. Handl.,
   Ny Földj, 26(2):128. 1894.

Valve linear to linear-elliptical with rounded ends. Axial area narrow,
linear. Central area variable in size, transverse; formed by the nearly equal
shortening of the central striae. Striae radiate throughout the valve except
about the central area where they are almost parallel. Striae, usually 26 in
10μ but may be finer. Length, 6-17μ. Breadth, 2.5-5μ.

The nominate variety resembles some of the varieties of *Navicula seminulum* Grun. in shape. It differs from *N. seminulum* in that the striae,
except those around the central area, are always 25 or more in 10μ; and
the central area is typically smaller, and the valve is not swollen in the
middle.

Type locality. — Belgium, Brussels.

U. S. distribution. — GEOGRAPHICAL: New England States, Middle Atlantic States, Southeastern States, Gulf Coast States, South Central States,
East Central States, West Central States, Plains States; Arizona, California.
ECOLOGICAL: Widely distributed in fresh water; sometimes found in slightly
brackish water.

16. **Navicula seminulum** Grun. var. **seminulum**   PL. 46, FIG. 19

Navicula seminulum Grun., Verh. Zool.-Bot. Ges. Wien, 10:552, pl. 4, fig. 3. 1860.

Margins of the valve parallel at the ends, becoming convex at the
center. This produces a swollen effect about the central area. Ends of the
valve rounded. Axial area narrow. Central area rectangular, transversely
widened. Striae radiate throughout the valve except around the central
area where they are almost parallel. Striae shortened about the central
area, often somewhat irregular in length; slightly more distant from each
other than in the rest of the valve. Striae very finely punctate (they are
difficult to see except under oblique light and oil immersion). Striae, 18-20
in 10μ. Length, 7-18μ. Breadth, 4-5μ.

Type locality. — [Austria], . . . in fontibus et rivules.

U. S. distribution. — GEOGRAPHICAL: New England States, Middle At-
lantic States, Southeastern States, South Central States, East Central States,
West Central States, Lakes States; Arizona, Oregon, California. ECOLOGI-
CAL: Fresh to slightly brackish water.

16. **Navicula seminulum** var. **hustedtii** Patr.   PL. 46, FIG. 20

Navicula seminulum var. *hustedtii* Patr., Proc. Acad. Nat. Sci. Philadelphia, 111:
   100, pl. 8, fig. 13. 1959.

Valve typically linear with broadly rounded ends; in very small specimens the valve may become elliptical. Axial area narrow. Central area

transverse, rounded, not very large. Striae radiate throughout the valve; indistinctly punctate. Striae, 18-22 in 10μ. Length, 4-18μ. Breadth, 3-5μ.

This variety differs from the nominate variety of the species in that it is typically linear and not swollen about the central area. The striae about the central area are radiate and not perpendicular to the central nodule, as is usually the case in the nominate variety.

This variety is closely related to *Navicula seminulum* var. *intermedia* Hust. (1942b, p. 110, figs. 25-28) from which it differs by the typical specimens being linear in shape whereas the larger specimens of *N. seminulum* var. *intermedia* are linear-elliptical. The striae radiate at a greater angle in this taxon than in *N. seminulum* var. *intermedia*. It differs from *N. minima* in its coarser striae.

Type locality. — U.S.A., South Carolina, Aiken County, near the mouth of Upper Three Runs. (*Holotype*—A-G.C. 4425a, Patrick, 1959.)

U. S. distribution. — Geographical: Known only from the type locality. Ecological: Slightly acid water low in mineral content; fairly rich in humates.

17. Navicula secura Patr. var. secura   pl. 46, fig. 21

Navicula secura Patr., Proc. Acad. Nat. Sci. Philadelphia, 111:100, pl. 8, fig. 11. 1959.

Valve linear-lanceolate with broad, rounded ends. Axial area distinct. Median ends of the raphe fairly distant, ending at the edges of the central area. Central area a broad, transverse fascia that extends almost to the margins of the valve. Central nodule distinct. Striae radiate throughout the valve; those bordering the fascia equally or unequally shortened. Striae, 33-35 in 10μ. Length, 13-20μ. Breadth, 5-7μ.

This species is very similar to *Navicula hangchowensis* Skv. (1937, p. 224, pl. 1, fig. 31), but differs from it in that the axial area of our taxon is wider and more distinct. Also, the striae are 33-35 in 10μ rather than 30 in 10μ. In *N. hangchowensis* the striae are slightly radiate or parallel at the ends of the valve, while in *N. secura* they are more strongly radiate. In shape and characteristics of the central area it is somewhat similar to *N. pseudoseminulum* Skv. (1935, p. 40, pl. 9, fig. 27) which, however, is a little larger and is more coarsely striated.

Type locality. — U.S.A., South Carolina, Aiken County, near the mouth of Upper Three Runs. (*Holotype*—A-G.C. 44254a, Patrick, 1959.)

U. S. distribution. — Geographical: Known only from the type locality. Ecological: Water of low mineral content; mesotrophic to eutrophic.

18. **Navicula vanheurckii** Patr. sp. nov. PL. 46, FIG. 22

Valva ellipticali apicibus rotundis. Area axiali angusta, distincta. Apicibus terminalibus raphidis versis in partibus adversis. In specie raphidi leniter sigmoidi. Area media magna, dilatata transverse, prope attacta margines valvae. Striis radiatis omnino maxima parte valvae, parallelis in area media ubi striae sunt breviores aut inaequales in longitudine. Striis circiter 28 in 10μ. Longitudine, 12-30μ. Latitudine, 5-9μ.

Valve elliptical with rounded ends. Axial area narrow, distinct. Terminal ends of raphe turned in opposite directions, thus giving the raphe a slightly sigmoid appearance. Central area large, transversely widened, nearly reaching the margins of the valve. Striae radiate throughout most of the valve, parallel at the central area where they may be equally shortened or irregular in length. Striae, 24-28 in 10μ. Length, 13-25μ. Breadth, 5-9μ.

Grunow and Van Heurck considered their specimens as illustrated with the name *Navicula rotaeana* in Van Heurck's *Synopsis des Diatomées de Belgique* (1880, pl. 14, fig. 17) to be the same entity as *Stauroneis rotaeana* Rabh. (1856a, No. 505; 1856b, p. 103, pl. 13, fig. 7). However, the specimens we have examined of material of Rabenhorst (1856a, No. 505) are *Navicula mutica* var. *cohnii* (Hilse) Grun. and not the same as *Navicula rotaeana* Grun. Therefore, the taxon which represents their specimens is described as new.

Type locality. — Uncertain, Belgium.

U. S. distribution. — GEOGRAPHICAL: Middle Atlantic States; New York, Indiana, Montana, Wyoming, Colorado. ECOLOGICAL: Oligohalobe, aerophil (often on moist rocks in springs), prefers alkaline water.

19. **Navicula orbiculata** Patr. var. **orbiculata** PL. 46, FIG. 23

Navicula orbiculata Patr., Proc. Acad. Nat. Sci. Philadelphia, 111:99, pl. 8, fig. 12. 1959.

Valve linear with rounded ends. Axial area narrow, distinct. Central area large, orbicular; formed by the regular shortening of the striae about the central nodule. Striae somewhat radiate at the center of the valve, parallel or slightly radiate at the ends; slightly curved. Striae, 24-32 in 10μ. Length, 9-13μ. Breadth, 4-6μ.

This species is similar to *Navicula dulcis* Krasske in form, angle of the striae, and shape of the axial area. It differs from *N. dulcis* in the shape of the central area. This area is large and orbicular in *N. orbiculata*, small and rectangular in *N. dulcis*. The striae are coarser in *N. orbiculata*, 24-32 in 10μ—not 34 or more in 10μ as in *N. dulcis*.

Type locality. — U.S.A., Texas, Orange County, Sabine River near the mouth. (*Holotype*—A-G.C. 8030, Patrick, 1959.)

U. S. distribution. — GEOGRAPHICAL: Known only from the type locality. ECOLOGICAL: Brackish water.

20. Navicula luzonensis Hust. var. luzonensis   PL. 46, FIG. 24

Navicula luzonensis Hust., Internat. Rev. Ges. Hydrobiol., 42:59, fig. 106. 1942.

Valve elliptical. Axial area narrow, linear. Raphe straight, filiform; median ends somewhat distant. Central area lacking. Striae slightly radiate throughout; closely punctate. Striae, 20-24 in 10μ. Puncta slightly finer than the striae. Length, 9-12μ. Breadth, 4-4.5μ.

This species is similar to *Navicula muralis* Grun. (1880b, pl. 14, figs. 26-28), but differs in that the striae are coarser and distinctly punctate. The shape of our specimens varies from that typified by Hustedt to those with very slightly produced ends.

Type locality. — Luzon; Buhisee . . . [Philippine Islands].

U. S. distribution. — GEOGRAPHICAL: Middle Atlantic States, South Central States; South Carolina, Texas, Ohio. ECOLOGICAL: Seems to prefer water of fairly high mineral content.

Navicula subgenus WARDIA Patr.

Navicula subgenus *Wardia* Patr., Not. Nat. Acad. Nat. Sci. Philadelphia, No. 324, p. 11. 1959.

Valve with strongly radiate striae throughout. Striae in the median portion of the valve irregular in length, usually alternately longer and shorter.

This subgenus is distinguished by the striae which are indistinctly punctate, strongly radiate throughout the valve, and irregular in length, usually alternately longer and shorter, about the central area. The terminal fissures of the raphe form a V. The axial area is narrow.

The alternately longer and shorter striae about the central area and radiate terminal striae relate this subgenus to some species in the subgenus *Punctulata,* but it differs in that the striae are not distinctly punctate.

Type species. — *Navicula wardii* Patr.

1. Navicula wardii Patr. var. wardii   PL. 47, FIG. 1

Navicula wardii Patr., Not. Nat. Acad. Nat. Sci. Philadelphia, No. 324, p. 11, fig. 2. 1959.

Valve linear with wedge-shaped ends. Axial area narrow. Central area large, rhomboidal. Striae strongly radiate throughout the valve; irregular in length at the center and usually alternately longer and shorter. Striae, 26 in 10μ at the center of the valve to 32 in 10μ at the ends. Length, 49-63μ. Breadth, 9-10μ.

This is the only species that we have seen belonging to this subgenus of *Navicula.*

Type locality. — U.S.A., Spring Hill (Mobile, Alabama?); fresh water. (*Holotype*—N.Y.B.G.-Ward D-4-21, Patrick, 1959.)

U. S. distribution. — GEOGRAPHICAL: Known only from the type locality.

Navicula subgenus BACILLUM Patr.

Navicula group *Bacillées* V. H., Syn. Diat. Belgique, p. 72. 1885.
Navicula subgenus *Bacillum* Patr., Not. Nat. Acad. Nat. Sci. Philadelphia, No. 324, p. 3. 1959.

Valve with thickened terminal nodules, sometimes transversely expanded. Raphe often lies between two thickened ribs.

The central area may be small or transversely widened. The axial area is variable in width. The striae are very finely punctate, and usually further apart at the center than in the rest of the valve. They are slightly radiate throughout the valve. This subgenus includes species recognized by Van Heurck as belonging to the groups *Bacillées* and *Americanées.*

As Cleve points out, *N. pupula* and *N. laevissima* (*N. bacilliformis*) are somewhat intermediate between *N.* subgenus *Minuscula* (includes Cleve's group *Mesoleiae*) and *N.* subgenus *Bacillum.* Their inclusion in either subgenus is somewhat arbitrary.

Type species. — *Navicula bacillum* Ehr.

KEY TO THE SPECIES OF THE SUBGENUS BACILLUM

1. Terminal nodules strongly expanded, reaching margins of the valve
   [4] *N. pupula* and vars.
1. Terminal nodules not strongly expanded 2
   2. Raphe enclosed in a distinct siliceous thickening 3
   2. Raphe not enclosed in a distinct siliceous thickening .... [5] *N. laevissima*
3. Axial area very broad .... [1] *N. americana* and var.
3. Axial area narrow 4
   4. Terminal fissures "comma" shaped .... [3] *N. subhamulata*
   4. Terminal fissures not "comma" shaped .... [2] *N. bacillum*

1. Navicula americana Ehr. var. americana PL. 47, FIG. 3

Navicula? americana Ehr., Phys. Abh. Akad. Wiss. Berlin, for 1841:417. 1843.
Navicula americana f. *minor* M. Perag & Hérib., *in* Hérib., Diat. Auvergne, p. 116, pl. 4, fig. 12. 1893.

Valve linear, broad; ends rounded. Sometimes the sides of the valve slightly concave. Axial area one-third to one-half the width of the valve. Ribs close to the raphe, forming a very narrow area. Central area orbicular. Striae radiate throughout the valve; finely punctate; slightly curved. Striae, 15-18 in 10μ; more distant from each other at the center of the valve. Length, 30-120μ. Breadth, 10-30μ.

This species is characterized by its broad axial area.

Type locality. — U.S.A., New York, West Point; fossil layer.

U. S. distribution. — Geographical: New England States, Middle Atlantic States, Southeastern States, Gulf Coast States, Lakes States; Washington, Oregon, California. Ecological: Oligohalobe (indifferent), alkaliphil, water of circumneutral pH.

1. **Navicula americana** var. **moesta** Temp. & Perag.   PL. 47, FIG. 2

Navicula americana var. *moesta* Temp. & Perag., Diat. Monde Entier, 2nd ed., p. 86. 1908.

Valve linear, concave in the middle portion; ends rounded. Axial area very broad, about two-thirds the width of the valve. Striae more coarsely punctate than in the nominate variety; sometimes irregular in length. Striae, 16-18 in 10μ. Length, about 130μ. Breadth, 26μ at the center of the valve to 30μ at the ends.

Wolle (1890, pl. 19, fig. 26) identifies a diatom which he calls *Navicula moesta* A.S. The specimen which Wolle illustrates may be this taxon.

Type locality. — U.S.A., Massachusetts, Essex County, Georgetown, Boldpatte Pond. (*Lectotype*—A-T. & P. 159, Patrick.)

U. S. distribution. — Geographical: Known only from the type locality.

2. **Navicula bacillum** Ehr. var. **bacillum**   PL. 47, FIGS. 4-5

Navicula bacillum Ehr., Phys. Abh. Akad. Wiss. Berlin, for 1838:130. 1840. Phys. Abh. Akad. Wiss. Berlin, for 1841:418, pl. 4(5), fig. 8. 1843.
Navicula pseudobacillum Grun. *in* Cl. & Grun., K. Svenska Vet.-Akad. Handl., Ny Följd, 17(2):45, pl. 2, fig. 52. 1880.
Navicula bastianii Perag. *in* Temp. & Perag., Diat. Monde Entier, 2nd ed., p. 183. 1909.

Valve linear, sides sometimes slightly concave; ends rounded. Axial area of distinctly different thickness than the narrow siliceous thickening enclosing the raphe. Central area distinct, more or less elliptical in shape. Clear, terminal areas variable in extension to sides of valve. Striae radiate and somewhat curved throughout the valve. Striae, 12-14 in 10μ at the center of the valve to 22 in 10μ at the ends. Length, 30-89μ. Breadth, 10-20μ.

This species is distinguished by the shape of the central and terminal nodules and the curvature of the striae.

Type locality.— Uncertain.

U. S. distribution.— GEOGRAPHICAL: New England States, Middle Atlantic States, Southeastern States, Gulf Coast States, South Central States, East Central States, Lakes States, Plains States; Wyoming, Utah, Washington, Oregon, California. ECOLOGICAL: Fresh to slightly brackish water; alkaliphil, circumneutral pH.

3. **Navicula subhamulata** Grun. var. **subhamulata**   PL. 47, FIG. 6

    Navicula subhamulata Grun. *in* V. H., Syn. Diat. Belgique, pl. 13, fig. 14. 1880.
        (text, p. 106. 1885.)

Valve linear, sometimes slightly swollen in the middle portion; ends rounded. Axial area narrow. Terminal fissures of the raphe long, slightly curved in the same direction. Central area not, or only slightly, wider than the axial area. Striae slightly radiate, 24-30 in 10μ. Length, 14-20μ. Breadth, 4-8μ.

This species is distinguished by the shape of the terminal fissures of the raphe and the fine, slightly radiate striae.

Type locality. — Belgium, Brussels; fresh water.

U. S. distribution. — GEOGRAPHICAL: Middle Atlantic States, Southeastern States, Gulf Coast States, South Central States; Indiana, Missouri, California. ECOLOGICAL: Seems to prefer fresh water with fairly high mineral content; mesotrophic.

4. **Navicula pupula** Kütz. var. **pupula**   PL. 47, FIG. 7

    Navicula pupula Kütz., Bacill., p. 93, pl. 30, fig. 40. 1844.

Valve linear-lanceolate with broad, rostrate ends. Axial area narrow. Central area a transverse fascia which almost reaches the margins of the valve. Terminal nodules transversely widened, clearly marked by the end striae which are thicker than the other striae. Terminal striae parallel or slightly radiate. Striae toward the center of the valve distinctly radiate; short and irregular in length about the central area. Striae, 13-17 in 10μ at the center of the valve to 26 in 10μ at the ends. Length, 20-40μ. Breadth, 7-11μ.

Kützing's original illustration shows two forms, one which is distinctly narrower at the apices and the other similar to the one we have illustrated. Our illustration is similar to Grunow's *Navicula pupula* var. *genuina* (1880a, p. 45) which he states was identified by Kützing himself.

I have examined Kützing's specimens of this taxon in the British Museum (Kütz. 925–B. M. 18726) from the River Main. They are the same taxon as our specimens and agree with Van Heurck's illustration in *Synopsis des Diatomées Belgique*, pl. 13, fig. 15 (1880).

Type locality. — Lebend in süssem Wasser bei Nordhausen [Germany].

U. S. distribution. — Geographical: New England States, Middle Atlantic States, Southeastern States, Gulf Coast States, South Central States, East Central States, West Central States, Lakes States, Plains States; Montana, Wyoming, Utah, Washington, California. Ecological: Seems to prefer fresh, circumneutral water of fairly high mineral content; halophilous.

4. **Navicula pupula** var. **capitata** Skv. & Meyer   pl. 47, fig. 8

> *Navicula pupula* var. capitata Skv. & Meyer, Proc. Sungaree River. Biol. Stat., (Harbin), 1(5):15, pl. 1, fig. 40. 1928.

This variety differs from the nominate variety of the species by the distinct, broadly capitate ends.

Type locality. — None is given with the original description.

U. S. distribution. — Geographical: New England States, Middle Atlantic States, Southeastern States, Gulf Coast States, South Central States, East Central States, West Central States, Lakes States, Plains States; Montana, Wyoming, Utah, Oregon, California. Ecological: Similar to that of the nominate variety.

4. **Navicula pupula** var. **elliptica** Hust.   pl. 47, fig. 11

> *Navicula pupula* var. *elliptica* Hust., Abh. Naturw. Ver. Bremen, 20:291, pl. 3, fig. 40. 1911.

Valve typically elliptical-lanceolate, narrowed toward rounded ends. Some specimens, as the one illustrated by Hustedt (1930, fig. 465c), are elliptical with rounded ends. Axial area narrow. Central area transverse, almost reaching the margins of the valve. Striae radiate, fine; 22-26 in 10μ. Length, $14\text{-}20\mu$. Breadth, $6\text{-}8\mu$.

Type locality. — Germany, Bremen, Wumme River.

U. S. distribution. — Geographical: Middle Atlantic States, Southeastern States; Ohio, Nebraska. Ecological: Seems to be similar to that of the nominate variety.

4. **Navicula pupula** var. **mutata** (Krasske) Hust.   pl. 47, figs. 9-10

> *Navicula mutata* Krasske, Bot. Arch., 27:354, fig. 16. 1929.
> *Navicula pupula* var. *mutata* (Krasske) Hust. *in* Pasch., Süssw.-Fl. Mitteleuropas, Heft 10, Aufl. 2, p. 282, fig. 467f. 1930.

Valve elliptical-lanceolate to elliptical with rostrate ends. The width of the rostrate ends is variable. Hustedt's figure has narrow, short, rostrate ends. The ends of our specimens are broader, although they are distinctly rostrate. Axial area narrow. Central area transverse, somewhat rectangular in shape. Striae radiate throughout most of the valve, almost parallel at the ends. Striae, 22-24 in 10μ at the center of the valve to 28 in 10μ at the ends. Length, $10\text{-}18\mu$. Breadth, $5\text{-}8\mu$.

Our specimens are not as abruptly rostrate as Hustedt's illustration, and the length-to-breadth ratio is a little greater. Since in other respects the specimens are the same, it seems unwise to make this a new variety.

Figure 10 is of a specimen with a more rounded central area than is typical for Navicula pupula var. mutata.

Type locality. — . . . im Abflusse des Comerauer Grossteiches bei Königs-wartha (Lausitzer Niederung) [Saxony].

U. S. distribution. — GEOGRAPHICAL: Southeastern States, South Central States, East Central States.

4. **Navicula pupula** var. **rectangularis** (Greg.) Grun.   PL. 47, FIG. 12

Stauroneis rectangularis Greg., Quart. Jour. Micr. Sci., 2:99, pl. 4, fig. 17.   1854.
Navicula pupula var. rectangularis (Greg.) Grun. in Cl. & Grun., K. Svenska Vet.-Akad. Handl., Ny Följd, 17(2):45.   1880.
Navicula pupula var. bacillaroides Grun. in Cl. & Grun., K. Svenska Vet.-Akad. Handl., Ny Följd, 17(2):45.   1880.

Valve linear in general outline, slightly swollen in the middle portion; ends broadly rounded, sometimes appearing slightly rostrate. Striae as in nominate variety. Length-to-breadth ratio, about 4:1. Length of the same range as that of the nominate variety. Hustedt (1961, p. 121) recognizes this taxon as a form rather than a variety of Navicula pupula.

Type locality. — Scotland, Mull; diatomaceous earth.

U. S. distribution. — GEOGRAPHICAL: New England States, Middle Atlantic States, Southeastern States; Florida, Tennessee, Indiana, Nebraska, Wyoming, Arizona, Oregon, California. ECOLOGICAL: Seems to prefer water of higher mineral content than the nominate variety; this variety has been found in salt bogs.

5. **Navicula laevissima** Kütz. var. **laevissima**   PL. 47, FIG. 13

Navicula laevissima Kütz. Bacill., p. 96, pl. 21, fig. 14.   1844.
Stauroneis wittrockii Lagerst., Bih. K. Svenska Vet.-Akad. Handl., 1(14):38, pl. 2, fig. 15.   1873.
Navicula bacilliformis Grun. in Cl. & Grun., K. Svenska Vet.-Akad. Handl., Ny Följd, 17(2):44, pl. 2, fig. 51.   1880.
Navicula wittrockii (Lagerst.) Temp. & Perag., Diat. Monde Entier, 2nd ed., p. 120. 1909.

Valve linear, slightly swollen in the middle portion; ends rounded. Axial area narrow; terminal clear area not large, wider than the axial area. Central area transverse, formed by the irregular shortening of the striae. Striae somewhat radiate; curved, the curvature more marked toward the ends of the valve. Striae, 12-15 in 10μ at the center of the valve to 20-22 in 10μ at the ends. Length, 32-45μ. Breadth, 8-10μ.

This species is related to *Navicula pupula* var. *bacillarioides* from which it is distinguished by the shape of the terminal areas, the curvature of the striae, and the shape of the central area.

I have seen isotype material of *N. laevissima* (B. M. 18820) and as Ross (1963) points out it is the correct name for this taxon.

Type locality. — Fossil in Bergmehl von San Fiore.

U. S. distribution. — GEOGRAPHICAL: New England States, Middle Atlantic States, Southeastern States, Gulf Coast States, East Central States, Lakes States, Plains States; Tennessee, Wyoming, Washington, California. ECOLOGICAL: Widely distributed in circumneutral fresh water.

Navicula subgenus PSEUDOFRICKIA Patr.

Navicula subgenus *Pseudofrickia* Patr., Not. Nat. Acad. Nat. Sci. Philadelphia, No. 324, pp. 8-9. 1959.

Valve with thickened siliceous ribs on each side of the raphe; thickened terminal nodules absent; transverse central area bound by thickened striae.

The central area forms a fascia which extends to the margins of the valve. The striae are not clearly punctate and appear as a line. The terminal fissures of the raphe appear to form a straight line.

This subgenus is closely related to the genus *Frickia*. It differs in that the ribs do not seem to be united under the raphe by a membrane. The central area forms a transverse fascia and is bounded by striae which are thicker than the other striae. Longitudinal lines are not present. Of the subgenera of the genus *Navicula*, it is most closely related to the *Bacillum*.

Type species. — *Navicula pseudofrickia* Patr.

1. **Navicula pseudofrickia** Patr. var. **pseudofrickia**   PL. 47, FIG. 14

Navicula pseudofrickia Patr., Not. Nat. Acad. Nat. Sci. Philadelphia, No. 324, p. 9, fig. 1. 1959.

Valve linear with rounded ends. Axial area bounded by two siliceous ribs which fuse at the central nodule. Median ends of the raphe usually turned slightly to one side. Central area forming a fascia on each side of the central nodule. Striae slightly radiate, sometimes parallel at the ends of the valve. Striae, 22-24 in 10μ. Length, 34-63μ. Breadth, 6-10μ.

This species resembles the genus *Frickia* in the structure of the terminal areas of the valve. It is also similar to *Frickia* in that the axial area is enclosed by two siliceous ribs. It is most closely related to *Navicula tignaria* Hust. (1942d, p. 59, figs. 103-104), but it is a much larger species and the striae are finer.

Type locality. — U.S.A., New Jersey, Passaic County, Newfoundland.

U. S. distribution. — GEOGRAPHICAL: Known only from the type locality.

Navicula subgenus NAVICULA

Valve with striae which are crossed by lines—not punctate.

This subgenus includes the species in the group or section which was formerly called *Lineolatae*. Since it includes the type of the genus *Navicula*, it must be called *Navicula* according to the *International Rules of Botanical Nomenclature*. This subgenus is most easily characterized by the cross-lineate striae.

The axial and central areas are variable. The striae at the ends of the valve may be radiate, parallel, or convergent. The striae are not broken to form irregular longitudinal areas.

Type species. — *Navicula tripunctata* (Müll.) Bory.

KEY TO THE SPECIES OF THE SUBGENUS NAVICULA

1. Striae crossed by a band formed by the internal pore opening as in *Pinnularia*
   [45] *N. walkerii*
1. Striae not so formed 2
   2. Apices of the valve clear, appearing of different thickness than the rest of the valve, terminal striae more strongly marked than the rest of the striae
      [55] *N. capitata*
   2. Apices and striae not so formed 3
3. Near apices of the valve a dark bar which appears to be due to a depression in the valve, crosses the valve . . . . [56] *N. inflexa*
3. Apices not so formed 4
   4. A short septum present at the apices of each valve
      [42] *N. incomposita* var. *minor*
   4. Septa not present 5
5. Isolated puncta present at the ends of the terminal striae . . . . . . [54] *N. cascadensis*
5. Striae not so formed 6
   .6. Terminal striae convergent or sometimes parallel 7
   6. Terminal striae radiate or sometimes parallel 39
7. Central area more strongly widened, transversely 8
7. Central area rhombic, lanceolate, or round; sometimes very small or indistinct 16
   8. Length of the valve, less than 25μ 9
   8. Length of the valve, more than 25μ 13
9. Valve elliptical-lanceolate; striae, less than 14 in 10μ 10
9. Valve linear-lanceolate with rounded or attenuate-rostrate ends; striae, 14 or more in 10μ 11

10. Valve with attenuate ends ....[53] *N. gravistriata*

10. Valve with rounded ends ....[23] *N. menisculus* var. *upsaliensis*

11. Valves with attenuated, rostrate ends ....[37] *N. canalis*

11. Valves with rounded ends 12

    12. Striae, not more than 16 in 10μ at the ends of the valve; distinctly radiate in
the middle portion of the valve ....[51] *N. dulcis*

    12. Striae, 18-19 in 10μ at the ends of the valve, slightly radiate in the middle
portion of the valve ....[50] *N. tenelloides*

13. Striae, 6-10 in 10μ ....[47] *N. aurora*

13. Striae, more than 9 in 10μ 14

    14. Valve elliptical-lanceolate with slightly rostrate ends
                          [23] *N. menisculus* var. *upsaliensis*

    14. Valve linear or linear-lanceolate or lanceolate 15

15. Valve with distinctly rostrate-capitate ends ....[5] *N. globulifera*

15. Apices rounded ....[17] *N. graciloides*

    16. Central area formed by the striae irregularly shortened, often alternately
longer and shorter 17

    16. Central area formed by striae regularly shortened, occasionally regularly
shortened on one side and slightly irregularly shortened on the other side
of the central nodule 23

17. Central area with an isolated punctum ....[21] *N. decussis*

17. Central area without an isolated punctum 18

    18. Valve, more than 100μ long; valve linear-lanceolate ......[43] *N. peticolasii*

    18. Valve, less than 75μ long 19

19. Valve with attenuate-rostrate or capitate ends 20

19. Valve with acute or rounded ends 21

    20. Valve broadly lanceolate; striae at the ends of the valve, not more than
18 in 10μ ....[1] *N. salinarum*

    20. Valve linear; terminal striae, 20-22 in 10μ ....[40] *N. bicephala*

21. Valve linear-lanceolate with rounded or acute ends, median striae usually much
longer than the other striae about the central area 22

21. Valve broadly lanceolate, central area otherwise formed ..[18] *N. pseudoreinhardtii*

    22. Striae at the center of the valve, 8-10 in 10μ ....[16] *N. cincta*

    22. Striae at the center of the valve, 12 or more in 10μ ..[7] *N. radiosa* var. *tenella*

23. Valves with distinctly narrowed, usually rostrate or capitate ends 24

23. Valves with apices truncate or rounded or acute; not as above 29

    24. Central area large or distinct 25

    24. Central area small, sometimes not distinct 28

25. Central area rounded, often slightly irregular in shape with striae being evenly
shortened on one side and irregular in length on the other, striae more than 12
in 10μ ....[2] *N. cryptocephala* and vars.

25. Central area rounded or irregular in shape; striae 12 or less in 10μ 26

    26. Valve linear to linear-lanceolate in shape 27

    26. Valve lanceolate; length, usually less than 60μ; central area large
                              [3] *N. rhynchocephala*

27. Striae moderately radiate, almost parallel around the central area; central area
irregular in shape, apices protracted, subrostrate ....[4] *N. viridula* var. *rostellata*

27. Central area large, rounded, sometimes somewhat asymmetrical; ends not so
protracted as above ....[4] *N. viridula* and vars.

1. Navicula salinarum Grun. var. salinarum   PL. 48, FIG. 1

Navicula salinarum Grun. *in* Cl. & Grun., K. Svenska Vet.-Akad. Handl., Ny
    Följd, 17(2):33, pl. 2, fig. 34. 1880.

Valve broadly lanceolate; narrowed toward the ends which are usually
rostrate to slightly capitate, but sometimes attenuated and rounded rather
than truly rostrate. Axial area distinct, widening toward the central area,
which is lanceolate-elliptical. Striae radiate throughout most of the valve,
parallel or slightly convergent at the ends; sometimes appearing curved
because of the convexity of the valve surface; more widely spaced and
alternately longer and shorter at the center of the valve. Striae, 14-18 in
10μ. Length, 23-41μ. Breadth, 8-12μ.

Type locality — Arctic Ocean, Kara Sea, Jamal Peninsula.

U. S. distribution. — GEOGRAPHICAL: New England States, Southeastern States, East Central States, West Central States, Plains States; Wyoming, California. ECOLOGICAL: Seems to prefer brackish water or fresh water of high mineral content.

1. **Navicula salinarum** var. **intermedia** (Grun.) Cl.   PL. 48, FIG. 2

> *Navicula cryptocephala* var. *intermedia* Grun. *in* V. H., Syn. Diat. Belgique, pl. 8, fig. 10. 1880.
>
> *Navicula salinarum* var. *intermedia* (Grun.) Cl., K. Svenska Vet.-Akad. Handl., Ny Földj, 27(3):19. 1895.

Valve lanceolate; narrowed toward the somewhat protracted, subcapitate to capitate ends. Axial area indistinct. Central area irregular in shape due to the striae being alternately longer and shorter. Striae radiate toward the middle portion of the valve, convergent at the ends; lineate. Striae, 14-18 in 10μ. Length, 25-50μ. Breadth, 7-10μ.

This taxon is closer to *Navicula salinarum* than to *N. cryptocephala* because the striae are alternately longer and shorter about the central area as they are in *N. salinarum* and not equally shortened as in *N. cryptocephala*.

Type locality. — Uncertain, Belgium.

U. S. distribution. — GEOGRAPHICAL: New England States, Middle Atlantic States, Southeastern States, Gulf Coast States, South Central States, East Central States, West Central States, Lakes States, Plains States; Arizona, California. ECOLOGICAL: Water of high mineral content to brackish water.

2. **Navicula cryptocephala** Kütz. var. **cryptocephala**   PL. 48, FIG. 3

> *Navicula cryptocephala* Kütz., Bacill., p. 95, pl. 3, figs. 20, 26. 1844.

Valve lanceolate with globose-capitate to rostrate-capitate ends. Axial area narrow; slightly wider at the center of the valve where it merges with the rounded, transverse central area. Central area often somewhat irregular in shape. Striae radiate throughout most of the valve, parallel or slightly convergent at the ends. Striae, 16-18 in 10μ. Length, 20-40μ. Breadth, 5-7μ.

In general shape, the nominate variety of this species resembles *Navicula rhynchocephala* Kütz. It differs from *N. rhynchocephala* in its smaller size and finer striation.

I have seen Kützing's specimens of this taxon in the British Museum and have designated Kützing's slide no. 459 (B.M. 18785) as the type.

Type locality. — Durch ganz Europa unter Oscillarien und andern Diatomeen.

U. S. distribution. — GEOGRAPHICAL: New England States, Middle Atlantic States, Southeastern States, Gulf Coast States, South Central States,

East Central States, West Central States, Lakes States, Plains States; Wyoming, Colorado, Washington, California. Ecological: Widely distributed in lakes, bogs, or rivers; fresh to slightly brackish water.

2. **Navicula cryptocephala** var. **exilis** (Kütz.) Grun.   pl. 48, fig. 4

> Navicula exilis Kütz., Bacill., p. 95, pl. 4, fig. 6. 1844. (ex partim according to Grunow.)
> Navicula cryptocephala var. minor Grun., Verh. Zool.-Bot. Ges. Wien, 10:527, pl. 4, figs. 28c-d. 1860. (?).
> Navicula cryptocephala var. exilis (Kütz.) Grun. in V. H., Syn. Diat. Belgique, pl. 8, fig. 2. 1880. (text, p. 85. 1885.)

Valve broadly lanceolate, narrowed toward somewhat rostrate ends. Axial area narrow. Central area transverse, somewhat irregular in shape. Striae radiate throughout most of the valve, parallel or slightly convergent at the ends. Striae, 18-20 in 10μ. Length, 17-19μ. Breadth, 4-6μ.

This variety is very similar to *Navicula cryptocephala* var. *veneta* (Kütz.) Rabh., except that it is more finely striated and smaller in size. It is questionably synonymous with *N. cryptocephala* var. *minor* Grun. Grunow, who made the original drawing of *N. cryptocephala* var. *exilis*, did not refer to *N. cryptocephala* var. *minor*. His original drawing of the latter variety does not show a central area, but otherwise it is somewhat similar to *N. cryptocephala* var. *exilis*.

Type locality. — In halbvertrockneten Wassergräben bei Nordhausen! [Germany.]

U. S. distribution. — Geographical: Middle Atlantic States, Plains States; Kentucky, Ohio, Wyoming. Ecological: Water of high mineral content; fresh to brackish water.

2. **Navicula cryptocephala** var. **veneta** (Kütz.) Rabh.   pl. 48, fig. 5

> Navicula veneta Kütz., Bacill., p. 95, pl. 30, fig. 76. 1844.
> Navicula cryptocephala var. veneta (Kütz.) Rabh., Fl. Europaea Alg., sect. 1, p. 198. 1864.
> Navicula cryptocephala var. pumila (Grun.) Cl., K. Svenska Vet.-Akad. Handl., Ny Följd, 27(3):14. 1895.

Valve linear-lanceolate to rhombic-lanceolate with slightly protracted ends. Striae radiate throughout most of the valve, parallel or slightly convergent at the ends. Striae, 14-16 in 10μ. Length, 13-26μ. Breadth, 5-6μ.

This taxon is best separated from *Navicula cryptocephala* var. *exilis* Grun. by its coarser striation and its linear to rhombic-lanceolate shape. The ends in variety *exilis* are subrostrate or obtuse.

I have examined Kützing's specimens of this taxon (Kütz. 1296—B. M. 18787). In some specimens the central area is not very distinct.

Type locality. — In halbsalzigen Wassergräben des botanischen Gartens zu Venedig! [Italy, Venice.]

U. S. distribution. — GEOGRAPHICAL: New England States, Middle Atlantic States, Southeastern States, Gulf Coast States, South Central States, East Central States, West Central States, Plains States; Colorado, Arizona, Oregon, California. ECOLOGICAL: Seems to prefer brackish water; also found in fresh water with high mineral content.

3. **Navicula rhynchocephala** Kütz. var. **rhynchocephala**   PL. 48, FIG. 6

Navicula rhynchocephala Kütz., Bacill., p. 152, pl. 30, fig. 35.   1844.

Valve lanceolate with protracted, rostrate to capitate ends. Axial area and central nodule apparently more thickly silicified than the rest of the valve and thus set off from the rest of the central area. Central area transverse, rounded. Striae radiate in the middle portion of the valve, parallel to slightly convergent at the ends; more distantly spaced at the center of the valve than at the ends. Striae, 8 in 10μ at the center of the valve to 12 in 10μ at the ends. Length, $35\text{-}60\mu$. Breadth, $10\text{-}13\mu$.

Cleve-Euler (1953b, p. 157) gives the following measurements: length, $35\text{-}80\mu$; breadth, $9\text{-}14\mu$; striae, $6.5\text{-}12$ in 10μ.

Type locality. — Germany, near Nordhausen.

U. S. distribution. — GEOGRAPHICAL: New England States, Middle Atlantic States, Southeastern States, Gulf Coast States, South Central States, East Central States, Lakes States, Plains States; Montana, Wyoming, Oregon, California. ECOLOGICAL: Widely distributed in fresh water; seems to prefer water of high mineral content, halophilous to indifferent to small amounts of chloride.

3. **Navicula rhynchocephala** var. **amphiceros** (Kütz.) Grun.

PL. 48, FIG. 7

Navicula amphiceros Kütz., Bacill., p. 95, pl. 3, fig. 39.   1844.
Navicula rhynchocephala var. *amphiceros* (Kütz.) Grun. *in* Cl. & Grun., K. Svenska Vet.-Akad. Handl., Ny Följd, 17(2):33.   1880.

Valve usually more broadly lanceolate than in the nominate variety; ends protracted and rounded—not slightly capitate. Striae coarser, 8-11 in 10μ. Length and breadth as in the nominate variety, except that the valves are usually a little shorter.

Type locality. — In süssem Wasser bei Nordhausen! [Germany].

U. S. distribution. — GEOGRAPHICAL: Connecticut, Maryland, Kansas. ECOLOGICAL: Similar to that of the nominate variety.

3. **Navicula rhynchocephala** var. **germainii** (Wallace) Patr. comb. nov.

PL. 48, FIG. 8

Navicula germainii Wallace, Not. Nat. Acad. Nat. Sci. Philadelphia, No. 331, p. 3,
pl. 2, figs. 1a-c. 1960.

Valve broadly lanceolate with protracted, rostrate-subcapitate apices.
Axial area narrow. Median ends of the raphe slightly turned to one side.
Terminal fissures small, distinct. Central area orbicular to elliptical in
shape. Striae lineate, appearing somewhat curved due to the convexity of
the valve; radiate throughout most of the valve, slightly convergent at the
apices. Striae, 13-14 in 10μ. Length, 34-37μ. Breadth, 7-10μ.

This variety differs from the nominate variety by its smaller size, finer
striae, and usually smaller central area.

Type locality. — U.S.A., Pennsylvania, Lancaster County, Little Muddy
Creek. Coll. J. H. Wallace, 1948 (*Lectotype*—A-G.C. 42397a, Wallace,
1960.)

U. S. distribution. — GEOGRAPHICAL: Middle Atlantic States, Southeastern States, Gulf Coast States, South Central States, East Central States,
West Central States; California.

4. **Navicula viridula** (Kütz.) Kütz. emend. V. H., var. **viridula**

PL. 48, FIG. 9

Frustulia viridula Kütz., Linnaea, 8:551, pl. 13, fig. 12. 1833. [description very
meager.]
Navicula viridula (Kütz.) Kütz., Bacill., p. 91, pl. 30, fig. 47; pl. 4, figs. 10, 15.
1844. [description not definitive; illustrations include more than one taxon.]
Navicula viridula (Kütz.) Kütz. *emend.* V. H., Syn. Diat. Belgique, pl. 7, fig. 25.
1880. (text, p. 84. 1885.)

Valve linear-lanceolate; narrowing to obtuse, rostrate ends. Axial area
narrow, distinct. Central area large, rounded. Axial area and central nodule
appearing more heavily silicified than the rest of the valve. Striae slightly
radiate throughout most of the valve, convergent toward the ends; regularly shortened and more distant from each other about the central area.
Striae, 8-10 in 10μ. Length, 35-80μ. Breadth, 10-15μ.

Type locality. — . . . in einem Teiche bei Markwerben unweit Weissenfels . . . [Germany].

U. S. distribution. — GEOGRAPHICAL: New England States, Middle Atlantic States, Southeastern States, Gulf Coast States, South Central States,
East Central States, Lakes States, Plains States; Wyoming, Colorado, Arizona, Oregon, California. ECOLOGICAL: Seems to prefer circumneutral,
slightly alkaline fresh water; oligohalobe.

4. **Navicula viridula** var. **avenacea** (Bréb. *ex* Grun.) V. H. PL. 48, FIG. 10

Navicula (*viridula* Kg. var. ?) *avenacea* Bréb. *ex* Grun. *in* Schneider, Naturw. Beitr. Kenntn. Kaukasusländer, p. 112, pl. 4, fig. 23. 1878.

Navicula viridula var. *avenacea* (Bréb. *ex* Grun.) V.H., Syn. Diat. Belgique, p. 84. 1885. [Van Heurck (1880, pl. 7, fig. 27) suggested relationship of *N. avenacea* Bréb. *ex* Grun. to *N. viridula*.]

Valve lanceolate, narrowed toward rounded ends. Axial and central areas as in the nominate variety. Striae radiate except at the ends where they are convergent. Striae, 10-12 in 10μ at the center of the valve to 14 in 10μ at the ends. Length, $30\text{-}60\mu$. Breadth, $8\text{-}10\mu$.

This variety differs from the nominate variety by its great variability in size, finer striae, and ends of the valve that are not slightly rostrate. Ecologically it has a wider salt tolerance than the nominate variety and is more common in polluted waters. This taxon should be kept distinct from the nominate variety of the species, but it is not sufficiently different to be maintained as a separate species. It is closely related to *Navicula vulpina* Kütz.

Type locality. — France, Falaise.

U. S. distribution. — GEOGRAPHICAL: Middle Atlantic States; Connecticut, Nebraska. ECOLOGICAL: Similar to nominate variety.

4. **Navicula viridula** var. **linearis** Hust.   PL. 48, FIG. 11

Navicula viridula var. *linearis* Hust., Arch. Hydrobiol. Suppl., 15(2):264, pl. 19, figs. 1-2. 1937.

Valve linear with parallel, sometimes slightly concave margins; ends wedge-shaped, rostrate. Axial and central areas as in the nominate variety. Terminal nodules distinct. Striae radiate except at the ends of the valve where they are convergent. Striae, 8-10 in 10μ. Length, $65\text{-}100\mu$. Breadth, $11\text{-}12\mu$.

Type locality. — . . . In Tobasee ziemlich häufig [Sumatra].

U. S. distribution. — GEOGRAPHICAL: Middle Atlantic States, Southeastern States, Gulf Coast States, South Central States, West Central States, Plains States; California. ECOLOGICAL: Soft, fresh water.

4. **Navicula viridula** var. **rostellata** (Kütz.?) Cl.   PL. 48, FIG. 12

Navicula rostellata Kütz., Bacill, p. 95, pl. 3, fig. 65. 1844.

Navicula rhynchocephala var. *rostellata* (Kütz.) Grun. *in* Cl. & Grun., K. Svenska Vet.-Akad. Handl., Ny Följd, 17(2):33. 1880.

Navicula viridula var. *rostellata* (Kütz.) Cl., K. Svenska Vet.-Akad. Handl., Ny Följd. 27(3):15. 1895.

Valve linear to linear-lanceolate with protracted, subrostrate ends.

Axial area narrow, distinct. Axial area may become wider on one side of the raphe than on the other, thus giving the central area on one side an elliptical appearance. Central area rounded, irregular in shape. Striae radiate at the center of the valve, slightly convergent toward the ends; lineate. Striae, 9-12 in 10μ. Length, 35-65μ. Breadth, 8-11μ.

As Van Heurck indicates (1880, pl. 7, fig. 23), it is doubtful if the taxon we are considering today under the name *rostellata* is the same one that Kützing had. Certainly when one examines Kützing's original illustration it appears to be very different. Hustedt, however, believes that the taxon recognized today is the same as Kützing's.

Van Heurck, Cleve, Hustedt, and others have pointed to the close relationship between their taxon and *Navicula viridula*. Hustedt states it is intermediate between *N. rhynchocephala* Kütz. and *N. viridula* Kütz. I am in agreement. It resembles *N. viridula* in the shape of the central area and the angle of the striae. In the shape of the valve it is more nearly like *N. rhynchocephala*.

H. L. Smith (A-H.L. Sm. 268, spec. typ.) misidentified this taxon as *N. rhynchocephala* var. *brevis* Grun.

Type locality. — In Regenpfützen auf Wangerooge!

U. S. distribution. — Geographical: New England States, Middle Atlantic States, Southeastern States, Gulf Coast States, South Central States, East Central States, Plains States; Nebraska, Arizona, California.

5. **Navicula globulifera** Hust. var. **globulifera**   pl. 48, fig. 13

Navicula globulifera Hust., Arch. Hydrobiol., 18:164, pl. 5, fig. 7. 1927.

Valve linear-lanceolate with distinctly rostrate-capitate ends. Axial area narrow. Raphe with distinct terminal fissures turned in the same direction. Central area variable in shape; may be rounded rectangular, sometimes reaching the margins of the valve. Hustedt (*loc. cit.*) illustrates a specimen in which the central area does not extend to the margin of the valve. Striae radiate at the center of the valve, convergent toward the ends; lineate. Apices of the valve without striae. Striae, 10-12 in 10μ at the center of the valve to 14 in 10μ at the ends. Length, 37-70μ. Breadth, 5-10μ.

This species is distinguished by the absence of striae at the apices of the valve which produces a broad, clear area at each end of the valve.

Type locality. — Japan, Aokikosee.

U. S. distribution. — Geographical: Pennsylvania. Ecological: Fresh water.

6. **Navicula gottlandica** Grun. var. **gottlandica**   PL. 48, FIG. 14

Navicula gottlandica Grun. *in* V. H., Syn. Diat. Belgique, pl. 8, fig. 8.   1880.

Valve lanceolate with protracted, subacute ends. Axial area distinct, narrow. Central area somewhat rounded, irregular in shape. Striae radiate at the center of the valve, convergent at the ends; distinctly lineate. Striae, 14 in 10μ at the center of the valve to 18 in 10μ at the ends. Length, 35-60μ. Breadth, 8-9μ.

This species is easily recognized by the protracted, subacute ends and the angle and number of the striae.

Type locality. — Uncertain, Belgium.

U. S. distribution. — GEOGRAPHICAL: Middle Atlantic States, Southeastern States; Ohio, Texas. ECOLOGICAL: Fresh to brackish water.

7. **Navicula radiosa** Kütz. var. **radiosa**   PL. 48, FIG. 15

Navicula radiosa Kütz., Bacill., p. 91, pl. 4, fig. 23.   1844.
Pinnularia radiosa (Kütz.) Rabh., Süssw.-Diat., p. 43, pl. 6, fig. 9.   1853.
Navicula radiosa var. *acuta* (W. Sm.) Grun., Verh. Zool.-Bot. Ges. Wien, 10:526. 1860.

Valve linear-lanceolate with acute, rounded ends. Axial area narrow, distinct. Axial area and central nodule often appearing more heavily silicified than the rest of the valve. Central area variable in size, transversely widened—not reaching the margins of the valve. Striae radiate throughout most of the valve, convergent at the ends. Striae, 10-12 in 10μ. Length, 40-120μ. Breadth, 10-19μ.

Kützing's original illustration shows the striae radiate at the ends of the valve, but no other workers have observed this arrangement.

Kützing's slide no. 400, Breckdorf (B. M. 18714) has specimens with striae of irregular length about the well defined central area, whereas the length of the striae about the central area is more regularly shortened in the Van Heurck collection, and the terminal striae are convergent.

Type locality. — Uncertain.

U. S. distribution. — GEOGRAPHICAL: New England States, Middle Atlantic States, Southeastern States, Gulf Coast States, South Central States, East Central States, West Central States, Lakes States, Plains States; Montana, Wyoming, Utah, Arizona, Washington, Oregon, California. ECOLOGICAL: Common in all types of circumneutral fresh water; oligohalobous to indifferent to salt concentration.

7. **Navicula radiosa** var. **parva** Wallace   PL. 48, FIG. 16

> *Navicula radiosa* var. *parva* Wallace, Not. Nat. Acad. Nat. Sci. Philadelphia, No.
> 331, pp. 3-4, pl. 1, fig. 5. 1960.

Valve linear-lanceolate with narrow axial area. Raphe structure as in the nominate variety. Central area somewhat elliptical in shape. Striae lineate, radiate in the middle portion of the valve; convergent toward the apices. Striae, 13-14 in 10μ. Length, 45-48μ. Breadth, 6-7μ.

This taxon is distinguished from the nominate variety by its smaller size and finer striae.

Type locality. — U.S.A., Florida, Santa Rosa County, Escambia River. Coll. R. Patrick, 1953. (*Holotype*—A-G.C. 4373b, Wallace, 1960.)

U. S. distribution. — GEOGRAPHICAL: Middle Atlantic States, Southeastern States, Gulf Coast States, East Central States. ECOLOGICAL: Prefers water of low mineral content.

7. **Navicula radiosa** var. **tenella** (Bréb. *ex* Kütz.) Grun.   PL. 48, FIG. 17

> *Navicula tenella* Bréb. *ex* Kütz., Sp. Alg., p. 74. 1849.
> *Navicula radiosa* var. *tenella* (Bréb. *ex* Kütz.) Grun. *in* V. H., Syn. Diat. Belgique,
> p. 84. 1885.

Valve lanceolate with acute ends. Axial area narrow, slightly widened toward the center of the valve. Central area small, often characterized by the median striae being longer than the rest and reaching almost to the central nodule. Striae coarser and radiate at the center of the valve, parallel at the ends. Striae, 15-18 in 10μ. Length, 25-65μ (less than 40μ in most of our specimens). Breadth, 5-7μ.

This variety differs from the nominate variety mainly in its finer striae and usually smaller size. It differs from *N. radiosa* var. *parva* by its finer striae and the shape of the central area.

Type locality. — France, near Falaise.

U. S. distribution. — GEOGRAPHICAL: New England States, Middle Atlantic States, Southeastern States, Gulf Coast States, South Central States, East Central States, West Central States, Lakes States, Plains States; California. ECOLOGICAL: Similar to that of the nominate variety.

8. **Navicula odiosa** Wallace var. **odiosa**   PL. 48, FIG. 18

> *Navicula odiosa* Wallace, Not. Nat. Acad. Nat. Sci. Philadelphia, No. 331, p. 5,
> pl. 2, fig. 4. 1960.

Valve linear-lanceolate with acute, somewhat rounded ends. Axial area narrow. Central area very small, only slightly wider that the axial area.

Striae radiate in the middle portion of the valve, parallel at the ends; lineate. Striae, 22-24 in 10μ. Length, about 15μ. Breadth, about 3μ.

This species is distinguished by its fine striae and their angle.

This taxon is similar to *Navicula aliena* Krasske (1938, p. 529).

Type locality. — U.S.A., Texas, Calhoun County, Mission Lake. Coll. J. H. Wallace, May, 1954. (*Holotype*—A-G.C. 6853a, Wallace, 1960.)

U. S. distribution. — GEOGRAPHICAL: Middle Atlantic States, Southeastern States, Gulf Coast States; California. ECOLOGICAL: Seems to prefer water of high conductivity.

9. **Navicula lanceolata** (Ag.) Kütz. var. **lanceolata**   PL. 48, FIGS. 19-20

Frustulia lanceolata Ag., Flora, 10:626. 1827.
Navicula lanceolata (Ag.) Kütz., Bacill., p. 94, pl. 28, fig. 38; pl. 30, fig. 48. 1844. [illustrations doubtful.]

Valve lanceolate, narrowed toward the ends which are rounded or slightly attenuate-rounded. Axial area narrow, distinct. Central area large, orbicular. Striae lineate-radiate throughout most of the valve, becoming convergent at the ends; regularly shortened about the central area. Striae, usually about 10 in 10μ in the middle of the valve to 14 in 10μ at the ends. Length, 27-50μ, but usually less than 40μ. Breadth, 6.5-12μ.

This species is characterized by the large orbicular central area, the shape of the valve, and the angle and number of the striae.

Mr. Sven Snogerup has kindly allowed me to examine portions of the only material in the Agardh Herbarium labeled *Frustulia lanceolata*. The handwriting on the label is that of J. G. Agardh. The only other notation is "Ge. B. A. + 4." The specimens are very common in this material; one of them is illustrated. It is evident from the examination of these specimens and those on Van Heurck slide no. 96 that they both belong to the same taxon although some variation in the shape of the ends of the valves is present.

Kützing (*loc. cit.*) shows by his figures that he considered this taxon to be variable in shape. He states that his taxon is synonymous with *Frustulia lanceolata* Kütz. (1833b, p. 542). In 1833 he gives Agardh as the authority for the name, but in his description questions whether they are the same. He cites exsiccatae specimens as being this taxon. On Kützing's slide no. 72 in his *Algarum Aquae Dulcis Germanicum* (1833), he has a few specimens which belong to the same taxon as Agardh's *Frustulia lanceolata*. These may be overlooked due to the common occurrence of *Navicula rhynchocephala* var. *germainii* (Wallace) Patr.

Type locality. — In ostio thermarum ad Carlsbad, demersa ubi aqua adhuc calida (25°R.). (*Lectotype*—Ag. Herb. "Ge. B. A. + 4," designated by Patrick.)

U. S. distribution. – GEOGRAPHICAL: New England States, Middle Atlantic States, Southeastern States, Gulf Coast States, South Central States, East Central States, West Central States, Lakes States, Plains States; Montana, Wyoming, Colorado, California. ECOLOGICAL: Widely distributed in fresh or slightly brackish water; seems to prefer water of high mineral content.

10. Navicula arenaria Donk. var. arenaria   PL. 48, FIG. 21

Navicula arenaria Donk., Quart. Jour. Micr. Sci., Ser. 2, 1:10, pl. 1, figs. 8-9. 1861.
Navicula lanceolata var. *arenaria* (Donk.) V. H., Syn. Diat. Belgique, p. 88. 1885.

Valve lanceolate with acute ends. Axial area narrow, distinct. Central area rounded, variable in size. Striae moderately radiate, parallel to slightly convergent at the ends, toward the central area almost parallel. Striae, 9-12 in 10μ. Length, 30-82μ. Breadth, 9-11μ.

Some writers have considered this taxon a variety of *Navicula lanceolata* (Ag.?) Kütz. It differs from this taxon by its coarser and less radiate striae.

Donkin in his original figure of this species shows a diatom with striae that are only slightly radiate throughout most of the valve as shown in our illustration. The central nodule is distinct but very small in one illustration (fig. 9). In figure 8 it is a little larger. Our specimen as his figure 9..

Type locality. – Uncertain.

U. S. distribution. – GEOGRAPHICAL: New Jersey, Kansas. ECOLOGICAL: Brackish water or water of high mineral content.

11. Navicula schroeteri var. escambia Patr.   PL. 49, FIG. 1

Navicula schroeteri var. *escambia* Patr., Proc. Acad. Nat. Sci. Philadelphia, 111:104, pl. 7, fig. 3. 1959.

Valve linear with broadly rounded ends. Axial area narrow, distinct. Terminal fissures of the raphe curved to one side and turned in the same direction. Central area large, more or less elliptical. Striae radiate; slightly curved; distinctly lineate, forming indistinct longitudinal lines. Striae, 12-14 in 10μ. Length, 33-50μ. Breadth, 7-9μ.

This variety differs from the nominate variety in that the ends of this taxon are broadly rounded. The central area is elliptical in this variety, whereas in the nominate variety it is rectangular. This species is related to *Navicula pavillardii* Hust. (1939, p. 635, figs. 86-90). It is similar to *N. symmetrica* Patr. (1944, p. 5, fig. 6), but differs in that the striae are coarser and more coarsely lineate.

Type locality. – U.S.A., Florida, Santa Rosa County, Escambia River, eight to nine miles from the mouth. (*Holotype*–A-G.C. 6564a, Patrick, 1959.)

U. S. distribution. — GEOGRAPHICAL: Middle Atlantic States, Gulf Coast States, South Central States; South Carolina. ECOLOGICAL: Fresh water of low mineral content.,

12. Navicula symmetrica Patr. var. symmetrica   PL. 49, FIG. 2

> *Navicula symmetrica* Patr., Bol. Mus. Nac. [Rio de Janeiro], Nova Sér., Bot., 2:5, fig. 6. 1944.

Valve linear to linear-lanceolate with rounded ends. Axial area and central nodule apparently more heavily silicified than the rest of the valve. Central area transverse, more or less rounded. Striae radiate throughout the valve; distinctly lineate; irregular in length at the center of the valve, but not alternately longer and shorter. Striae, 15-17 in 10μ. Length, 32-35μ. Breadth, 5-7μ. (*Holotype*—A.G.C. 25740, Patrick, 1944.)

This taxon is characterized by the striae that are radiate throughout the valve and by the heavily silicified axial and central areas.

Type locality. — Brazil, Rio Grande do Sul; current water at roadside near Lagoa dos Quadros.

U. S. distribution. — GEOGRAPHICAL: Middle Atlantic States, Southeastern States, Gulf Coast States, South Central States, East Central States, Plains States; California.

13. Navicula tripunctata (O. F. Müll.) Bory var. tripunctata

PL. 49, FIG. 3

> *Vibrio tripunctatus* O. F. Müll., Animal. Infus., p. 52, pl. 7, fig. 2. 1786.
> *Navicula transversa* Bory, Encyclop. Method., p. 563. 1824.
> *Navicula tripunctata* (O. F. Müll.) Bory, Encyclop. Method., p. 563. 1824.
> *Navicula gracilis* Ehr., Phys. Abh. Akad. Wiss. Berlin, for 1830: 64, 67, 69. 1832; for 1831:79. 1832.

Valve almost linear with obtuse, rounded ends. Axial area narrow, disstinct. Central area rectangular, almost reaching the margins of the valve. Striae slightly radiate at the center of the valve, parallel at the ends; distinctly lineate. Striae, 11-12 in 10μ. Length, 33-60μ. Breadth, 6-10μ.

This species is easily recognized by the large rectangular central area and the almost parallel striae.

In 1822, Bory (p. 128) described the genus *Navicula*. He stated that *Vibrio tripunctatus* O. F. Müll. was the type. In 1824, Bory (*loc. cit.*) synonymized *Navicula* (*Vibrio*) *tripunctatus* with *N. transversa* Bory. Ehrenberg, in 1838 (p. 176) stated that *N. transversa* Bory and *N. gracilis* Ehr. were the same.

Type locality. — Germany, Berlin.

U. S. distribution. — GEOGRAPHICAL: New England States, Middle Atlantic States, Southeastern States, South Central States, East Central States, West Central States, Plains States; Montana, Colorado, New Mexico, Arizona, California. ECOLOGICAL: Widely distributed in many kinds of fresh water, also in slightly brackish water.

13. Navicula tripunctata var. schizonemoides (V. H.) Patr.

PL. 49, FIG. 4

Schizonema neglectum Thwaites, Ann. Mag. Nat. Hist., Ser. 2, 1:171, pl. 12(J), figs. 1-4. 1848.

Navicula gracilis var. *schizonemoides* V. H., Syn. Diat. Belgique, p. 83. 1885. [as *Schizonema neglectum* Thwaites, pl. 7, figs. 9-10. 1880.]

Navicula tripunctata var. *schizonemoides* Patr., Proc. Acad. Nat. Sci. Philadelphia, 111:106, pl. 7, fig. 2. 1959.

Distinguished from the nominate variety of the species in that the central area is smaller and does not have the rectangular shape. In other characteristics similar to the nominate form.

Type locality. — Occurring amongst other *Diatomaceae* from fresh or slightly brackish water near Bristol [England].

U. S. distribution. — GEOGRAPHICAL: New England States, Middle Atlantic States, Southeastern States, Gulf Coast States, South Central States, East Central States, West Central States, Plains States; Utah, Arizona, California. ECOLOGICAL: Widely distributed in fresh water; seems to prefer water of fairly high mineral content.

14. Navicula angusta Grun. var. angusta

PL. 49, FIG. 5

Navicula angusta Grun., Verh. Zool.-Bot. Ges. Wien, 10:528, pl. 5, fig. 19. 1860.

Navicula cincta var. *angusta* (Grun.) Cl., K. Svenska Vet.-Akad. Handl., Ny Följd, 27(3):17. 1895.

Navicula cari var. *angusta* (Grun.) Cl.-Eul., K. Svenska Vet.-Akad. Handl., Fjärde Ser., 4(5):153, fig. 810b. 1953.

Valve linear-lanceolate with slightly rostrate, rounded ends. Axial area narrow. Central area transverse, rounded, almost reaching the margins of the valve. Terminal nodules distinct, not large. Striae radiate at the center of the valve to convergent at the ends. Striae, 12-14 in 10μ. Length, 43-65μ. Breadth, 5-7μ. Length-to-breadth ratio, 7:1-10:1.

In the original description Grunow suggested that this might be only a small alpine form of *Navicula radiosa* Kütz., yet it appears in great numbers and is rather constant. Van Heurck (1880, pl. 7, fig. 17) believed the species to be related to *N. cari* Ehr. The distinctive characteristics of the taxon are the shape of the central area and the slightly rostrate ends. The striae number is also less than that found in *N. cari*.

Type locality. — Habitat in rivulis alpium austriacarum (prope Schladming detexi auctumno 1859).

U. S. distribution. —GEOGRAPHICAL: New England States, Middle Atlantic States, Southeastern States, South Central States, Plains States; Wyoming. ECOLOGICAL: Seems to prefer mountainous areas.

15. **Navicula heufleri** Grun. var. **heufleri**   PL. 49, FIG. 6

Navicula heufleri Grun., Verh. Zool.-Bot. Ges. Wien, 10:528, pl. 3, figs. 32a-b.   1860.
Navicula cincta var. *heufleri* (Grun.) V. H., Syn. Diat. Belgique, p. 82.   1885.
    [as *Navicula* (*cincta* var.) *heufleri* (Grun.) V. H., pl. 7, fig. 12.   1880.]

Valve linear-lanceolate with slightly protracted, obtusely rounded ends. Axial area narrow. Central area lanceolate. Striae not more than 10-12 in 10μ. Length, 20-32μ. Breadth, 4-6μ.

This species should not be considered a variety of *Navicula cincta* (Ehr.) Ralfs. It does not have the type of central area that is so characteristic of *N. cincta*, and the striae are much coarser than in that taxon.

Type locality. — Austria, ruins of Schloss Gloggnitz.

U. S. distribution. — GEOGRAPHICAL: New England States, Middle Atlantic States, Southeastern States, Gulf Coast States, West Central States, Plains States; Montana, Oregon. ECOLOGICAL: Prefers alkaline or slightly brackish water.

15. **Navicula heufleri** var. **leptocephala** (Bréb. *ex* Grun.) Perag. PL. 49, FIG. 7

Navicula leptocephala Bréb. *ex* Grun. *in* V. H., Syn. Diat. Belgique, pl. 7, fig. 16.
    1880.
Navicula cincta var. *leptocephala* Bréb. *ex* V. H., Syn. Diat. Belgique, p. 82.   1885.
Navicula heufleri var. *leptocephala* (Bréb. *ex* Grun.) Perag., Mar. France, p. 99,
    pl. 12, fig. 32, 1897, text 1908.

This taxon is very similar to the nominate variety. It differs in that the ends are rounded and slightly protracted, and the striae are a little finer, 13-14 in 10μ.

In the past this taxon has been considered a variety of *Navicula cincta* (Ehr.) Ralfs. However, as in the nominate variety of this species, it differs from *N. cincta* in the shape of the central area and in the coarser striation. The structure of the central area and the fineness of the striae are two of the most important characteristics in the identification of *N. cincta*.

Type locality. — Austruweel pies d'Anvers [Belgium].

U. S. distribution. — GEOGRAPHICAL: Virginia, Tennessee, Nebraska, Texas. ECOLOGICAL: Seems to prefer water of high mineral content or brackish water.

16. **Navicula cincta** (Ehr.) Ralfs var. **cincta**   PL. 49, FIG. 8

Pinnularia cincta Ehr., Mikrogeol., pl. 10(2), figs. 6a-e.   1854.
Navicula cincta (Ehr.) Ralfs *in* Pritch., Hist. Infusoria, 4th ed., p. 901.   1861.

Valve linear-lanceolate with broadly rounded ends. Axial area narrow, indistinct. Central area transverse: sometimes formed by the striae at the center of the valve being shorter than the others and more distant from each other; at other times the two central striae reach almost to the central nodule while those on each side are much shorter, thus giving the central area an irregular appearance. Striae radiate toward the center of the valve and convergent at the ends. Striae, 8-10 in 10μ at the center of the valve to 17 in 10μ at the ends. Length, $10\text{-}42\mu$. Breadth, $4\text{-}8\mu$.

Type locality. — Kieselguhr von Franzensbad [Czechoslovakia, N. W. Bohemia].

U. S. distribution. — GEOGRAPHICAL: New England States, Middle Atlantic States, Southeastern States, Gulf Coast States, South Central States, East Central States, West Central States, Plains States; Arizona, Oregon, California. ECOLOGICAL: Prefers slightly brackish or slightly alkaline or hard water.

17. **Navicula graciloides** A. Mayer var. **graciloides**   PL. 49, FIGS. 9-10

Navicula graciloides A. Mayer, Kryptog. Forsch., 1:203, 212, pl. 7, fig. 60.   1919.

Valve linear with more or less wedge-shaped, rounded ends. Axial area narrow. Central area transverse, irregular, more or less oval. Striae strongly radiate and somewhat bent near the central area, convergent at the ends. Striae, 10-13 in 10μ. Length, $30\text{-}40\mu$. Breadth, $6\text{-}8\mu$.

This species is easily separated from *Navicula gracilis* Ehr. by the strongly radiate striae and the rounded central area.

Type locality. — Reichenhall und Umgebung . . . Selten im Thumsee [Germany, Upper Bavaria].

U. S. distribution. — GEOGRAPHICAL: Connecticut, Maryland, Indiana. ECOLOGICAL: Fresh to slightly brackish water; circumneutral pH.

18. **Navicula pseudoreinhardtii** Patr. var. **pseudoreinhardtii**
PL. 49, FIG. 11

Navicula pseudoreinhardti Patr., Proc. Acad. Nat. Sci. Philadelphia, 111:104, pl. 7, fig. 9.   1959.

Valve broadly lanceolate, narrowed toward rounded ends. Axial area narrow, distinct. Central area irregular in shape due to the unequal shortening of the striae. The median stria on each side of the raphe often much longer or shorter than the striae adjacent to them. Striae radiate and sometimes curved near the center of the valve, parallel to slightly convergent at the ends; lineate. Striae, 18-20 in 10μ. Length, $15\text{-}25\mu$. Breadth, $4\text{-}7\mu$.

The most characteristic feature of this species is the central area. The central striae are very irregular in length and produce an appearance similar to that of *Navicula reinhardtii* Grun., but the striae are much finer, do not necessarily alternate in length, and the frustules are smaller than those of *N. reinhardtii*. However, *N. pseudoreinhardtii* does seem to be closely related to this group in which the striae are always alternately longer and shorter about the central area.

Type locality. — U.S.A., South Carolina, Aiken County, Savannah River near the Allendale Bridge at Mile 134 from the mouth. (*Holotype*—A.G.C. 4737a, Patrick, 1959.)

U. S. distribution. — GEOGRAPHICAL: South Carolina, Florida.

19. **Navicula reinhardtii** (Grun.) Grun. var. **reinhardtii** PL. 49, FIG. 12

Stauroneis reinhardti Grun., Verh. Zool.-Bot. Ges. Wien, 10:566, pl. 6, fig. 19. 1860.
Navicula reinhardti (Grun.) Grun. *in* Cl. & Grun., K. Svenska Vet.-Akad. Handl., Ny Földj, 17(2):32. 1880.

Valve oblong, more or less abruptly swollen in the middle portion; ends broadly rounded. Axial area narrow. Central area transverse. Striae radiate and somewhat curved at the center of the valve, transverse at the ends; coarsely lineate; more widely spaced at the center of the valve and irregularly, alternately longer and shorter. Striae, 7-9 in 10μ. Length, $35\text{-}70\mu$. Breadth, $11\text{-}18\mu$.

Type locality. — [Germany], ... in lacu "Skienitz See" dicto marchionatus Brandenburgensis . . . .

U. S. distribution. — GEOGRAPHICAL: New England States, Middle Atlantic States, Southeastern States, East Central States, Lakes States, Plains States; Utah, Washington, Oregon. ECOLOGICAL: Seems to prefer fresh water of high mineral content or slightly brackish water.

19. **Navicula reinhardtii** var. **elliptica** Hérib. PL. 49, FIG. 13

Navicula reinhardtii var. *elliptica* Hérib., Diat. Foss. Auvergne, vol. 2, p. 8. 1903.

Valve elliptical. Axial area a little wider than in the nominate variety. Central area transverse, characterized by the striae being irregularly alternately longer and shorter. Striae radiate, near the apices less radiate, almost parallel. Striae, 8-11 in 10μ. Length, $26\text{-}40\mu$. Breadth, $15\text{-}19\mu$.

Héribaud gives no description or figure for his variety, but says: "C'est la forme représentée par Van-Heurck, *Syn*. pl. 7, fig. 6 . . . " The figure cited is of a specimen from La Hulpe, Belgium, on V. H. type slide no. 79.

Type locality. — Belgium, La Hulpe.

U. S. distribution. — Geographical: Oregon.

20. **Navicula gastrum** (Ehr.) Kütz. var. **gastrum**   PL. 49, FIG. 14

Pinnularia gastrum Ehr., Phys. Abh. Akad. Wiss. Berlin, for 1841:421, pl. 3(7), fig. 23. 1843.
Navicula gastrum (Ehr.) Kütz., Bacill., p. 94, pl. 28, fig. 56. 1844.
Navicula varians Greg., Trans. Micr. Soc. London, New Ser., 3:11, pl. 2, figs. 27-28 (in part). 1855.
Navicula gastrum f. *maxima* Temp. & Perag., Diat. Monde Entier, 2nd ed., p. 194. 1910.

Valve lanceolate to elliptical-lanceolate with obtuse, slightly protracted ends. Axial area narrow, slightly widened toward the center area. Central area transverse, irregular in shape. Striae radiate throughout the valve; irregular in length at the central area. The striae at the central area may be alternately longer and shorter; the median striae may be much longer than the others, or they may be irregular in length without any definite pattern. Striae, 8-10 in 10μ at the center of the valve to 12 in 10μ at the ends. Length, 25-60μ. Breadth, 12-20μ.

This species is closely related to *Navicula anglica* Ralfs and *N. placentula* Ehr. Cleve (1895, p. 23) states they intergrade. More study is needed to determine whether they should be kept as distinct species. Except for the general shape of the valve, one cannot be sure that the taxon which Ehrenberg and Kützing had in mind is the same as the one we recognize as *N. gastrum* today. Both Ehrenberg and Kützing illustrate specimens in which the striae are parallel and no central area is present. Kützing illustrates specimens with somewhat more rostrate ends.

It is also closely related to the nominate variety of *N. exigua* (Greg.) Grun.

Type locality. — Mexico, Vera Cruz; among marine algae on the coast.

U. S. distribution. — Geographical: New England States, Middle Atlantic States, Southeastern States,,South Central States, East Central States, West Central States, Lakes States, Plains States; Wyoming, Nevada, Oregon, California. Ecological: Fresh to slightly brackish water.

21. **Navicula decussis** Østr. var. **decussis**   PL. 49, FIG. 15

Navicula decussis Østr., Danske Diat., p. 77, pl. 2, fig. 50. 1910.

Valve elliptical-lanceolate with distinctly capitate ends. Axial area narrow, distinct. Central area irregular in shape, formed by striae which are alternately longer and shorter; an isolated punctum sometimes present. Striae radiate throughout most of the valve, parallel or slightly convergent at the ends; lineate. Striae, 16-20 in 10μ. Length, 16-25μ. Breadth, 6-8μ.

Østrup does not mention the presence of an isolated punctum in his original description. Dr. Reimer has seen some of Østrup's slides in Copenhagen. They are not mounted in a medium of high refractive index, and thus such a punctum might have been overlooked. In A. Schmidt's *Atlas der Diatomaceen-Kunde* (1936, pl. 401, figs. 12-13) a specimen is illustrated which has the punctum.

Type locality. — Denmark, Sjaelland, Fure Sø Ostf.

U. S. distribution. — GEOGRAPHICAL: Middle Atlantic States, Southeastern States; Florida, Tennessee, Ohio, Montana, California. ECOLOGICAL: Fresh water; circumneutral pH.

22. **Navicula hambergii** Hust. var. **hambergii**   PL. 49, FIG. 16

> *Navicula hambergii* Hust. *in* Hamberg, Naturw. Untersuch. Sarekgeb. Schwedisch-Lappland, Band 3, Bot., p. 562, pl. 17, fig. 2. 1924.
> *Navicula quadripartita* Hust. *in* A. S., Atlas Diat., pl. 400, figs. 12-15. 1934. Described: Arch. Hydrobiol. Suppl., 15(2):263, pl. 18, figs. 35-37. 1937.

Valve elliptical-lanceolate with slightly to distinctly rostrate ends. Axial area distinct, becoming wider toward the center of the valve. Central area with one long stria on each side extending to the axial area, each median stria being flanked by two shorter ones. These central striae are more widely spaced than the striae in the rest of the valve. Striae slightly radiate throughout the valve; lineate. Striae, 14-16 in 10μ except at the central area where there are less in 10μ. Cleve-Euler (1953b, p. 194) says that the striae may be 17 in 10μ at the center of the valve to 20 in 10μ at the ends. Length, 17-25μ. Breadth, 6-7.5μ.

This species is most easily characterized by the central area which has the middle striae much longer than those on either side.

Type locality. — Sarekgebirge, . . . in einem Bach (956m.) auf dem Ostabhang des Sakok [Germany].

U. S. distribution. — GEOGRAPHICAL: Pennsylvania. ECOLOGICAL: Oligohalobe and aerophil, preferring mossy rocks on the edge of water.

23. **Navicula menisculus** var. **upsaliensis** (Grun.) Grun.

PL. 49, FIGS. 17-18

> *Navicula* (*menisculus* Schum. var.?) *upsaliensis* Grun. *in* Cl. & Grun., K. Svenska Vet.-Akad. Handl., Ny Földj, 17(2):33. 1880.
> *Navicula menisculus* var. *upsaliensis* (Grun. *in* Cl. & Grun.) Grun. *in* V. H., Syn. Diat. Belgique, pl. 8, figs. 23-24. 1880.

Valve elliptical-lanceolate with slightly rostrate ends. Axial area narrow. Central area small, rounded. Striae radiate toward the center of the valve, parallel to slightly convergent at the ends. Striae, 9-12 in 10μ at the center of the valve, finer toward the apices. Length, 13-40μ. Breadth, 8-15μ.

This variety differs from the nominate variety in that the apical striae are parallel or convergent—not radiate. Also the striae are more finely punctate than in the nominate variety.

This taxon differs from *N. peregrina* (Ehr.) Kütz. in size, shape, and form of the central area.

According to Van Heurck, his type slides nos. 80 and 190 contain specimens of *Navicula menisculus* Schum. However, since the striae are parallel or slightly convergent at the ends, these specimens belong to this taxon rather than to the nominate variety. These specimens are the same as those on Cleve and Möller type slide no. 242 which are identified as this variety.

Type locality. — Upsala . . . [Sweden].

U. S. distribution. — GEOGRAPHICAL: New York, Iowa, Nebraska.

24. Navicula minnewaukonensis Elm. var. minnewaukonensis

PL. 49, FIG. 19

Navicula minnewaukonensis Elm., Univ. Nebraska Stud., 21:78, pl. 9, figs. 331-332. 1922.

Valve broadly lanceolate, oblong, or elliptical with somewhat wedge-shaped or rounded ends; sometimes constricted below rounded ends. Axial area narrow. Central area rounded, small, about one-third the breadth of the valve. Striae radiate throughout most of the valve, parallel at the ends; distantly placed and somewhat irregular in length around the central area. Striae, 14-16 in 10μ. Length, 15-20μ. Breadth, 4-6μ.

This taxon is distinguished by the shape of the valve and the striae number.

Type locality. — U.S.A., North Dakota, Devils Lake; in sand on shore of Bird Island.

U. S. distribution. — GEOGRAPHICAL: Known only from the type locality. ECOLOGICAL: Water of high mineral content.

25. Navicula anglica var. subsalsa (Grun.) Cl.   PL. 49, FIG. 20

Navicula tumida var. *subsalsa* Grun., Verh. Zool.-Bot. Ges. Wien, 10:537, pl. 4, fig. 43b. 1860.

Navicula anglica var. *subsalina* Grun. *in* V. H., Syn. Diat. Belgique, pl. 8, fig. 31. 1880. (text, p. 87. 1885.)

Navicula anglica var. *subsalsa* (Grun.) Cl., K. Svenska Vet.-Akad. Handl., Ny Följd, 27(3):22. 1895.

Valve lanceolate with rostrate ends. Axial area narrow, distinct. Central area small, transversely widened. Cleve-Euler (1953b, p. 141, figs. 790g-k) describes and illustrates specimens in which the central area is quite variable in size. Striae radiate except at the center of the valve where they are almost parallel; striae nearest the apices slightly radiate or almost parallel. Striae, 8-12 in 10μ. Length, 28-40μ. Breadth, 9-15μ.

The nominate variety of this species is elliptical in shape with distinctly capitate ends. The striae are very radiate and are distinctly radiate about the central area. Van Heurck (1880, pl. 8, fig. 30) illustrates a specimen which he names *Navicula anglica* Ralfs but which is really this variety of the species. Since many workers refer to Van Heurck, a great deal of confusion has arisen as to just what *N. anglica* Ralfs var. *anglica* really is. If one refers to the original illustration of this taxon which was published as *Navicula tumida* W. Sm. (1853, p. 53, pl. 17, fig. 146), it is clear that the ends of the valve are distinctly capitate and the striae are radiate—not almost parallel—about the central area.

Elmore (1921, p. 79) in his work on Nebraska diatoms lists several specimens as *N. anglica* Ralfs which are not that taxon.

Type locality. — . . . in Sumpfgräben bei Weissenbach in Unterösterreich . . . [Lower Austria].

U. S. distribution. — GEOGRAPHICAL: Pennsylvania, Alabama. ECOLOGICAL: Hard, or slightly brackish water; circumneutral pH.

26. Navicula latens Krasske var. latens   PL. 49, FIG. 21

> *Navicula latens* Krasske, Arch. Hydrobiol., 31:41. 1937. (*in* A. S., Atlas Diat., pl. 398, figs. 49-51. 1934; and [as *N. tecta* var. *latens* (Krasske) Hust.] pl. 403, fig. 37. 1936).

Valve elliptical-lanceolate with rostrate, sometimes slightly capitate ends. Axial area narrow, linear. Central area transverse; an isolated punctum present on one side. Striae radiate throughout the valve; irregular in length about the central area. Striae, 14-16 in 10μ at the center of the valve, closer at the ends. Length, 24-27μ. Breadth, 8-9μ.

Type locality. — Credner-See Rügen [Island, Baltic Sea].

U. S. distribution. — GEOGRAPHICAL: Florida.

27. Navicula clementis Grun. var. clementis   PL. 49, FIG. 22

> *Navicula clementis* Grun., *in* Beitr. Palaeont. Österreich-Ungarns, Band 2, p. 144, pl. 30, fig. 52. 1882.

Valve elliptical-lanceolate, slightly asymmetrical; narrowed to the rostrate ends. Axial area narrow. Central area transverse, irregular in shape due to the uneven length of the striae. Two isolated puncta are present on one side of the central nodule. Striae radiate throughout the valve; alternately longer and shorter in the middle portion. Striae finely but distinctly lineate, the arrangement of the lineae sometimes giving the appearance of longitudinal lines near the margins of the valve. Striae, 8-10μ at the center of the valve to 16 in 10μ at the ends. Length, 28-40μ. Breadth, 12-15μ.

Type locality. — Dūbravica.

U. S. distribution. — Geographical: Middle Atlantic States, Southeastern States; Tennessee. Ecological: Oligohalobe, littoral, often an aerophil, prefers circumneutral to slightly alkaline water.

28. **Navicula exigua** Greg. *ex* Grun. var. **exigua**   pl. 49, fig. 23

Navicula or *Pinnularia exigua* Greg., Quart. Jour. Micr. Sci., 2:99, pl. 4, fig. 14. 1854. (provisional name.)
Navicula exigua Greg. *ex* Grun. *in* V. H., Syn. Diat. Belgique, pl. 8, fig. 32. 1880.

Valve broadly elliptical with somewhat protracted, rounded ends. Axial area narrow, distinct. Central area transverse, more or less rectangular in shape. Striae radiate throughout the valve; irregular in length and more or less alternately longer and shorter about the central area. Striae, 12-14 in 10μ. Length, 17-30μ. Breadth, 9-12μ.

This taxon differs from Gregory's illustration of *Pinnularia exigua* in that his figure shows no central area and the striae appear to be less radiate. In his description Gregory says that the striae are radiate. This taxon as illustrated is the same as that figured by Van Heurck. Many authors have incorrectly called the capitate form the nominate variety.

Type locality. — Scotland, Mull; diatomaceous earth.

U. S. distribution. — Geographical: New England States, Middle Atlantic States, Southeastern States, Gulf Coast States, South Central States, East Central States, Lake States; California. Ecological: Fresh water; circumneutral pH, with moderate hardness.

28. **Navicula exigua** var. **capitata** Patr.   pl. 49, fig. 24

Navicula exigua var. *capitata* Patr., Farlowia, 2(2):179, pl. 1, fig. 8. 1945.

Valve linear-elliptical with rostrate-capitate ends. Axial area narrow. Central area large, irregularly rectangular. Striae strongly radiate at the center of the valve, parallel or slightly radiate at the ends; finely lineate; irregular in length at the central area. Striae, 14-16 in 10μ. Length, 22-30μ. Breadth, 10-11μ.

This variety differs from the nominate variety mainly in its shape and more numerous striae.

Type locality. — U.S.A., Pennsylvania, Pike County, Shohola Falls. (*Holotype*—A-G.C. 2200, Patrick, 1945.)

·U. S. distribution. — GEOGRAPHICAL: New England States, Middle Atlantic States, Southeastern States, West Central States, Lakes States, Plains States; California. ECOLOGICAL: Fresh water; seems to prefer water of less than 100 p.p.m. hardness ($CaCO_3$).

29. Navicula laterostrata Hust. var. laterostrata   PL. 49, FIG. 25

Navicula laterostrata Hust., Internat. Rev. Ges. Hydrobiol. 13:357, fig. 4. 1925.

Valve lanceolate to elliptical-lanceolate, constricted at the rostrate ends. Axial area narrow, distinct. Central area distinct. Striae radiate throughout the valve; irregular in length about the central area, sometimes alternately longer and shorter. Striae about 15 in 10μ at the center of the valve to 24 in 10μ at the ends. Length, $20\text{-}30\mu$. Breadth, $8\text{-}10\mu$.

The most distinguishing characteristics of this diatom are the shape of the valve and the orbicular shaped central area surrounded by striae of irregular length. Our specimens have striae parallel at the ends.

Type locality. — Schlawasee? . . . Silesia interior [Slawa, Poland].

U. S. distribution. — GEOGRAPHICAL: New England States, Middle Atlantic States; Texas. ECOLOGICAL: Seems to prefer water of high mineral content.

30. Navicula placentula (Ehr.) Kütz. var. placentula   PL. 50, FIG. 1

Pinnularia placentula Ehr., Phys. Abh. Akad. Wiss. Berlin, for 1841:421, pl. 3(7), fig. 22. 1843.
Navicula placentula (Ehr.) Kütz., Bacill., p. 94. 1844. (*non descr.*)

Valve elliptical-lanceolate, narrowed toward wedge-shaped, subrostrate ends. Axial area narrow, distinct. Central area rounded. Striae radiate throughout the valve; coarsely lineate—not alternately longer and shorter about the central area. Striae, 6-12 in 10μ. Length, $30\text{-}70\mu$. Breadth, $14\text{-}28\mu$.

The striae are usually given as 6-9 in 10μ. Many specimens in the United States have striae 9 in 10μ at the center of the valve to 12 in 10μ at the ends. The higher striae number is characteristic of a taxon which has been called *Navicula placentula* var. *latiuscula* (Grun.) Meist. or *N. gastrum* var. *latiuscula* Grun. This variety is not distinctly separate from the nominate variety of this species since the shape and striae number are quite variable.

In 1844, Kützing cites *Navicula placentula* (Ehr.). In his description he says the illustration is "pl. 2, fig. 57c"; however "c" is not included on the plate. His description and figure 57 would indicate that his taxon is not that of Ehrenberg. According to the *International Code of Botanical Nomenclature* (1956, Art. 55), the name must be retained for Ehrenberg's taxon, but the name combination is credited to Kützing even though he misidentified it. Grunow (1880a, p. 34, pl. 2, fig. 36) was the first to use Ehrenberg's taxon correctly in the genus *Navicula.*

Type locality. — Vera-Cruz . . . Die Formen von Vera-Cruz sind See-formen . . . [Mexico].

U. S. distribution. — Geographical: New England States, Middle Atlantic States, Gulf Coast States, East Central States, Plains States; Michigan, Oregon. Ecological: Oligohalobe (indifferent), alkaliphil, saproxen; sometimes found in warm water.

31. **Navicula subfasciata** Patr. var. **subfasciata**   PL. 50, FIG. 2

> *Navicula subfasciata* Patr., Proc. Acad. Nat. Sci. Philadelphia, 111:106, pl. 7, fig. 4. 1959.

Valve linear-lanceolate with distinct, rostrate to capitate ends. Axial area narrow. Median ends of the raphe "drop-like." Central area transverse, not reaching the margins of the valve. Striae very radiate except around the central area where they are almost parallel; lineate; irregularly shortened about the central area. Striae, 24-26 in 10μ. Length, 15-18μ. Breadth, 3-5μ.

The most distinctive characteristic of this species is the shape of the central area. The enlarged ends of the raphe at the central nodule is also characteristic. This species is related to *Navicula dicephala* Ehr., but differs in general outline and in the shape of the central area.

Type locality. — U.S.A., South Carolina, Aiken County, Savannah River at Mile 175 from the mouth of the river. (*Holotype*—A·G.C. 44259a, Patrick, 1959.)

U. S. distribution. — Geographical: South Carolina, Tennessee. Ecological: Fresh water of low mineral content.

32. **Navicula elginensis** (Greg.) Ralfs var. **elginensis**   PL. 50, FIG. 3

> *Pinnularia elginensis* Greg., Quart. Jour. Micr. Sci., 4:9, pl. 1, fig. 33.   1856.
> *Navicula elginensis* (Greg.) Ralfs *in* Pritch., Hist. Infusoria, 4th ed., p. 902.   1861.
> *Navicula dicephala* var. *minor* Grun. *in* V. H., Syn. Diat. Belgique, pl. 8, fig. 33. 1880.
> *Navicula dicephala* f. *minor* Grun. *in* V. H., Syn. Diat. Belgique, pl. 8, fig. 33. Följd, 27(3):21.   1895.

Valve broadly linear, sometimes slightly lanceolate, with capitate to rostrate ends. Margins of the valve on each side of the central area usually parallel. Axial area narrow. Central area distinct, transverse; may be somewhat rounded or rectangular. Striae radiate throughout the valve except at the ends where they are parallel or radiate. Striae, 9-11 in 10μ at the center of the valve to 14 in 10μ at the ends. Length, 20-40μ. Breadth, 8-14μ.

I have examined specimens in Ehrenberg's collection of *Pinnularia dicephala* (Book 8, No. 2, Degensdorf). They are very similar in appearance to *P. biceps* Greg. The specimens which we have and those which recent authors have called "*P. dicephala*" really belong to *P. elginensis* Greg. This, Grunow has suggested in Van Heurck (1880, pl. 8, fig. 34). I have examined specimens of *P. elginensis* from Dr. Gregory's collection (B.M. 11751) from Elgin which are the same as our taxon. The striae are radiate throughout most of the valve except at the very end where they are parallel or very slightly radiate.

Type locality. — Uncertain, probably Elgin [Scotland]. (*Lectotype*—B.M. 11751, Patrick.)

U. S. distribution. — GEOGRAPHICAL: New England States, Middle Atlantic States, Southeastern States, Gulf Coast States, South Central States, East Central States, West Central States, Lakes States, Plains States; Wyoming, Utah, Arizona, Oregon. ECOLOGICAL: Tolerant of a wide range of conditions in fresh to slightly brackish water.

32. **Navicula elginensis** var. **lata** (M. Perag.) Patr. comb. nov.

PL. 50, FIG. 4

Navicula dicephala var. *lata* M. Perag. *in* Temp. & Perag., Diat. Monde Entier, 2nd ed., p. 56. 1908.

Valve linear-elliptical to elliptical with rostrate to rostrate-capitate ends. Axial area narrow, distinct. Central area a broad, transverse fascia which does not reach the margins of the valve. Striae distinctly radiate at the center of the valve, feebly radiate to almost parallel at the ends; coarsely lineate; irregularly shortened about the central area. Striae, 12-14 in 10μ. Length, about 30μ. Breadth, about 11μ.

This taxon differs from the nominate variety by its larger central area.

Type locality. — U.S.A., Connecticut, Bristol, Fall Mountain; from springs and streams at 800 feet.

U. S. distribution. — GEOGRAPHICAL: Known only from the type locality.

32. **Navicula elginensis** var. **neglecta** (Krasske) Patr. comb. nov.

PL. 50, FIG. 5

Navicula neglecta Krasske, Bot. Arch., 27:354, fig. 5. 1929.
Navicula dicephala var. *neglecta* (Krasske) Hust. *in* Pasch., Süssw.-Fl. Mitteleuropas, Heft 10, Aufl. 2, p. 303, fig. 527. 1930.

Margins of valve triundulate; ends rostrate to slightly capitate. Axial area narrow; central area transversely widened. Striae at the ends of the valve parallel or slightly radiate. Striae, 10-14 in 10μ. Length, $22-23\mu$. Breadth, $8-9\mu$.

This taxon is related to *Navicula dicephala* var. *undulata* Østr. (1920, p. 25, pl. 3, fig. 33). Our taxon differs in that the undulations of the margins of the valve are much weaker and the striae at the apices are parallel to convergent.

Type locality. — Germany, Dresden.

U. S. distribution. — GEOGRAPHICAL: Middle Atlantic States, Southeastern States.

32. Navicula elginensis var. rostrata (A. Mayer) Patr. comb. nov.

PL. 50, FIG. 6

Navicula dicephala var. *rostrata* A. Mayer, Denkschr. Bayer. Bot. Ges. Regensburg, 13(N.F. 7):114, pl. 1, figs. 42a-b.   1917.

Valve linear-lanceolate with broadly rostrate ends. Axial area narrow. Central area rectangular, not reaching the margins of the valve. Striae radiate throughout the valve except about the central area where they are almost parallel. Striae, 9-11 in 10μ at the center of the valve to 13 in 10μ at the ends. Length, $33\text{-}36\mu$. Breadth, $10\text{-}12\mu$.

This variety is mainly distinguished from the nominate variety by its rostrate—not capitate—ends and the shape of the central area.

Type locality. — Germany, Bavaria, Donaualtheim.

U. S. distribution. — GEOGRAPHICAL: Montana.

33. Navicula explanata Hust. var. explanata   PL. 50, FIG. 7

Navicula explanata Hust., Schweizerische Zeitschr. Hydrol., 11:207, figs. 7-8   1948.

Valve lanceolate with protracted, rostrate ends. Axial area narrow. Terminal fissures of the raphe turned in opposite directions. Central area transverse, not reaching the margins of the valve. Striae radiate at the center of the valve, parallel at the ends; lineate. Striae, 10 in 10μ at the center of the valve to 20 in 10μ at the ends. Length, $28\text{-}40\mu$. Breadth, $9\text{-}12\mu$.

This species is quite similar to *Navicula elginensis* var. *rostrata* described above. However, it differs in that it is lanceolate in shape, the striae are parallel—not radiate—at the ends, the striae are much closer at the ends of the valve than in the center, and the ends of the raphe are turned in opposite directions.

Type locality. — Poland, near "Gaj bei Konin."

U. S. distribution. — GEOGRAPHICAL: Connecticut, Utah.

34. **Navicula hustedtii** Krasske var. **hustedtii**   PL. 50, FIG. 8

Navicula hustedtii Krasske, Bot. Arch., 3:198, fig. 3. 1923.
Navicula hustedtii f. *philippina* Skv., Philippine Jour. Sci., 64:290, pl. 1, fig. 44. 1938.

Valve lanceolate to elliptical-lanceolate with capitate ends. Axial area narrow. Central area transverse, rounded, somewhat variable in size. Striae radiate throughout the valve. Striae, 20 in 10μ at the center of the valve; often becoming much closer toward the ends, 26-28 in 10μ. Length, $10\text{-}15\mu$. Breadth, $4\text{-}5\mu$.

Our specimens are intermediate between *Navicula hustedtii* and *N. hustedtii* f. *philippina*. They are similar to the former in the number of striae, and to the latter in the shape of the central area. This indicates that these forms intergrade and are really part of the same taxon.

Type locality. — Auf Steinen einer Quelle über dem Bahnhof Wellerode (Söhre bei Cassel) [Germany].

U. S. distribution. — GEOGRAPHICAL: Middle Atlantic States; Texas, Indiana, Missouri. ECOLOGICAL: Brackish water.

35. **Navicula dystrophica** Patr. var. **dystrophica**   PL. 50, FIG. 9

Navicula dystrophica Patr., Proc. Acad. Nat. Sci. Philadelphia, 111:102, pl. 7, fig. 5. 1959.

Valve linear with somewhat wedge-shaped, rostrate ends. Axial area distinct, narrow. Central area not clearly differentiated from the axial area. Terminal striae parallel or slightly convergent, other striae radiate except the median one on each side of the central area. Striae only slightly shortened about the central area; sometimes striae on one side of this area shorter than those on the opposite side. Striae about the central area farther apart than those in the rest of the valve. Striae, 26-28 in 10μ. Length, $10\text{-}15\mu$. Breadth, $2.8\text{-}4\mu$.

This species is very similar in size and general shape to *Navicula brehmioides* Hust. (1952, p. 404, fig. 118), but the ends are more protracted than in Hustedt's species. The number of striae in 10μ is similar, and in both species the striae may be slightly convergent at the ends. Hustedt states that in his taxon the striae are finely punctate. In this taxon they are finely lineate. In Hustedt's taxon the median striae are much shorter than the other striae.

This taxon is somewhat similar to *Navicula iniqua* Krasske (1932, p. 116, pl. 3, fig. 20). However, in *N. dystrophica* the striae are more numerous, and they are parallel or slightly convergent at the ends. In *N. iniqua* they are radiate at the ends.

It is also similar to *Navicula pinnularioides* f. *continua* Cl.-Eul. (1934, p. 67, pl. 4, fig. 111) which is a larger species with coarser striae.

Type locality. — U.S.A., South Carolina, Aiken County, near the mouth of Upper Three Runs. (*Holotype*—A-G.C. 44254, Patrick, 1959.)

U. S. distribution. — GEOGRAPHICAL: Known only from the type locality. ECOLOGICAL: Soft, acid, fresh water.

36. **Navicula notha** Wallace var. **notha**   PL. 50, FIGS. 10-11

> *Navicula notha* Wallace, Not. Nat. Acad. Nat. Sci. Philadelphia, No. 331, p. 4, pl. 1, figs. 4A-D. 1960.

Valve linear-lanceolate with attenuated, rostrate, sometimes slightly capitate apices. Axial area very narrow, sometimes indistinct. Central area small, rounded, sometimes asymmetrical. Striae radiate in the middle portion of the valve, parallel or slightly convergent toward the apices; lineate. Striae, 16-17 in 10μ. Length, 19-32μ. Breadth, 4-5μ.

This taxon is distinguished by its shape and the number of the striae.

Type locality. — U.S.A., Virginia, Louisa County, North Anna River. Coll. J. H. Wallace, September 24, 1954. (*Holotype*—A-G.C. 4613b, Wallace, 1960.)

U. S. distribution. — GEOGRAPHICAL: Middle Atlantic States, Southeastern States, Gulf Coast States, South Central States, East Central States; California. ECOLOGICAL: Seems to prefer water of low mineral content.

37. **Navicula canalis** Patr. var. **canalis**   PL. 50, FIG. 12

> *Navicula canalis* Patr., Bol. Mus. Nac. [Rio de Janeiro], Nova Sér., Bot., 2:6, fig. 7. 1944.

Valve linear-lanceolate with attenuated, rostrate ends. Axial area narrow. Central area small, not distinct. Striae somewhat radiate throughout most of the valve, parallel or slightly convergent toward the ends. Striae, 15-17 in 10μ. Length, 22μ. Breadth, 5μ. (*Holotype*—A-G.C. 25741, Patrick, 1944.)

Type locality. — Brazil, Rio Grande do Sul, near Lagoa dos Quadros.

U. S. distribution. — GEOGRAPHICAL: Middle Atlantic States, Southeastern States, Gulf Coast States, South Central States, East Central States, West Central States, Plains States. ECOLOGICAL: Seems to prefer water of low mineral content.

38. **Navicula falaisensis** var. **lanceola** Grun.   PL. 50, FIG. 13

> *Navicula falaisensis* var.? *lanceola* Grun. *in* V. H., Syn. Diat. Belgique, pl. 14, fig. 6B. 1880.

Valve linear with attenuated, rostrate ends. Axial area narrow, distinct. Central area elliptical, distinct. Striae radiate, finely lineate. Striae, 23-27 in 10μ. Length, 27-29μ. Breadth, 4-5μ.

Type locality. — Uncertain, Belgium.

U. S. distribution. — GEOGRAPHICAL: New York, Wyoming.

39. **Navicula ilopangoensis** Hust. var. **ilopangoensis**   PL. 50, FIG. 14

Navicula ilopangoensis Hust., Ergebn. Deutschen Limnol. Venezuela-Exped. 1952, 1:114, fig. 37. 1956.

Valve narrow, linear-lanceolate with produced rostrate ends. Axial area narrow. Raphe straight; median ends slightly broadened; terminal fissures indistinct. Central area inconspicuous or lacking. Striae very slightly radiate, becoming parallel toward the ends; indistinctly lineate. Striae, 22-24 in 10μ. Length, 22-32μ. Breadth, 3-4μ.

Type locality. — Lago de Ilopango in El Salvador.

U. S. distribution. — GEOGRAPHICAL: Texas. ECOLOGICAL: Brackish water.

40. **Navicula bicephala** Hust. var. **bicephala**   PL. 50, FIG. 15

Navicula bicephala Hust., Bot. Not., for 1952:398, fig. 106. 1952.

Valve linear with parallel to slightly convex sides; ends protracted, subcapitate to capitate. Axial area very narrow. Raphe straight; terminal ends curved in the same direction. Central area small, orbicular. Striae radiate except at the ends where they are convergent; indistinctly lineate. Striae, 16-18 in 10μ becoming 20-22 in 10μ at the ends. Length, 20-26μ. Breadth, 3-4μ.

This diatom is very similar to *Navicula longicephala* Hust. (1944, p. 277, fig. 17). The latter, however, has uniformly shortened central striae forming a distinctly circular central area, whereas *N. bicephala* has striae irregularly shortened at the central area. In addition, *N. longicephala* has parallel striae at the ends, not convergent as in *N. bicephala*. *N. dicephaloides* Fusey (1948, p. 349, figs. 50, 52) also has the same general shape as *N. bicephala*, but is distinguished by the coarser striae that are radiate throughout and by the presence of a rather large central area.

Type locality. — In Süsswasser Ansammlungen auf den Kerguelen [Kerguelen Island].

U. S. distribution. — GEOGRAPHICAL: Middle Atlantic States, Southeastern States; Tennessee. ECOLOGICAL: Soft circumneutral water in the United States.

41. Navicula contraria Patr. var. contraria   PL. 50, FIG. 16

Navicula contraria Patr., Proc. Acad. Nat. Sci. Philadelphia, 111:101, pl. 7, fig. 10.
1959.

Valve lanceolate with broadly rounded ends. Axial area narrow.
Terminal fissures of the raphe turned in opposite directions. Central area
transverse, rounded. Striae slightly radiate throughout the valve; lineate;
more or less regularly shortened about the central area. Striae, 12-13 in
10μ at the center of the valve to 16-18 in 10μ toward the ends. Length,
$33-41\mu$. Breadth, $13-21\mu$.

The most distinctive characteristics of this species are the terminal
fissures (turned in opposite directions), the shape of the central area, and
the coarsely lineate striae.

This species is closely related to the marine species, *Navicula diversi-
punctata* Hust. and *N. omegopsis* Hust. It differs from them in its shape,
the absence of puncta in the central area, and the coarsely lineate rather
than punctate striae.

Type locality. — U.S.A., South Carolina, Aiken County, Savannah River
at Mile 134 from the mouth near Allendale Bridge. (*Holotype*—A-G.C.
4737a, Patrick, 1959.)

U. S. distribution. — GEOGRAPHICAL: Known only from the type locality.
ECOLOGICAL: Soft circumneutral water.

42. Navicula incomposita var. minor Hagelst.   PL. 50, FIG. 17

Navicula incomposita var. *minor* Hagelst., New York Acad. Sci., Sci. Surv. Porto
Rico & Virgin Isl., 8(3):386, pl. 7, fig. 3.   1939.

Valve lanceolate with obtusely rounded ends. Diaphragm or septum
present at each end of the valve. Axial area narrow, linear. Raphe straight;
median ends broadened; terminal ends curving in the same direction. Central area inconspicuous or lacking. Striae radiate throughout most of the
valve, nearly parallel at the ends; lineate. Arrangement of the central striae
variable, more distant than the other striae, individual striae sometimes
lacking. Striae, 15-16 in 10μ at the center of the valve to 18-21 in 10μ
toward the ends. Length, $20-45\mu$. Breadth, $6.5-10\mu$.

The nominate variety has not been observed from the United States.
It is a larger form (to 85μ) and, according to Hagelstein, has more or less
irregularly spaced striae throughout the valve. None of the forms observed
in collections from the United States exceeds 45μ in length, and the irregular spacing of the striae is confined to those at the center of the valve.

Type locality. — Porto Rico, Santa Isabel.

U. S. distribution. — GEOGRAPHICAL: Texas. ECOLOGICAL: Warm, brackish water.

43. **Navicula peticolasii** M. Perag. var. **peticolasii**   PL. 50, FIG. 18

Navicula (*peregrina* var.?) *peticolasii* M. Perag. *in* Temp. & Perag., Diat. Monde Entier, 2nd ed., p. 195. 1910.

Valve lanceolate with rounded ends. Axial area narrow, widening in the middle portion between the ends and the central area. Raphe filamentous. Central area transverse, irregular in shape. Striae radiate at the center of the valve, convergent at the ends; lineate; alternately longer and shorter about the central area. Striae, 7-9 in 10μ. Length, $210\text{-}300\mu$. Breadth, about 35μ.

Peragallo questions if this is a variety of *Navicula peregrina*. I believe it to be a separate taxon because of the angle of the striae and the fact that they are alternately longer and shorter about the central area. Also, the shape of the central area is different.

Type locality. — U.S.A., Oregon, Klamath County, Swan Lake. (*Lectotype*—A-T.&.P. 365, Patrick.)

U. S. distribution. — GEOGRAPHICAL: Oregon, California.

44. **Navicula vulpina** Kütz. var. **vulpina**   PL. 50, FIG. 19

Navicula vulpina Kütz., Bacill., p. 92, pl. 3, fig. 43.   1844.

Valve linear-lanceolate, tapering to rounded ends. Axial area narrow, widening toward the large oval to circular central area. Striae radiate toward the center of the valve, convergent at the ends; coarsely lineate, the lineae sometimes forming irregular longitudinal lines. Striae, 10-12 in 10μ. Length, $50\text{-}140\mu$. Breadth, $10\text{-}20\mu$.

This species is easily characterized by its large central area and large terminal nodules.

Type locality. — In Süsswassergräben bei Nordhausen [Germany].

U. S. distribution. — GEOGRAPHICAL: Middle Atlantic States; New York, Ohio, Michigan. ECOLOGICAL: Fresh water, mesotrophic.

45. **Navicula walkeri** Sov. var. **walkeri**   PL. 51, FIG. 1

Navicula walkerii Sov., Trans. American Micr. Soc., 77(2):120, pl. 3, figs. 27-28. 1958.

Valve lanceolate to somewhat rhombic-lanceolate with obtuse, rounded apices. Axial area one-quarter to one-fifth the breadth of the valve. Raphe filamentous with well-developed "comma" shaped terminal fissures. Central area orbicular. Striae radiate throughout most of the valve, more or less convergent at the apices; lineate; crossed by a band similar to that found in *Pinnularia*. Striae, 9-10 in 10μ. Length, $108\text{-}194\mu$. Breadth, $22\text{-}29\mu$.

The striae seem to be formed as in *Caloneis* except that the external membrane is lineate; internally a small pore is present which forms a longitudinal line. Thus the structure of the striae has the characteristics of the subgenus *Navicula* of *Navicula* and of *Caloneis*. Sovereign states the structure of the striae has the characteristics of *Navicula* and *Pinnularia*. However, since the internal opening seems to be a small pore rather than a band-like opening as in *Pinnularia*, I think it is more like that of *Caloneis*.

This species is distinguished by the structure of the striae.

Type locality. — U.S.A., Oregon, Crater Lake National Park, Bay on Wizard island. (*Holotype*—Cal. Acad. Sci. H.T.-3469, Sov. 491-5, Sovereign, 1960.)

U. S. distribution. — GEOGRAPHICAL: Oregon.

46. Navicula ludloviana A. S. var. ludloviana   PL. 51, FIG. 2

Navicula ludloviana A. S., Atlas Diat., pl. 46, fig. 15.   1876.

Valve lanceolate with obtuse, subtruncate ends. Axial area broad, widening into an orbicular central area. Terminal nodules large. Raphe filamentous. Striae radiate throughout the valve; lineate; more distantly placed at the center of the valve and alternately longer and shorter. Striae, 6-7 in 10μ at the center of the valve to 8-9 in 10μ at the ends. Length, $90\text{-}132\mu$. Breadth, $23\text{-}33\mu$.

This diatom is mainly characterized by the broad axial area, the large central area, and by the striae in the central area being alternately longer and shorter.

Type locality. — U.S.A., Washington, Fort Ludlow.

U. S. distribution. — GEOGRAPHICAL: Washington, Oregon, California.

47. Navicula aurora Sov. var. aurora   PL. 51, FIGS. 3-4

Navicula aurora Sov., Trans. American Micr. Soc., 77(2):120, pl. 3, figs. 29-31. 1958.

Navicula peregrina var. *truncata* M. Perag. *in* Temp. & Perag., Diat. Monde Entier, 2nd ed., p. 59.   1908.

Valve elliptical-lanceolate to linear-lanceolate with broadly rounded, slightly protracted apices. Axial area distinct, usually one-fifth to one-sixth the breadth of the valve; widening toward the central area which is more or less irregularly rectangular. The raphe has distinct terminal fissures. Striae lineate, radiate in the middle portion of the valve; parallel, occasionally slightly convergent at the apices. Striae about the central area are irregular in length, but not regularly alternately longer and shorter. Striae, 6-10 in 10μ. Length, $57\text{-}128\mu$. Breadth, $15\text{-}26\mu$.

This species is distinguished by the shape of the axial and central areas and the angle of the striae. The thickness of the striae varies with the plane of focus. The holotype which we have illustrated has the striae more irregular about the central area than the specimen illustrated by Sovereign.

This taxon is closely related to *Navicula peregrina*. Indeed it is very similar to a specimen which is referred to this species in A. Schmidt's Atlas Diat. (1876, pl. 47, fig. 60). It mainly differs by the shape of the valve and the coarser striae. This illustration of A. Schmidt, however, is not typical of the nominate variety of the species. In general it seems to differ from *N. peregrina* by its wider axial area, more irregularly shaped central area, and finer striae. It is also closely related to *N. reinhardti* from which it differs by the shape of the central area and the coarser striae. It does not seem to be so closely related to *N. ludloviana* to which Sovereign refers. It differs from *N. kefvingensis* (Ehr.) Kütz. by the shape of the central area and the striae being parallel or slightly convergent—not radiate—at the apices.

Type locality. — U.S.A., Oregon, Douglas County, Diamond Lake. (*Holotype*—Cal. Acad. Sci. H.T.-3468, Sov. 498-7, Sovereign, 1960.)

U. S. distribution. — GEOGRAPHICAL: Widespread in the Pacific Northwest. ECOLOGICAL: Found in water of pH 6.5-9.

48. Navicula peregrina (Ehr.) Kütz. var. peregrina   PL. 51, FIG. 5

Pinnularia peregrina Ehr., Phys. Abh. Akad. Wiss. Berlin, for 1841:421, pl. 1(1), figs. 5-6; pl. 2(4), fig. 1; pl. 2(6), fig. 22; pl. 3(1), fig. 3.   1843.
Navicula peregrina (Ehr.) Kütz., Bacill., p. 97, pl. 28, fig. 52.   1844.

Valve lanceolate, usually narrowed toward broadly rounded ends. Ends sometimes acute. Axial area narrow, distinct. Central area transversely widened; usually rounded, sometimes almost rectangular. Striae radiate throughout most of the valve, becoming parallel to slightly convergent toward the ends; lineate. Striae, 5-6 in 10μ at the center of the valve to 8 in 10μ at the ends. Length, $36\text{-}150\mu$. Breadth, $10\text{-}30\mu$.

Ehrenberg, in his original description of this species, illustrates several specimens. The shape of our specimen most closely resembles that shown in pl. 1(1), fig. 6. The angle of the striae is more similar to that found in pl. 3(1), fig. 3.

Type locality. — Maluinen- oder Falklands-Inseln; aus einem Theilchen einer Seeconferve . . . [South America; from a piece of a marine conferva].

U. S. distribution. — GEOGRAPHICAL: New England States, Middle Atlantic States, Southeastern States, Gulf Coast States, East Central States, Lakes States, Plains States; Montana, Wyoming, Washington, Oregon, California. ECOLOGICAL: Seems to prefer water of high mineral content or brackish water.

49. **Navicula oblonga** (Kütz.) Kütz. var. **oblonga**   PL. 51, FIG. 6

Frustulia oblonga Kütz., Linnaea, 8:548, pl. 14, fig. 24. 1833.
Navicula oblonga (Kütz.) Kütz., Bacill., p. 97, pl. 4, fig. 21. 1844.
Pinnularia oblonga Rabh., Süssw.-Diat., p. 45, pl. 6, fig. 6. 1853.

Valve linear or slightly lanceolate; narrower at the truncate, rounded ends. Axial area distinct; approximately one-fourth the breadth of the valve, becoming wider toward the center. Raphe filamentous with distinct terminal fissures. Central area transverse, rounded. Terminal nodules distinct. Striae radiate throughout most of the valve and bent near the margins, convergent at the ends; lineate. Striae, 6-9 in 10μ. Length, 70-220μ. Breadth, 13-24μ.

Kützing's second illustration (1844, pl. 4, fig. 21) shows the striae to be radiate throughout the valve. However, a specimen from Kützing's exsiccatae (Dec. 8, No. 71, 1833a, *Frustulia oblonga*) shows the striae to be convergent at the ends of the valve, and lineate.

Type locality. — Uncertain, Germany.

U. S. distribution. — GEOGRAPHICAL: New England States, Middle Atlantic States, Gulf Coast States, East Central States, Lakes States, Plains States; Wyoming, Utah, Washington, Oregon. ECOLOGICAL: Seems to prefer water of high mineral content; alkaline or slightly brackish.

50. **Navicula tenelloides** Hust. var. **tenelloides**   PL. 51, FIG. 7

Navicula tenelloides Hust., Arch. Hydrobiol. Suppl., 15(2):269, pl. 19, fig. 13. 1937.

Valve linear-lanceolate with rounded ends. Axial area narrow. Central area small. Striae slightly radiate at the center of the valve, convergent at the ends. Striae, 15 in 10μ at the center of the valve to 20 in 10μ at the ends. Length, 16-19μ. Breadth, 3-4μ.

This species differs from *Navicula tenella* in the smaller size and the more broadly rounded ends.

Type locality. — East Java . . . Abfluss und Quellzufluss des Ranu Lamongan [?] . . . Quelle am Ranu Pakis [?] . . . .

U. S. distribution. — GEOGRAPHICAL: Middle Atlantic States, Southeastern States, South Central States, East Central States, Plains States; Florida. ECOLOGICAL: Aerophil; pH, 7.5-7.8.

51. **Navicula dulcis** Patr. var. **dulcis**   PL. 51, FIG. 8

Navicula dulcis Patr., Proc. Acad. Nat. Sci. Philadelphia, 111:102, pl. 7, fig. 7. 1959.

Valve lanceolate, narrowed toward rounded ends. Axial area narrow.

Central area reaching the margins of the valve. Striae radiate at the center of the valve, parallel or slightly convergent at the ends; very broad; lineate. Striae, 14-16 in 10µ. Length, 11-16µ. Breadth, 2.5-4µ.

This species is quite similar to *Navicula subcostulata* Hust. (1934b, p. 386, fig. 13), but differs from it in that its ends are more rounded than those of *N. subcostulata*. *Navicula subcostulata* lives in water of low conductivity, whereas this species lives in brackish water or water of high conductivity.

Type locality. — U.S.A., Texas, Orange County, Sabine River near the mouth, on diatometer. (*Holotype*—A-G.C. 8035, Patrick, 1959.)

U. S. distribution. — GEOGRAPHICAL: Known only from the type locality. ECOLOGICAL: Brackish water.

52. **Navicula costulata** Grun. var. **costulata** PL. 51, FIG. 9

Navicula costulata Grun. *in* Cl. & Grun., K. Svenska Vet.-Akad. Handl., Ny Földj, 17(2):27. 1880.

Valve rhombic-lanceolate with acute ends. Axial area indistinct. Central area broad, transverse, extending to the margins of the valve. Striae strongly radiate in the middle portion of the valve, parallel or slightly radiate at the ends; distant from each other. Striae, 7-10 in 10µ. Length, 12-20µ. Breadth, 4-5µ.

The strongly radiate striae that are distant from each other, and the wide central area, characterize this species.

Type locality. — Uncertain.

U. S. distribution. — GEOGRAPHICAL: New York, California. ECOLOGICAL: Alkaliphil or slightly brackish water.

53. **Navicula gravistriata** Patr. var. **gravistriata** PL. 51, FIG. 10

Navicula gravistriata Patr., Proc. Acad. Nat. Sci. Philadelphia, 111:103, pl. 7, fig. 8. 1959.

Valve elliptical-lanceolate with narrow, rounded, somewhat attenuated ends. Axial area narrow. Central area transverse, formed by the middle stria on each side of the raphe being much shorter. Striae radiate in the middle portion of the valve, parallel to slightly convergent at the ends; distinctly lineate; broad. Striae, 11-13 in 10µ. Length, 12-22µ. Breadth, 4-7µ.

The possibility that this was a new taxon was first noted by Mrs. B. G. Stepka.

Some of the smaller forms of *Navicula abunda* Hust. (1955b, p. 27, pl. 9, figs. 10-12) are similar to this species in the shape of the axial and central area and in the angle of the striae. The main differences are in the shape of the valve, the length-to-breadth ratio, the lesser number of striae in 10μ, and the smaller size range.

Type locality. — U.S.A., Texas, Orange County, Sabine River near the mouth of Cow Bayou. (*Holotype*—A-G.C. 8031, Patrick, 1959.)

U. S. distribution. — GEOGRAPHICAL: Known only from the type locality. ECOLOGICAL: Slightly brackish to brackish water.

54. **Navicula cascadensis** Sov. var. **cascadensis**   PL. 51, FIG. 11·

Navicula cascadensis Sov., Trans. American Micr. Soc., 77(2):118-119, pl. 3, figs. 32-33. 1958.

Valve elliptical to elliptical-lanceolate with rounded apices. Axial area narrow, distinct. Terminal nodules of the raphe at some distance from the ends of the valve. Central area only slightly wider than the axial area. Striae radiate, lineate. Striae near the ends of the valve shorter than the rest, due to the presence of a row of two to three puncta on each side of the axial area. Striae, 9-11 in 10μ, more numerous at the ends of the valves. Length, 11-21μ. Breadth, 6-9μ.

This species is distinguished by the characteristic structure of the striae and the rows of puncta extending from the apices of the valve.

Type locality. — U.S.A., Oregon, Douglas County, Diamond Lake.

U. S. distribution. — GEOGRAPHICAL: Oregon. ECOLOGICAL: Lake water of pH 8.1-8.8. (*Holotype*—Cal. Acad. Sci. H.T.-3467, Sov. 489-6, Sovereign, 1960.)

55. **Navicula capitata** Ehr. var. **capitata**   PL. 52, FIGS. 1-2

Navicula capitata Ehr., Infusionsthierchen, p. 185, pl. 13, fig. 20. 1838.
Pinnularia capitata Ehr., Ber. Akad. Wiss. Berlin, for 1848:18. 1848.
Pinnularia digitus Ehr., Mikrogeol., pl. 33(A)8, fig. 15. 1854.
Navicula humilis Donk., Nat. Hist. British Diat., p. 67, pl. 10, figs. 7a-b. 1870-1873.
Navicula hungarica var. *capitata* (Ehr.) Cl., K. Svenska Vet.-Akad. Handl., Ny Följd, 27(3):16. 1895.

Valve elliptical-lanceolate with rostrate to capitate ends. Ends of the valve devoid of striae, forming a clear area which appears to be of different thickness from the rest of the valve. Axial area indistinct. Central area small, formed by the center striae being shorter than the rest. Striae radiate throughout most of the valve, convergent at the ends; the terminal ones more heavily marked than the rest. Striae, 8-10 in 10μ. Length, 12-47μ. Breadth, 5-10μ.

Mr. Ross agrees with me that specimens on B. M. 12291 which Mr. Ross states are part of Donkin's type material, represent Donkin's species correctly. I, therefore, designate the specimen we have drawn as the lectotype of *Navicula humilis*.

Type locality. — Germany, Berlin.

U. S. distribution. — GEOGRAPHICAL: New England States, Middle Atlantic States, Southeastern States, Gulf Coast States, West Central States, Lakes States, Plains States; Wyoming, Arizona, Washington. ECOLOGICAL: Seems to tolerate a wide variation in the chemistry of the water.

55. **Navicula capitata** var. **hungarica** (Grun.) Ross   PL. 52, FIG. 3

> *Navicula hungarica* Grun., Verh. Zool.-Bot. Ges. Wien, 10:539, pl. 3, fig. 30. 1860.
> *Navicula capitata* var. *hungarica* (Grun.) Ross, Natl. Mus. Canada Bull., No. 97, pt. 2, p. 192. 1947.

Valve linear-lanceolate to rhombic-lanceolate with broadly rounded ends. Axial area indistinct. Central area small, formed by the median striae being shorter than the others. As in the nominate variety, terminal striae more strongly marked than the rest. Striae radiate toward the center of the valve to convergent at the ends. Striae, 8-11 in 10μ. Length, $10-36\mu$. Breadth, $4-10\mu$.

This variety differs from the nominate variety in that the ends are not capitate.

Type locality. — . . . Ad litora meridionalia lacus Peisonis Hungariae in aqua subsalsa . . . [Hungary].

U. S. distribution. — GEOGRAPHICAL: New England States, Middle Atlantic States, Southeastern States, Gulf Coast States, South Central States, East Central States, West Central States, Plains States; California. ECOLOGICAL: Seems to tolerate a great variety of water conditions.

55. **Navicula capitata** var. **luneburgensis** (Grun.) Patr. comb. nov.

PL. 52, FIG. 4

> *Navicula hungarica* var. *luneburgensis* Grun., *in* Beitr. Palaeont. Österreich-Ungarns, Band 2, p. 156, pl. 30, figs. 43-44. 1882.

Valve lanceolate with acute ends. Axial area indistinct. Ends of the valve devoid of striae, appearing to be of a different thickness from the rest of the valve. Central area rounded, distinct. Striae radiate toward the center of the valve, convergent toward the ends. Striae, 5 in 10μ at the center of the valve, 10 in 10μ at the ends. Length, $12-36\mu$. Breadth, $5-8\mu$.

This taxon is characterized by its lanceolate shape and acute ends.

Type locality. — Germany, Oberohe.

U. S. distribution. — GEOGRAPHICAL: Middle Atlantic States; Tennessee, Texas. ECOLOGICAL: Slightly brackish water.

56. **Navicula inflexa** (Greg.) Ralfs var. **inflexa**   PL. 52, FIG. 5

Pinnularia inflexa Greg., Trans. Micr. Soc. London, New Ser., 4:48, pl. 5, fig. 20. 1856.

Navicula inflexa (Greg.) Ralfs *in* Pritch., Hist. Infusoria, 4th ed., p. 905. 1861.

Valve lanceolate to elliptical-lanceolate with acute, rounded ends. A dark band present near each apex. Axial area narrow, distinct. Central area rounded. Striae strongly radiate; distinctly lineate; regularly or somewhat irregularly shortened at the central area. Striae, 8-11 in 10μ. Length, 33-75μ. Breadth, 7-9μ.

This species is characterized by the dark bands extending across the ends of the valve.

Gregory chose the species name because he believed the dark bands near the apices to be caused by depressions.

Type locality. — Scotland, post-Tertiary sands of Glenshira.

U. S. distribution. — GEOGRAPHICAL: Connecticut, New Jersey. ECOLOGICAL: Brackish water.

Navicula subgenus TUSCULA (Hust.) Patr.

Navicula sect. *Tusculae* Hust., Abh. Naturw. Ver. Bremen, 34(3):287. 1957.

Navicula subgenus *Tuscula* (Hust.) Patr., Not. Nat. Acad. Nat. Sci. Philadelphia, No. 324, p. 10. 1959.

Valve with striae broken into sections. Striae lineate at the center of the valve. On the margins of the valve striae sometimes composed of a double row of puncta.

The raphe may be straight or undulate. The striae are radiate throughout the valve, but they are almost parallel at the center of the valve.

This subgenus is closely related to the subgenus *Navicula*, which is characterized by lineate striae; however, the striae are not broken into sections as in this subgenus.

Type species. — *Navicula tuscula* Ehr.

1. **Navicula caroliniana** Patr., var. **caroliniana**   PL. 52, FIG. 6

Navicula caroliniana Patr., Proc. Acad. Nat. Sci. Philadelphia, 111:107, pl. 7, fig. 11. 1959.

Valve lanceolate with slightly attenuated, semirostrate, rounded ends. Axial area narrow. Raphe undulate. Central area transverse, irregular in shape. Striae radiate throughout the valve; broken to form irregular longitudinal lines; irregular in length about the central area where they may be alternately longer and shorter. On the margins of the valve, the striae sometimes give the appearance of being composed of two rows of puncta. Striae, 11-12 in 10μ. Length, 44-45μ. Breadth, 15-16μ.

This species belongs in the same group as *Navicula tuscula* Ehr. It differs from this taxon by its undulate, filamentous raphe and coarser striae. It is also similar to *N. konstantinii* Skabich. (1952, p. 40) in both the structure of the striae and the undulate raphe.

Type locality. — U.S.A., South Carolina, Aiken County, Savannah River at Mile 175 from the mouth of the river.

U. S. distribution. — GEOGRAPHICAL: Known only from the type locality. ECOLOGICAL: Soft circumneutral water.

2. **Navicula tuscula** Ehr. var. **tuscula**   PL. 52, FIG. 7

Navicula tuscula Ehr., Ber. Akad. Wiss. Berlin, for 1840:215.   1840.
Stauroneis punctata Kütz., Bacill., p. 106, pl. 21, fig. 9.   1844.
Navicula punctata (Kütz.) Donk., Nat. Hist. British Diat., p. 36, pl. 5, fig. 12. 1870-1873.
Navicula tuscula f. *rostrata* Hust. *in* Pasch., Süssw.-Fl. Mitteleuropas, Heft 10, Aufl. 2, p. 308.   1930.

Valve linear-lanceolate to elliptical-lanceolate with protracted, rostrate to capitate ends. Axial area narrow. Central area transverse, narrow, irregular in shape. Raphe straight. Striae radiate throughout most of the valve, radiate or transverse at the ends. The cross-lineate striae are broken up into segments which have a superficially punctate appearance. However, on careful examination these short segments are lineate. The segments of the striae produce irregular longitudinal lines. Striae, 12-14 in 10μ. Length, $12-70\mu$. Breadth, $7-22\mu$.

The distinctive characteristics of this species are the structure of the striae together with the structure of the central area. Most of the specimens from the United States show a double row of puncta composing the striae near the margins of the valve. This is also true for specimens from Kützing's collection from the type locality labeled *Navicula tuscula* (A-G.C. 13099). It is impossible to see such a double row of puncta on Van Heurck's slide, though this may be due to the refractive index of the medium. Otherwise our specimens seem to belong to the same taxon as those of Van Heurck.

This species is sometimes placed in the subgenus *Navicula*, but the structure of the striae is quite different although they are lineate.

Type locality. — Italy, Santa Fiora; fossil.

U. S. distribution. — GEOGRAPHICAL: New England States, Middle Atlantic States, East Central States, Lakes States, Plains States.

Navicula subgenus LAEVISTRIATA (Cl.) Patr.

Navicula subgenus *Laevistriata* Patr., Not. Nat. Acad. Nat. Sci. Philadelphia, No. 324, p. 7.   1959.

Valve more or less lanceolate. Axial area linear, abruptly dilated around the central nodule to an orbicular space or transverse fascia, or uniting with the central area in a lanceolate space. Striae usually coarse, radiate, and smooth or costate as in *Pinnularia*. Sometimes they appear slightly punctate but this is not characteristic of this subgenus. Longitudinal lines or furrows not present. Cleve states that the terminal fissures of the raphe are usually small and indistinct. In the specimens I have seen, they are distinct and variable in size.

This subgenus is closely related to the genus *Pinnularia*, particularly that section of the genus in which the striae are not crossed by bands. It might well be considered a transitional group between these two genera. It is also related to the genus *Caloneis*.

Type species. — *Navicula elegans* W. Sm.

1. **Navicula elegans** W. Sm. var. **elegans**   pl. 52, figs. 8-9

> *Navicula elegans* W. Sm., Syn. British Diat., vol. 1, p. 49, pl. 16, fig. 137. 1853.
> *Navicula elegans* var. *cuspidata* Cl., K. Svenska Vet.-Akad. Handl., Ny Följd, 27(3):68. 1895.

Valve lanceolate with somewhat wedge-shaped or rostrate ends. Axial area narrow. Raphe broad; median ends turned to one side. Central area large, orbicular. Striae strongly radiate throughout most of the valve, often somewhat curved; convergent at the ends. Striae, 8-12 in 10μ. Length, 60-115μ. Breadth, 20-30μ.

This species is characterized by the strongly radiate striae and the shape of the axial and central areas. The original material of William Smith contained specimens with wedge-shaped and rostrate ends. They seem to intergrade. For this reason we have synonymized *Navicula elegans* var. *cuspidata* Cl.

Type locality. — England, Poole Bay; marine or brackish water.

U. S. distribution. — Geographical: New England States, Middle Atlantic States; Oregon. Ecological: Fresh to brackish water.

2. **Navicula palpebralis** Bréb. *ex* W. Sm. var. **palpebralis**   pl. 52, fig. 10

> *Navicula palpebralis* Bréb. *ex* W. Sm., Syn. British Diat., vol. 1, p. 50, supp. pl. 31, fig. 273. 1853.

Valve broadly lanceolate to elliptical-lanceolate with subacute ends. Axial and central areas forming a broad lanceolate space. Raphe filamentous. Striae radiate throughout the valve. Striae, 10-12 in 10μ. Length, 38-80μ. Breadth, 13-24μ.

William Smith in his description of this species says nothing about the striae being finely lineate. However, when one examines his figures the striae appear to be finely lineate. We have examined isotype material and have found indications that the striae might be indistinctly cross lineate, but could not be sure as the slides are air mounts. Our specimens from the United States show no signs of such cross lineation.

Whether this taxon is a member of the subgenus may be questioned on this point.

The nominate variety of this species is distinguished by the broad, lanceolate space formed by the axial and central areas and by the subacute ends of the valve.

Type locality. — England, Poole Bay; marine.

U. S. distribution. — GEOGRAPHICAL: Middle Atlantic States; Nebraska. ECOLOGICAL: Brackish to marine water, or water of high mineral content.

3. **Navicula yarrensis** var. **americana** Cl. PL. 52, FIG. 11

Navicula yarrensis var. *americana* Cl., K. Svenska Vet.-Akad. Handl., Ny Földj, 27(3):69. 1895.

Valve linear-lanceolate with almost parallel sides; ends somewhat wedge-shaped. Axial area narrow; widening into a small, more or less lanceolate central area. Striae radiate in the middle portion of the valve, parallel to slightly convergent at the ends. Striae, 5-8 in 10μ. Length, 90-95μ. Breadth, 18-25μ.

This variety is distinguished from the nominate variety by the shape of the valve, the slightly finer striae, and the axial area which is usually narrower.

Type locality. — Brackish water, Atlantic coast of U. S., Quincy, Massachusetts.

U. S. distribution. — GEOGRAPHICAL: New England States; New Jersey. ECOLOGICAL: Brackish water; often in estuaries.

Names of Taxa reported from the U. S. (fresh water) which could not be verified by a specimen from a public herbarium.

Navicula aequalis (Ehr.) Kütz. = *Pinnularia aequalis* Ehr. (recorded by Ehrenberg).

Navicula ammophila var. *flanatica* (Grun.) Cl. = *Navicula flanatica* Grun. (recorded by Tempère & Peragallo and Curtis).

Navicula amphioxys Ehr. = *Pinnularia amphioxys* Ehr. (recorded by Ehrenberg).

Navicula apiculata Bréb. = *Navicula crucifera* Grun. *in* A. S. (recorded by De Toni and Schultze).

Navicula arata Grun. (recorded by Cleve and Boyer).

Navicula arverna M. Perag. & Hérib. *in* Hérib. (recorded by Tempère & Peragallo).

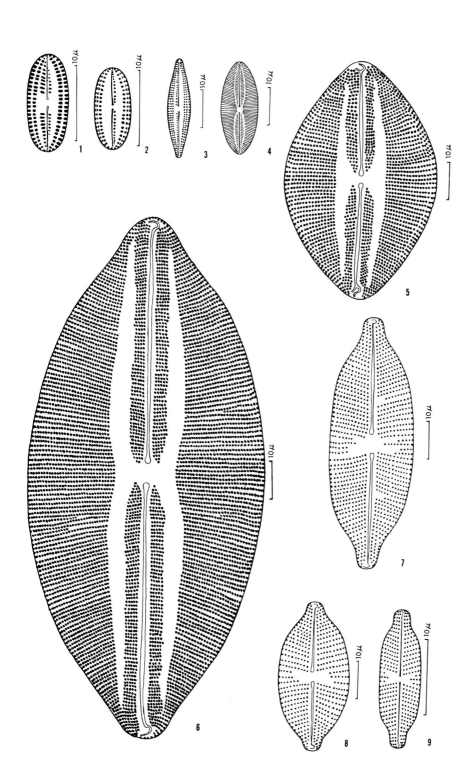

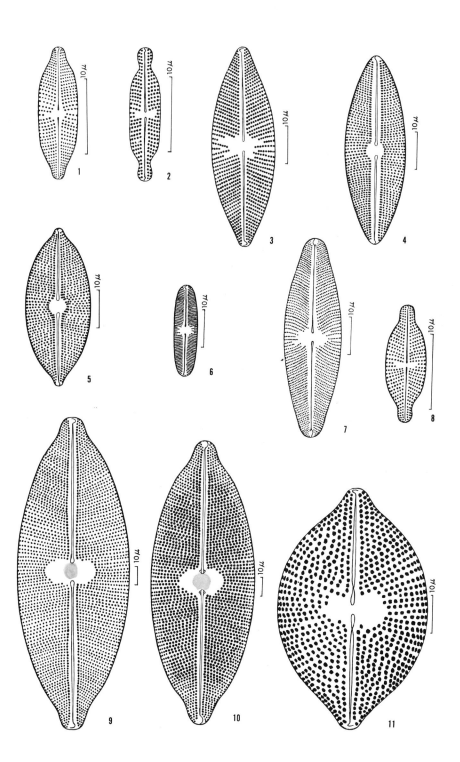

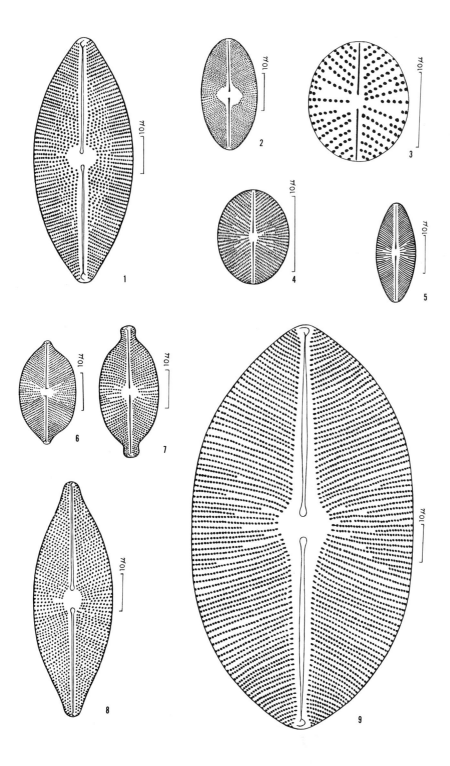

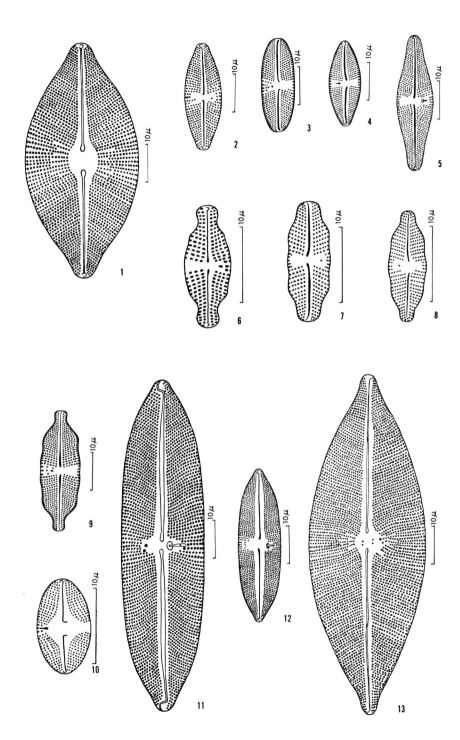

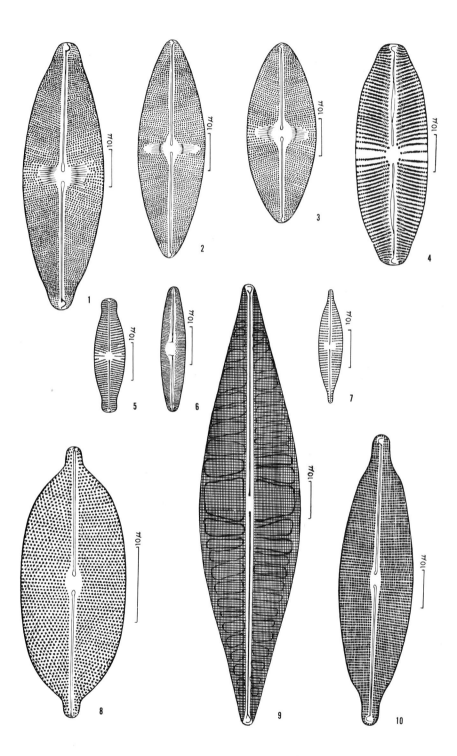

Fig. 1.   *Navicula cuspidata* var. *major* A-Boyer H-7-6, Ohio, Columbus.

Fig. 2.   *Navicula cuspidata* var. *obtusa* var. nov. A-Boyer A-6-15, Colorado, Radford Peak (drawing of Holotype).

Fig. 3a–b.   *Navicula guatemalensis* A-G.C. 5850, Nebraska, Cherry Co., Dewey Lake.

Fig. 4.   *Navicula halophila* A-V.H. 12, Belgium, Blankenberghe.

Fig. 5.   *Navicula halophila* f. *tenuirostris* A-G.C. 7054, Ohio, Allen Co., Ottawa River, Station 1.

Fig. 6.   *Navicula gregaria* A-V.H. 94, England, Northumberland.

Fig. 7.   *Navicula accomoda* A-G.C. 8029, Texas, Victoria Co., Guadalupe River.

Fig. 8.   *Navicula biconica* A-G.C. 44492, South Carolina, Aiken Co., Savannah River (drawing of Holotype).

Fig. 9.   *Navicula spicula* A-V.H. 9, Wales, Swansea Dock (drawing of Lectotype).

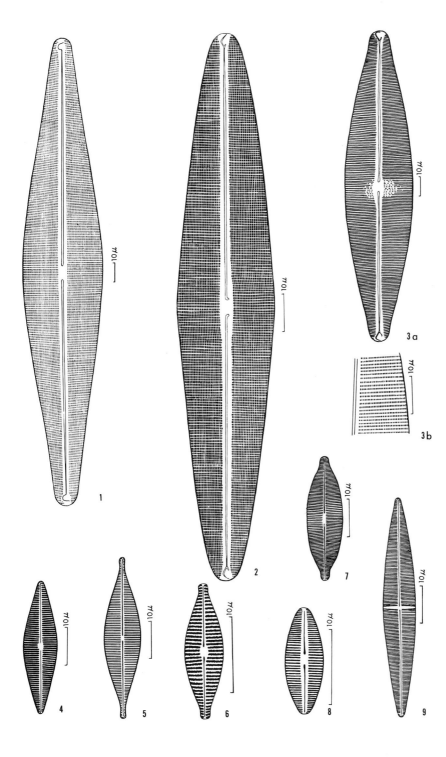

PLATE 45

Fig. 1a–b.   *Navicula bergenensis* A-G.C. 4148a, New York, Genesee Co., Bergen Swamp.

Fig. 2.   *Navicula crucicula* A-V.H. 112, England, Yorkshire.

Fig. 3.   *Navicula protracta* A-V.H. 99, England, Cheshire, Great Mols.

Fig. 4.   *Navicula sabiniana* A-G.C. 8030, Texas, Orange Co., Sabine River (drawing of Holotype).

Fig. 5.   *Navicula aikenensis* A-G.C. 4737a, South Carolina, Aiken Co., Savannah River (drawing of Holotype).

Fig. 6.   *Navicula integra* A-V.H. 55, Great Britain.

Fig. 7.   *Navicula sanctaecrucis* A-G.C. 8116, Texas, Victoria Co., Guadalupe River.

Fig. 8.   *Navicula monmouthiana-stodderi* A-Boyer D-6-25, New Hampshire, Grafton Co., The Flume, White Mountains.

Fig. 9.   *Navicula confervacea* A.G.C. 4723a, Pennsylvania, Montgomery Co., Schuylkill River.

Fig. 10.   *Navicula confervacea* var. *peregrina* A-G.C. 1609, Florida, Putnam Co.

Fig. 11.   *Navicula keeleyi* A-G.C. 2197, Pennsylvania, Pike Co., Shohola Falls (drawing of Holotype).

Fig. 12.   *Navicula convergens* A-G.C. 3954a, South Carolina, Aiken Co., Savannah River (drawing of Holotype).

Fig 13.   *Navicula elmorei* sp. nov. N.Y.B.G.-Elm. 704, Nebraska, pool one mile west of Fremont (drawing of Holotype).

Fig. 14.   *Navicula perpusilla* A-V.H. 212, Scotland.

Fig. 15.   *Navicula poconoensis* A-G.C. 2188, Pennsylvania, Pike Co., Greeley (drawing of Holotype).

Fig. 16.   *Navicula gibbosa* A-G.C. 44264a, South Carolina, Aiken Co., Savannah River.

Fig. 17.   *Navicula hassiaca* A-G.C. 4074a, South Carolina, Aiken Co., Savannah River.

Fig. 18.   *Navicula duomedia* A-G.C. 44264a, South Carolina, Aiken Co., Savannah River (drawing of Holotype).

Fig. 19.   *Navicula contenta* var. *biceps* A-G.C. 8097, Texas, Orange Co., Sabine River.

Fig. 20.   *Navicula pennsylvanica*, nom. nov. A-G.C. 2188, Pennsylvania, Pike Co., Greeley (drawing of Holotype).

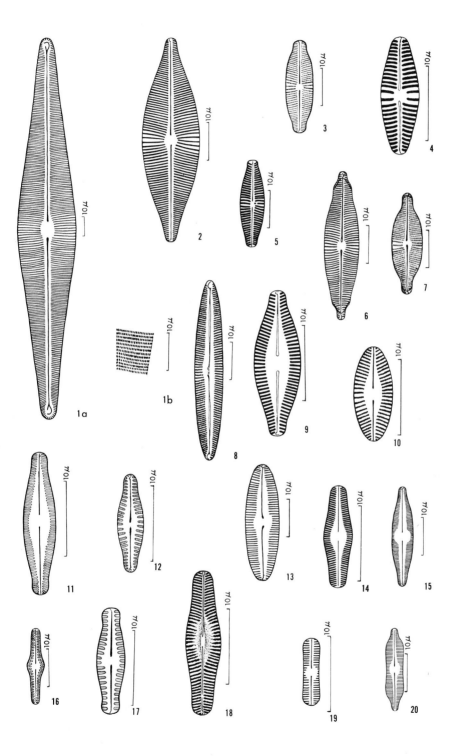

PLATE 46

Fig. 1 – 2.   *Navicula arvensis* A-G.C. 3972a, South Carolina, Aiken Co., Upper Three Runs Creek.

Fig. 3.   *Navicula gysingensis* A-G.C. 44254, South Carolina, Aiken Co., Upper Three Runs Creek.

Fig. 4.   *Navicula subtilissima* A-G.C. 4359a, Florida, Escambia Co., Escambia River, Station 2.

Fig. 5.   *Navicula pelliculosa* A-V.H. 145, France, Falaise.

Fig. 6.   *Navicula paucivisitata* A-G.C. 44274, South Carolina, Aiken Co., Savannah River (drawing of Holotype).

Fig. 7.   *Navicula festiva* A-G.C. 10637d, Germany, Hesse, Meissner Mountains in *Polytrichum commune*.

Fig. 8.   *Navicula latelongitudinalis* A-G.C. 44258a, South Carolina, Aiken Co., Savannah River (drawing of Holotype).

Fig. 9.   *Navicula jaernefeltii* A-G.C. 3978a, South Carolina, Aiken Co., Upper Three Runs Creek.

Fig. 10.   *Navicula simula* A-G.C. 44259a, South Carolina, Aiken Co., Savannah River (drawing of Holotype).

Fig. 11.   *Navicula ventralis* var. *chilensis* A-G.C. 44456, Florida, Santa Rosa Co., Escambia River.

Fig. 12 –13.   *Navicula lateropunctata* A-G.C. 4072a, South Carolina, Aiken Co., Upper Three Runs Creek (drawing of Type).

Fig. 14.   *Navicula minuscula* A-G.C. 6775a, Utah, Cache Co., Providence Creek.

Fig. 15.   *Navicula muralis* A-V.H. 144, Great Britain.

Fig. 16.   *Navicula atomus* A-V.H. 149, Belgium, Antwerp.

Fig. 17 –18.   *Navicula minima* A-V.H. 142, Belgium, Brussels.

Fig. 19.   *Navicula seminulum* A-V.H. 141, Belgium, Groendael.

Fig. 20.   *Navicula seminulum* var. *hustedtii* A-G.C. 4425a, South Carolina, Aiken Co., Upper Three Runs Creek (drawing of Holotype).

Fig. 21.   *Navicula secura* A-G.C. 44254a, South Carolina, Aiken Co., Upper Three Runs Creek (drawing of Holotype).

Fig. 22.   *Navicula vanheurckii* sp. nov. A-G.C. 2142, Pennsylvania, Monroe Co., Tobyhanna Creek.

Fig. 23.   *Navicula orbiculata* A-G.C. 8030, Texas, Orange Co., Sabine River (drawing of Holotype).

Fig. 24.   *Navicula luzonensis* A-G.C. 6622a, Texas, Guadalupe Co., Guadalupe River, Station 3.

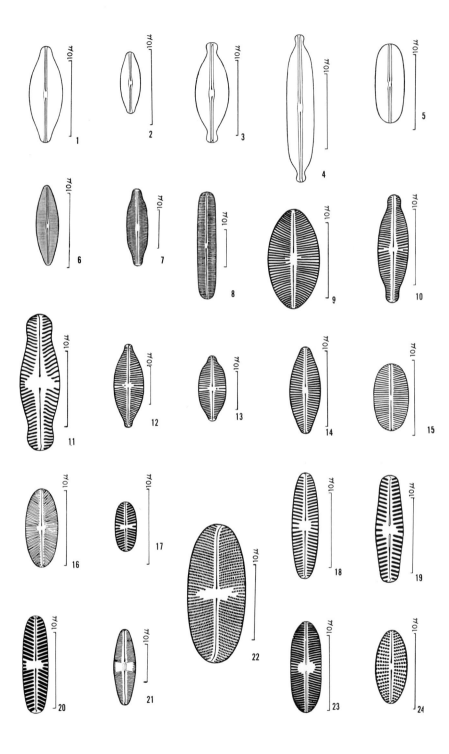

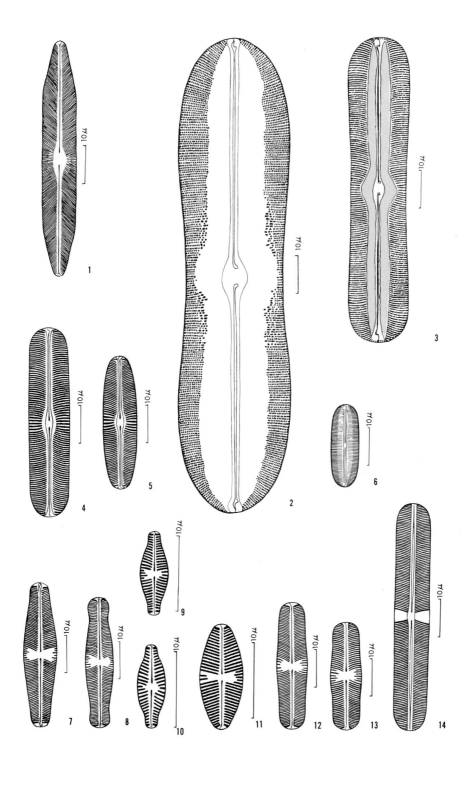

PLATE 48

Fig. 1. *Navicula salinarum* A-V.H. 95, Germany, Holstein Wedel.
Fig. 2. *Navicula salinarum* var. *intermedia* A-V.H. 92, England, Teignmouth.
Fig. 3. *Navicula cryptocephala* A-G.C. 10349, Germany, in a gutter near Freiburg in Baden.
Fig. 4. *Navicula cryptocephala* var. *exilis* A-V.H. 93, Belgium, Laeken (Isotype).
Fig. 5. *Navicula cryptocephala* var. *veneta* A-Cl. & Möll. 255, France, Mouth of the Somme, Hourdel.
Fig. 6. *Navicula rhynchocephala* A-V.H. 186, England, Hull.
Fig. 7. *Navicula rhynchocephala* var. *amphiceros* A-Cl. & Möll. 323, Japan, Vega Expedition.
Fig. 8. *Navicula rhynchocephala* var. *germanii* comb. nov. A-G.C. 42397a, Pennsylvania, Lancaster Co., Little Muddy Creek (drawing of Lectotype).
Fig. 9. *Navicula viridula* A-G.C. 4515a, Pennsylvania, Lancaster Co.
Fig. 10. *Navicula viridula* var. *avenacea* A-G.C. 11090, France, Falaise (Isotype).
Fig. 11. *Navicula viridula* var. *linearis* A-G.C. 4649a, Georgia, Screven Co., Savannah River.
Fig. 12. *Navicula viridula* var. *rostellata* A-V.H. 87, Bengal.
Fig. 13. *Navicula globulifera* A-G.C. 2123, Pennsylvania, Wayne Co., Mill Creek.
Fig. 14. *Navicula gottlandica* A-Cl. & Möll. 161, Sweden, Gottland, Fårön (Isotype).
Fig. 15. *Navicula radiosa* A-V.H. 85, Belgium, Rouge-Cloître.
Fig. 16. *Navicula radiosa* var. *parva* A-G.C. 437b, Florida, Santa Rosa Co., Escambia River (drawing of Holotype).
Fig. 17. *Navicula radiosa* var. *tenella* A-V.H. 107 Belgium, Brussels.
Fig. 18. *Navicula odiosa* A-G.C. 6853a, Texas, Calhoun Co., Mission Lake (drawing of Holotype).
Fig. 19. *Navicula lanceolata* A-V.H. 96, Great Britain.
Fig. 20. *Navicula lanceolata* Univ. Bot. Mus. Lund-Ag. Herb. *Frustulia lanceolata* "Ge. B. A. + 4" (drawing of Lectotype).
Fig. 21. *Navicula arenaria* A-V.H. 8, England, Blyth Sand, North.

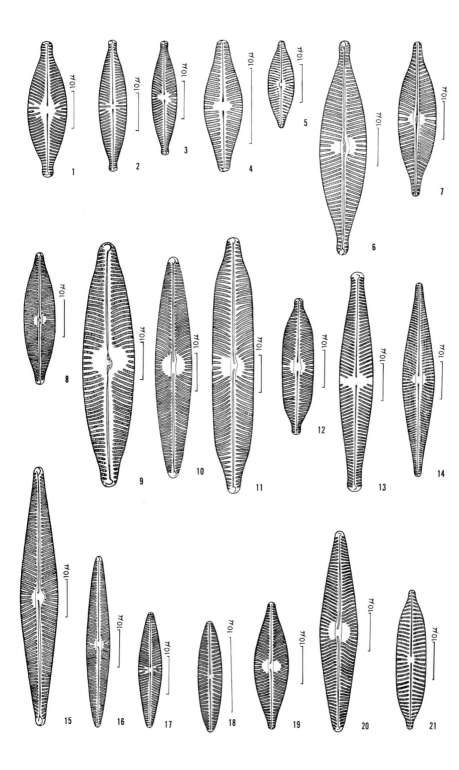

PLATE 49

Fig. 1.   *Navicula schroeteri* var. *escambia* A-G.C. 6564a, Florida, Santa Rosa
Co., Escambia River (drawing of Holotype).

Fig. 2.   *Navicula symmetrica* A-G.C. 25740, Brazil, Rio Grande do Sul.

Fig. 3.   *Navicula tripunctata* A-V.H. 81, England, Ulverston, Gill Banks.

Fig. 4.   *Navicula tripunctata* var. *schizonemoides* A-V.H. 234, England, near
Hull, Bromfleet.

Fig. 5.   *Navicula angusta* A-V.H. 140, Scotland, Lochnagar.

Fig. 6.   *Navicula heufleri* A-G.C. 5690, Nebraska, Chase Co., Field Museum.

Fig. 7.   *Navicula heufleri* var. *leptocephala* comb. nov. A-V.H. 84, Belgium,
near Antwerp.

Fig. 8.   *Navicula cincta* A-V.H. 82, Bohemia, Franzensbad.

Fig. 9.   *Navicula graciloides* A-G.C. 1950, Indiana, Marshall Co., algae of
Maxinkuckee Lake.

Fig. 10.   *Navicula graciloides* A-G.C. 1715, Connecticut, Linsley Pond.

Fig. 11.   *Navicula pseudoreinhardtii* A-G.C. 4737a, South Carolina, Aiken Co.,
Savannah River (drawing of Holotype).

Fig. 12.   *Navicula reinhardtii* A-V.H. 79, Belgium, La Hulpe.

Fig. 13.   *Navicula reinhardtii* var. *elliptica* A-T. & P. 366, Oregon, Klamath Co.,
Swan Lake.

Fig. 14.   *Navicula gastrum* A-G.C. 2544b, Michigan, Douglas Lake.

Fig. 15.   *Navicula decussis* A-G.C. 5348, Montana, Missoula Co.

Fig. 16.   *Navicula hambergii* A-G.C. 2188, Pennsylvania, Pike Co., Greeley.

Fig. 17.   *Navicula menisculus* var. *upsaliensis* A-V.H. 80, Belgium, Rouge-
Cloître.

Fig. 18.   *Navicula menisculus* var. *upsaliensis* A-V.H. 190, Belgium, Pool in the
park at Antwerp

Fig. 19.   *Navicula minnewaukonensis* N.Y.B.G.-Elm. 634, North Dakota, Devils
Lake, Bird Island (Isotype)

Fig. 20.   *Navicula anglica* var. *subsalsa* A-Boyer K-1-6, Alabama, Montgomery.

Fig. 21.   *Navicula latens* A-G.C. 45697, Florida, Santa Rosa Co., Escambia
River.

Fig. 22.   *Navicula clementis* A-V.H. 99, Great Britain.

Fig. 23.   *Navicula exigua* A-Cl. & Möll. 261, Finland.

Fig. 24.   *Navicula exigua* var. *capitata* A-G.C. 2200, Pennsylvania, Pike Co.,
Shohola Falls (drawing of Holotype).

Fig. 25.   *Navicula laterostrata* A-G.C. 6614a, Texas, Guadalupe River.

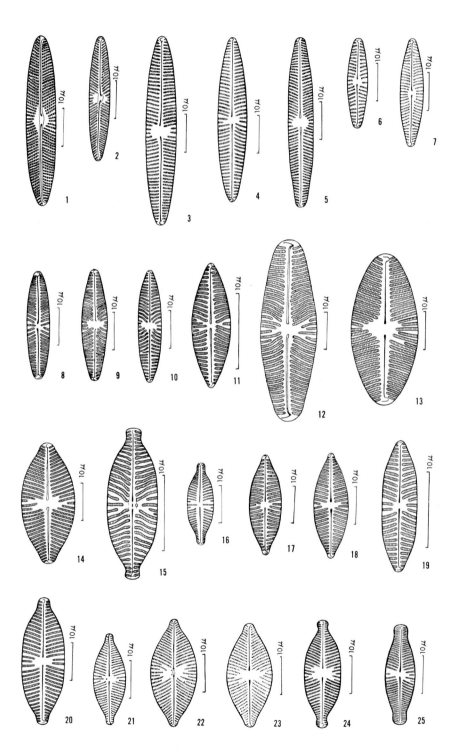

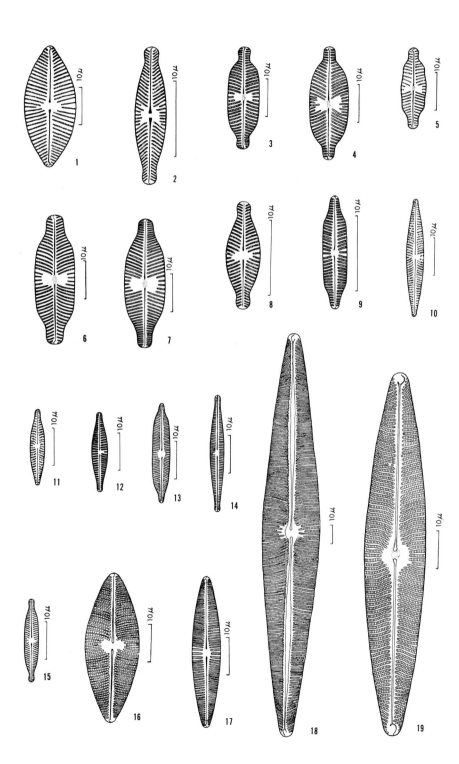

PLATE 51

Fig. 1.   *Navicula walkeri* Cal. Acad. Sci. H. T.-3469, Sov. 491-5, Oregon, Crater Lake National Park, Bay on Wizard Island (drawing of Holotype).

Fig. 2.   *Navicula ludloviana* A-Boyer E-2-21, California, Shasta Co., Pitt River.

Fig. 3–4.   *Navicula aurora* Cal. Acad. Sci. H.T.-3468, Sov. 489-7, Oregon, Douglas Co., Diamond Lake (drawing of Holotype).

Fig. 5.   *Navicula peregrina* A-V.H. 186, England, Hull.

Fig. 6.   *Navicula oblonga* A-V.H. 132, England, Finnety.

Fig. 7.   *Navicula tenelloides* A-G.C. 4436a, Florida, Santa Rosa Co., Escambia River.

Fig. 8.   *Navicula dulcis* A-G.C. 8035, Texas, Orange Co., Sabine River (drawing of Holotype).

Fig. 9.   *Navicula costulata* A-V.H. 71, Belgium, Rouge-Cloître.

Fig. 10.   *Navicula gravistriata* A-G.C. 8031, Texas, Orange Co., Sabine River.

Fig. 11.   *Navicula cascadensis* Cal. Acad. Sci. H.T.-3467, Sov. 489-6, Oregon, Douglas Co., Diamond Lake (drawing of Holotype).

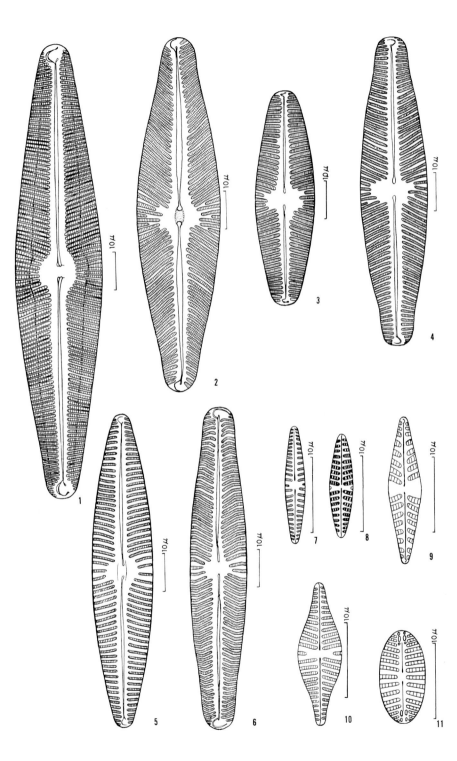

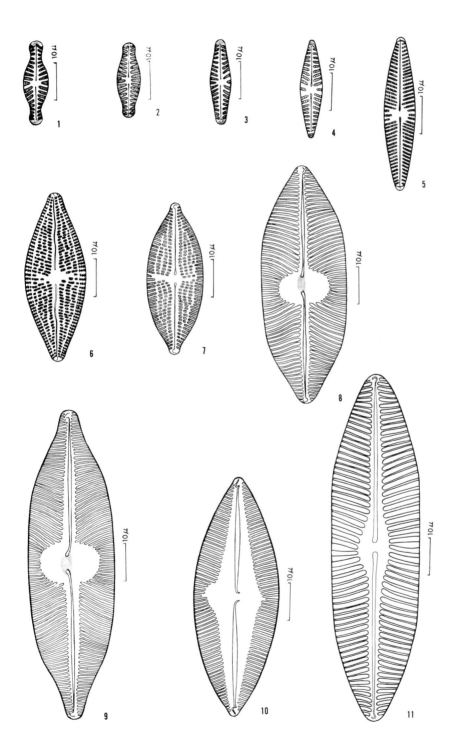

Navicula bicapitellata Hust. (recorded by Hohn).

Navicula cancellata var. *retusa* (Bréb.) Cl. = *Navicula retusa* Bréb. (recorded by Curtis).

Navicula carolinensis Ehr. (recorded by Ehrenberg).

Navicula cocconeis (Ehr.) DeT. = *Pinnularia cocconeis* Ehr. (recorded by Ehrenberg).

Navicula cuspidata var. *danaica* Grun. *in* Cl. (recorded by Cleve).

Navicula cuspidata var. *heribaudi* Perag. *in* Hérib. = *Navicula elsaethum* Pant. (recorded by Silva).

Navicula digito-radiata (Greg.) Ralfs = *Navicula digito-radiata* Greg. (recorded by Elmore and Tempère & Peragallo).

Navicula eiowana Ehr. (recorded by Ehrenberg).

Navicula exsul A. S. = *Navicula clavata* var. *exsul* (A. S.) Cl. (recorded by Cleve & Möller).

Navicula falaisiensis Grun. *in* V. H. (recorded by Tempère & Peragallo).

Navicula forcipata Grev. (recorded by Cleve & Möller).

Navicula gallica var. *nitzschioides* Grun. (recorded by Cleve & Möller).

Navicula guttata Grun. *in* Cl. & Grun. = *Navicula peragalli* Brun. = *Navicula guttata* var. *peragalli* (Brun) Cl. (recorded by Tempère & Peragallo).

Navicula hasta Pant. (recorded by Hohn and Boyer).

Navicula hasta var. *punctata* Boyer (recorded by Boyer).

Navicula heroina A. S. = *Pinnularia major* var. *heroina* (A. S.) Cl. (recorded by Tempère & Peragallo).

Navicula hexapla A. S. (recorded by A. Schmidt).

Navicula lanceolata f. *minuta* Rabh. (recorded by De Toni).

Navicula lanceolata var. *cymbula* (Donk.) Cl. = *Navicula cymbula* Donk. (recorded by Curtis).

Navicula leptorhynchus Ehr. (recorded by Ehrenberg).

Navicula leptostigma Ehr. (recorded by Ehrenberg).

Navicula limosa var. *undulata* Grun. *in* V. H. (recorded by Chase, Tempère & Peragallo, and Britton).

Navicula lirata Ehr. (recorded by Ehrenberg).

Navicula lucidula Grun. *in* V. H. (recorded by Palmer and Silva).

Navicula lyra var. *elliptica* A. S. (recorded by Tempère & Peragallo).

Navicula maculata var. *lanceolata* Heid. (recorded by Boyer).

Navicula oculata Krasske = *Navicula occulta* Krasske (recorded by Young *in* Hohn).

Navicula ohiensis Ehr. (recorded by Ehrenberg).

Navicula pennata A. S. (recorded by Sister Maloney).

Navicula perrotettii (Grun.) Grun. (recorded by Cleve).

Navicula platalea Ehr. (recorded by Ehrenberg).

Navicula pusilla var. *lanceolata* (Grun.) Grun. *in* Cl. & Grun. (recorded by Boyer).

Navicula radiosa var. *subrostrata* Cl. (recorded by Cleve).

Navicula rotaeana var. *excentrica* Grun. *in* V. H. (recorded by Hohn).

Navicula scutelloides var. *mocarensis* Grun. (recorded by Tempère & Peragallo).

Navicula septenaria L. W. Bail. (recorded by De Toni).

Navicula similis Krasske (recorded by Hohn).

Navicula stauroneiformis (recorded by Curtis and Wolle).

Navicula stauroparva Grun. = *Navicula stauroptera* var. *parva* (Ehr.) Grun. = *Stauroptera parva* Ehr. (recorded by Curtis and Ehrenberg).

Navicula subinflata Grun. (recorded by Curtis).

Navicula verecunda Hust. *in* A. S. (recorded by Hohn).

Names of taxa which were misidentified or for which the original description cannot be found.

Navicula diagonalis (recorded by Bailey).

Navicula humerosa Bréb. (recorded by De Toni and Boyer).

Navicula major f. *maxima* (recorded by Tempère & Peragallo).

Navicula major var. *dilatata* M. Perag. (recorded by Tempère & Peragallo).

Navicula minuta (recorded by Lackey).

Navicula polystricta var. *circumstricta* Grun. (recorded by Deming) = *Navicula hennedy* var. *circumsecta* (Grun.) Cl. = *Navicula polystricta* Grun.

Navicula radians (recorded by Curtis).

Navicula retusa var. *elongata* (recorded by Cleve & Möller).

Navicula scutum Schum. (recorded by Elmore).

Navicula staurifera Thomas (recorded by De Toni and Chase).

Navicula timodis? = *Navicula trinodis* (recorded by Palmer).

*Taxa Recorded Since 1960

Navicula abducta Mang. (recorded by Hohn & Hellerman, 1963).

Navicula achthera Hohn & Hellerm. (recorded by Hohn & Hellerman, 1963).

---

* See page 671 for additional taxa.

Navicula adnata Hust. (recorded by Hohn, 1961).

Navicula adversa Krasske (recorded by Hohn & Hellerman, 1963).

Navicula agma Hohn & Hellerm. (recorded by Hohn & Hellerman, 1963).

Navicula agrestis Hust. (recorded by Hohn & Hellerman, 1963).

Navicula alea Hohn & Hellerm. (recorded by Hohn & Hellerman, 1963).

Navicula amnicola Hohn & Hellerm. (recorded by Hohn & Hellerman, 1963).

Navicula amphibola var. *polymorpha* Fusey (recorded by Reimer, 1961).

Navicula anatis Hohn & Hellerm. (recorded by Hohn & Hellerman, 1963).

Navicula anglica Ralfs (recorded by Hohn, 1961; Woodson & Holoman, 1964; and Lipscomb, 1964).

Navicula argutiola Hohn & Hellerm. (recorded by Hohn & Hellerman, 1963).

Navicula asymbasia Hohn & Hellerm. (recorded by Hohn & Hellerman, 1963).

Navicula bacula Hohn & Hellerm. (recorded by Hohn & Hellerman, 1963).

Navicula begeri Krasske (recorded by Hohn & Hellerman, 1963).

Navicula bryophila Østr. (recorded by Reimer, 1961).

Navicula bryophila Peters. (recorded by Stoermer, 1962).

Navicula caduca Hust. (recorded by Hohn & Hellerman, 1963).

Navicula canoris Hohn & Hellerm. (recorded by Hohn & Hellerman, 1963).

Navicula caractacus Hohn & Hellerm. (recorded by Hohn, 1961; Hohn & Hellerman, 1963).

Navicula carniolensis Hust. (recorded by Hohn, 1961; Hohn & Hellerman, 1963).

Navicula caterva Hohn & Hellerm. (recorded by Hohn & Hellerman, 1963).

Navicula cincta var. *rostrata* Reim. (recorded by Reimer, 1962; Shobe, Stoermer, & Dodd, 1963).

Navicula cinna Hohn & Hellerm. (recorded by Hohn & Hellerman, 1963).

Navicula contortula Sov. (recorded by Sovereign, 1963).

Navicula cremorne Hohn & Hellerm. (recorded by Hohn & Hellerman, 1963).

Navicula cryptocephala f. *minuta* Peters. (recorded by Hohn & Hellerman, 1963).

Navicula cryptocephala f. *terrestris* Lund (recorded by Lund, 1961).

Navicula dailyi Reim. (recorded by Reimer, 1961).

Navicula dicephala var. *abiskoensis* (Hust.) A. Cl. (recorded by Stoermer, 1962).

Navicula dicephala var. *subcapitata* Grun. (recorded by Stoermer, 1962; Shobe, Stoermer, & Dodd, 1963).

Navicula distinctastriata Hohn & Hellerm. (recorded by Hohn & Hellerman, 1963).

Navicula ebor Hohn & Hellerm. (recorded by Hohn & Hellerman, 1963).

Navicula elaphros Hohn & Hellerm. (recorded by Hohn & Hellerman, 1963).

Navicula evexa Sov. (recorded by Sovereign, 1963).

Navicula friesneri Reim. (recorded by Reimer, 1961).

Navicula fritschii Lund (recorded by Dodd & Stoermer, 1962; Stoermer, 1962).

Navicula frugalis Hust. (recorded by Hohn & Hellerman, 1963).

Navicula gastrum var. *exigua* (Greg.) Grun. (recorded by Stoermer, 1962).

Navicula genovefea Fusey (recorded by Hohn & Hellerman, 1963).

Navicula gibbula Cl. (recorded by Dodd & Stoermer, 1962).

Navicula habena Hohn & Hellerm. (recorded by Hohn & Hellerman, 1963).

Navicula imbellis Hohn & Hellerm. (recorded by Hohn & Hellerman, 1963).

Navicula indianensis Reim. (recorded by Reimer, 1961).

Navicula indifferens Hust. (recorded by Hohn & Hellerman, 1963).

Navicula infrenis Hohn & Hellerm. (recorded by Hohn & Hellerman, 1963).

Navicula insociabilis Krasske (recorded by Reimer, 1961).

Navicula kincaidii Sov. (recorded by Sovereign, 1963).

Navicula lagerheimii var. *intermedia* Hust. (recorded by Hohn & Hellerman, 1963).

Navicula lagerstedtii Cl. (recorded by Stoermer, 1962).

Navicula lalia Hohn & Hellerm. (recorded by Hohn, 1961; Hohn & Hellerman, 1963).

Navicula lapidosa Krasske (recorded by Hohn & Hellerman, 1963).

Navicula levanderi Hust. (recorded by Hohn & Hellerman, 1963).

Navicula litos Hohn & Hellerm. (recorded by Hohn & Hellerman, 1963).

Navicula lundstroemii Cl. (recorded by Hohn, 1961).

Navicula mediahelos Hohn & Hellerm. (recorded by Hohn, 1961; Hohn & Hellerman, 1963).

Navicula menisculus (recorded by Jackson, Nemerow, & Rand, 1964).

Navicula menisculus Schum. (recorded by Woodson & Holoman, 1964).

Navicula mica Hohn & Hellerm. (recorded by Hohn & Hellerman, 1963).

Navicula migma Hohn & Hellerm. (recorded by Hohn & Hellerman, 1963).

Navicula minima var. *okamurae* Skv. (recorded by Reimer, 1961).

Navicula minthe Hohn & Hellerm. (recorded by Hohn & Hellerman, 1963).

Navicula multigramma Hohn & Hellerm. (recorded by Hohn & Hellerman, 1963).

Navicula nemoris Hohn & Hellerm. (recorded by Hohn, 1961; Hohn & Hellerman, 1963).

Navicula nimbus Hohn & Hellerm. (recorded by Hohn & Hellerman, 1963).

Navicula nugalis Hohn & Hellerm. (recorded by Hohn & Hellerman, 1963).

Navicula nyassensis f. *minor* O. Müll. (recorded by Hohn & Hellerman, 1963).

Navicula nyassensis var. *capitata* O. Müll. (recorded by Hohn, 1961; Hohn & Hellerman, 1963).

Navicula obdurata Hohn & Hellerm. (recorded by Hohn & Hellerman, 1963).

Navicula oblongata Kütz. (recorded by Woodson & Holoman, 1964).

Navicula oppugnata Hust. (recorded by Shobe, Stoermer, & Dodd, 1963).

Navicula oxigua (Greg.) Müll. (recorded by Lipscomb, 1964).

Navicula parablis Hohn & Hellerm. (recorded by Hohn & Hellerman, 1963).

Navicula perpusilla var. *distans* Cl.-Eul. (recorded by Reimer, 1961).

Navicula perventralis Hust. (recorded by Hohn & Hellerman, 1963).

Navicula placentula f. *rostrata* A. Mayer (recorded by Hohn & Hellerman, 1963).

Navicula potzgeri Reim. (recorded by Reimer, 1961; Shobe, Stoermer, & Dodd, 1963).

Navicula potzgeri var. *quadripunctata* Reim. (recorded by Reimer, 1961).

Navicula pragma Hohn & Hellerm. (recorded by Hohn & Hellerman, 1963).

Navicula pseudopelliculosa Mang. (recorded by Hohn & Hellerman, 1963).

Navicula pseudosilicula var. *olympica* Sov. (recorded by Sovereign, 1963).

Navicula pupula f. *minutula* Choln. (recorded by Hohn & Hellerman, 1963).

Navicula rainierensis Sov. (recorded by Sovereign, 1963).

Navicula recava Hohn & Hellerm. (recorded by Hohn & Hellerman, 1963).

Navicula riparia Hust. (recorded by Hohn & Hellerman, 1963).

Navicula rivalis Hohn & Hellerm. (recorded by Hohn & Hellerman, 1963).

Navicula rugula Hohn & Hellerm. (recorded by Hohn & Hellerman, 1963).

Navicula sagitta Hohn & Hellerm. (recorded by Hohn & Hellerman, 1963).

Navicula schroteri Meist. (recorded by Hohn & Hellerman, 1963).

Navicula seminuloides var. *sumatrensis* Hust. (recorded by Hohn & Hellerman, 1963).

Navicula simplex Krasske (recorded by Shobe, Stoermer, & Dodd, 1963).

Navicula spirata Hust. (recorded by Hohn & Hellerman, 1963).

Navicula stankovici Hust. (recorded by Shobe, Stoermer, & Dodd, 1963).

Navicula stroemii Hust. (recorded by Reimer, 1961).

Navicula subhalophila Hust. (recorded by Hohn & Hellerman, 1963).

Navicula subminuscula Mang. (recorded by Hohn & Hellerman, 1963).

Navicula submolesta (recorded by Blum, 1963).

Navicula submolesta Hust. (recorded by Hohn & Hellerman, 1963).

Navicula subrhynchocephala Hust. (recorded by Hohn & Hellerman, 1963).

Navicula taedia Wall. (recorded by Hohn & Hellerman, 1963).

Navicula tantula Hust. (recorded by Reimer, 1961).

Navicula umbra Hohn & Hellerm. (recorded by Hohn & Hellerman, 1963).

Navicula venerablis Hohn & Hellerm. (recorded by Hohn & Hellerman, 1963).

Navicula ventralis Krasske (recorded by Hohn & Hellerman, 1963).

Navicula wulfii Peters. (recorded by Hohn & Hellerman, 1963).

Navicula zanoni Hust. (recorded by Hohn & Hellerman, 1963).

Genus **Oestrupia** Heid.

Heid. *ex* Hust., Ber. Deutschen Bot. Ges., 53(1):16. 1935.

The generic name *Östrupia* was proposed by Heiden in Schmidt's *Atlas* (1906, pl. 264) for certain species of *Caloneis*. No description of the genus was given. In *Deutsche Südpolar-Expedition* 1901-1903, Band 8, Heft 5 (1928, p. 591) Heiden and Kolbe state that this genus includes species belonging to Grunow's group *Quadriseriatae* of the genus *Navicula*. However, since there appears to have been no description of Grunow's group, the name was invalid until described by Hustedt in 1935 (*loc. cit.*).

Valve strongly convex, linear to lanceolate in shape, sometimes slightly constricted. Due to the convexity of the valve the raphe is sometimes raised well above the rest of the valve. The central area is distinct; the axial area is variable in width on each side of the raphe. A siliceous rib or ribs divide the striae into one or more segments. The striae appear to be chambers with openings, as in *Caloneis* or *Pinnularia*, sometimes apparent. The striae are usually radiate.

This genus is closely related to *Pinnularia* and *Caloneis*, but differs in the presence of the siliceous longitudinal ribs.

The species of this genus are found in marine or brackish water.

Since Hustedt did not designate a type species for this genus, I herewith designate as the type species *Oestrupia powelli* (Lewis) Heid. *ex* Hust.

Type species. — Oestrupia powelli (Lewis) Heid. *ex* Hust.

1. **Oestrupia powelli** (Lewis) Heid. *ex* Hust. var. **powelli** PL. 53, FIG. 1

Navicula powelli Lewis, Proc. Acad. Nat. Sci. Philadelphia, 13:65, pl. 2, fig. 2. 1861.

Caloneis powelli var. *atlantica* Cl., K. Svenska Vet.-Akad. Handl., Ny Följd, 26(2): 63. 1894.

Östrupia powelli (Lewis) Heid. *ex* Hust., Ber. Deutschen Bot. Ges., 53(1):17. 1935.

Valve linear with cuneate ends. Axial area narrow, distinct. A longitudinal line which broadens toward the middle of the valve bisects the striae on each side of the raphe. It usually joins the central area at the central nodule. Central area rhomboidal or somewhat angular in shape. The costate striae appear somewhat radiate due to the convexity of the valve. Striae, 7-11 in 10μ. Length, usually 50-100μ; Lewis states to 150μ. Breadth, 15-30μ.

This species is easily distinguished by the structure of the longitudinal ribs and the structure of the striae.

This taxon was previously assigned to the genus *Oestrupii* by Heiden, but since he did not describe the genus his erection of the genus was not valid.

Type locality. — [U.S.A., Long Island] Black Rock Harbor.

U. S. distribution. — GEOGRAPHICAL: New England States; New Jersey. ECOLOGICAL: Brackish to marine water.

Genus **Caloneis** Cl.

Cl., K. Svenska Vet.-Akad. Handl., Ny Följd, 26(2):46. 1894.

Frustules without intercalary bands or septa. Valve of variable shape, usually linear-lanceolate to elliptical; symmetrical to the apical and transverse axes. Axial and central area variable in shape. Terminal fissures of the raphe usually distinct. The structure of the striae is similar to that of *Pinnularia* in that the striae are transverse chambers which open to the interior of the valve by one or more small openings. These openings on each stria are at more or less the same distance from the edge of the valve and appear as longitudinal lines or narrow bands. Depending on the number of openings in the striae, one or several longitudinal lines are present. The striae are costae-like in appearance.

The striae are often parallel throughout most of the valve and are often radiate near the apices.

Hustedt (1935, pp. 7-17) has given a very good description of the structure of the frustule of the species of this and related genera. He points out the close relationship between *Pinnularia*, *Caloneis*, and the subgenus *Laevistriatae* of *Navicula*. A careful study of the species found in these genera and subgenus may reveal that they all belong to the same genus, or that a reassorting of the species in these groups needs to be made in accordance with recent findings.

Type species. — *Navicula amphisbaena* Bory [= *Caloneis amphisbaena* (Bory) Cl.].

KEY TO THE SPECIES OF CALONEIS

1. Axial and central areas without lunate markings 2
1. Axial and central areas, or just central areas, with lunate markings 12
    2. Longitudinal line on each side of the raphe marginal 3
    2. Longitudinal line or lines on each side of the raphe removed from the margin   8
3. Transverse fascia absent 4
3. Transverse fascia present 5
    4. Valve triundulate or abruptly swollen in the middle of the valve
                                           [7] *C. ventricosa* and vars.
    4. Valve linear . . . . [9] *C. bacillaris* var. *thermalis*
5. Valve more or less triundulate or abruptly swollen in the middle of the valve
                                           [7] *C. ventricosa* and vars.
5. Valve without triundulations 6
    6. Fascia very broad . . . . [8] *C. hyalina*
    6. Fascia narrow or moderately broad 7
7. Ends of the valve wedge-shaped, fascia narrow . . . . [6] *C. wardii*
7. Ends of the valve rounded or very slightly rostrate . . . . [10] *C. bacillum*
    8. A single longitudinal line or a narrow band present on each side of the
        raphe 9
    8. Two longitudinal lines or a distinct and fairly broad band present on each
        side of the raphe 10
9. Axial area narrow, linear . . . . [2] *C. fenzlii*
9. Axial area linear-lanceolate . . . . [4] *C. oregonica* and var.
    10. Axial and central areas forming a linear or linear-lanceolate hyaline area 11
    10. Axial and central areas forming a broadly lanceolate hyaline area
                                         [1] *C. amphisbaena* and var.
11. Area in the middle portion of the valve less than one-quarter the breadth of the
    valve . . . . [5] *C. liber*
11. Area in the middle portion of the valve about one-third the breadth of the valve
                                           [3]*C. permagna*
    12. Valve triundulate or biconstricted 13
    12. Valve not triundulate or biconstricted 16
13. Markings extending most of the length of the axial area, faintly striated
                                           [15] *C. speciosa*
13. Markings confined to the central area 14
    14. Valve triundulate or slightly biconstricted, ends of the valve rounded, usually
        slightly cuneate . . . . [12] *C. limosa*
    14. Valve strongly biconstricted 15
15. Ends of the valve cuneate . . . . [13] *C. lewisii*
15. Ends of the valve cuneate, apiculate-rostrate . . . . [13] *C. lewisii* var. *inflata*
    16. Axial area narrow, valve linear with rounded ends . . . . [11] *C. alpestris*
    16. Axial area broad, valve lanceolate, with cuneate, rounded ends . . [14] *C. hebes*

1. **Caloneis amphisbaena** (Bory) Cl. var. **amphisbaena**   PL. 53, FIG. 2

Navicula amphisbaena Bory, Encyclop. Method., p. 565. 1824.
Pinnularia amphisbaena (Bory) Ehr., Mikrogeol., pl. 33(11), fig. 7. 1854.
Caloneis amphisbaena (Bory) Cl., K. Svenska Vet.-Akad. Handl., Ny Földj, 26(2): 58. 1894.

Valve elliptical with capitate to rostrate-capitate ends. Axial area widening into a large, more or less rhomboidal, central area. Raphe filamentous, appearing twisted near the central nodules; terminal fissures distinct. Two longitudinal lines on each side of the raphe which divide the striae into thirds. Striae radiate throughout most of the valve, parallel to convergent at the ends. Striae, 15-18 in 10μ. Length, 36-80μ. Breadth, 20-30μ.

In this species the two longitudinal lines enclose a broad but irregularly wide chamber as described by Hustedt (1935, pp. 7-17). These chambers are more distinct on the inner surface of the valve than on the outer. The width of each chamber (band) is very small at the central nodule as compared with that in the area between the central nodule and the ends.

This taxon is characterized by the shape of the central area, the shape of the ends, and the position of the longitudinal lines.

Type locality. — Dans la Marne, sous le pont de Charenton . . . [France].

U. S. distribution. — GEOGRAPHICAL: New England States, Middle Atlantic States, Southeastern States, Gulf Coast States, South Central States, East Central States, West Central States, Lakes States, Plains States; New Mexico, California. ECOLOGICAL: Fresh to slightly brackish water.

1. **Caloneis amphisbaena** var. **subsalina** (Donk.) Cl.   PL. 53, FIG. 3

Navicula subsalina Donk., Nat. Hist. British Diat., p. 24, pl. 4, fig. 2. 1870-1873.
Caloneis amphisbaena var. *subsalina* (Donk.) Cl., K. Svenska Vet.-Akad. Handl., Ny Földj, 26(2):58. 1894.

This variety differs from the nominate variety by its rostrate-apiculate ends and its broader elliptical shape. Striae, 12-14 in 10μ in center to 18 in 10μ toward the apices. Length, 50-90μ. Breadth, 22-32μ.

Van Heurck, in his *Synopsis des Diatomées de Belgique* (1880, pl. 11, fig. 6), shows a figure of this taxon with drawn-out ends and a more lanceolate shape. Our illustration agrees with Donkin's original figure.

W. Smith (1853, p. 51) was the first one to recognize this taxon, but he did not describe it.

Type locality. — Lewes, East Sussex, England [as *Navicula amphisbaena* var. β].

U. S. distribution. — GEOGRAPHICAL: New York. ECOLOGICAL: Brackish water.

2. **Caloneis fenzlii** (Grun.) Patr. comb. nov., var. **fenzlii**   PL. 53, FIG. 4

Navicula fenzlii Grun., Verh. Zool.-Bot. Ges. Wien, 13:153. 1863.
Caloneis amphisbaena var. fenzlii (Grun.) Cl., K. Svenska Vet.-Akad. Handl., Ny
    Följd, 26(2):59. 1894.

Valve lanceolate with rounded ends. Axial area distinct, narrow. Central area large, rounded. Striae in specimen I have seen not resolvable into puncta. In very oblique light may appear to be slightly granular. Striae radiate throughout most of the valve; may appear almost parallel at the center. A distinct longitudinal line is located one-fourth to one-third the distance between the margin of the valve and the axial area. Striae, 12-14 in 10μ. Length, 80-90μ. Breadth, 30-38μ.

The specimen which I have seen is from Boyer's collection. In his *Diatoms of North America* he calls it *Caloneis brevis* var. *vexans* (Grun.) Cl. However, when one examines the description and original illustration of Grunow's diagnosis of variety *vexans*, it is evident that he did not have a taxon with a distinct longitudinal line. Boyer's specimen seems to belong to *Navicula fenzlii* Grun. as diagnosed by the description and illustration. This species has distinct longitudinal lines and agrees with Boyer's specimens more nearly in shape than does *C. brevis* var. *vexans*. I have not seen any of Grunow's specimens, but our specimens are the same as Grunow's illustration of *N. elegans* (1860, p. 534, pl. 4, fig. 37) on which Grunow bases his description of *N. fenzlii*.

Type locality. — Am Ufer des Neusiedler Sees.

U. S. distribution. — GEOGRAPHICAL:New Jersey.

3. **Caloneis permagna** (J. W. Bail.) Cl. var. **permagna**   PL. 53, FIG. 5

Pinnularia permagna J. W. Bail., Smithsonian Contr. Knowl., 2(8):40, pl. 2, figs. 28,
    38. 1851.
Navicula permagna (J. W. Bail.) Edwards, Trans. Micr. Soc. London, New Ser.,
    7:91. 1859.
Navicula bivittata Pant., Beitr. Foss. Bacill. Ungarns, vol. 2, p. 43, pl. 5, fig. 83.
    1889.
Caloneis permagna (J. W. Bail.) Cl., K. Svenska Vet.-Akad. Handl., Ny Följd,
    26(2):59. 1894.
Caloneis bivittata var. rostrata Heid. in A. S., Atlas Diat., pl. 263, fig. 2. 1906.
Caloneis permagna var. lewisiana Boyer, Diat. Philadelphia, p. 68, pl. 21, fig. 2.
    1916.

Valve elliptical-lanceolate to linear-lanceolate. The apices of the valve apiculate in the shorter elliptical forms and attenuated, broadly rounded in the more linear forms. Axial area a broad, linear-lanceolate space. Central area not differentiated from the axial area. Striae radiate throughout most of the valve, parallel at the ends. Two longitudinal lines forming a band removed from the outer margin, but on the outer half of the striae. Striae, 9-13 in 10μ, usually finer toward the ends of the valve. Length, 85-220μ. Breadth, 35-55μ.

Bailey states "with punctato-striate marginal bands." It is hard to know just what Bailey means by this statement. The bands have the typical pore openings characteristic in *Caloneis*.

Although later workers have divided this species into various taxa, Bailey in his original description and, particularly in his illustrations shows a range in variation to include the taxa listed as synonyms. Since they seem to intergrade, I see no reason to separate them.

Type locality. — Hudson River, at West Point [New York, U.S.A.].

U. S. distribution. — GEOGRAPHICAL: New England States, Middle Atlantic States; California. ECOLOGICAL: Brackish water.

4. **Caloneis oregonica** (Ehr.) Patr. comb. nov., var. **oregonica**

PL. 53, FIG. 6

Pinnularia oregonica Ehr., Ber. Akad. Wiss. Berlin, for 1845:79-80. 1845. [illustrated, Phys. Abh. Akad. Wiss. Berlin, for 1870, pl. 2(1), figs. 10-11. 1871.]
Navicula oregonica (Ehr.) Kütz., Sp. Alg., p. 71. 1849.
Navicula formosa Greg., Trans. Micr. Soc. London, New Ser., 4:42, pl. 5, fig. 6. 1856.
Caloneis formosa (Greg.) Cl., K. Svenska Vet.-Akad. Handl., Ny Följd, 26(2):57. 1894.

Valve linear-lanceolate with rounded ends. Axial area narrow at the ends, but soon widening to a space which is slightly less than one-third the breadth of the valve in width. Central area rounded. Striae radiate, sometimes almost parallel at the ends. Longitudinal line formed by the small "chambers" on the striae nearer the margin than the axial area. Striae, 9-15 in 10μ. Length, 75-165μ. Breadth, 15-35μ.

This species is closely related to *Caloneis latiuscula* (Kütz.) Cl. from which it mainly differs by the shape of the valve and the longitudinal lines being further from the margins of the valve.

To this species may belong the taxon which in Van Heurck's *Synopsis des Diatomées de Belgique* (1885, p. 102; 1880, pl. 11, fig. 3; type sl. no. 133) is called *Navicula liburnica* Grun. However, it has a much narrower axial area.

An examination of Ehrenberg's figures (1871) shows that the taxa of Ehrenberg and Gregory are the same.

Type locality. — Fossilis in Oregonia.

U. S. distribution. — GEOGRAPHICAL: New England States, Middle Atlantic States, Southeastern States, Gulf Coast States, South Central States, Plains States; Utah, California. ECOLOGICAL: Brackish to marine water.

4. Caloneis oregonica var. quadrilineata (Grun. *ex* Cl.) Patr. comb. nov.

PL. 53, FIG. 7

Navicula quadrilineata Grun. *in* Cl. & Möll., Diatoms, pt. 4, slide no. 204. 1879.
  (*nom. nud.*)
Caloneis formosa var. *quadrilineata* Grun. *ex* Cl., K. Svenska Vet.-Akad. Handl., Ny
  Földj, 26(2):58. 1894.

This variety differs from the nominate variety in its more linear valve
with somewhat cuneate ends, its narrower axial area, and its two longitudinal
lines near each margin of the valve instead of one. Striae, 15-17 in 10μ.
Length, 44-66μ. Length-to-breadth ratio, about 4:1.

Type locality. — U.S.A., California, Oakland; brackish water. (*Lectotype*—A-Cl. & Möll. 204, Patrick.)

U. S. distribution. — GEOGRAPHICAL: Known only from the type locality.

5. Caloneis liber (W. Sm.) Cl. var. liber

PL. 53, FIG. 9

Navicula liber W. Sm., Syn. British Diat., vol. 1, p. 48, pl. 16, fig. 133. 1853.
Navicula maxima Greg., Quart. Jour. Micr. Sci., 3:41, pl. 4, fig. 19. 1855.
Caloneis liber (W. Sm.) Cl., K. Svenska Vet.-Akad. Handl., Ny Földj, 26(2):54.
  1894.

Valve linear, sometimes with slightly concave sides; ends rounded or
somewhat cuneate. Axial area narrow, one-sixth to one-fifth the width of
the valve. Central area a little wider than the axial area, rounded. Central
nodule distinct. Striae parallel throughout most of the valve to slightly
radiate at the ends. Two longitudinal lines on each side of the raphe. Striae
usually about 20 in 10μ—sometimes as few as 13 in 10μ. Length, 80-170μ.
Breadth, 13-24μ.

The specimens of *Navicula maxima* illustrated by Gregory in 1856
(1856b, pl. 5, fig. 2) more nearly agree with our specimens than that illustrated by Gregory in 1855 (*loc. cit.*).

Type locality. — England, coast of Sussex, Sept. 1851. Marine.

U. S. distribution. — GEOGRAPHICAL: Middle Atlantic States; Florida,
Michigan (?), Nevada. ECOLOGICAL: Inland saline lakes; marine.

6. Caloneis wardii Cl. var. wardii

PL. 53, FIG. 8

Caloneis wardii Cl., K. Svenska Vet.-Akad. Handl., Ny Földj, 26(2):57, pl. 3,
  figs. 39-41. 1894.
Navicula campbellii M. Perag. *in* Temp. & Perag., Diat. Monde Entier, 2nd ed.,
  p. 100. 1908.

Valve linear with cuneate ends which are a little attenuated, rostrate.
Axial area about one-fifth the breadth of the valve. Central area a narrow
fascia. Striae parallel throughout most of the valve, slightly radiate at the

ends. Longitudinal line on each side of the valve, nearer the margin than the raphe. Striae, 18 in 10μ near the center of the valve to 21 in 10μ near the ends. Length, 40-90μ. Breadth, about 15μ.

Type locality. — Brackish water; Bristol, Connecticut (Ward) [U.S.A.].

U. S. distribution. — GEOGRAPHICAL: Connecticut, Pennsylvania. ECO-LOGICAL: Brackish water.

7. **Caloneis ventricosa** (Ehr.) Meist. var. **ventricosa**   PL. 54, FIG. 3

Navicula ventricosa Ehr., Phys. Abh. Akad. Wiss. Berlin, for 1838:130, pl. 4, fig. 10i. 1839.
Navicula silicula Ehr., Phys. Abh. Akad. Wiss. Berlin, for 1841:419. 1843.
Navicula leptogongyla Ehr., Phys. Abh. Akad. Wiss. Berlin, for 1841:418. 1843.
Caloneis silicula (Ehr.) Cl., K. Svenska Vet.-Akad. Handl., Ny Följd, 26(2):51. 1894.
Caloneis ventricosa (Ehr.) Meist., Beitr. Kryptog.-Fl. Schweiz, 4(1), p. 116, pl. 17, fig. 4. 1912.

Valve biconstricted; median portion swollen. Ends broadly clavate and rounded, sometimes somewhat cuneate. Axial and central areas forming a linear-lanceolate space which is widened and rounded at the central nodule. Striae parallel or almost parallel, sometimes slightly radiate at the ends. A longitudinal line near each edge of the valve. Striae, 16-20 in 10μ. Length, 50-85μ. Breadth, 13-15μ.

This taxon has recently been named by many authors as *Caloneis silicula* (Ehr.) Cl. However, Ehrenberg in the legend of pl. 21, fig. 37 of the *Mikrogeologie* states that "N. silicula 1844 = N. ventricosa 1838" (1839). Since *N. ventricosa* is the older name it is the valid one.

Navicula limosa var. *gibberula* (Kütz.) Grun. (1860, p. 544, pl. 5, fig. 8A) is not *N. gibberula* Kütz., but rather Grunow's specimen represents a synonym of this species. Many authorities consider *N. limosa* Kütz. and *N. gibberula* Kütz. to be the same taxon. I have examined type material of Kützing in the British Museum and find these species to be synonymous with *C. schumanniana* Grun. which is a later homonym.

Type locality. — Mergel von Oran in Afrika.

U. S. distribution. — GEOGRAPHICAL: New England States, Middle Atlantic States, Southeastern States, South Central States, East Central States, Plains States; Utah, Washington, Oregon, California. ECOLOGICAL: Tolerant of a wide range of fresh-water conditions.

7. **Caloneis ventricosa** var. **alpina** (Cl.) Patr. comb. nov.   PL. 54, FIG. 1

Caloneis silicula var. alpina Cl., K. Svenska Vet.-Akad. Handl., Ny Följd, 26(2):51. 1894.

This variety differs from the nominate variety by the weaker constriction of the valve, the less cuneate ends, and the wider axial area. Striae, 18-22 in 10μ. Length, 20-45μ; Hustedt (1930, p. 238) states—rarely 40μ. Breadth, 7-8μ.

This taxon has been wrongly named *Navicula silicula* by Grunow in Van Heurck's *Synopsis des Diatomées de Belgique* (1880, pl. 12, fig. 21). Also, Lagerstedt (1873, p. 30, pl. 1, fig. 6) incorrectly called it *N. limosa* Kütz.

Type locality. — Spetzb[ergen], Brandewijne B, (Lagerstedt's specimen).

U. S. distribution. — GEOGRAPHICAL: New York, Pennsylvania, Illinois. ECOLOGICAL: Typically in mountainous regions.

7. **Caloneis ventricosa** var. **minuta** (Grun.) Mills   PL. 54, FIG. 2

> *Navicula ventricosa* var. *minuta* Grun. *in* V.H., Syn. Diat. Belgique, p. 103. 1885; f. *minuta?* Grun., pl. 12, fig. 26. 1880.
> *Caloneis silicula* var. *minuta* (Grun.) Cl., K. Svenska Vet.-Akad. Handl., Ny Följd, 26(2):52. 1894.
> *Caloneis ventricosa* var. *minuta* (Grun.) Mills Index Diat., Vol. 2, p. 1177. 1934.

This taxon differs from the nominate variety by its somewhat cuneate ends, smaller size, usually finer striae, and very broad transverse fascia. Striae, 21-22 in 10μ. Length, 22-33μ. Breadth, 6-7μ.

The name *"silicula"* is illegitimate for this species. See note under *Caloneis ventricosa*.

Type locality. — Eaux douces. — Louvain (P. G.) [Belgium].

U. S. distribution. — GEOGRAPHICAL: Southeastern States; Tennessee, Kansas, California(?).

7. **Caloneis ventricosa** var. **subundulata** (Grun.) Patr. comb. nov.
PL. 54, FIG. 4

> *Navicula ventricosa* var. *subundulata* Grun. *in* Cl. & Grun., K. Svenska Vet.-Akad. Handl., Ny Följd, 17(2):29, pl. 1, fig. 16. 1880.
> *Caloneis silicula* var. *subundulata* (Grun. *in* Cl. & Grun.) Ross, Natl. Mus. Canada Bull., No. 97, pt. 2, p. 208. 1947.

This variety resembles the nominate variety in the shape of the valve and the narrow axial area. It differs in that the central area forms a broad transverse fascia. Striae, 18-20 in 10μ. Length, 40-60μ. Breadth, at the center of the valve, 9-13μ.

This taxon is the same as Donkin's (1870-1873, p. 74, pl. 12, fig. 7) which he erroneously called *Navicula ventricosa* Ehr.

The taxa called varieties of *Caloneis ventricosa* Ehr. need to be carefully studied and separated, perhaps into two species. The separation would be made mainly on the basis of the presence of a transverse fascia. Hustedt does not believe the transverse fascia to be an important characteristic. However, it does seem to be a basis for two groups of variations in other characters.

Type locality. — Karisches Meer.

U. S. distribution. — GEOGRAPHICAL: New England States, Southeastern States, South Central States; Iowa, Michigan, California.

7. Caloneis ventricosa var. truncatula (Grun.) Meist. PL. 54, FIG. 5

Navicula ventricosa var. *truncatula* Grun. *in* V. H., Syn. Diat. Belgique, pl. 12, fig. 25. 1880.
Caloneis silicula var. *truncatula* (Grun.) Cl., K. Svenska Vet.-Akad. Handl., Ny Följd, 26(2):52. 1894.
Caloneis ventricosa var. *truncatula* (Grun.) Meist., Beitr. Kryptog.-Fl. Schweiz, 4(1), p. 116, pl. 17, fig. 5. 1912.

This taxon differs from the nominate variety in that the valve is only slightly constricted, the ends of the valve are not swollen, and the central area is only slightly swollen. The transverse fascia is usually a little narrower than in the nominate variety. Striae, 20-22 in 10μ. Length, 30-42μ. Breadth, 7-10μ.

The name "*silicula*" is illegitimate for this species. (See note under the nominate variety.)

Type locality. — Uncertain, Belgium.

U. S. distribution. — GEOGRAPHICAL: Middle Atlantic States, Southeastern States, Gulf Coast States, South Central States, East Central States, Lakes States; Iowa, Utah. ECOLOGICAL: Seems to like fresh water with a little calcium. Also found in slightly brackish water.

8. Caloneis hyalina Hust. var. hyalina PL. 54, FIG. 6

Caloneis hyalina Hust., Arch. Hydrobiol. Suppl., 15(2):281, pl. 15, figs. 8-10. 1937.

Valve linear-lanceolate with rounded ends. Axial area narrow. Central area a broad transverse fascia. Striae parallel. A longitudinal line apparent near each margin of the valve. Striae, 34-38 in 10μ. Length, 12-28μ. Breadth, 4-5μ.

Hustedt states that the longitudinal line was not apparent on his specimens. With oblique light it is sometimes apparent on our specimens.

Type locality. — Java.

U. S. distribution. — GEOGRAPHICAL: New England States, Middle Atlantic States, Southeastern States, South Central States, East Central States; California. ECOLOGICAL: Soft and hard fresh water.

9. Caloneis bacillaris var. thermalis (Grun.) A. Cl.　　　PL. 54, FIG. 7

Navicula bacillaris var. *thermalis* Grun. *in* V. H., Syn. Diat. Belgique, pl. 12, fig. 27. 1880.

Caloneis bacillaris var. *thermalis* (Grun.) A. Cl., Bih. K. Svenska Vet.-Akad. Handl., 21, Afd. 3(2):16. 1895.

Valve linear to slightly gibbous in the middle portion; ends rounded. Axial area narrow near the ends, becoming wider toward the center where it joins the central area to form a somewhat rounded space. Striae parallel to very slightly radiate, particularly at the ends of the valve. Longitudinal line on each side of the valve near the margin. Striae, 18-23 in 10μ. Length, $34\text{-}55\mu$. Breadth, $8\text{-}10\mu$.

This taxon is somewhat variable in shape. Our specimens most nearly resemble that of the center figure in Van Heurck's plate 12, fig. 27.

Type locality. — Uncertain, Belgium.

U. S. distribution. — GEOGRAPHICAL: Nebraska. ECOLOGICAL: Found in water of high mineral content.

10. Caloneis bacillum (Grun.) Cl. var. bacillum　　　PL. 54, FIG. 8

Stauroneis bacillum Grun., Verh. Zool.-Bot. Ges. Wien, 13:155, pl. 4, figs. 16a-b. 1863.

Navicula fasciata Lagerst., Bih. K. Svenska Vet.-Akad. Handl., 1(14):34, pl. 2, fig. 11. 1873.

Navicula lacunarum Grun. *in* V. H., Syn. Diat. Belgique, pl. 12, fig. 31. 1880.

Navicula fontinalis Grun. *in* V. H., Syn. Diat. Belgique, pl. 12, fig. 33. 1880.

Caloneis bacillum (Grun.) Cl., Diatomiste, 2(17):99. 1894.

Caloneis fasciata (Lagerst.) Cl., K. Svenska Vet.-Akad. Handl., Ny Följd, 26(2):50. 1894.

Valve usually linear with parallel sides, sometimes slightly linear-lanceolate; ends rounded or very slightly rostrate. Axial area distinct, narrow; gradually widening toward the center of the valve. Central area a transverse fascia; usually moderately broad. Striae parallel to slightly radiate. Striae usually 24-30 in 10μ; in a few specimens they have been found to be 22 in 10μ, but this is not typical of this taxon. A more or less distinct longitudinal line near each margin of the valve. Length, $15\text{-}45\mu$. Breadth, $4\text{-}9\mu$.

The specimens of this taxon resemble those of *Caloneis ventricosa* var. *truncatula*, but differ in that the margins are not slightly triundulate and the striae are finer.

I have carefully studied the original description of *Stauroneis bacillum* Grun. and of *Navicula fasciata* Lagerst. I can find no significant difference between these two taxa. Lagerstedt states that longitudinal lines are present on his taxon and Grunow shows them in his illustration. I cannot understand why Hustedt (1930, p. 316, fig. 569) has synonymized *N. fasciata* Lagerst. with a *Pinnularia.*

This species belongs to the same group of species of *Caloneis* as *C. ventricosa.*

Type locality. — In aqua subsalsa ad litora Angliae prope Newhaven (legi August 1861).

U. S. distribution. — GEOGRAPHICAL: New England States, Middle Atlantic States, Southeastern States, Gulf Coast States, South Central States, East Central States, West Central States, Lakes States, Plains States; Utah, Oregon, California. ECOLOGICAL: Soft, hard, or slightly brackish water; lakes, rivers, bogs. Often found in standing alkaline waters.

11. Caloneis alpestris (Grun.) Cl. var. alpestris PL. 54, FIG. 9

Navicula alpestris Grun., Verh. Zool.-Bot. Ges. Wien, 10:545, pl. 5, fig. 4. 1860.
Caloneis alpestris (Grun.) Cl., K. Svenska Vet.-Akad. Handl., Ny Földj, 26(2):53. 1894.

Valve linear or slightly swollen in the middle portion; ends rounded. Axial area about one-fourth the width of the valve. Central area elliptical to rhomboidal in shape. On each side of the central nodule is a crescent-shaped siliceous thickening. Striae almost parallel at the center of the valve to radiate at the ends. Longitudinal line or band submarginal, sometimes indistinct. Striae, 20-24 in 10μ. Length, 45-92μ. Breadth, 6-15μ.

This species is related to *Caloneis limosa* which it resembles in general type of structure.

Type locality. — In rivulis et fontibus alpium Austriacarum.

U. S. distriution. — GEOGRAPHICAL: New England States, East Central States, West Central States, Lakes States; California. ECOLOGICAL: Likes calcium and cool climates; mesotrophic.

12. Caloneis limosa (Kütz.) Patr. comb. nov., var. limosa PL. 54, FIG. 10

Navicula limosa Kütz., Bacill., p. 101, pl. 3, fig. 50. 1844.
Navicula gibberula Kütz., Bacill., p. 101, pl. 3, fig. 50. 1844.
Navicula trochus Ehr., Mikrogeol., pl. 16(1), fig. 13. 1854.
Navicula schumanniana Grun. *in* V. H., Syn. Diat. Belgique, pl. 11, fig. 21. 1880. (text, p. 99. 1885.)
Caloneis schumanniana (Grun.) Cl., K. Svenska Vet.-Akad. Handl., Ny Földj, 26(2):53. 1894.
Navicula schumanniana var. *biconstricta* (Grun.) Reich., Arch. Hydrobiol., 1:232, fig. 5. 1906.

Valve slightly biconstricted or triundulate, inflated in the middle portion; ends broadly rounded and usually slightly cuneate. Axial area narrow, widening to the elliptical central area. On each side of the central area is a crescent-shaped, siliceous thickening. Striae almost parallel at the center of the valve to radiate at the ends. An indistinct, submarginal longitudinal line present on each side of the valve. Striae, 16-20 in 10μ. Length, 22-50μ. Breadth, 8-14μ.

I have examined isotype material from Kützing's herbarium (Kütz. no. 420-B.M. no. 18827) and have found *Navicula limosa* to be identical with *N. schumanniana* Grun. I have designated by a ring a lectotype on this slide.

This species is distinguished by the crescent-shaped markings at the central area, the lack of a transverse fascia, and the shape of the valve.

Type locality. — Bei Nordhausen in Süsswassergräben. (*Lectotype*— Kütz. 420–B.M. 18827, Patrick.)

U. S. distribution. — Geographical: New England States, Gulf Coast States, East Central States, West Central States, Lakes States, Plains States; Colorado, Oregon. Ecological: Seems to prefer water with a fair amount of calcium; also found in brackish water.

13. **Caloneis lewisii** Patr. var. **lewisii**   PL. 54, FIG. 11

Navicula trochus var.? *biconstricta* Grun. *in* Schneider, Naturw. Beitr. Kenntn. Kaukasusländer, pp. 112-113 pl. 3, fig. 6. 1878.
Caloneis lewisii Patr., Farlowia, 2(2):172. 1945.

Valve biconstricted with rounded, cuneate ends. Axial area narrow. Central area large rhomboidal with two lunate markings, one on each side of the central nodule. Striae parallel, occasionally slightly radiate about the central area. Longitudinal bands or lines indistinct. Striae, 18-20 in 10μ except in the middle of the valve. Length, 27-42μ. Breadth, 8-11μ.

This species is distinguished by the shape of the valve and the characteristics of the central area.

This taxon, by mistake, was identified by Lewis (1861) as *Navicula trinodis* W. Sm. (1856, p. 94) which is a much smaller and a finer striated diatom of very different shape. I have examined isotype material of *Navicula trinodis* W. Sm. belonging to Dr. Arnott (A-J. W. Bail. 1021). A discussion of this species is given by Patrick (*loc. cit.*). The name *Caloneis schumanniana* var. *trinodis* (Lewis) Cl. (1894) and *Caloneis trinodis* (Lewis) Meister (1912) must also be considered as misidentifications of W. Smith's species.

In 1945 (*loc. cit.*) when I named this taxon, I was unaware of the existence of any of Lewis' material from the type locality. Since then, I have found his type slide at the Academy of Natural Sciences.

Type locality. — Northam's Pond [Newport, Rhode Island], locality of Lewis' specimen. (*Holotype*—A-G.C. 2018. Patrick.)

U. S. distribution. — GEOGRAPHICAL: New England States, Middle Atlantic States, Southeastern States, Gulf Coast States, East Central States, West Central States, Lakes States, Plains States; Montana, Wyoming, Colorado, New ·Mexico, Washington, Oregon, California. ECOLOGICAL: Fresh to brackish water.

13. **Caloneis lewisii** var. **inflata** (Schultze) Patr. comb. nov.

PL. 54, FIG. 12

Navicula trinodis var. *inflata* Schultze, Bull. Torrey Bot. Club, 16:101, pl. 90, fig. 7. 1889.

This variety differs from the nominate variety by the cuneate ends of the valve which, instead of being rounded, are drawn out into rostrate apices. Striae and characteristics of the central area as in the nominate variety. Length, about 40μ. Breadth, 13-14μ at the center of the valve.

Schultze (1889, p. 101, pl. 90, fig. 7) describes the striae as being linear-punctate. This is not the case in our specimens. They are not resolvable into puncta. In a few instances one can imagine that they may be very finely punctate.

Type locality. — Fresh water, Clifton, in pond near the old town road [Staten Island, New York, U.S.A.].

U. S. distribution. — GEOGRAPHICAL: New England States, Middle Atlantic States.

14. **Caloneis hebes** (Ralfs) Patr. comb. nov., var. **hebes**   PL. 54, FIG. 13

Navicula obtusa W. Sm., Syn. British Diat., vol. 1, p. 50, pl. 16, fig. 140. 1853. (questionable) (*non* Ehr. 1843.)
Navicula hebes Ralfs *in* Pritch., Hist, Infusoria, 4th ed., p. 896. 1861.
Caloneis obtusa (W. Sm.) Cl., K. Svenska Vet.-Akad. Handl., Ny Följd, 26(2):54. 1894.

Valve linear with slightly convex margins; ends broad, truncate, wedge-shaped to slightly capitate wedge-shaped. Axial and central areas uniting to form a moderately broad, lanceolate space. On each side of the central area a long, thickened marking. Straie parallel to slightly radiate throughout the valve. Longitudinal lines indistinct, near the margins of the valve. Striae, 15-17 in 10μ. Length, 50-60μ. Breadth, 16-17μ.

This species was apparently first described by W. Smith under a later homonym, *Navicula obtusa*. Unfortunately W. Smith used a wrong illustration for this species (1853, pl. 16, fig. 140). His description is not very definite, but could apply to the specimens I have seen. I have examined material from the United States, from the type locality, and specimens identified by Grunow (A-V.H. 75) as being this species; and they are all the same. Likewise, Cleve and Möller slide no. 168 contains specimens which are this taxon. Donkin (1870-1873, p. 23, pl. 3, fig. 12) first correctly illustrated this species and described it as *N. hebes* Ralfs. I have designated as a lectotype A-Feb. 3367 which may have belonged to William Smith and is from the type locality.

Type locality. — Fresh water. Raasay Earth [Island of Raasay, Hebrides, Scotland]. (*Lectotype*—A-Feb. 3367, Patrick.)

U. S. distribution. — Geographical: New England States; Kansas. Ecological: Fresh water, particularly in cool water.

15. **Caloneis speciosa** Hust. *ex* Boyer var. **speciosa**   PL. 54, FIG. 14

Caloneis speciosa Hust. *ex* Boyer, Proc. Acad. Nat. Sci. Philadelphia, 78. Suppl.: 310. 1927.

Valve strongly biconstricted with the central segment slightly larger than the terminal segments. Ends broadly rounded. Axial area broad, widening into an elliptical central area. On each side of the central nodule are lunate markings which extend almost the whole length of the valve. These lunate markings are more or less distinctly striated. Striae radiate throughout most of the valve, parallel at the ends. Longitudinal line marginal. Striae, 8-10 in 10μ. Length, 55-90μ. Breadth, 18-25μ.

This species is easily distinguished by its characteristic lunate markings.

This species was invalidly described by Hustedt *in* A. Schmidt's *Atlas* as *Navicula speciosa* (1913, pl. 295, figs. 8-9) which was a later homonym, and subsequently he changed the name to *N. pseudoschumanniana* in the *Atlas* (1914, legend, pl. 309). Since it was published without a description, it has not been validly described.

Type locality. — U.S.A., Washington, Jacoma [Tacoma].

U. S. distribution. — Geographical: Colorado, Washington. Ecological: Fresh water.

Taxa Recorded Since 1960

Caloneis bacillum var. *fontinalis* Hust. (recorded by Reimer, 1962).
Caloneis pseudoclevei Choln. (recorded by Hohn, 1961).
Caloneis pulchra Messik. (recorded by Hohn, 1961).
Caloneis salebrastriata Hohn (recorded by Hohn, 1961).

Genus **Pinnularia** Ehr. nom. cons.

Ehr., Ber. Akad. Wiss. Berlin, for 1843: 45. 1843.

The frustules are typically linear or linear-lanceolate, usually occurring singly or occasionally in filaments. Very large and very small species are found in this genus. Intercalary bands and septa are absent. The structure of the "costa-like" striae are chambers which open to the interior of the valve. The margins of these openings appear to form a band of variable width which crosses the striae. Such apparent bands are commonly seen on the larger species. On some of the small species it is obscure. The raphe may appear as a line or a filament. In some species it is twisted in various ways. The axial and central areas are usually distinct but variable in shape. Two large plate-like chloroplasts are usually present in each frustule.

This genus is most closely related to *Caloneis*, and perhaps further study will show these two genera should be united. This genus is also closely related to *Navicula* subgenus *Laevistriata*.

Type species. — Navicula (*Pinnularia*) *nobilis* Ehr. [= *Pinnularia nobilis* (Ehr.) Ehr.] (Designated by Boyer.)

KEY TO THE SECTIONS OF PINNULARIA

1. Axial and central areas forming a broad space in the center of the valve, striae very short ....*Pinnularia* section *Brevistriatae* (p. 620)
1. Axial and central areas not so formed 2
    2. Striae distant from each other, typically broad and fairly few in 10μ
                          Pinnularia section *Distantes* (p. 617)
    2. Striae not distant from each other 3
3. Striae not apparently crossed by lines or bands 4
3. Striae crossed by lines or bands 6
    4. Frustules small, striae fine, parallel or only slightly radiate
                  Pinnularia section *Parallelistriatae* (p. 591)
    4. Frustules variable in size, striae usually not parallel throughout most of the valve 5
5. Valve, usually less than 75μ in length, usually linear or linear-lanceolate in shape, apices of valve usually distinctly capitate, axial area narrow
                  Pinnularia section *Capitatae* (p. 592)
5. Valve usually large, apices of valve typically not somewhat drawn out and capitate, striae definitely radiate in middle portion of valve
                  Pinnularia section *Divergentes* (p. 602)
    6. Raphe filamentous ....*Pinnularia* section *Maior* (p. 627)
    6. Raphe appears to be twisted at least twice, complex in appearance
                  Pinnularia section *Pinnularia* (p. 635)

Pinnularia section **Parallelistriatae** (Cl.) Patr. sect. nov.

Pinnularia group *Parallelistriatae* Cl., K. Svenska Vet.-Akad. Handl., Ny Földj, 27(3):73. 1895.

Frustuli parvis, area axiali augusta striis semper ferme parallelis sed interdum aliquantulum radiatis et convenientibus. Striis semper ferme maioribus quam 15 in 10μ saepe amplius 20 in 10μ.

Frustules small, axial area narrow. Striae usually parallel but may be somewhat radiate or convergent. Striae, usually greater than 15 in 10μ, often over 20 in 10μ.

Several species of this section resemble small species of the genus *Caloneis*. They differ in that a longitudinal line or band on each side of the raphe is absent.

Cleve (*loc. cit.*) describes this group under the name *Parallelistriatae*; however, perhaps through an error it is listed as *Gracillimae* in his systematic treatment.

Type species. — *Pinnularia gracillima* Greg.

1. **Pinnularia sublinearis** (Grun.) Cl. var. **sublinearis**   PL. 55, FIG. 1

Navicula sublinearis Grun. *in* V. H., Syn. Diat. Belgique, pl. 6, figs. 25-26. 1880.
Pinnularia sublinearis (Grun.) Cl., K. Svenska Vet.-Akad. Handl., Ny Följd, 27(3):74. 1895.

Valve linear or slightly swollen in the middle portion with rounded ends. Axial area narrow, becoming wider near the central nodule. Central area not differentiated from the axial area. Striae very fine and their structure not distinct; radiate throughout most of the valve, parallel at the ends. Striae, 21-25 in 10μ. Length, $20\text{-}30\mu$. Breadth, $4\text{-}5\mu$.

This species is distinguished by its narrow axial area, small central area, and fine striae.

Cleve (*loc. cit.*) states that the striae are convergent at the ends. Grunow's illustration and our specimens have striae which are parallel at the ends. Depending on the curvature of the valve they might appear as convergent.

Because of the fineness of the striae, it is difficult to be sure that the striae are of the structure found in the genus *Pinnularia*. Perhaps the electron microscope will be helpful in deciding whether the taxon is a *Pinnularia* or should be placed, as it originally was, in the genus *Navicula*.

Type locality. — Not known.

U. S. distribution. — Geographical: New York, Pennsylvania, Indiana.

Pinnularia section **Capitatae** (Cl.) Patr. sect. nov.

Pinnularia group *Capitatae* Cl., K. Svenska Vet.-Akad. Handl., Ny Följd, 27(3):73. 1895.

Frustuli parvis. Valvis linearibus aut lineari-lanceolatis. Apicibus capitatis aut rostratis praeter in *P. mormonorum*. Striis radiatis aut convenientibus sed non valide angulatis.

This section is composed of mostly small species which are usually linear or linear-lanceolate. The apices of the valve are more or less capitate or rostrate. Only in one species, *P. mormonorum*, is the end of the valve rounded.

This section is closely related to the section *Divergentes*. It differs in that the striae are not strongly radiate or strongly convergent or both. The striae in this section are radiate in the middle portion of the valve and slightly radiate, parallel, or convergent toward the apices.

Type species. – Pinnularia biceps Greg.

KEY TO THE SPECIES OF THE SECTION CAPITATAE

1. **Pinnularia appendiculata** (Ag.) Cl. var. **appendiculata**

PL. 55, FIG. 2

Frustulia appendiculata Ag., Flora, 10:626. 1827.
Pinnularia appendiculata (Ag.) Cl., K. Svenska Vet.-Akad. Handl., Ny Följd, 27(3):75. 1895.

Valve linear with somewhat attenuated, rostrate-capitate, slightly wedge-shaped apices. Axial area narrow, widening into the central area. Central area a broad, transverse fascia. Terminal nodules large; terminal fissures of the raphe distinct. Striae radiate at the center of the valve, strongly convergent at the ends. Striae, 16-18 in 10μ. Length, 18-36μ. Breadth, 4-6μ.

Type locality. — Ad Carlsbad, ad parietes verticales prope Tepl ubi vapor calidus ex ostio thermarum adscendit [Czechoslovakia].

U. S. distribution. — GEOGRAPHICAL: New England States, Middle Atlantic States, Southeastern States, Gulf Coast States, East Central States, Lakes States, Plains States; Wyoming. ECOLOGICAL: Aerophil; widely distributed in fresh water.

2. **Pinnularia braunii** (Grun.) Cl. var. **braunii**   PL. 55, FIG. 3

Navicula brauniana Grun. *ex* A. S., Atlas Diat., pl. 45, figs. 77-78. 1876.
Navicula braunii Grun. *in* V. H., Syn. Diat. Belgique, pl. 6, fig. 21. 1880. (text, p. 79. 1885.)
Pinnularia braunii (Grun.) Cl., K. Svenska Vet.-Akad. Handl., Ny Följd, 27(3):75. 1895.

Valve lanceolate with capitate to subcapitate apices. Axial area widening toward the center of the valve into a broad lanceolate space. Central area a broad, transverse fascia. Raphe filamentous. Striae strongly radiate at the center of the valve, convergent at the ends. Striae, 10-12 in 10μ. Length, 30-60μ. Breadth, 8-12μ.

This species is distinguished by the shape of the axial and central areas, the angle of the striae, and the shape of the valve.

Type locality. — Loka [Sweden].

U. S. distribution. — GEOGRAPHICAL: New England States, Middle Atlantic States, Southeastern States; Illinois, Nebraska, California. ECOLOGICAL: Seems to prefer cool water of low mineral content.

2. **Pinnularia braunii** var. **amphicephala** (A. Mayer) Hust.

PL. 55, FIG. 4

Pinnularia amphicephala A. Mayer, Denkschr. Bayer. Bot. Ges. Regensburg, 13(N.F. 7):136, pl. 2, figs. 15-16. 1917.
Pinnularia braunii var. *amphicephala* (A. Mayer) Hust. *in* Pasch., Süssw.-Fl. Mitteleuropas, Heft 10, Aufl. 2, p. 319, fig. 578. 1930.

Valve linear or with slightly convex margins; apices rostrate-capitate. Axial area about one-fourth the breadth of the valve; widening toward the central area which is a broad, transverse fascia. Raphe filamentous; terminal fissures and terminal nodules distinct. Striae radiate at the center of the valve, convergent toward the ends. Striae, 11-14 in 10μ. Length, 48-55μ. Breadth, 7-8μ.

This taxon is distinguished from the nominate variety by the linear valve, the narrower axial area, and the less attenuated apices.

Type locality. — ... aus einem Weiherabfluss bei Holzheim (Oberpfalz bei Klardorf) [Regensburg, Germany].

U. S. distribution. — GEOGRAPHICAL: Middle Atlantic States, Southeastern States, South Central States; Indiana. ECOLOGICAL: Seems to prefer cool water of low mineral content.

3. **Pinnularia hilseana** Jan. var. **hilseana**   PL. 55, FIG. 5

Pinnularia hilseana Jan. *in* Hilse, Jahres-Ber. Schlesischen Ges. Vaterl. Kult., 38:82. 1860.

Valve linear with distinctly capitate, somewhat attenuated ends. Axial area narrow, widening slightly as it approaches the central area. Central area a transverse fascia which is definitely wider in the transverse axis than in the apical axis. Terminal fissures and terminal nodules distinct. Striae radiate in the middle portion of the valve, strongly convergent toward the ends. Striae, 12-13 in 10μ at the center of the valve to 13-16 in 10μ at the ends. Length, 28-40μ. Breadth of middle portion of the valve does not vary much, 4-5μ.

Cleve (1895, p. 75) has synonymized this species with the nominate variety of *Pinnularia subcapitata* Greg. I do not believe that these two taxa are the same. *Pinnularia hilseana* is characterized by the distinctive shape of the capitate ends and the fairly large, distinct terminal nodules. Hustedt considers this taxon a variety of *P. subcapitata.* However, since this taxon has a very constant and characteristic morphology and has, so far as I can determine, been found only in acid water (usually bogs), it seems well to maintain it as a separate species. O. Müller (1898, p. 66, fig. 14) calls a taxon with triundulate margins *P. subcapitata* var. *hilseana,* but this is not the same as the type of this species.

Type locality. — ... Graben auf dem Rücken der Eule . . . [Eulen Range of the Sudeten Mountains].

U. S. distribution. — GEOGRAPHICAL: Connecticut, Pennsylvania, Indiana, Nebraska (?). ECOLOGICAL: In acid water, usually bogs.

4. **Pinnularia termitina** (Ehr.) Patr. comb. nov., var. **termitina**

PL. 55, FIG. 6

Navicula termitina Ehr., Mikrogeol., p. 159, pl. 33(4), fig. 4.   1854.

Valve slender, sometimes the margins slightly undulate, with rostrate-capitate ends. Axial area one-fourth to one-third the breadth of the valve, widening into a central area which is a transverse fascia. Terminal nodules large and terminal fissures distinct. Raphe filamentous. Striae radiate in the middle portion of the valve, and convergent toward the ends. Striae,

12-14 in 10μ. Length, 38-41μ. Breadth, 4-5μ. Length-to-breadth ratio, about 8:1.

This species differs from *Pinnularia hilseana* Jan. by its larger terminal nodules and fairly wide axial area that gradually widens toward the central area. In *P. hilseana* Jan. the axial area is very narrow all the way to the central area, and the terminal nodules are smaller. It differs from *P. biceps* f. *petersenii* by its large terminal nodules, its greater length-to-breadth ratio, and the more linear shape of the valve.

A. Schmidt in *Atlas der Diatomaceen-kunde* (1876, pl. 45, fig. 64) cites this taxon as *Navicula* (*Pinnularia*) *termitina* Ehr.

Type locality. — Andamanen—Inseln.

U. S. distribution. — GEOGRAPHICAL: Connecticut. ECOLOGICAL: Seems to prefer acid bogs.

5. Pinnularia burkii Patr. var. burkii   PL. 55, FIG. 7

Pinnularia burkei Patr., Farlowia, 2(2):189, pl. 3, fig. 1.   1945.

Valve lanceolate with rostrate-capitate ends. Axial area broad, widening toward the central area which is a broad, transverse fascia. Striae radiate at the center of the valve, convergent toward the ends. Striae, 16-18 in 10μ. Length, 18-22μ. Breadth, 3-4μ.

Type locality. — [U.S.A., Pennsylvania], Pike County, Greeley; (squeezings from *Sphagnum* in swamp). (*Holotype*—A-G.C. 2189, Patrick, 1945.)

U. S. distribution. — GEOGRAPHICAL: Known only from the type locality. ECOLOGICAL: Acid water of low mineral content.

6. Pinnularia subcapitata Greg. var. subcapitata   PL. 55, FIGS. 8-10

Pinnularia subcapitata Greg., Quart. Jour. Micr. Sci., 4:9, pl. 1, fig. 30.   1856.
Pinnularia subcapitata var. *stauroneiformis* (V. H.) A. Mayer, Denkschr. Bayer. Bot. Ges. Regensburg, 13 (N.F. 7):35, pl. 3, fig. 26.   1917.

Valve linear with capitate to subcapitate ends. Axial area narrow. Central area rounded, or elliptical with its greatest length in the apical axis; often forming a transverse fascia. Terminal nodules small but distinct. Striae somewhat radiate at the center of the valve, convergent at the ends. Due to the convexity of the valve, the striae appear on superficial examination to be more radiate than they really are. Striae, 12-13 in 10μ; sometimes toward the center of the valve, 10 in 10μ. Length, 24-50μ. Breadth, 4-6μ. Length-to-breadth ratio, 6:1-9:1.

Pinnularia hilseana Jan. has been synonymized with the nominate variety of this species. However, I consider it distinct (see discussion under *P. hilseana*).

Gregory, in the original description, says the apices of the valve are subcapitate, but his illustration shows a specimen with distinctly capitate ends. His original illustration shows a narrow axial area and a small central area with no indication of the presence of a fascia.

Type locality. — Scotland, gatherings from Elgin, Elchies, and several other Banffshire localities, also in Lochlevin and elsewhere.

U. S. distribution. — GEOGRAPHICAL: New England States, Middle Atlantic States, Southeastern States, Plains States; Oregon, California. ECOLOGICAL: Prefers water of low mineral content.

6. **Pinnularia subcapitata** var. **paucistriata** (Grun.) Cl.   PL. 55, FIG. 11

> *Navicula subcapitata* var. *paucistriata* Grun. *in* V. H., Syn. Diat. Belgique, pl. 6, fig. 23. 1880.
>
> *Pinnularia subcapitata* var. *paucistriata* (Grun. *in* V. H.) Cl., K. Svenska Vet.-Akad. Handl., Ny Följd, 27(3):75. 1895.

Valve linear with broadly rostrate, rounded ends. Axial area distinct, uniting with the central area to form a very broad, transverse fascia. Striae radiate toward the center of the valve, convergent toward the ends. Due to the large central area, only about three-fourths of the valve is striated. Striae, 12-13 in 10μ. Length, 28-32μ. Breadth, 5-8μ.

This variety is easily separated from the nominate variety by the broad central area and the shape of the ends of the valve.

The length-to-breadth ratio of our specimens is less than that shown in Van Heurck's illustration (*loc. cit.*), and the transverse fascia is not quite as wide.

Type locality. — Belgium.

U. S. distribution. — GEOGRAPHICAL: New England States, Middle Atlantic States, East Central States; Oregon. ECOLOGICAL: Seems to prefer fresh water of low mineral content.

7. **Pinnularia microstauron** (Ehr.) Cl. var. **microstauron**

PL. 55, FIG. 12

> *Stauroptera microstauron* Ehr., Phys. Abh. Akad. Wiss. Berlin, for 1841:423, pl. 1(4), fig. 1. 1843.
>
> *Navicula bicapitata* var. *hybrida* Grun. *in* V. H., Syn. Diat. Belgique, pl. 6, fig. 9. 1880.
>
> *Pinnularia microstauron* (Ehr.) Cl., Acta Soc. Fauna Fl. Fennica, 8(2):28. 1891.

Valve linear with usually broadly rostrate ends; occasionally somewhat rounded. Axial area narrow, usually less than one-fourth the breadth of the valve, widening toward the central area which is a transverse fascia. Striae somewhat radiate at the center of the valve, convergent toward the apices.

The angle of the striae in Ehrenberg's original illustration was much less than in the specimens which are considered to belong to this taxon by most workers. Striae, 10-13 in 10μ. Length, 25-90μ. Breadth, 7-11μ. Length-to-breadth ratio seems to be quite variable; in the more typical specimens it seems to vary between 5:1 and 6.4:1.

This taxon is quite variable and needs a great deal more study to determine if all of the so-called variants really are one taxon. Ehrenberg's original illustration (*loc. cit.*) shows the apices to be narrower than the main body of the valve and the striae almost parallel. Cleve and later workers such as Hustedt have considered as this taxon specimens with apices which are broader in relation to the rest of the valve and with striae more radiate and convergent than as illustrated by Ehrenberg.

It is doubtful if *Navicula brebissonii* var. *subproducta* Grun. *in* V. H. (1880, pl. 5, fig. 9) should be considered a synonym of the nominate variety of this species.

Type locality. — Brazil, from soil on roots of plants from Rio de Janeiro.

U. S. distribution. — Geographical: New England States, Middle Atlantic States, Southeastern States, Gulf Coast States, South Central States, East Central States, West Central States, Plains States; New Mexico, Utah, California. Ecological: Tolerates a wide range of pH and mineral content, but seems to prefer oligotrophic, slightly acid water.

8. **Pinnularia mormonorum** (Grun.) Patr. comb. nov., var. **mormonorum**   PL. 55, FIG. 13

Navicula mormonorum Grun. *in* A. S., Atlas Diat., pl. 44, figs. 24-26.   1876.

Valve broadly linear with rounded ends that are as broad as the middle portion of the valve. Axial area distinct, narrow, becoming broader toward the large central area. Striae slightly radiate at the center of the valve, convergent toward the ends. Striae, 7-9 in 10μ. Length, 35-60μ. Breadth, 10-12μ. Length-to-breadth ratio, 4:1-5:1.

This taxon should not be considered a variety of *Pinnularia brebissonii* because it differs in the angle of the striae, the convexity of the valve, and the shape of the axial and central areas. *P. brebissonii* var. *linearis* f. *curta* O. Müll., *P. brebissonii* var. *curta* (O. Müll.) Meist., and *Navicula brebissonii* var. *curta* (O. Müll.) Temp. & Perag. may be synonymous with this taxon.

Type locality. — Salt Lake, Utah [U.S.A.].

U. S. distribution. — Geographical: Pennsylvania, Texas, Utah.

9. **Pinnularia biceps** Greg. var. **biceps** PL. 55, FIGS. 14-15

Pinnularia interrupta W. Sm., Syn. British Diat., vol. 1, p. 59, pl. 19, fig. 184. 1853. (exclusive of synonyms.)

Pinnularia biceps Greg., Quart. Jour. Micr. Sci., 4:8, pl. 1, fig. 28. 1856.

Navicula bicapitata Lagerst., Bih. K. Svenska Vet.-Akad. Handl., 1(14):23, pl. 1, fig. 5. 1873.

Pinnularia interrupta f. stauroneiformis Cl., K. Svenska Vet.-Akad. Handl., Ny Följd, 27(3):76. 1895.

Pinnularia termes var. stauroneiformis (V. H.) Hofmann, Österreichische Bot. Zeitschr., 64:213, pl. 8, figs. 9a-b. 1914.

Navicula (Pinnularia) interrupta f. bicapitata (Lagerst.) Fritsch, Ann. S. African Mus., 9:592. 1918.

Pinnularia biceps f. stauroneiformis (Cl.) Ross, Natl. Mus. Canada Bull., No. 97, pt. 2, p. 201. 1947.

Valve linear with distinctly capitate apices. In some of the specimens with transverse fascias, the valve appears slightly concave. Axial area distinct, narrow, widening a little near the central area. Central area rhomboidal, somewhat rounded or a transverse fascia. The head of the transverse fascia is quite variable. Raphe filamentous; terminal fissures distinct, terminal nodules large. Striae radiate at the center of the valve, convergent toward the ends of the valve. Striae, 9-14 in 10μ. Length, 30-80μ. Breadth, 9-16μ. Length-to-breadth ratio, 3:1-5:1.

This species is closely related to *Pinnularia mesolepta* from which it mainly differs by the straight or slightly concave rather than triundulate margins.

William Smith (1856, p. 96) states that it is accidental whether or not a transverse fascia is present in *P. interrupta* because intermediate forms have been found. He considers his species the same as Gregory's taxon. Therefore, on this basis one cannot recognize two distinct taxa. He considered Gregory's name incorrect because it is not the same as *Navicula biceps* Ehr. which is an *Anomoeoneis*. Ross (*loc. cit.*) gives a clear discussion of this nomenclatural problem, and why *P. interrupta* is incorrect.

I have examined Ehrenberg's specimens of *Navicula dicephala* (Book 8, No. 2, Degensdorf, one of the localities cited by Ehrenberg [1838] for this species) which is synonymized by Ehrenberg in his notes, with *Pinnularia dicephala* (1841). These specimens are very similar to *P. biceps*. Further study may show that this is the correct name for this species.

Type locality. — Scotland, Elgin, Elchier and Lochleven.

U. S. distribution. — GEOGRAPHICAL: New England States, Middle Atlantic States, Southeastern States, Gulf Coast States, South Central States, East Central States, West Central States; Montana, Wyoming, California. ECOLOGICAL: Seems to prefer fresh water of low mineral content.

9. Pinnularia biceps f. petersenii Ross   PL. 55, FIG. 16

Pinnularia interrupta f. minor Peters. in Bot. Iceland, vol. 2, pt. 2, p. 405, fig. 25.
    1928.
Pinnularia biceps f. petersenii Ross, Natl. Mus. Canada Bull., No. 97, pt. 2, p. 201;
    pl. 9, fig. 11? 1947.

Valve linear with rostrate to subcapitate apices. Axial area distinct, widening toward the central area which is a transverse fascia. Striae radiate at the center of the valve, convergent toward the apices. Striae, 12-14 in 10μ. Length, $22\text{-}30\mu$. Breadth, $4.5\text{-}6\mu$.

This form is distinguished from the nominate variety by its smaller size and its larger central area in proportion to the length of the valve.

Ross (loc. cit., pl. 9, fig. 11) illustrates a form which is quite different from that which was originally described by Petersen. (Ross, personal communication, states his specimens are small forms of P. microstauron.) Ross points out that Petersen's name for this taxon is a later homonym.

Type locality. — Near hot spring, Iceland on ground in front of house (Hlad) Mödrn vellir (Kjós) 6/8.

U. S. distribution. — GEOGRAPHICAL: New England States, Middle Atlantic States, Southeastern States, Gulf Coast States, South Central States. ECOLOGICAL: Widely distributed in circumneutral water.

10. Pinnularia mesolepta (Ehr.) W. Sm. var. mesolepta

PL. 55, FIGS. 17-18

Navicula mesolepta Ehr., Phys. Abh. Akad. Wiss. Berlin, for 1841:419, pl. 4(2),
    fig. 4. 1843.
Pinnularia mesolepta (Ehr.) W. Sm., Syn. British Diat., vol. 1, p. 58, pl. 19, fig. 182.
    1853.
Pinnularia mesolepta var. stauroneiformis (Grun.) Cl., K. Svenska Vet.-Akad. Handl.,
    Ny Földj, 27(3):76. 1895.

Valve linear with triundulate margins, the central inflation narrower than the other two. Apices rostrate-capitate, somewhat attenuated but broad. Axial area distinct, less than one-fourth the breadth of the valve. Raphe filamentous; terminal fissures and terminal nodules large, distinct. Central area rhomboidal or a transverse fascia. Striae strongly radiate at the center of the valve, convergent at the ends. Striae, 10-14 in 10μ. Length, $30\text{-}65\mu$. Breadth, $9\text{-}12\mu$.

This species is closely related to *Pinnularia biceps*. It is distinguished by the distinctly triundulate margins which do not seem to intergrade with the straight margins of *P. biceps*. It also seems to prefer water of a lower pH. It is distinguished from *P. nodosa* (Ehr.) W. Sm. by the length-to-breadth ratio and the central inflation being narrower than the other two.

Type locality. — Labrador, Okak.

U. S. distribution. — GEOGRAPHICAL: New England States, Middle Atlantic States, Southeastern States, Gulf Coast States, South Central States, East Central States, Lakes States, Plains States; Wyoming, Oregon, California. ECOLOGICAL: Seems to prefer fresh water of low mineral content, usually circumneutral to slightly acid.

10. **Pinnularia mesolepta** var. **angusta** Cl.   PL. 55, FIG. 19

> *Pinnularia mesolepta* var. *angusta* Cl., K. Svenska Vet.-Akad. Handl., Ny Följd, 27(3):76. 1895.

Valve linear with triundulate margins and attenuated, rostrate ends. Axial area narrow, distinct, about one-fourth the width of the valve, and widening into the central area which is a transverse fascia. Striae radiate in the middle portion of the valve (though not as strongly as in the nominate variety) and convergent at the ends. Striae, 10-13 in 10μ. Length, 42-80μ. Breadth, 7-10μ. Length-to-breadth ratio, 6:1-8:1.

This taxon is distinguished from the nominate variety by its slender valve and its somewhat attenuated, rostrate ends.

Type locality. — Uncertain. Fresh water: Upsala, Sweden! Ringkiöbing, Denmark (Atl.), Harz (Atl.), Maine, Bridgetown! Demerara River! Rio Purus, Brazil!

U. S. distribution. — GEOGRAPHICAL: Maine, Georgia, Wyoming. ECOLOGICAL: Prefers circumneutral water of low mineral content.

11. **Pinnularia nodosa** (Ehr.) W. Sm. var. **nodosa**   PL. 55, FIGS. 20-21

> *Navicula nodosa* Ehr., Infusionsthierchen, p. 179, pl. 13, fig. 9. 1838.
> *Pinnularia nodosa* (Ehr.) W. Sm., Syn. British Diat., vol. 2, p. 96. 1856.
> *Pinnularia nodosa* f. *capitata* Cl., K. Svenska Vet.-Akad. Handl., Ny Följd, 27(3): 87. 1895.

Valve linear, triundulate, central inflation broader than the other two; ends rostrate to rostrate-capitate. Raphe narrow, filiform; terminal fissures distinct, "comma" shaped, Axial area distinct, one-fourth to one-third the breadth of the valve, widening into the central area. Central area usually a transverse fascia, though sometimes the striae are not interrupted and the transverse fascia is absent. Striae radiate at the center of the valve, convergent at the ends. Striae, 7-11 in 10μ. Length, 35-75μ. Breadth at the widest portion of the valve which is usually at the central nodule, 9-18μ.

The nominate variety and forma *capitata* seem to intergrade, so I have united them.

This species is closely related to *Pinnularia mesolepta* (Ehr.) W. Sm. from which it differs in the length-to-breadth ratio and the central inflation being larger than the other two.

Type locality. — Bei Berlin [Germany].

U. S. distribution. — GEOGRAPHICAL: New England States, Middle Atlantic States, Southeastern States, Gulf Coast States, West Central States, Lakes States, Plains States; Washington. ECOLOGICAL: Seems to prefer cool water and water of low mineral content although sometimes found in other types of water.

Pinnularia section Divergentes (Cl.) Patr. sect. nov.

Pinnularia group *Divergentes* Cl., K. Svenska Vet.-Akad. Handl., Ny Följd, 27(3):73. 1895.

Pinnularia group *Tabellarieae* Cl., K. Svenska Vet.-Akad. Handl., Ny Följd, 27(3):73. 1895.

Valvis linearibus, lanceolatis aut ellipticis. Striis radiatis valide in media parte valvae et convenientibus distincte ad apices; aut radiatis distincte in media parte valvae, et convenientibus valide ad apices; aut radiatis valide in media parte valvae et radiatis ad apicem valvae. Area axiali distincta et saltem quarta latitudinis valvae in media parte.

The diatoms belonging to this section of *Pinnularia* are characterized by having strongly radiate striae at the center of the valve and distinctly convergent striae at the ends of the valve. In some taxa the middle striae are radiate and the terminal striae strongly convergent; in others the middle striae are strongly radiate and distinctly but not strongly convergent; and in some the middle striae are strongly radiate and the terminal striae strongly convergent. The axial area is distinct and often one-fourth or more the breadth of the valve.

Most of the taxa belonging to this group are over 40μ long although some species such as *P. obscura, P. intermedia,* and *P. brebissonii* may be less than 40μ long. Some of the species are characterized by having long "bayonet" shaped terminal fissures whereas in other species they are curved.

Pinnularia obscura and *P. intermedia* are intermediate between this section and *Pinnularia* section *Distantes* and might be placed in either section.

Cleve, who first erected the various groups of *Pinnularia,* states that the *Tabellarieae* are closely related to the *Divergentes* and that *P. legumen* is intermediate.

Type species. — *P. divergens* W. Sm.

KEY TO THE SPECIES OF THE SECTION DIVERGENTES

1. Raphe with distinctly "bayonet"-shaped terminal fissures 2
1. Raphe with terminal fissures shaped as a "question mark" or intermediate between this shape and a "bayonet" shape 10

1. **Pinnularia divergens** W. Sm. var. **divergens**   PL. 56, FIG. 1

Pinnularia divergens W. Sm., Syn. British Diat., vol. 1, p. 57, pl. 18, fig. 177. 1853.
Navicula divergens (W. Sm.) Grun., Verh. Zool.-Bot. Ges. Wien, 10:523.´ 1860.

Valve linear to linear-lanceolate with rostrate, rounded ends. Axial area one-fourth to one-third the width of the valve, gradually widening toward the central area. Central area a transverse fascia, on each side of which there is a rounded thickening. Raphe filamentous; terminal fissures "bayonet" shaped. Striae strongly radiate at the center of the valve, strongly convergent at the ends. Striae, 9-12 in 10μ. Length, 50-140μ. Breadth, 13-20μ.

This species is distinguished by the rounded thickenings present on each side of the central area.

W. Smith (*loc. cit.*) states the striae are about 4.5 in 10μ. However, specimens from the type locality (Rabh., Alg. Sach. Mitteleuropas No. 2211) have striae 9-10 in 10μ.

Type locality. — Fresh water, Premnay Peat [Aberdeenshire, Scotland?]. Dolgelly Earth [Merionethshire, Wales?].

U. S. distribution. — Geographical: New England States, Middle Atlantic States, Southeastern States, East Central States, Lakes States, Plains States; Montana, Washington, Oregon. Ecological: Cool water of low mineral content.

1. **Pinnularia divergens** var. **bacillaris** (M. Perag.) Mills   pl. 56, fig. 2

Navicula divergens var. *bacillaris* M. Perag. *in* Temp. & Perag., Diat. Monde Entier, 2nd ed., p. 58. 1908.
Pinnularia divergens var. *bacillaris* (M. Perag. *in* Temp. & Perag.) Mills, Index Diat., pt. 17, p. 1280. 1934.

Valve linear with slightly convex margins and rounded or slightly swollen ends. Axial area about one-third the breadth of the valve, widening into a narrow transverse fascia with rounded thickenings on the edge of the valve. Terminal nodules large. Raphe filamentous; terminal fissures "bayonet" shaped. Striae strongly radiate at the center of the valve, strongly convergent at the ends. Striae, 10-11 in 10μ. Length, 67μ. Breadth, 13μ.

This taxon, in shape of valve and shape of axial and central areas, is very similar to a taxon in A. Schmidt's *Atlas der Diatomaceen-kunde* (1876, pl. 44, figs. 6-7) which he calls *Navicula divergens* W. Sm. They are not the nominate variety as described by W. Smith. Cleve (1895, p. 79) has synonymized these figures with *Pinnularia divergens* var. *elliptica*. They are not variety *elliptica* as originally described. However, they are apparently the same as Peragallo's description of variety *bacillaris*. I have thoroughly examined our slides of Peragallo's type material. The specimen illustrated is the only one that fits his description and, therefore, one can assume it is the one he meant. His description is very short and not very definitive.

Type locality. — Bunnel's Pond, Bristol, Connecticut (Dépôt fossile d'eau douce), [U.S.A.]. (*Lectotype*—A-T.&P. 106, Patrick.)

U. S. distribution. — Geographical: Connecticut, Washington. Ecological: Cool water, mountainous regions.

1. **Pinnularia divergens** var. **elliptica** Cl. PL. 56, FIG. 3

Navicula? *divergens* var. *elliptica* O'Meara, Proc. Roy. Irish Acad. Ser. 2:345. 1875.
Navicula divergens var. *elliptica* Grun., Denkschr. Akad. Wiss. Wien, Math.-
Naturw. Cl., 48:98, pl. 1, fig. 19. 1884.
Pinnularia divergens var. *elliptica* Cl., K. Svenska Vet.-Akad. Handl., Ny Följd,
27(3):79. 1895.

Valve linear-elliptical, narrowing toward rounded ends. Axial area one-
fourth to one-fifth the breadth of the valve, widening into the rhomboid
central area on each side of which is the thickening characteristic of *Pinnularia divergens*. Raphe filamentous; terminal fissures "bayonet" shaped.
Striae radiate at the center of the valve, convergent toward the ends. Striae,
7-11 in 10μ. Length, 50-100μ. Breadth, 15-26μ. Length-to-breadth ratio,
3:1-4:1.

Cleve (1895, p. 79) states that figures 6 and 7 of plate 44 in A. Schmidt's
Atlas der Diatomaceen-kunde are of this taxon, though Schmidt designates
them as *Navicula divergens* W. Sm. Also, they differ in shape from variety
elliptica as originally described by Grunow. Our taxon, as illustrated, corresponds to Grunow's variety *elliptica* in shape as well as in other characteristics. It is difficult from the single sentence description of O'Meara to know
just what is his taxon.

The taxon listed by Boyer seems to be intermediate between *P. divergens* var. *bacillaris* and variety *elliptica*.

Type locality. — Franz Josefs-Land.

U. S. distribution. — GEOGRAPHICAL: New England States, Middle Atlantic States; Michigan. ECOLOGICAL: Seems to prefer cool water.

1. **Pinnularia divergens** var. **parallela** (Brun) Patr. comb. nov.

Pinnularia parallela Brun, Diatomiste, 2:pl. 14, fig. 7. 1895. PL. 56, FIG. 4
Navicula (Pinnularia) divergens var. *parallela* (Brun) Freng., Anal. Soc. Cient.
Argentina, 97:102, pl. 3, fig. 24. 1924.

Valve linear with rounded ends as broad as the middle portion of the
valve or a little narrower. Axial area one-third the breadth of the valve,
widening toward the central area. Central area a transverse fascia with
rounded, hemispherical thickenings on each margin. Raphe filamentous;
terminal fissures "bayonet" shaped. Striae strongly radiate at the center
of the valve, convergent toward the ends. Striae, 7-8 in 10μ. Length,
140-150μ. Breadth, 20-28μ. Length-to-breadth ratio, 5:1-7.5:1.

This taxon is distinguished from the nominate variety by its linear shape
and rounded, rather than slightly rostrate, ends. The striae are also coarser.

The specimen I have illustrated does not have quite as broad apices
as the original illustration of Brun.

Type locality. — Plages à roseaux des bords des lacs Genève et de
Zürich . . . .

U. S. *distribution.* — Geographical: New England States; Pennsylvania.
Ecological: In mountainous areas; seems to prefer cool water of low mineral content.

1. **Pinnularia divergens** var. **undulata** (M. Perag. & Hérib.) Hust.
   Patr.   pl. 56, fig. 5

   Navicula divergens var. *undulata* M. Perag. & Hérib. *in* Hérib., Diat. Auvergne,
       p. 89, pl. 4, fig. 2.   1893.
   Pinnularia divergens var. *undulata* (M. Perag. & Hérib.) Hust. *in* Pasch., Süssw.-Fl.
       Mitteleuropas, Heft. 10, Aufl. 2, p. 323, fig. 589.   1930.

Valve with triundulate margins and rounded or rostrate-rounded ends.
Axial area distinct, about one-third to one-fourth the breadth of the valve,
widening into the central area. Central area a narrow transverse fascia with
rounded thickenings present on each margin of the valve. Raphe filamentous, sometimes slightly twisted; terminal fissures "bayonet" shaped.
Striae strongly radiate at the center of the valve, strongly convergent near
the ends. Striae, 8-11 in 10μ. Length, 80-105μ. Breadth, at the central
nodule, 18-20μ.

This taxon is distinguished from the nominate variety by its triundulate
margins. Héribaud and Peragallo state that the striae are 8 in 10μ rather
than 14.5 in 10μ as in the nominate variety. I have found them as fine as
11 in 10μ. Also, the length-to-breadth ratio in our specimens and that
illustrated by Hustedt (1930, fig. 291) is greater than that of the original
illustration. Likewise, the ends of the valve are more rostrate than rounded
in our specimen. However, since forms have been seen which seem to intergrade, it seems better to consider them all the same taxon.

Type locality. — Puy-de-Dôme. Fossile: Dépôt de Saint-Saturnin
[France].

U. S. *distribution.* — Geographical: Maryland, North Carolina.

2. **Pinnularia schweinfurthii** (A. S.) Patr. comb. nov., var. **schweinfurthii**   pl. 56, fig. 6

   Navicula schweinfurthi A. S., Atlas Diat., pl. 44, figs. 4-5.   1876.
   Pinnularia divergens var. *schweinfurtii* (A.S.) Cl., K. Svenska Vet.-Akad. Handl.,
       Ny Földj, 27(3):79.   1895.

Valve linear; either becoming narrower toward the broadly rounded
ends or not becoming narrower with ends as broad as the middle portion
of the valve. Axial area distinct, about one-fourth the breadth of the valve;
suddenly widening into the central area. Terminal fissures of the raphe
slightly curved, "bayonet" shaped. Central area a narrow transverse fascia
in which indistinct puncta are sometimes present. The transverse fascia

plus the widening of the axial area produce a somewhat rhombic-shaped space. Striae radiate in the middle portion of the valve and convergent toward the ends. The angle of the striae is not as great as that in many of the species belonging to the *Divergentes* group. Striae, 7-8 in 10μ at the center of the valve to 10-11 in 10μ near the ends. Length, 110-145μ. Breadth, 20-22μ.

Our specimens differ from those illustrated by A. Schmidt in that the ends are more broadly rounded and the terminal striae are not quite as strongly convergent. However, these variations do not seem to be enough to make a separate variety. This taxon does not belong to *Pinnularia divergens* because it lacks the rounded thickenings in the central area near the margins of the valve.

Type locality. — Grosse Seriba Gattas.

U. S. distribution. — GEOGRAPHICAL: Maine. ECOLOGICAL: Cool water in mountainous areas.

3. **Pinnularia caudata** (Boyer) Patr. comb. nov., var. **caudata**

PL. 57, FIG. 1

Pinnularia viridis var. *caudata* Boyer, Diat. Philadelphia, p. 104, pl. 30, fig. 18. 1916.

Valve linear-lanceolate with broad, rostrate ends. Axial area distinct, about one-fifth the breadth of the valve, widening into a large orbicular central area. Raphe filamentous, terminal fissures "bayonet" shaped. Striae radiate in the middle portion of the valve, strongly convergent at the ends. The curvature of the valve gives the appearance of a narrow band near the margins. Striae, 11-13 in 10μ. Length, 40-45μ. Breadth, 9-11μ.

This taxon was referred by Boyer to the species *Pinnularia viridis*. However, on careful examination it does not seem to be very closely related to that species. It differs in that the striae are strongly convergent near the terminal nodules and distinctly radiate near the middle portion of the valve. The terminal fissures are "bayonet" shaped and not curved as is typical for the *Complexae*. Also this taxon does not have the complex raphe characteristic of *P. viridis*.

Boyer states the valve is elliptical-lanceolate, but his illustration and the specimens on the slide which he designates as containing this taxon are linear-lanceolate.

Type locality. — U.S.A., Pennsylvania, Newtown Square, fresh water. (*Lectotype*—A-Boyer V-5-2, Patrick.)

U. S. distribution.—GEOGRAPHICAL: Known only from the type locality.

4. **Pinnularia legumen** (Ehr.) Ehr. var. **legumen**   PL. 57, FIG. 2

Navicula legumen Ehr., Ber. Akad. Wiss. Berlin, for 1841:144. 1841. [The name
   is listed, but the taxon is not described. This is the oldest reference to the
   name I have found.]
Pinnularia legumen (Ehr.) Ehr., Phys. Abh. Akad. Wiss. Berlin, for 1841: pl. 4(1),
   fig. 7. 1843.

Valve linear to slightly lanceolate with triundulate margins and subrostrate, broadly rounded ends. Axial area one-third to a little less than one-
fourth of the breadth of the valve (except near the apices of the valve),
widening toward the central area which is large and orbicular in shape.
Raphe filamentous; terminal fissures "bayonet" or somewhat curved in
shape. Striae strongly radiate at the center of the valve; convergent toward
the ends—not interrupted at the central area. Striae, 8-12 in 10μ. Length,
60-130μ. Breadth, 15-23μ.

This species is very similar to *Pinnularia divergens* var. *undulata*, but
differs in that the central area does not form a fascia or possess a thickening
on each side of the valve.

Type locality. — West Point, New York; fossil [U.S.A.].

U. S. distribution. — GEOGRAPHICAL: New England States, Middle Atlantic States, Southeastern States, Gulf Coast States, South Central States,
West Central States, Plains States; Wyoming, Oregon. ECOLOGICAL: Seems
to prefer water of low nutrient content.

5. **Pinnularia mesogongyla** Ehr. var. **mesogongyla**   PL. 57, FIG. 3

Pinnularia mesogongyla Ehr., Phys. Abh. Akad. Wiss. Berlin, for 1841:421. 1843.
Pinnularia gibba var. *mesogongyla* (Ehr.) Hust. *in* Pasch., Süssw.-Fl. Mitteleuropas,
   Heft 10, Aufl. 2, p. 327, fig. 603. 1930.

Valve linear, slightly to distinctly gibbous in the middle portion. Ends
broad, rounded; sometimes slightly capitate, but this is not the condition
in the more typical forms. Axial area distinct, usually about one-third the
breadth of the valve, widening toward the central area which is large and
elliptical in shape. Central nodule more or less distinct. Raphe filamentous
with "bayonet" shaped or slightly curved terminal fissures. Terminal nodules
distinct. Striae strongly radiate at the center of the valve; strongly convergent toward the ends. Striae, 11-12 in 10μ. Length, 60-80μ. Breadth,
12-15μ.

As Cleve (1895, p. 84) points out, Ehrenberg 1870 (published 1871)
figures what appear to be several distinct taxa which he calls this species.
Cleve had selected Ehrenberg's figure 16 on plate 2 as the correct one for
this taxon. It is the one which seems to be his and our taxon.

Hustedt (*op. cit.*) makes this taxon a variety of *Pinnularia gibba*. I do not believe that this should be done, as the shape of the valve and the shape of the central area are different.

Pinnularia decurrens Ehr. (*Navicula decurrens* (Ehr.) Grun.) seems to be the same species, but I have seen none of Ehrenberg's or Grunow's specimens.

Type locality. — U.S.A., "Andower" (probably Andover), Mass. Also mentions Boston, Mass.

U. S. distribution. — Geographical: New England States, Middle Atlantic States, Southeastern States, Gulf Coast States, East Central States, West Central States, Plains States; Utah. Ecological: Usually in water of low mineral content.

6. Pinnularia sillimanorum Ehr. var. sillimanorum   PL. 57, FIG. 4

Pinnularia sillimanorum Ehr., Phys. Abh. Akad. Wiss. Berlin, for 1841:421.   1843.
Navicula sillimanorum (Ehr.) Kütz., Bacill., p. 100.   1844.

Valve lanceolate with large, distinctly capitate ends. Axial area about one-third the breadth of the valve, widening into a large, orbicular central area which often has irregular blotches on it. Raphe filamentous; terminal fissures "bayonet" shaped. Striae strongly radiate at the center of the valve, and strongly convergent at the ends. Striae, 9-11 in 10μ. Length, 110-150μ. Breadth, 32-35μ.

This species is distinguished by the shape of the valve, the shape of the terminal fissures, and the angle of the striae.

Type locality. — . . . in dem Lager am Castell bei West-Point, New York, (fossil) [U.S.A.].

U. S. distribution. — Geographical: New England States. Ecological: Prefers cool, acid water.

7. Pinnularia stomatophora (Grun.) Cl. var. stomatophora

PL. 57, FIG. 5

Navicula stomatophora Grun. *in* A. S., Atlas Diat., pl. 44, figs. 27-29.   1876.
Pinnularia stomatophora (Grun. *in* A. S.) Cl., Acta Soc. Fauna Fl. Fennica, 8(2):27.   1891.

Valve linear, sometimes with slightly convex sides; ends rounded. Axial area distinct, one-fourth to one-third the breadth of the valve; widening toward the central area. Central area a transverse fascia with a lunate marking on each side of the central nodule. Raphe filamentous; terminal fissures "bayonet" shaped. Striae radiate in the middle portion of the valve, convergent toward the ends. Striae, 12-14 in 10μ. Length, 59-110μ. Breadth, 9-11μ.

This species is distinguished by the markings in the central area, the "bayonet" shaped terminal fissures, and the distinctly convergent and radiate striae.

It is closely related to *Pinnularia substomatophora* Hust.

Type locality. — Pudasjärvi . . . [Finland].

U. S. distribution. — GEOGRAPHICAL: New England States, Middle Atlantic States, Plains States (?); Montana, Oregon. ECOLOGICAL: Cool water of low mineral content.

8. **Pinnularia substomatophora** Hust. var. **substomatophora**

PL. 57, FIG. 6

> *Pinnularia substomatophora* Hust. *in* A. S., Atlas Diat., pl. 392, fig. 14. 1934.
>   Arch. Hydrobiol. Suppl., 14:160, pl. 2, fig. 14. 1935.

Valve linear with parallel or slightly swollen sides and rounded ends. Axial area distinct, about one-third the breadth of the valve, widening toward the central area which is a transverse fascia. Raphe filamentous with distinct, "bayonet" shaped terminal fissures. Striae strongly radiate at the center of the valve, strongly convergent toward the apices. Striae, 11-13 in 10μ. Length, 55-65μ. Breadth, 8-9μ.

This species is distinguished from *Pinnularia stomatophora* by the lack of the characteristic markings in the central area and the more strongly divergent and convergent striae.

Type locality. — Sumatra, Kieselgur vom Tobasee.

U. S. distribution. — GEOGRAPHICAL: Pennsylvania. ECOLOGICAL: Cool, slightly acid water of low mineral content, in lakes or bogs.

9. **Pinnularia bogotensis** (Grun.) Cl. var **bogotensis**   PL. 57, FIG. 7

> *Navicula bogotensis* Grun. *in* A. S., Atlas Diat., pl. 44, figs. 30-31. 1876.
> *Pinnularia bogotensis* (Grun.) Cl., K. Svenska Vet.-Akad. Handl., Ny Följd, 27(3):
>   83-84. 1895.

Valve linear, narrowing toward the rounded ends. Axial area about one-third the breadth of the valve throughout most of its length, widening into the central area which is a fairly broad transverse fascia. Raphe filamentous with "bayonet" shaped terminal fissures. Terminal nodules large. Striae strongly divergent in the middle portion of the valve, strongly convergent toward the ends. Striae, 12-14 in 10μ. Length, 100-110μ. Breadth, 11-13μ.

This taxon is distinguished by the shape of the broad axial and central areas.

Type locality. — Uncertain, Neu-Granada [Colombia]; French's Pond. (*Lectotype*—A-H.L. Sm. 681, Patrick.)

U. S. distribution. — GEOGRAPHICAL: New England States, Middle Atlantic States. ECOLOGICAL: Commonly found in somewhat acid ponds with water of low mineral content.

9. Pinnularia bogotensis var. undulata (M. Perag.) Boyer

PL. 57, FIG. 8

Navicula bogotensis var. *undulata* M. Perag. *in* Temp. & Perag., Diat. Monde Entier, 2nd ed., p. 56. 1908.

Pinnularia bogotensis var. *undulata* (M. Perag. *in* Temp. & Perag.) Boyer, Proc. Acad. Nat. Sci. Philadelphia, 79(Suppl.):439. 1927.

Valve linear; margins triundulate with the widest portion of the valve at the central area; ends broadly rounded. Axial area broad, between one-third and one-half the breadth of the valve, widening into the central area which is a broad transverse fascia. Raphe filamentous; terminal fissures "bayonet" shaped. Terminal nodules a broad, clear area about the terminal fissures. Striae distinctly radiate toward the center of the valve, strongly convergent toward the ends. Striae, 12-13 in 10μ. Length, 83-100μ. Breadth, 10-11μ.

This variety is distinguished from the nominate variety by its triundulate margins and broader axial area. Our specimen, although on a slide with Boyer's label on it, was probably part of Tempère and Peragallo's material which originally was collected by Terry.

Type locality. — Fall Mountain, Bristol, Connecticut (Sources et ruisseaux à 800 pieds d'altitude) [U.S.A.].

U. S. distribution. — GEOGRAPHICAL: Connecticut. ECOLOGICAL: Small brook, flowing from a mountain spring.

10. Pinnularia sudetica Hilse var. sudetica

PL. 57, FIG. 9

Pinnularia sudetica Hilse, Jahres-Ber. Schlesischen Ges. Vaterl. Kult., 38:82. 1860.

Valve linear, narrowing toward rounded or somewhat acute ends. Axial area one-third to one-fourth the breadth of the valve, widening toward the central area. Raphe filamentous; terminal fissures "question mark" shaped; terminal nodules large. Central area large, elliptical, central nodule distinct. Striae radiate in the middle portion of the valve and strongly convergent toward the ends; crossed by a narrow band near the margins of the valve. Striae, 12-14 in 10μ. Length, 50-90μ. Breadth, 11-12μ.

This species is distinguished by its large terminal nodules, filamentous raphe, and narrow band crossing the striae near the margins of the valve. It is not swollen in the middle portion of the valve.

This taxon is not a variety of *Pinnularia viridis* (Nitz.) Ehr. It belongs to the section *Divergentes* and not the section *Pinnularia* because of its filamentous raphe. *Navicula commuta* Grun. as illustrated in A. Schmidt's *Atlas der Diatomaceen-Kunde* (1876, pl. 45, figs. 36-37) does not seem to be this species.

Hustedt (1930, p. 335) names a taxon *P. viridis* var. *sudetica* (Hilse) Hérib. However, on the examination of Hilse's type material, it is evident that Hustedt's taxon is not that of Hilse. The raphe of Hustedt's taxon is complex and the shape of the valve is different.

Type locality. — Gesammelt zu Pfingsten 1860 auf dem Rücken der Eule in einer Höhe von 3000 Fuss [Eulen Range of the Sudeten Mountains]. (*Lectotype*—A-G.C. 11806, Patrick.)

U. S. distribution. — GEOGRAPHICAL: Middle Atlantic States; Connecticut, North Carolina. ECOLOGICAL: *Sphagnum* bog.

11. **Pinnularia abaujensis** (Pant.) Ross var. **abaujensis**

PL. 58, FIG. 1-2

> *Frustulia acrosphaeria* Bréb., Consid. Diat., p. 19. 1838.
> *Pinnularia acrosphaeria* (Bréb.) Rabh., Süssw.-Diat., p. 45, pl. 6, fig. 36. 1853.
>   [published in late May, according to research of W. Stearn (British Museum).]
> *Navicula abaujensis* Pant., Beitr. Foss. Bacill. Ungarns, Theil 2, p. 41, pl. 3, fig. 54. 1889.
> *Pinnularia abaujensis* (Pant.) Ross, Natl. Mus. Canada Bull., No. 97, pt. 2, p. 199, pl. 10, fig. 1. 1947.

Valve linear-lanceolate with swollen, rounded or subcapitate ends. The length-to-breadth ratio and the shape of the ends of the valve are quite variable. The width of the axial area is also variable, but is usually greater than one-fourth the width of the valve. The axial area widens into a large central area whose width is variable; sometimes it forms a transverse fascia on one or both sides of the raphe. The raphe is filamentous with rounded "question mark" shaped terminal fissures. The striae are radiate at the center of the valve and convergent toward the apices. Striae, 9-13 in 10μ. Length, 50-140μ. Breadth, 7-13μ.

This taxon which is quite variable can be distinguished by its linear-lanceolate shape, the somewhat swollen apices, the angle of the striae, and a central area which is large although variable in shape.

I have examined specimens of *Frustulia acrosphaeria* from Brébisson's collection which were collected in Falaise and appear to be isotype material. One of these is illustrated. I have also examined W. Smith's specimens of *Pinnularia gibba* (B. M. 23589—lectotype, Patrick) which he has labeled as being the same as his illustration (1853, pl. 19, fig. 183). The Brébisson specimen and the W. Smith specimen belong to the same taxon, pl. 58, figs. 1, 2. W. Smith refers to Brébisson specimens under the name *Navicula acros-*

phaeria Kütz. However, since the name *P. acrosphaeria* was published by W. Smith for another taxon before Rabenhorst made this combination, the next name used for this species in the genus *Pinnularia* must be applied. This is *Pinnularia abaujensis* (Pant.) Ross.

Although it is evident from Pantocsek's description that his taxon and the one we are considering are the same, neither Mr. Ross nor I have seen Pantocsek's type. Pantocsek, in the legend of his plate, questions whether his taxon may be a variety of *P. gibba*. *P. smithii* (Woodhead and Tweed) belongs to this taxon.

I have examined many specimens in Ehrenberg's herbarium which were labeled *P. gibba* and *P. tabellaria*. In rings on mica circles labeled as these two taxa there are quite diverse specimens which we would today consider as belonging to different species. It is clear that Ehrenberg has confused these two taxa or has considered that they intergrade. Specimens of *P. gibba* from two localities cited by Ehrenberg in 1841 ("Reale de Monte Mexico # 4, Box 22, 822 B card" and "Atolonilco el Grande, Mexico #2") are certainly not the taxon referred to this name by Hustedt and other modern workers and is not the same as our taxon.

Type locality. — Falaise.

U. S. distribution. — GEOGRAPHICAL: New England States, Middle Atlantic States, Southeastern States, Gulf Coast States, South Central States, East Central States, West Central States, Lakes States, Plains States; Wyoming. ECOLOGICAL: Widely distributed in water of low mineral content.

11. **Pinnularia abaujensis** var. **linearis** (Hust.) Patr. comb. nov.

PL. 58, FIG. 3

> *Pinnularia gibba* var. *linearis* Hust. *in* Pasch., Süssw.-Fl. Mitteleuropas, Heft 10, Aufl. 2, p. 327, fig. 604. 1930.

Valve linear with rounded ends. Axial area about one-fourth the breadth of the valve, widening toward the central area which is large and forms a transverse fascia. Raphe filamentous, terminal fissures "question mark" shaped. Striae radiate in the middle portion of the valve, convergent toward the ends. Striae, 9-11 in 10μ. Length, $60-85\mu$. Breadth at the center, $8-12\mu$.

This taxon is closely related to the nominate variety of *P. abaujensis*, but differs in the size and shape of the central and axial areas and the shape of the valve.

Elmore (1921, p. 67, pl. 22, figs. 823-824) has misidentified this taxon as *P. rangoonensis* Grun. *ex* Cl. (1895, p. 83).

Type locality. — Not given, but probably fresh water, central Europe.

U. S. distribution. — GEOGRAPHICAL: New York, Nebraska, Oregon.

11. **Pinnularia abaujensis** var. **rostrata** (Patr.) Patr. comb. nov.
PL. 58, FIG. 4

Pinnularia gibba var. *rostrata* Patr., Farlowia, 2(2):192, pl. 3, fig. 6. 1945.

Valve linear with rostrate, rounded apices. Axial area broad, about one-third the breadth of the valve, widening toward the central area which is rounded and a little wider than the axial area. Raphe filamentous with rounded terminal fissures which are "question mark" shaped. Striae somewhat radiate at the center of the valve and more strongly convergent toward the apices. Striae tend to be fewer and somewhat irregular in spacing about the central area. Striae, 8-11 in 10μ. Length, 65-79μ. Breadth, 8-11μ.

This taxon differs from the nominate variety by its rostrate apices that are narrower than the main body of the valve and by the shape of the central area which does not form a transverse fascia.

Type locality. — U.S.A., Monroe County, Pocono Lake Preserve, Pocono Lake, Pennsylvania. (*Holotype*—A-G.C. 2213, Patrick, 1945.)

U. S. distribution. — GEOGRAPHICAL: Pennsylvania. ECOLOGICAL: Found in water of low mineral content which is slightly acid.

11. **Pinnularia abaujensis** var. **subundulata** (A. Mayer *ex* Hust.) Patr. comb. nov.
PL. 58, FIG. 5

Pinnularia gibba f. *subundulata* A. Mayer *ex* Hust. *in* Pasch., Süssw.-Fl. Mitteleuropas, Heft 10, Aufl. 2, p. 327, fig. 601. 1930.

Valve linear with margins definitely, but not deeply, triundulate; rostrate to slightly capitate apices. Apices almost as wide as the middle portion of the valve. Axial area narrow toward the apices, widening toward the central area which is a transverse fascia. Terminal nodules distinct. Striae strongly radiate toward the middle portion of the valve and convergent toward the apices. Striae, 10-13 in 10μ. Length and breadth as in the nominate variety.

This form is distinguished from the nominate variety by its triundulate margins, shape of the valve, and shape of the axial and central areas.

Type locality. — Not given by Hustedt.

U. S. distribution. — GEOGRAPHICAL: Middle Atlantic States, Southeastern States; Arizona. ECOLOGICAL: Prefers water of low mineral content.

12. **Pinnularia brebissonii** (Kütz.) Rabh. var. **brebissonii**
PL. 58, FIG. 6

Navicula brebissonii Kütz., Bacill., p. 93, pl. 3, fig. 49; pl. 30, fig. 39. 1844.
Pinnularia stauroneiformis W. Sm., Syn. British Diat., vol. 1, p. 57, pl. 19, fig. 178. 1853.

Pinnularia brebissonii (Kütz.) Rabh., Fl. Europaea Alg., sect. 1, p. 222. 1864.
Pinnularia microstauron var. brebissonii (Kütz.) Hust. in Pasch., Süssw.-Fl. Mittel-
    europas, Heft 10, Aufl. 2, p. 321, fig. 584. 1930.

Valve linear-elliptical, gradually narrowing to rounded ends. Axial
area narrow, distinct; gradually widening toward the central area which is
a transverse fascia. Terminal fissures of the raphe intermediate between
"bayonet" and "comma" shapes. Striae radiate at the center of the valve,
convergent toward the ends. Striae, 10-14 in 10μ. Length, $40\text{-}60\mu$. Breadth,
$9\text{-}11\mu$.

This taxon is distinguished by its uniform shape, angle of the striae,
and structure of the axial and central areas. I have examined Kützing's
type material no. 412 (B. M. 18755) in the British Museum. The specimens
are the same as the one illustrated here and the same as that illustrated
by Van Heurck (1880, pl. 5, fig. 7).

Kützing states that Frustulia bipunctata Bréb. (1838, p. 18) is the
same as his taxon. However, Brébisson did not describe his taxon but only
lists the name—it is, therefore, invalidly published and cannot be used.
A. Mayer (1912, pp. 184-188) discusses the relation of Pinnularia microstauron and P. brebissonii, unites them under the name P. microstauron, and then divides the species into two sections each with its
varieties and forms. This institutes a very complex nomenclature which
I do not believe solves anything. Some workers such as A. Mayer (op. cit.)
state that the structure of the central area and the divergence of the
striae in P. brebissonii are variable and may resemble these structures in
P. microstauron and, therefore, these two taxa should be united. In the
specimens I have examined, which are from many different parts of the
United States, P. brebissonii is characterized by distinctly convergent and
divergent striae with a definite break where the direction of the striae
changes, rounded ends of the valve, usually a well-developed fascia at
the central area, although this character does seem to vary a little, and a
length-to-breadth ratio of 4:1-5:1. Certainly if one compares Ehrenberg's
original description and illustration of Stauroptera microstauron on which
the nominate variety of P. microstauron is based, it is a very different
entity than Navicula brebissonii Kütz. whose type material I have examined
(B. M. No. 18755-lectotype). For these reasons I prefer to retain them
as separate species.

Pinnularia stauroneiformis W. Sm. is synonymous with this taxon. I
have examined a slide from the collection of W. Smith (A-122, W. Sm.-178)
from the type locality and find it is the same. The only difference is that
the terminal striae are slightly less convergent at the apices.

Type locality. — In süssem Wasser Falaise: De Brébisson! [France.]
(Lectotype—B. M. 18755, Patrick.)

U. S. distribution. — GEOGRAPHICAL: New England States, Middle Atlantic States, East Central States, West Central States, Lakes States, Plains States; Texas (?), Montana, Wyoming, Colorado, New Mexico, Utah, California. ECOLOGICAL: Seems to prefer cool water of low mineral content.

12. **Pinnularia brebissonii** var. **diminuta** (Grun.) Cl.   PL. 58, FIG. 7

> *Navicula brebissonii* var. *diminuta* Grun. *in* V. H., Syn. Diat. Belgique, pl. 5, fig. 8. 1880. (text, p. 77. 1885.)
>
> *Pinnularia brebissonii* var. *diminuta* (Grun. *in* V. H.) Cl., K. Svenska Vet.-Akad. Handl., Ny Följd, 27(3):78. 1895.
>
> *Pinnularia microstauron* var. *brebissonii* f. *diminuta* (Grun. *in* V. H.) Hust. *in* Pasch., Süssw.-Fl. Mitteleuropas, Heft 10, Aufl. 2, p. 322, fig. 585. 1930.

Valve linear-lanceolate, gradually narrowing to rounded ends. Axial area widening toward the central area which is a transverse fascia. Striae radiate at the center of the valve, strongly convergent toward the ends. Striae, 10-12 in 10μ. Length, 20-33μ. Breadth, 7-8μ.

This variety differs from the nominate variety in that it is smaller and the striae are not quite as strongly angled.

On Kützing's slide, on which the type of the nominate variety occurs, there are specimens of this taxon.

Type locality. — Frahan (Delogne) [Belgium].

U. S. distribution. — GEOGRAPHICAL: Middle Atlantic States; South Carolina.

13. **Pinnularia divergentissima** (Grun.) Cl. var. **divergentissima**

PL. 58, FIG. 8

> *Navicula divergentissima* Grun. *in* V. H., Syn. Diat. Belgique, pl. 6, fig. 32. 1880.
>
> *Pinnularia divergentissima* (Grun. *in* V.H.) Cl., K. Svenska Vet.-Akad. Handl., Ny Följd, 27(3):77. 1895.

Valve linear to linear-lanceolate with obtuse to rostrate-capitate ends. Axial area narrow, widening only slightly toward the central area. Central area a broad transverse fascia. Terminal fissures intermediate between the "comma" shape and "bayonet" shape. Striae strongly radiate toward the center of the valve, strongly convergent toward the ends. Striae, 12-14 in 10μ. Length, 28-40μ. Breadth, 5-7μ.

Type locality. — Not given.

U. S. distribution. — GEOGRAPHICAL: Ohio, Wyoming. ECOLOGICAL: Prefers cold water, often found in mountainous country.

14. **Pinnularia obscura** Krasske var. **obscura**   PL. 58, FIG. 9

Pinnularia obscura Krasske, Hedwigia, 72(3):117, pl. 3, fig. 22. 1932.

Valve linear with somewhat rostrate, wedge-shaped ends, or linear-elliptical with rounded ends. Axial area narrow. Central area a broad, transverse fascia. Striae radiate toward the middle of the valve, strongly convergent at the ends. Striae, 13-15 in 10μ. Length, 12-22μ. Breadth, 3-5μ.

This species is characterized by its strongly convergent striae at the ends of the valve and the broad, transverse central area.

Type locality. — Vereinzelt an nassen Felsen an der neuen Autostrasse im Stubachtale [Hohen Tauern, Austrian Alps].

U. S. distribution. — GEOGRAPHICAL: Middle Atlantic States, Southeastern States, Gulf Coast States, South Central States, East Central States, Plains States; California. ECOLOGICAL: Found in a wide variety of fresh waters, often associated with moss.

15. **Pinnularia intermedia** (Lagerst.) Cl. var. **intermedia**

PL. 58, FIG. 10

Navicula intermedia Lagerst., Bih. K. Svenska Vet.-Akad. Handl., 1(14):23, pl. 1, fig. 3. 1873.
Pinnularia intermedia (Lagerst.) Cl., K. Svenska Vet.-Akad. Handl., Ny Följd, 27(3):80. 1895.

Valve linear with slightly narrower, rounded apices. Valve slightly concave in the middle portion. Axial area narrow, becoming a little wider near the central area which is a broad, transverse fascia. Central nodule elongate. Raphe with median ends somewhat distant from each other. Striae radiate in the middle portion of the valve, convergent toward the apices. Striae, 7-10 in 10μ. Length, 18-42μ. Breadth, 5-8μ.

Type locality. — Spitzbergen, Parry's Island . . . .

U. S. distribution. — GEOGRAPHICAL: South Dakota, Wyoming. ECOLOGICAL: Prefers cool water of low mineral content.

Pinnularia section **Distantes** (Cl.) Patr. sect. nov.

Pinnularia group *Distantes* Cl., K. Svenska Vet.-Akad. Handl., Ny Följd, 27(3):73. 1895.

Valve lanceolata ad ellipticam aut linearem, interdum tumita in media parte valvae. Striis latis, positis procul ab inter se.

Valve lanceolate to elliptical or linear, sometimes swollen in the middle portion of the valve.

The distinguishing characteristics of this section are the broad, flat striae which are distantly placed from each other.

Type species. — Pinnularia lata (Bréb.)Rabh.

1. **Pinnularia alpina** W. Sm. var. **alpina**   PL. 58, FIGS. 11-12

> *Pinnularia alpina* W. Sm., Syn. British Diat., vol. 1, p. 55, pl. 18, fig. 168. 1853.
> *Navicula alpina* (W. Sm.) Ralfs *in* Pritch., Hist. Infusoria, 4th ed., p. 906. 1861.

Valve elliptical-lanceolate to linear-lanceolate with broadly rounded ends. Axial area usually less than one-third the breadth of the valve. Raphe filamentous; terminal fissures large, sinuous; median ends of the raphe turned slightly to one side. Axial and central areas forming a lanceolate space which is somewhat rounded, particularly on one side in the region of the central area. Central nodule also broader on one side than on the other. Striae radiate throughout most of the valve, parallel or slightly convergent at the ends. Striae, 2.5-4 in 10μ. Length, 100-280μ. Breadth, 38-56μ.

This species is distinguished by the peculiar shape of the terminal fissures and the shape of the valve.

Type locality. — Fresh water: subalpine. Mountains of Aberdeen, Dr. Dickie [Scotland]. (*Lectotype*—A-115, W. Sm. 68, Patrick.)

U. S. distribution. — GEOGRAPHICAL: Indiana (?), Washington. ECO-LOGICAL: Subalpine in water of low mineral content.

2. **Pinnularia borealis** Ehr. var. **borealis**   PL. 58, FIG. 13

> *Pinnularia borealis* Ehr., Phys. Abh. Akad. Wiss. Berlin, for 1841:420, pl. 1(2),
>   fig. 6; pl. 4(1), fig. 5; pl. 4(5), fig. 4. 1843.
> *Navicula borealis* (Ehr.) Kütz., Bacill., p. 96, pl. 28, figs. 68, 72. 1844.

Valve broadly linear with rounded ends. Axial area narrow. Median ends of the raphe turned slightly to one side; terminal fissures distinct. Central area rounded, transverse. Striae usually parallel; sometimes slightly radiate toward the center of the valve and slightly convergent near the ends. Striae, 4-6 in 10μ. Length, 28-110μ. Breadth, 7-18μ.

This species is distinguished by its slightly curved raphe and the shape of the axial and central areas.

Type locality. — Uncertain, Chile.

U. S. distribution. — GEOGRAPHICAL: New England States, Middle Atlantic States, Southeastern States, Gulf Coast States, South Central States, East Central States, West Central States, Lakes States, Plains States; Montana, Wyoming, Colorado, Washington, Oregon, California. ECOLOGICAL: Prefers cool water of low mineral content. Often found in rivers, but also in ponds.

2. **Pinnularia borealis** var. **rectangularis** Carlson   PL. 58, FIG. 14

Pinnularia borealis var. *rectangularis* Carlson *in* Schwedischen Südpolar-Exped. 1901-1903, Band 4, Lief. 14, p. 21, pl. 3, fig. 15.   1913.

Valve linear with rounded ends. Axial area broad, almost one-half the breadth of the valve. Raphe somewhat curved with "comma" shaped terminal fissures. Central area formed by shortening or absence of median striae. Striae widely spaced; more or less alternating on opposite sides of the valve, not usually opposite each other which is the more usual case in diatoms. Striae almost parallel, 5-6 in 10μ. Length, $18-42\mu$. Breadth, $4.5-10\mu$.

This taxon is distinguished by the placement of the striae and the shape of the raphe and terminal fissures.

Our specimens differ from the one originally illustrated by Carlson in that they lack the median striae and are somewhat smaller in size. Fritsch (1918, p. 593, text fig. 40f) illustrated a specimen with the striae interrupted on each side of the central nodule.

Hustedt (1934a, pl. 385, fig. 28) described this taxon as new, but under this same name. His specimen also had a transverse fascia.

Type locality. — Falklands.

U. S. distribution. — GEOGRAPHICAL: Southeastern States; New Jersey Ohio.

3. **Pinnularia lata** (Bréb.) Rabh. var. **lata**   PL. 59, FIGS. 1-2

Frustulia lata Bréb., Consid. Diat., p. 18.   1838.
Pinnularia lata (Bréb.) Rabh., Süssw.-Diat., p. 42.   1853.
Pinnularia megaloptera Ehr., Mikrogeol., pl. 3(1), fig. 4.   1854.
Pinnularia costata Ehr., Mikrogeol., pl. 4(2), fig. 5.   1854.
Navicula costata (Ehr.) Hérib., Diat. Auvergne, p. 87, pl. 4, fig. 7.   1893. [non *N. costata* Kütz.]
Navicula megaloptera (Ehr.) Hérib., Diat. Auvergne, p. 88, pl. 4, fig. 6.   1893.
Pinnularia lata var. *costata* (Ehr.) Meist., Beitr. Kryptog.-Fl. Schweiz, 4(1), p. 157, pl. 26, fig. 11.   1912.

Valve broadly linear with rounded ends. Axial area distinct, somewhat variable in breadth but usually one-fourth to one-third the breath of the valve. Raphe filamentous, sometimes twisted as it approaches the central area; terminal fissures large, "question mark" shaped. Central area large, rounded. Striae somewhat radiate in the middle portion of the valve and parallel to convergent toward the ends. Striae, 2.5-5 in 10μ. Length, $70-160\mu$. Breadth, $24-40\mu$.

Kützing's taxon *Navicula lata* (Bréb.) Kütz. (1844, p. 92, pl. 3, fig. 51) does not seem to belong to this species.

Ehrenberg, in plate legends in *Mikrogeologie*, indicates that *Pinnularia costata* and *P. megaloptera* are probably the same species.

This taxon is also illustrated in A. Schmidt's *Atlas der Diatomaceen-kunde* (1876, pl. 45, figs. 5-8), but is erroneously called *N. pachyptera*.

I have examined Brébisson's specimens from Falaise (Rabh. Alg. Sachsens resp. Mitteleuropas No. 501) and find they are the same as ours.

Type locality. — Falaise [France].

U. S. distribution. — GEOGRAPHICAL: New England States, Middle Atlantic States, Gulf Coast States, East Central States, Plains States; Montana, Washington. ECOLOGICAL: Seems to prefer cool water of low mineral content, often slightly acid; commonly found in lakes and bogs.

3. **Pinnularia lata** var. **pachyptera** (Ehr.) Meist.   PL. 59, FIG. 3

> *Pinnularia pachyptera* Ehr., Phys. Abh. Akad. Wiss. Berlin, for 1841:421, pl. 4(2),
>   fig. 9.   1843.
> *Pinnularia lata* var. *pachyptera* (Ehr.) Meist., Beitr. Kryptog.-Fl. Schweiz, 4(1),
>   p. 157, pl. 26, fig. 12.   1912.

Valve linear, swollen about the central area. Apices rounded. Axial area broad, about one-third the breadth of the valve. Raphe filamentous, usually twisted as it approaches the central area; terminal fissures large, "question mark" shaped. Central area large, rounded. Striae radiate throughout most of the valve, parallel to slightly convergent near the ends. Striae, 3-4.5 in 10μ. Length, 50-125μ. Breadth, 14-32μ.

This taxon is mainly differentiated from the nominate variety by being gibbous in the middle portion of the valve. It is also often smaller and the striae are a little finer than in the nominate variety.

William Smith (1853, p. 55, pl. 18, fig. 167) erroneously called this taxon *Pinnularia lata*.

Type locality. — Okak auf Labrador.

U. S. distribution. — GEOGRAPHICAL: New England States; Washington. ECOLOGICAL: Same as the nominate variety.

Pinnularia section Brevistriatae (Cl.) Patr. sect. nov.

Pinnularia group *Brevistriatae* Cl., K. Svenska Vet.-Akad. Handl., Ny Följd, 27(3):73.
   1895.

Valvis semper ferme linearibus, interdum tumidis aut concavis ad mediam partem valvae; interdum lanceolatis leviter. Area axiali lata, semper ferme dimidia pars latitudinis valvae in media parte. Striis parallelis aut radiatis leviter aut convenientibus.

Valves usually linear, sometimes swollen or concave toward the middle portion of the valve; occasionally slightly lanceolate. Axial area broad usually in the middle portion of the valve, at least one-half the breadth of the valve. Striae parallel or only slightly radiate or convergent.

Type species. — *Pinnularia brevicostata* Cl.

KEY TO THE SPECIES OF THE SECTION BREVISTRIATAE

1. Valve swollen in the middle portion or triundulate 2
1. Valve linear or slightly concave 8
    2. Valve triundulate . . . . [8] *P. formica*
    2. Valve swollen in the middle of the valve 3
3. Central area granular 4
3. Central area not granular 5
    4. Raphe flexuose, axial area appears thickened on each side of the raphe
                                           [5] *P. cuneicephala*
    4. Raphe straight, axial area not thickened on each side of the raphe
                                 [3] *P. acrosphaeria* and var.
5. Axial area thickened on each side of the raphe 6
5. Axial area not thickened on each side of the raphe 7
    6. Raphe flexuose . . . . [5] *P. cuneicephala*
    6. Raphe straight . . . . [4] *P. singularis*
7. Apices of the valve distinctly swollen . . . . [7] *P. boyeri*
7. Apices of the valve rounded or only very slightly swollen . . . . [2] *P. brevicostata*
    8. Apices of the valve wedge-shaped, narrower than the middle portion of the
       valve; margins straight or slightly concave . . . . [1] *P. acuminata* and vars.
    8. Apices of the valve broad, rounded or slightly rostrate, valve linear 9
9. Length of the valve, more than 70μ . . . . [2] *P. brevicostata*
9. Length of the valve, less than 60μ . . . . [6] *P. parvula*

1. **Pinnularia acuminata** W. Sm. var. **acuminata**   PL. 59, FIG. 4

    Pinnularia acuminata W. Sm., Syn. British Diat., vol. 1, p. 55, pl. 18, fig. 164.
    1853.

Valve linear; sometimes with slightly convex sides; narrowing toward the wedge-shaped, sometimes slightly rounded ends. Axial area broad throughout most of the length of the valve, much narrower near the apices. Raphe filamentous with distinct "question mark" shaped terminal fissures. Ends of the raphe at the central nodule turned to one side. Striae parallel to slightly radiate toward the apices. Striae, 8-10 in 10μ. Length, 55-90μ. Breadth, 11-18μ. Length-to-breadth ratio in specimens I have seen, 5:1-6:1.

    This species is distinguished by its broad axial area, its filamentous raphe, and the wedge-shaped apices of the valve. Its filamentous raphe distinguishes it from *Pinnularia inconstans* A. Mayer (1917, p. 46) which has a complex raphe.

    P. T. Cleve (1895, p. 85) misidentified this taxon as *Navicula hemiptera* Kg. R. Ross of the British Museum has examined Kützing's packets from Trinidad as well as those from Falaise sent by Brébisson. He concludes that *Pinnularia hemiptera* Kütz. is not the correct name for this taxon. He has examined isotype material of W. Smith and finds specimens of our taxon in it which are undoubtedly his *P. acuminata*.

Type locality. — Fresh water. Premnay Peat.

U. S. distribution. — GEOGRAPHICAL: New England States, Middle Atlantic States, Southeastern States; Kansas (?), Washington. ECOLOGICAL: Water of low mineral content, often in swamps or lakes.

1. **Pinnularia acuminata** var. **bielawskii** (Hérib. & Perag.) Patr. comb. nov.   PL. 59, FIG. 5

> *Navicula hemiptera* var. *bielawskii* Hérib. & Perag., Diat. Auvergne, p. 85, pl. 4, fig. 10. 1893.
>
> *Pinnularia hemiptera* var. *bielawskii* (Hérib. & Perag.) Sov., Trans. American Micr. Soc., 77(2):123. 1958.

Valve linear with rounded, slightly narrower toward the apices. Axial area broad, uniting with the central area to form a linear or slightly lanceolate area. Central area sometimes producing a somewhat rounded shape to the broad lanceolate area. Terminal fissures large, "comma" shaped. Striae parallel at the ends of the valve, slightly radiate toward the middle portion of the valve. Striae, 9-10 in 10μ. Length, 55-90μ. Breadth, 11-17μ.

This taxon is distinguished from the nominate variety by its linear shape, rounded—not wedge-shaped—apices, and its narrower central area.

Type locality. — Puy-de-Dôme. Fossil Dépt des Queyrades No. 2 AR.

U. S. distribution. — GEOGRAPHICAL: Washington, Oregon. ECOLOGICAL: Water of pH 7-8.4.

1. **Pinnularia acuminata** var. **instabilis** (A. S.) Patr. comb. nov.
                                                        PL. 59, FIG. 6

> *Navicula instabilis* A. S., Atlas Diat., pl. 43, figs. 37, 39. 1876.

Valve linear; often in specimens we have seen, slightly constricted in the middle portion. Apices of the valve distinctly wedge-shaped, sometimes slightly apiculate. Raphe filamentous with large terminal fissures and distinct terminal nodules. Striae parallel to slightly radiate, crossed by a more or less distinct band. Striae, 8-10 in 10μ. Length, 86-100μ. Breadth, 20-22μ. Length-to-breadth ratio, 4:1-5:1.

This variety differs from the nominate variety in its usually broader axial area and its smaller length-to-breadth ratio.

Type locality. — Demarara River [British Guiana].

U. S. distribution. — GEOGRAPHICAL: New England States; Florida.

1. **Pinnularia acuminata** var. **interrupta** (Cl.) Patr. comb. nov.

PL. 59, FIG. 7

Pinnularia hemiptera var. *interrupta* Cl., K. Svenska Vet.-Akad. Handl., Ny Följd, 27(3):85. 1895.

Valve linear with angular, wedge-shaped ends. Axial area lanceolate, broad. Median ends of the raphe turned to one side. Central area a transverse fascia. Striae radiate in the middle portion of the valve and parallel near the apices. Striae, 8-11 in 10μ. Length, 40-80μ. Breath, 11-16μ.

This taxon differs from the nominate variety in its more lanceolate axial area, the presence of a transverse fascia, and the more radiate striae.

Type locality. — Japan, lignite (Brun Coll.).

U. S. distribution. — GEOGRAPHICAL: Alabama, Washington, Oregon.

2. **Pinnularia brevicostata** Cl. var. **brevicostata**   PL. 60, FIG. 1

Pinnularia brevicostata Cl., Acta Soc. Fauna Fl. Fennica, 8(2):25, pl. 1, fig. 5. 1891.

Pinnularia brevicostata var. *leptostauron* Cl., Acta Soc. Fauna Fl. Fennica, 8(2):25. 1891.

Valve linear with parallel margins, sometimes slightly swollen at the central nodule; ends broadly rounded. Axial area broad, about one-half the breadth of the valve. Raphe filamentous; terminal fissures "comma" shaped. Striae short; parallel or slightly radiate at the center of the valve and parallel to slightly convergent at the ends. Striae may be absent in the middle of the valve or continuous. Striae, 7-10 in 10μ. Length, 70-135μ. Breadth, 12-20μ.

This species is distinguished by its linear shape and very broad axial area.

Type locality. — Uncertain, Finland.

U. S. distribution. — GEOGRAPHICAL: New England States; Pennsylvania. ECOLOGICAL: Seems to prefer cool water of low mineral content.

3. **Pinnularia acrosphaeria** W. Sm. var. **acrosphaeria**   PL. 60, FIGS. 2-3

Pinnularia acrosphaeria W. Sm., Syn. British Diat., vol. 1, p. 58, pl. 19, fig. 183. 1853.

Pinnularia acrosphaeria var. *sandvicensis* A. S., Atlas Diat., pl. 43, figs. 14-15. 1876.

Navicula acrosphaeria var. *minor* M. Perag. & Hérib. *in* Hérib., Diat. Auvergne, p. 93. 1893.

Pinnularia acrosphaeria f. *minor* Cl., K. Svenska Vet.-Akad. Handl., Ny Följd, 27(3):86. 1895.

Valve linear, swollen in the middle portion; ends rounded, usually somewhat swollen, often almost as wide as the median portion of the valve. Axial area broad, about one-third the breadth of the valve and covered with small granules. Raphe filiform; terminal fissures distinct, semicircular. Central area not differentiated from the axial area. Striae parallel or slightly radiate. Striae, 6-14 in 10μ. Length, 30-180μ. Breadth, 8-20μ.

This species is distinguished by the broad, granular axial area.

William Smith (*loc. cit.*) gave the name *Pinnularia acrosphaeria* to this taxon. Rabenhorst a few months later in 1853 made the combination *Pinnularia acrosphaeria* for Brébisson's *Frustulia acrosphaeria* which is not this taxon. Dr. William Stearns of the British Museum has ascertained that volume one of William Smith's *A Synopsis of the British Diatomaceae* was published in 1853 before Rabenhorst's *Die Süsswasser-Diatomaceen* (*Bacillarien*).

I have examined specimens of William Smith which he indicates are the specimens on which his illustration of *P. acrosphaeria* is based. One of these is illustrated.

Type locality. — Fresh water near Lewes, September 1850, W. Sm.

U. S. distribution. — Geographical: New England States, Middle Atlantic States, Southeastern States, Gulf Coast States, Plains States; Wyoming, Washington, California. Ecological: Seems to prefer littoral areas of circumneutral lakes and ponds.

3. **Pinnularia acrosphaeria** var. **turgidula** Grun. *ex* Cl.   PL. 60, FIG. 4

> *Pinnularia acrosphaeria* var. *turgidula* Grun. *ex* Cl., K. Svenska Vet.-Akad. Handl., Ny Följd, 27(3):86. 1895.
>
> *Navicula acrosphaeria* var. *dilata* Temp. & Perag., Diat. Monde Entier, 2nd ed., p. 20. 1908.

Valve linear, strongly gibbous in the middle portion; apices strongly capitate, cuneate. Axial area distinct, much narrower than in the nominate variety, granulate. Raphe as in the nominate variety. Striae radiate in median portion of the valve, somewhat convergent or parallel toward the ends. Around the terminal nodules the striae may appear radiate due to the shape of the valve. Striae, 10-12 in 10μ. Length, 48-70μ. Breadth, 12-15μ.

Type locality. — Fresh water. Waltham Mass! [U.S.A.].

U. S. distribution. — Geographical: New England States, Middle Atlantic States; Washington. Ecological: Prefers circumneutral water of low mineral content.

4. **Pinnularia singularis** (A.S.) Cl. var. **singularis**   PL. 60, FIG. 5

> *Navicula singularis* A. S., Atlas Diat., pl. 43, fig. 20. 1876.
>
> *Pinnularia singularis* (A. S.) Cl., K. Svenska Vet.-Akad. Handl., Ny Följd, 27(3):86. 1895.

Valve linear, slightly gibbous in the middle portion; ends cuneate-capitate. Axial area more than one-half the breadth of the valve; the part adjacent to the raphe seems to be a little thicker than the rest of the area. Raphe filamentous; terminal fissures "comma" shaped. Striae parallel or slightly radiate at the center of the valve and parallel or slightly convergent at the ends. Striae, 6-8 in 10μ. Length, 70-110μ. Breadth, 9-19μ.

This species is closely related to *Pinnularia brevicostata* Cl. It differs mainly in the shape of the valve; also, the striae are usually a little coarser.

Type locality. — N. Celebes.

U. S. distribution. — GEOGRAPHICAL: Massachusetts.

5. **Pinnularia cuneicephala** (Mann) Patr. comb. nov., var. **cuneicephala**
PL. 60, FIG. 7

Pinnularia integra Grun. *ex* Cl., K. Svenska Vet.-Akad. Handl., Ny Följd, 27(3):87. 1895. (A. S., Atlas Diat., pl. 43, fig. 19. 1876.) [non *P. integra* W. Sm. 1856.]
Navicula cuneicephala Mann, Jour. Washington Acad., 14(1):30, pl. 4, fig. 5. 1924.

Valve linear, usually swollen in the middle portion, although Cleve says the margins may be parallel; ends cuneate, often somewhat subcapitate. Axial and central areas forming a broad area about one-half the breadth of the valve. Raphe flexuose; terminal fissures small but distinct. A siliceous region or thickening extending along each side of the raphe; the rest of the central area often mottled. Striae short; almost parallel throughout most of the valve, somewhat radiate toward the middle portion and convergent toward the ends. Striae, 7 in 10μ. Length, 110-120μ. Breadth, 16-17μ.

This taxon is distinguished both by the shape of the valve and the characteristics of the central area.

Type locality. — Fresh water: Uncertain, America (Crane Pond, Waltham Mass.)! French Pond (Atl.).

U. S. distribution. — GEOGRAPHICAL: New England States; New Jersey. ECOLOGICAL: Cool, fresh water of low mineral content.

6. **Pinnularia parvula** (Ralfs) Cl.-Eul. var. **parvula**　　PL. 60, FIG. 6

Pinnularia parva Greg., Quart. Jour. Micr. Sci., 2:98, pl. 4, fig. 11. 1854.
Navicula parvula Ralfs *apud.* Pritch., Hist. Infusoria, 4th ed., p. 908. 1861.
Pinnularia parvula (Ralfs *apud.* Pritch.) Cl.-Eul. *in* Sverige, Geol. Undersokn., Ser. C, No. 309, p. 72. 1922. [*non* Hust. 1937] (*nom. nud.*).

Valve linear, gradually tapering to the rounded or slightly rostrate-capitate ends. Axial area broad, a little more than one-third the breadth of the valve, widening toward the central area which is not differentiated from the axial area. Raphe filamentous. Striae almost parallel to slightly

radiate in the middle portion of the valve and slightly convergent toward
the apices. Striae, 8-11 in 10μ. Length, 40-65μ. Breadth, 7-8μ.

Cleve (1895, p. 87) gives a little wider range for the length and breadth
of the valve. This is because he includes as synonyms some taxa which we
do not believe are synonymous.

Ross (1947, p. 200) states that *Pinnularia parva* Greg. cannot be used
for this species because it was a provisional name.

Type locality. — Diatomaceous earth from Mull [Scotland].

U. S. distribution. — Geographical: New England States, Middle Atlantic States, Southeastern States, South Central States, East Central States.
Ecological: Seems to prefer slightly acid water of low mineral content.

7. **Pinnularia boyeri** Patr. sp. nov.   pl. 60, fig. 8

Pinnularia tabellaria auct. non Ehr.: Boyer, Proc. Acad. Nat. Sci. Philadelphia,
79(2) Suppl.:438. 1927.
Pinnularia tabellaria var. *stauroneiformis* (V. H.) Boyer, Proc. Acad. Nat. Sci.
Philadelphia, 79(2), Suppl.:439. 1927.

Valva tenui, tumida in media parte et in apicibus rotundatis late aliquantulum capitatis. Area axiali distincta, semper ferme circiter dimidium
latitudinis valvae, dilatanti in aream magnam mediam interdum ad margines
valvae extendentem. Raphidi fiiliformi fissuris terminalibus formatis similibus signo interrogationis—non formatis gladio. Striis radiatis in media parte
valvae convenientibus ad apices. Striis 10-14 in 10μ. Longitudine 100-200μ.
Latitudine, 15-22μ.

Valve slender, gibbous in the middle portion and at the broadly
rounded, somewhat capitate ends. Axial area distinct, usually about one-
half the breadth of the valve; widening into a large central area which
sometimes extends to the margins of the valve. Raphe filamentous; terminal
fissures "question mark" shaped—not typically "bayonet" shaped. Striae
radiate at the center of the valve and convergent at the ends. Striae, 10-14
in 10μ. Length, 100-200μ. Breadth, 15-22μ.

This species is distinguished by its shape and its broad central area.

Because specimens have been found which intergrade from no transverse fascia at the central area to a distinct one, it seems better to consider
variety *stauroneiformis* a synonym of the nominate taxon.

I have examined many specimens of *Pinnularia tabellaria* in Ehrenberg's
collection (see discussion under *P. abaujensis*). None of them is the same
as Boyer's taxon which he has mistakenly called *P. tabellaria* Ehr.

Type locality. — U.S.A., New Hampshire. (*Holotype*—A-Boyer V-5-5,
Patrick.)

U. S. distribution. — Geographical: New England States, Middle Atlantic States, Gulf Coast States, East Central States, West Central States,

Lakes States, Plains States; New Mexico. ECOLOGICAL: Usually in lakes and ponds, prefers water of low mineral content.

8. **Pinnularia formica** (Ehr.) Patr. comb. nov., var. **formica**

PL. 61, FIGS. 1-2

Navicula formica Ehr., Phys. Abh. Akad. Wiss. Berlin, for 1841:418. 1843.
Navicula peripunctata Brun, Mém. Soc. Phys. Hist. Nat. Genève, 31(2)1:37, pl. 16, fig. 11. 1891.
Pinnularia nodosa var. *formica* (Ehr.) Cl., K. Svenska Vet.-Akad. Handl., Ny Följd, 27(3):87. 1895.

Valve with undulate margins, the median portion strongly swollen; ends distinctly capitate. Axial area broad, widening into a broad, lanceolate central area. Raphe filamentous; terminal nodules and terminal fissures large. Striae radiate at the center of the valve and strongly convergent toward the ends; submarginal through most of the valve, becoming longer toward the apices, sometimes interrupted in the middle portion. Striae, 9-12 in 10μ. Length, $75\text{-}105\mu$. Breadth, $11\text{-}14\mu$ at the central nodule.

The taxon is characterized by the undulate valve with its strongly swollen middle portion, and the broad axial and central areas. Cleve considered this taxon a variety of *Pinnularia nodosa*, but the distinctive shape of the valve and the characteristics of the central and axial areas are sufficiently distinct to regard it as a separate taxon.

Navicula polyonca Bréb. *ex* Kütz. [*Pinnularia polyonca* (Bréb.) W. Sm.] may be closely related, but the striae seem to be longer than is characteristic for *P. formica*. Therefore, the synonymy of these two taxa is questionable. Certainly *Pinnularia undulata* Greg. which Smith cites as a synonym of *Pinnularia polyonca* is a different taxon. Lewis' specimen (1861, p. 67, pl. 2, fig.7) which is this taxon is misidentified as *P. polyonca* Bréb.

Type locality. — U.S.A., Maine, Blue Hill Pond; fossil.

U. S. distribution. — GEOGRAPHICAL: New England States, Middle Atlantic States, Southeastern States, Gulf Coast States, South Central States. ECOLOGICAL: Seems to prefer fresh water of low mineral content.

Pinnularia Section **Maior** (Cl.) Patr. sect. nov.

Pinnularia group *Maior* Cl., K. Svenska Vet.-Akad. Handl., Ny Följd, 27(3):88. 1895.

Frustulis magnis semper ferme amplius 100μ in longitudine. Area axiali minori quam tertia parte latitudinis valvae et semper ferme circiter quarta parte latitudinis valvae.

The species of *Pinnularia* belonging to this section are large, usually 100μ or more in length. The axial area is relatively narrow, its width is less than one-third the width of the valve; usually its width is about one-fourth that of the valve. The raphe is filamentous or undulate but not complex.

Type species. — *Frustulia maior* Kütz. = *P. maior* (Kütz.) Rabh.

KEY TO THE SPECIES OF THE SECTION MAIOR

1. Valve with striae, less than 12 in 10μ 2
1. Valve with striae, 14 or more in 10μ, valve very convex .... [3] *P. rupestris*
    2. Valve lanceolate .... [6] *P. dactylus* var. *dariana*
    2. Valve linear or swollen in the middle 3
3. Valve swollen in the middle 4
3. Valve linear 8
    4. Ends of the valve broad 5
    4. Ends of the valve distinctly narrower than the middle portion of the valve
                                                                        [1] *P. clevei*
5. Middle portion of the valve very swollen, much broader than the ends
                                                                [2] *P. maior* var. *pulchella*
5. Middle portion of the valve about the same width or a little broader than the
    ends of the valve 6
    6. Ends of the valve rounded—not swollen; striae at the apices distinctly
        convergent .... [2] *P. maior* and vars.
    6. Ends of the valve swollen 7
7. Ends of the valve distinctly wedge-shaped, striae only slightly convergent at
    the apices .... [9] *P. bihastata*
7. Ends of the valve rounded, slightly wedge-shaped; striae distinctly convergent
    at the apices .... [4] *P. latevittata* var. *domingensis*
    8. Axial area asymmetrically dividing the valve .... [8] *P. torta*
    8. Axial area symmetrically dividing the valve 9
9. Valve in colonies joined together by their girdle faces .... [7] *P. socialis*
9. Valve not so joined 10
    10. Central area a transverse fascia .... [5] *P. cardinaliculus*
    10. Central area rounded, not a transverse fascia 11
11. Valve with filamentous raphe .... [4] *P. latevittata*
11. Valve with undulate raphe .... [6] *P. dactylus*

1. **Pinnularia clevei** Patr. var. **clevei**   PL. 61, FIG. 3

Pinnularia clevei Patr., Farlowia, 2(2):193, pl. 3, figs. 7-10.   1945.

Valve slender, swollen in the middle, narrowing toward rounded ends. Axial area broad, one-fourth to one-third the breadth of the valve. Raphe filamentous; terminal fissures distinct, "question mark" shaped. Central area a little wider than, but not clearly differentiated from the axial area. Striae radiate in the middle portion of the valve, convergent toward the ends; crossed by a narrow band. Striae, about 9 in 10μ. Length, 112-145μ. Breadth, 16-22μ.

This species is characterized by the shape of the valve, the shape of the axial and central areas, and the large terminal nodules.

P. T. Cleve (1891, p. 24, pl. 1, fig. 3) confuses this taxon with *Pinnularia esox* Ehr. which is really a *Caloneis* (Patrick, *op. cit.*). The apices of his specimens are more truncate than ours.

Type locality. — U.S.A., Monroe County, Jaggie's Bog [Pennsylvania]. (*Holotype*—A.G.C. 2225, Patrick, 1945.)

U. S. distribution. — GEOGRAPHICAL: Pennsylvania. ECOLOGICAL: In bogs with acid water of low mineral content.

2. **Pinnularia maior** (Kütz.) Rabh. var. **maior**   PL. 61, FIG. 4

Frustulia maior Kütz., Linnaea, 8:547, pl. 14, fig. 25. 1833.
Navicula major (Kütz.) Kütz., Bacill., p. 97, pl. 4, figs. 19-20. 1844.
Pinnularia major (Kütz.) Rabh., Süssw.-Diat., p. 42, pl. 6, fig. 5, pl. 10 supp., fig. 4. 1853.

Valve linear, swollen in the middle with rounded ends which are often slightly swollen. Axial area distinct, one-fourth to one-fifth the breadth of the valve. Raphe filamentous with distinct terminal fissures. Central area usually not much wider than the axial area; elliptical, somewhat asymmetrical in shape. Striae radiate in the middle portion of the valve and convergent at the ends; crossed by a distinct band. Striae, 5-7 in 10μ. Length, 140-200μ. Breadth, 25-40μ.

This taxon is distinguished by the shape of the valve, the axial and central areas, and the angle of the striae.

I have examined specimens in the Kützing herbarium in the British Museum (B.M. 18732) which were in Kützing's possession at the time he described *Pinnularia maior*. They are as our figure.

Type locality. — Germany, Halle.

U. S. distribution. — GEOGRAPHICAL: New England States, Middle Atlantic States, Southeastern States, Gulf Coast States, South Central States, East Central States, West Central States, Lakes States, Plains States; Arizona, Washington, Oregon, California. ECOLOGICAL: Widely distributed in water of fairly low mineral content.

2. **Pinnularia maior** var. **pulchella** Boyer   PL. 61, FIG. 5

Pinnularia major var. *pulchella* Boyer, Diat. Philadelphia, p. 102, pl. 28, fig. 2. 1916.

Valve slender, strongly gibbous in the middle portion; ends somewhat swollen and rounded. Axial area about one-fourth the breadth of the valve. Raphe filamentous; terminal fissures "question mark" shaped. Central area asymmetrical, rounded; about one-third the breadth of the valve. Striae almost parallel throughout most of the valve, radiate in the middle portion and slightly convergent at the ends; crossed by a broad band. Striae, 6-7 in 10μ. Length, 220-273μ. Breadth at the center of the valve, about 40μ.

This variety is distinguished from the nominate variety by the shape of the valve and the width of the band which crosses the striae. It seems to be closely related to *Pinnularia latevittata* var. *domingensis* Cl.

Type locality. — U.S.A., New Jersey, Hammonton Pond. (*Lectotype—* A-Boyer 426, Patrick.)

U. S. distribution. — GEOGRAPHICAL: New England States; New Jersey. ECOLOGICAL: Slightly acid ponds or lakes in water of very low mineral content.

2. **Pinnularia maior** var. **transversa** (A.S.) Cl.   PL. 61, FIG. 6

Navicula transversa A. S., Atlas Diat., pl. 43, figs. 5-6.   1876.
Pinnularia major var. *transversa* (A. S.) Cl., Acta Soc. Fauna Fl. Fennica, 8(2):24.
    1891.

Valve very slender, slightly swollen in the middle and at the ends. Axial area about one-third the breadth of the valve. Raphe filamentous; terminal fissures distinct. Central area asymmetrical, somewhat elliptical or rounded in shape. Striae radiate in the middle portion of the valve and convergent toward the ends; crossed by a distinct band. Striae, 8-9 in 10μ. Length, 170-220μ. Breadth, 17-20μ. Length-to-breadth ratio, 10:1-12:1.

This taxon is distinguished from the nominate variety by its greater length-to-breadth ratio, finer striae, and broader axial area.

Type locality. — Monticello (America).

U. S. distribution. — GEOGRAPHICAL: New England States, Middle Atlantic States, Southeastern States (fossil?), Gulf Coast States, East Central States, West Central States; Washington. ECOLOGICAL: Seems to prefer cool water of low mineral content.

3. **Pinnularia rupestris** Hantz. var. **rupestris**   PL. 61, FIG. 7

Pinnularia rupestris Hantz. in Rabh., Alg. Sachsens resp. Mitteleuropas, Exsicc. 1203.
    1861.
Navicula rupestris (Hantz. in Rabh.) A. S., Atlas Diat., pl. 45, figs. 38-44.   1876.
Pinnularia viridis var. *rupestris* (Hantz. in Rabh.) Cl., K. Svenska Vet.-Akad. Handl.,
    Ny Följd, 27(3):92.   1895.

Valve linear, narrowed toward the rounded ends. Surface of valve convex. Slightly constricted in the middle portion of the valve. Axial area between one-fourth and one-fifth the breadth of the valve; somewhat wider toward the asymmetrical central area which is scarcely wider than the axial area on one side and somewhat rounded on the other. Raphe filamentous with distinct "question mark" shaped terminal fissures. Central nodule usually appearing thicker than the central area. Striae appearing curved due to the convexity of the valve; radiate in the middle portion of the valve, parallel to convergent toward the ends. Longitudinal band not evident. Striae, 14 in 10μ in the middle portion of the valve to 15 in 10μ toward the apices. Length, 47-75μ. Breadth, 8-10μ.

This species is distinguished by the strongly convex shape of the valve, the fineness of the striae, and the shape of the axial and central area.

Cleve (*loc. cit.*) made the species a variety of *Pinnularia viridis.* With this I cannot agree as the raphe is filamentous—not convex. I have, therefore, placed it in the section *Maior.*

Type locality. — Krippengrund i.d. sächs. Schweiz. Ges. v. Gesangl. Bieue September, 1861. (*Lectotype*—A-G.C. 11084, Patrick.)

U. S. distribution. — GEOGRAPHICAL: New England States; Kansas (?), Washington (?). ECOLOGICAL: Seems to prefer cool water of low mineral content.

4. Pinnularia latevittata Cl. var. latevittata PL. 61, FIG. 8

Pinnularia latevittata Cl., Diatomiste, 2(17):103. 1894.
Navicula latevittata (Cl.) Temp. & Perag., Diat. Monde Entier, 2nd ed., p. 21. 1908.

Valve linear with parallel margins and broadly rounded ends. Axial area between one-fourth and one-third the breadth of the valve. Raphe filamentous; terminal fissures "question mark" shaped. Central area asymmetrical, more rounded on one side of the central nodule than the other; a little broader than the axial area. Striae almost parallel throughout most of the valve, becoming somewhat divergent in the middle portion and slightly covergent at the ends; crossed by a broad band. Striae, about 6 in 10μ; in A. Schmidt's *Atlas* (1876, pl. 42, fig. 5) they are shown as 10-12 in 10μ. Length, 180-185μ. Breadth, 30-33μ.

This species is distinguished by the shape of the valve and of the central area and by the broad band which crosses the striae. It is closely related to *Pinnularia dactylus* from which it is distinguished by its filamentous—not undulate—raphe.

Type locality. — Trouvé fossile à Puerte Monte Chili (Atlas).

U. S. distribution. — GEOGRAPHICAL: Southeastern States; Connecticut, Washington.

4. Pinnularia latevittata var. domingensis Cl. PL. 62, FIG. 1

Pinnularia latevittata var. *domingensis* Cl., Diatomiste, 2(17):103, pl. 7, fig. 3. 1894.
Navicula latevittata var. *domingensis* (Cl.) Temp. & Perag., Diat. Monde Entier, 2nd ed., p. 289. 1911.

Valve linear, gibbous in the middle; ends swollen and slightly cuneate-rounded. Axial area one-fourth to one-third the breadth of the valve. Raphe filamentous; terminal fissures "question mark" shaped. Central area distinct, rounded. Striae distinctly radiate in the middle·portion of the valve and convergent toward the ends; crossed by a broad band. Striae, 5-8 in 10µ. Length, 150-360µ. Breadth, 22-45µ.

This large diatom is distinguished from the nominate variety by the shape of the valve, the shape of the central area, and the more strongly radiate striae.

Type locality. — Rég. trop., à San-Nicolas . . . [Ecuador].

U. S. distribution. — Geographical: New England States; New Jersey. Ecological: In lakes and bogs in acid water of low mineral content.

5. **Pinnularia cardinaliculus** Cl. var. **cardinaliculus**   pl. 62, figs. 2-3

Pinnularia cardinaliculus Cl., K. Svenska Vet.-Akad. Handl., Ny Följd, 27(3):79, pl. 1, fig. 12. 1895.

Valve linear with parallel margins and rounded ends. Axial area between one-third and one-fourth the breadth of the valve, somewhat wider toward the central area which is a transverse fascia. Raphe filamentous with more or less "bayonet" shaped terminal fissures. Striae almost parallel, slightly divergent toward the middle part of the valve and parallel to slightly convergent toward the apices. Striae, 8-9 in 10µ. Length, 80-135µ. Breadth, 15-18µ.

This species is characterized by its "bayonet" shaped terminal fissures and almost parallel striae, together with the structure of the axial and central areas. The shape of the terminal fissures shows its close relation to some species of the section *Divergentes*.

This taxon is similar to *Pinnularia cardinalis* (Ehr.) W. Sm. from which it differs in that it has a simple raphe, "bayonet" shaped terminal fissures, and no distinct band crossing the striae.

Tempère and Peragallo in their 2nd edition of *Diatomées du Monde Entier* (1912, p. 337, no. 695) have specimens which they refer to as "*Navicula cardinalis* Ehr. var." They belong to the nominate variety of this taxon.

Type locality. — Uncertain.

U. S. distribution. — Geographical: New England States; Pennsylvania, Michigan. Ecological: Seems to prefer water of low mineral content.

6. **Pinnularia dactylus** Ehr. var. **dactylus**   pl. 62, fig. 4

Pinnularia dactylus Ehr., Phys. Abh. Akad. Wiss. Berlin, for 1841:420, pl. 4(1), fig. 3. 1843.
Pinnularia gigas Ehr., Phys. Abh. Akad. Wiss. Berlin, for 1841:421. 1843.
Navicula dactylus (Ehr.) Kütz., Bacill., p. 98, pl. 28, fig. 59c. 1844.
Navicula gigas (Ehr.) Kütz., Bacill., p. 98. 1844.

Valve broadly linear, sometimes narrower toward the rounded ends. Axial area one-fourth to one-third the breadth of the valve, widening toward the central area which is sometimes a little wider and rounded. Raphe undulate, but not complex; terminal fissures large, "question mark" shaped. Striae almost parallel throughout most of the valve, slightly radiate at the center, and slightly convergent toward the ends; crossed by a broad band. Striae, 4-5 in 10μ. Length, 160-320μ. Breadth, 30-50μ.

This taxon is distinguished by its large size, broadly linear shape, and broad, filamentous, somewhat undulate raphe.

Type locality. — . . . in dem Lager am Castell bei West-Point, New York (fossil) [U.S.A.].

U. S. distribution. — GEOGRAPHICAL: New England States, Middle Atlantic States, Southeastern States, Gulf Coast States, East Central States; Washington, Oregon. ECOLOGICAL: In swamps or ponds; seems to prefer water of low mineral content.

6. **Pinnularia dactylus** var. **dariana** (A.S.) Cl.   PL. 63, FIG. 1

Navicula dariana A. S., Atlas Diat., pl. 42, figs. 24-25. 1876.
Pinnularia dactylus var. *dariana* (A. S.) Cl., K. Svenska Vet.-Akad. Handl., Ny Följd, 27(3):90. 1895.

Valve lanceolate with rounded ends. Axial area one-fifth to one-fourth the breadth of the valve, widening toward the asymmetrically rounded central area. Raphe filamentous, oblique—not complex. Terminal fissures large, "question mark" shaped. Striae slightly radiate in the middle portion of the valve to slightly convergent toward the ends; crossed by a distinct band. Striae, 6-8 in 10μ. Length, 180-240μ. Breadth, 41-45μ.

This taxon is distinguished from the nominate variety by the shape of the valve.

Type locality. — Uncertain.

U. S. distribution. — GEOGRAPHICAL: New England States, Middle Atlantic States, Southeastern States, Gulf Coast States; Oregon, California. ECOLOGICAL: In water of low mineral content.

7. **Pinnularia socialis** (T. C. Palm.) Hust. var. **socialis**   PL. 63, FIG. 2

Navicula socialis T. C. Palm., Proc. Acad. Nat. Sci. Philadelphia, 62:461, pl. 35, figs. 1-2. 1910.
Pinnularia socialis (T. C. Palm.) Hust. *in* A. S., Atlas Diat., pl. 294, fig. 28. 1913.

Four to eight frustules joined on their girdle faces by a "siliceous cement." Valve broadly linear with rounded ends. Axial area about one-third the breadth of the valve. Raphe filamentous; terminal fissures large, "question mark" shaped. Central area usually not distinguished from the axial area though sometimes slightly rounded. Striae slightly radiate in the middle portion of the valve and slightly convergent at the ends, otherwise almost parallel. Striae, 8-9 in 10μ. Length, 60-120μ. Breadth, 13-27μ.

This taxon is distinguished by the fact that the frustules occur in groups of four to eight.

Type locality. — U.S.A., fresh water; swampy pools near Media, Pennsylvania.

U. S. distribution. — GEOGRAPHICAL: New England States, Middle Atlantic States; Alabama. ECOLOGICAL: Swampy pools and bogs.

8. **Pinnularia torta** (Mann) Patr. comb. nov., var. **torta**   PL. 63, FIG. 3

> *Pinnularia major* var. *asymmetrica* Cl., K. Svenska Vet.-Akad. Handl., Ny Följd, 27(3):89, pl. 1, fig. 22. 1895.
> *Navicula major* var. *asymetrica* (Cl.) Temp. & Perag., Diat. Monde Entier, 2nd ed., p. 120. 1909.
> *Navicula torta* Mann, Jour. Washington Acad., 14:31, pl. 4, fig. 6. 1924.

Valve linear with rounded ends. Axial area about one-third the breadth of the valve, dividing the valve asymmetrically. Raphe also asymmetrically placed, filamentous; terminal fissures distinct, "comma" shaped. Central area large, elliptical in shape. Striae radiate in the middle portion of the valve and convergent toward the ends; crossed by a broad band. Striae, 7-8 in 10μ. Length, 140-260μ. Breadth, 20-30μ.

This taxon is distinguished by its asymmetrical axial area and raphe. Mann (*loc. cit.*) states that this taxon is related to *Navicula trevelyana* Donk.

Type locality. — U.S.A., Massachusetts, Waltham.

U. S. distribution. — GEOGRAPHICAL: New England States; New Jersey. ECOLOGICAL: In swamps and ponds, in acid water of low mineral content.

9. **Pinnularia bihastata** (Mann) Patr. comb. nov., var. **bihastata**

PL. 63, FIG. 4

> *Pinnularia trigonocephala* Cl., K. Svenska Vet.-Akad. Handl., Ny Följd, 27(3):88, pl. 1, fig. 21. 1895 (non Ehr. 1854).
> *Navicula bihastata* Mann, Jour. Washington Acad., 14:30, pl. 4, fig. 2. 1924.

Valve linear, slightly gibbous in the middle and at the broadly cuneate, subcapitate ends. Axial area about one-fourth the breadth of the valve. Raphe filamentous; terminal fissures "question mark" shaped. Central area large, rounded. Striae radiate in the middle portion of the valve, somewhat convergent toward the ends. In some specimens a broad band crossing the striae is evident. Striae, 6-7 in 10μ. Length, 145-200μ. Breadth, 24-28μ.

This species is distinguished by the slightly swollen, cuneate apices of the valve and the structure of the central and axial areas.

The name *Pinnularia trigonocephala* cannot be used for this taxon as this name was used by Ehrenberg [1854, pl. 34 (8), fig. 11] for another taxon.

Type locality. — U.S.A., California, Big Lake.

U. S. distribution. — GEOGRAPHICAL: New England States; New Jersey, California. ECOLOGICAL: Found in lakes in water of fairly low mineral content.

Pinnularia section **Pinnularia**

Pinnularia group *Complexae* Cl., K. Svenska Vet.-Akad. Handl., Ny Földj, 27(3):73. 1895.

Frustulibus magnis semper ferme linearibus aut tumitis leviter in media parte valvae. Raphe multiplici.

This section is characterized by having a complex raphe. They are typically large diatoms which are linear or slightly swollen at the central area.

Type species. — *Navicula (Pinnularia) nobilis* Ehr. [= *Pinnularia nobilis* (Ehr.) Ehr.]

KEY TO THE SPECIES OF THE SECTION PINNULARIA

1. Valve linear, slightly swollen at the central area 2
1. Valve linear 3
  2. Striae, 4-5 in 10μ . . . . [5] *P. nobilis*
  2. Striae, about 7 in 10μ . . . . [4] *P. gentilis*
3. Valve with narrow axial area, less than one-fifth the breadth of the valve
                                                  [8] *P. viridis* and vars.
3. Valve with axial area one-fourth or more the breadth of the valve 4
  4. Valve with central area a transverse fascia 5
  4. Valve with central area typically not forming a fascia 6
5. Striae, 4-5 in 10μ; ends of the valve almost as broad as the middle portion of the valve . . . . [2] *P. cardinalis*
5. Striae, 6-8 in 10μ; ends of the valve narrower than the middle portion of the valve . . . . [1] *P. aestuarii*
  6. Central area asymmetrical, elliptical-lanceolate or rounded in shape 7
  6. Central area not asymmetrical, only slightly, if at all, wider than the axial area . . . . [6] *P. ruttneri*
7. Striae, 4-5 in 10μ 8
7. Striae, 6-8 in 10μ . . . . [8] *P. viridis* var. *minor*
  8. Striae strongly radiate in the middle portion of the valve . . . . [3] *P. flexuosa*
  8. Striae slightly radiate in the middle portion of the valve . . . . [7] *P. streptoraphe*

1. **Pinnularia aestuarii** Cl. var. **aestuarii**   PL. 63, FIG. 5

> *Pinnularia aestuarii* Cl., K. Svenska Vet.-Akad. Handl., Ny Följd, 27(3):93, 94, pl.
>   1, fig. 16. 1895.
> *Navicula stauroneiformis* Elm., Univ. Nebraska Stud., 21:66, pl. 7, figs. 206-207.
>   1922.

Valve linear with parallel margins and rounded ends. Axial area about one-third the breadth of the valve. Central area a transverse fascia. Raphe complex; terminal fissures "question mark" shaped. Striae parallel. throughout most of the valve, slightly radiate toward the center, slightly convergent toward the ends. Striae crossed by a band which is quite variable in distinctness, one-third to one-half the length of the striae in breadth. Striae, 6-8 in 10μ. Length, $82-120\mu$. Breadth, $15-16\mu$.

This species is distinguished by the broad axial area, the transverse fascia, and the low number of striae.

Some of Elmore's specimens seem to be smaller and more finely striated than is typical for the nominate variety. However, one of the specimens illustrated seems to belong to the nominate variety.

Type locality. — Uncertain.

U. S. distribution. — GEOGRAPHICAL: Plains States; Connecticut, Delaware, Wyoming. ECOLOGICAL: In water of high mineral content.

2. **Pinnularia cardinalis** (Ehr.) W. Sm. var. **cardinalis**   PL. 63, FIG. 6

> *Navicula (Pinnularia) cardinalis* Ehr., Ber. Akad. Wiss. Berlin, for 1840:213.   1840.
> *Stauroneis cardinalis* (Ehr.) Kütz., Bacill., p. 106, pl. 29, fig. 10b. 1844.
> *Pinnularia cardinalis* (Ehr.) W. Sm., Syn. British Diat., vol. 1, p. 55, pl. 19, fig. 166.
>   1853.

Valve linear with broadly rounded ends. Axial area distinct, about one-third to one-fourth the breadth of the valve. Central area a transverse fascia; central nodule thickened. Raphe complex, with distinct terminal fissures. Striae slightly radiate in the middle portion of the valve, parallel to slightly convergent near the ends; crossed by a broad band. Striae, 4-5 in 10μ. Length, $150-320\mu$. Breadth, $30-45\mu$.

This species is differentiated from other species of this group by the size and shape of the central and axial areas combined with the number and angle of the striae.

Stauroptera cardinalis Ehr. (1854, pl. 17(1), fig. 4) does not seem to be this species because the raphe is not complex and the striae are more strongly radiate.

Type locality. — Fossilis ad Santafioram [Italy].

U. S. distribution. — GEOGRAPHICAL: New England States, Middle Atlantic States, East Central States, Lakes States. ECOLOGICAL: Prefers cool water of low mineral content.

3. **Pinnularia flexuosa** Cl. var. **flexuosa** PL. 63, FIG. 7

Pinnularia flexuosa Cl., K. Svenska Vet.-Akad. Handl., Ny Földj, 27(3):93, pl. 1, fig. 23. 1895.
Navicula flexuosa (Cl.) Temp. & Perag., Diat. Monde Entier, 2nd ed., p. 440. 1913.

Valve linear to linear-elliptical, sometimes slightly swollen in the central portion and at the ends. Axial area distinct, less than one-third the breadth of the valve. In our specimens about one-fourth the breadth of the valve. Central area rounded, somewhat asymmetrical. Raphe complex; terminal fissures distinct, "question mark" shaped. Striae radiate in the middle portion of the valve to convergent at the ends; crossed by a broad band. Striae, 4-5 in 10μ. Length, $150\text{-}270\mu$. Breadth, $35\text{-}48\mu$.

Boyer (1927b, p. 448) reports a specimen from Port Townsend, Washington in which the striae are unilaterally interrupted.

This species is closely related to *Pinnularia streptoraphe* Cl. from which it differs mainly in its larger size, greater angle of striation, and sometimes more elliptical central area. It might be considered a variety of *P. streptoraphe*.

Type locality. — Uncertain, Canada (Eralton Lake), United States (Cherryfield, Crane Pond).

U. S. distribution. — GEOGRAPHICAL: New England States; New Jersey. ECOLOGICAL: In ponds and bogs; seems to prefer cool, somewhat acid water.

4. **Pinnularia gentilis** (Donk.) Cl. var. **gentilis** PL. 64, FIG. 1

Navicula gentilis Donk., Nat. Hist. British Diat., p. 69, pl. 12, fig. 1. 1870-1873.
Pinnularia gentilis (Donk.) Cl., K. Svenska Vet.-Akad. Handl., Ny Földj, 27(3):92. 1895.

Valve linear, sometimes slightly swollen in the median portion and at the rounded ends. Axial area about one-third the breadth of the valve. Central area fairly large, elliptical. Raphe complex; terminal fissures distinct, "question mark" shaped; terminal nodules large. Striae radiate in the middle portion of the valve, convergent toward the ends; crossed by a broad band. Striae, about 6-7 in 10μ throughout most of the valve, sometimes finer toward the apices. Length, $140\text{-}260\mu$. Breadth, $22\text{-}36\mu$.

This species is very closely related to *Pinnularia nobilis*. It differs in the size of the valve and the fineness of the striae.

Type locality. — Fresh water; frequent. In hilly districts; Cheviots, Northumberland . . . [England].

U. S. distribution. — GEOGRAPHICAL: New England States, Middle Atlantic States, Southeastern States; Washington, Oregon. ECOLOGICAL: Seems to prefer lakes, ponds, or bogs; in water of low mineral content.

5. **Pinnularia nobilis** (Ehr.) Ehr. var. **nobilis**   PL. 64, FIG. 2

Navicula (*Pinnularia*) *nobilis* Ehr., Ber. Akad. Wiss. Berlin, for 1840:214. 1840.
Pinnularia nobilis (Ehr.) Ehr., Phys. Abh. Akad. Wiss. Berlin, for 1841:384, pl.
     2(1), fig. 25; pl. 2(2), fig. 3. 1843.
Navicula nobilis (Ehr.) Kütz., Bacill., p. 98, pl. 4, fig. 24. 1844.

Valve linear, slightly swollen in the middle portion; ends broadly
rounded. Axial area throughout most of its length one-fourth to one-third
the breadth of the valve. Central area rounded, usually somewhat asymmetrical; central nodule usually evident. Raphe complex; terminal fissures
distinct, "question mark" shaped. Striae radiate in the middle portion of
the valve, convergent toward the ends; crossed by a broad band. Striae,
4-5 in 10μ. Length, 200-350μ. Breadth, 34-50μ.

Van Heurck (1896, p. 164) states that this taxon may be 400μ long
and the striae may be 6 in 10μ.

This taxon is distinguished by the swelling in the middle portion of
the valve and the coarseness of the striae.

I have examined Ehrenberg's specimens of *Pinnularia nobilis* (Reale
de Monte, Mexico, No. 3--822-B) and they are the same taxon as our
specimens.

Type locality. — Uncertain. Fossilis ad Santafioram [Italy] et in America
boreali frequens.

U. S. distribution. — GEOGRAPHICAL: New England States, Middle Atlantic States, Gulf Coast States, South Central States, East Central States,
Lakes States, Plains States; Wyoming, Washington, Oregon. ECOLOGICAL:
Seems to prefer slightly acid to circumneutral fresh water of low mineral
content.

6. **Pinnularia ruttneri** Hust. var. **ruttneri**   PL. 64, FIG. 3

Pinnularia ruttneri Hust. *in* A. S., Atlas Diat., pl. 390, figs. 6-7. 1934. Arch. Hydro-
     biol. Suppl., 14:162. 1935.

Valve linear, sometimes slightly swollen in the middle portion; narrowing toward rounded ends. Axial area about one-third the breadth of the
valve, slightly wider toward the center. Central area hardly wider than
the axial area; central nodule distinct. Raphe complex; median ends of
the raphe turned slightly to one side; terminal fissures large, "question
mark" shaped. Striae slightly radiate toward the center of the valve, convergent toward the ends; crossed by a fairly narrow band. Striae, 6-7 in
10μ. Length, 150-250μ. Breadth, 18-23μ.

This species is distinguished by the lack of differentiation of the
central area from the axial area and the structure of the raphe.

Type locality. — Tobasee, Sumatra, f. S.

U. S. distribution. — GEOGRAPHICAL: Connecticut, Oregon. ECOLOGICAL: Acid fresh water of low mineral content.

7. **Pinnularia streptoraphe** Cl. var. **streptoraphe** PL. 64, FIG. 4

Pinnularia streptoraphe Cl., Acta Soc. Fauna Fl. Fennica, 8(2):23. 1891.
Navicula streptoraphe (Cl.) Temp. & Perag., Diat. Monde Entier, 2nd ed., p. 104. 1908.

Valve broadly linear with rounded ends. Axial area distinct but less than one-third the breadth of the valve. Raphe complex; terminal fissures distinct, "question mark" shaped. Central area more or less asymmetrical, rounded. Striae almost parallel throughout most of the valve, becoming slightly radiate in the middle portion and slightly convergent toward the ends; crossed by a broad band. Striae, about 5 in 10μ. Length, $135\text{-}260\mu$. Breadth, $20\text{-}35\mu$.

This species is related to *Pinnularia viridis* but differs in its more broadly linear shape, the number of the striae—which in this taxon are coarser—wider axial area, and the more strongly twisted raphe.

Since P. T. Cleve (*op. cit.*) refers to A. Schmidt's illustration (1876, pl. 42, fig. 7), this or the specimen on which the illustration is based becomes the type.

Type locality. — Ohlajärri [Finland].

U. S. distribution. — GEOGRAPHICAL: New England States, Middle Atlantic States, Southeastern States, East Central States; Wyoming. ECOLOGICAL: Lakes, ponds, or bogs in water of low mineral content; seems to prefer acid water.

8. **Pinnularia viridis** (Nitz.) Ehr. var. **viridis** PL. 64, FIG. 5

Bacillaria viridis Nitz., Neue Schrift. Naturf. Ges. Halle, 3(1):97, pl. 6, figs. 1-3. 1817.
Navicula viridis (Nitz.) Ehr., Poggendorff's Ann. Phys. u. Chem. 38(5), p. 226, Pl. 3, fig. 1. 1837.
Pinnularia viridis (Nitz.) Ehr., Phys. Abh. Akad. Wiss. Berlin, for 1841:305, 385, pl. 1(1), fig. 7; pl. 1(3), fig. 3; pl. 1(4), fig. 3; pl. 2(1), fig. 22; pl. 2(3), fig. 1; pl. 2(5), fig. 2; pl. 2(6), fig. 21; pl. 3(1), figs. 1-2. 1843.

Valve linear, narrowing toward rounded ends. Axial area narrow, about one-fifth the breadth of the valve. Central area somewhat rounded, small. Raphe complex; terminal fissures distinct, "question mark" shaped. Striae almost parallel throughout most of the valve, somewhat radiate about the central area, convergent toward the ends; crossed by a band of variable distinctness. Striae, 6-9 in 10μ. Length, $50\text{-}170\mu$. Breadth, $10\text{-}30\mu$.

The nominate variety of this species is distinguished by the narrow axial area, small central area, and almost parallel striae throughout most of the valve.

I have examined Ehrenberg's specimens of *Pinnularia viridis* (Reale de Monte, Mexico—822 a, Strip 1, No. 5) and they belong to the same taxon as our specimens, although the axial area is wider.

Type locality. — Germany, Halle (in Priestley material).

U. S. distribution. — Geographical: New England States, Middle Atlantic States, Southeastern States, Gulf Coast States, South Central States, East Central States, West Central States, Lakes States, Plains States; Montana, Wyoming, Colorado, New Mexico, Arizona, Washington, California. Ecological: Found in water of higher mineral content than many of the species belonging to the *Pinnularia;* seems to prefer circumneutral water.

8. **Pinnularia viridis** var. **commutata** (Grun.) Cl.   pl. 64, fig. 6

> *Navicula viridis* var. *commutata* Grun. *in* V. H., Syn. Diat. Belgique, pl. 5, fig. 6. 1880. [non *Navicula commutata* Grun. *in* A. S., Atlas Diat., pl. 45, figs. 35-37. 1876.]
> *Pinnularia viridis* var. *fallax* Cl., K. Svenska Vet.-Akad. Handl., Ny Följd, 27(3):91. 1895.
> *Navicula viridis* var. *fallax* (Cl.) Hust., Süssw.-Diat. Deutschlands, p. 47. 1909.
> *Pinnularia viridis* var. *commutata* (Grun. *in* V. H.) Cl., K. Svenska Vet.-Akad. Handl., Ny Följd, 27(3):91. 1895. (excl. descr.)

Valve linear, narrowing toward rounded ends. Axial area narrow, one-fourth to one-fifth the breadth of the valve. Central area variable; small, somewhat elliptical, and usually asymmetrical; or widened unilaterally or bilaterally into a transverse fascia. Raphe complex; terminal fissures small but distinct. Striae slightly parallel throughout most of the valve, almost parallel at the center and parallel to slightly convergent toward the ends; crossed by a band which varies in distinctness. Striae, 9-12 in 10μ. Length, $45-110\mu$. Breadth, $9-20\mu$.

This taxon is distinguished from the nominate variety by its finer striae and central area of variable shape.

Cleve (*loc. cit.*) mistakenly believed his taxon was the same as *Navicula viridis* var. *commutata* Grun. *in* V. H. The name *commutata* has to be used for Grunow's taxon. A new name will have to be found for the taxon Cleve identified as *P. viridis* var. *commutata* (Grun.) Cl.

Type locality. — Uncertain.

U. S. distribution. — Geographical: New England States, Middle Atlantic States, Southeastern States, Plains States; Wyoming, Washington. Ecological: Seems to prefer cool water of low mineral content.

8. **Pinnularia viridis** var. **minor** Cl.   PL. 64, FIG. 7

> *Pinnularia viridis* var. *minor* Cl., Acta Soc. Fauna Fl. Fennica, 8(2):22, pl. 1, fig. 2. 1891.
>
> *Pinnularia streptoraphe* var. *minor* (Cl.) Cl., K. Svenska Vet.-Akad. Handl., Ny Följd, 27(3):93. 1895.

Valve linear, narrowing toward its rounded ends. Axial area one-third to one-fourth the breadth of the valve, widening into an asymmetrical central area usually rounded on one side. Sometimes the central area forms a stauros on one or both sides. Raphe complex. Striae somewhat radiate toward the middle portion of the valve, convergent toward the apices. The band crossing the striae usually narrow or not evident with the light microscope. Striae, 6-8 in 10μ. Length, 85-100μ. Breadth, 15-17μ.

This variety differs from the nominate variety mainly by its broader axial area and the shape of the central area.

The shape of the valve and the more radiate striae make this more logically a variety of *Pinnularia viridis* as originally proposed by Cleve, than of *P. streptoraphe*. It differs from *P. viridis* var. *commutata* by its coarser striae and broader axial area.

Type locality. — Padasjoki, Tavastehus än.

U. S. distribution. — GEOGRAPHICAL: Massachusetts, New Jersey.

Names of Taxa reported from the U. S. (fresh water) which could not be verified by a specimen from a public herbarium.

Pinnularia acrosphaeria var. *laevis* (M. Perag. & Hérib.) Cl. = *Navicula acrosphaeria* var. *laevis* A.S. (recorded by Tempère & Peragallo).

Pinnularia alpina var. *elongata* (M. Perag. & Hérib.) Mills = *Navicula alpina* var. *elongata* M. Perag. *in* Temp. & Perag. (recorded by Tempère & Peragallo).

Pinnularia borealis var. *caraccana* (Ehr.) Brun = *Navicula borealis* var. *caraccana* (Ehr.) DeT. (recorded by De Toni).

Pinnularia borealis var. *subacuta* Ehr. (recorded by Ehrenberg).

Pinnularia borealis var. *truncata* Ehr. (recorded by Ehrenberg).

Pinnularia conspicua (A.S.) Cl. = *Navicula conspicua* A.S. (recorded by Curtis).

Pinnularia dactylus var. *demerarae* Cl. (recorded by Boyer).

Pinnularia decurrens Ehr. = *Navicula decurrens* (Ehr.) Kütz. (recorded by Ehrenberg, Tempère & Peragallo, Curtis, and Elmore).

Pinnularia divergens var. *sublinearis* Cl. (recorded by Boyer and Cleve).

Pinnularia flaminula A.S. (T.&P. slide no. 884 which records this species from the United States has specimens similar in shape, but on specimens I have seen the shape of the terminal fissures and nodules are not correct for this taxon.)

Pinnularia flexuosa var. *cuneata* (Temp. & Perag.) Mills = *Navicula flexuosa* var. *cuneata* Temp. & Perag. (recorded by Tempère & Peragallo).

Pinnularia globiceps var. *krockii* (Grun.) Cl. (recorded by Hohn).

Pinnularia gracillima Greg. = *Navicula gracillima* (Greg.) Ralfs *in* Pritch. (recorded by Hohn and Tempère & Peragallo).

Pinnularia isostauron (Ehr.) Cl. = *Stauroptera isostauron* Ehr. = *Pinnularia icostauron* (Ehr.) Grun. (recorded by Cleve, Ehrenberg, and Tempère & Peragallo).

Pinnularia lata var. *rabenhorstii* (Grun.) Cl. = *Pinnularia lata* var. *thuringiaca* (Rabh.) A. Mayer (recorded by Boyer).

Pinnularia leptogongyla Ehr. (recorded by Ehrenberg).

Pinnularia longa Greg. (recorded by Lewis).

Pinnularia macilenta (Ehr.) Ehr. = *Navicula macilenta* Ehr. (recorded by Hohn, Ehrenberg, Cleve, and Tempère & Peragallo).

Pinnularia major var. *heroina* (A.S.) Cl. (Tempère & Peragallo in *Diat. du Monde Entier, 2nd ed.,* No. 103 record this taxon. I have found on their slides specimens similar to this taxon, but with striae too strongly radiate and convergent.)

Pinnularia major var. *linearis* Cl. = *Pinnularia major* var. *andesitica* (Pant.) Ross (recorded by Boyer and Cleve).

Pinnularia major var. *subacuta* (Ehr.) Cl. = *Navicula subacuta* (Ehr.) Ralfs *in* Pritch. (recorded by Tempère & Peragallo).

Pinnularia major var. *turgidula* Cl. (recorded by Cleve).

Pinnularia mesotyla Ehr. (recorded by Ehrenberg).

Pinnularia molaris (Grun.) Cl. = *Navicula macra* Grun. *in* A.S. (recorded by Boyer, Hohn, Sovereign, and Curtis).

Pinnularia sabae Ehr. = *Navicula sabae* (Ehr.) DeT. (recorded by Ehrenberg).

Pinnularia secernenda (A.S.) Cl. (recorded by Boyer and Cleve).

Pinnularia stauroptera var. *interrupta* Cl. (recorded by Boyer and Cleve).

Pinnularia stauroptera var. *semicruciata* Cl. (recorded by Cleve).

Pinnularia vespa Ehr. (recorded by Ehrenberg).

°Taxa Recorded Since 1960

Pinnularia amblys Hohn & Hellerm. (recorded by Hohn & Hellerman, 1963).

Pinnularia convexa Sov. (recorded by Sovereign, 1963).

° See page 672 for additional taxa.

Pinnularia cumvibia Hohn & Hellerm. (recorded by Hohn & Hellerman, 1963).

Pinnularia gibba f. *curta* Rabh. (recorded by Hohn & Hellerman, 1963).

Pinnularia instita Hohn & Hellerm. (recorded by Hohn & Hellerman, 1963).

Pinnularia interrupta var. *sinica* Skv. (recorded by Hohn & Hellerman, 1963).

Pinnularia lundii Hust. (recorded by Hohn & Hellerman, 1963).

Pinnularia makahana Sov. (recorded by Sovereign, 1963).

Pinnularia nubila Sov. (recorded by Sovereign, 1963).

Pinnularia obtusa Sov. (recorded by Sovereign, 1963).

Pinnularia palousiana Sov. (recorded by Sovereign, 1963).

Pinnularia platycephala f. *ornata* Sov. (recorded by Sovereign, 1963).

Pinnularia pluviana Sov. (recorded by Sovereign, 1963).

Pinnularia polyonca (Bréb.) W. Sm. (recorded by Schumacher & Whitford, 1961) = P. formica (Ehr.) Patr.

Pinnularia rivularis Hust. (recorded by Hohn & Hellerman, 1963).

Pinnularia stomatophora Grun. (recorded Shobe, Stoermer, & Dodd, 1963).

Pinnularia stricta Hust. (recorded by Hohn & Hellerman, 1963).

Pinnularia subcapitata var. *hybrida* (Grun.) Freng. (recorded by Hohn & Hellerman, 1963).

Pinnularia subpalousiana Sov. (recorded by Sovereign, 1963).

Pinnularia umbrosa Sov. (recorded by Sovereign, 1963).

Pinnularia undulata var. *subundulata* Grun. (recorded by Reimer, 1961).

Genus **Scoliopleura** Grun.

Grun., Verh. Zool.-Bot. Ges. Wien, 10:554. 1860.

Valve highly arched and somewhat twisted; elongate in shape with diagonal, sigmoid axial area and raphe. Longitudinal siliceous thickening (axial band) enclosing axial area and raphe; the outer margins of this thickening appear as longitudinal "lines" on either side of the axial area. Striae mostly parallel but may appear somewhat diagonal or (near valve extremities) convergent; broken into distinct puncta.

Type species. — *Scoliopleura peisonis* Grun. [designated by Boyer, 1927].

1. **Scoliopleura peisonis** Grun. var. **peisonis**   PL. 64, FIG. 8

Scoliopleura peisonis Grun., Verh. Zool.-Bot. Ges. Wien, 10:554, pl. 5, fig. 25. 1860.

Valve highly arched; linear-elliptical with slightly convex to parallel sides and obtusely rounded extremities. Axial area narrow, diagonal, sigmoid. Central area rather small, ovoid or oblong. Raphe sigmoid as the axial area, enclosed in a longitudinal furrow. Outer proximal raphe ends curved in opposite directions. Distal raphe ends indistinct. Margin of longitudinal furrow forming two "lines," one on each side of, and parallel to, the axial area. Striae parallel, punctate. Striae, 12-16 in 10μ. Puncta, 16-18 in 10μ. Length, $35\text{-}80\mu$. Breadth, $10\text{-}18\mu$.

The furrow on both sides of the axial area appears to be structurally quite similar to the axial band in *Neidium hitchcockii*. Further study of this genus may show it to be more closely related to the genera *Neidium* and/or *Gyrosigma* than to *Caloneis* or *Diploneis* as suggested by Cleve (1894, p. 105).

Type locality. — [Europe], Ad litora meridionalia lacus Peisonis Hungariae in aqua stagnanti verosimiliter subsalsa.

U. S. distribution. — Geographical: Utah, (Great Salt Lake). Ecological: Insufficiently known, but certainly tolerant of waters with high specific conductivity.

Names of taxa reported from the U. S. which
are of uncertain application.

Navicula alternans Schum. = *Scoliopleura?* *alternans* (Schum.) DeT. (recorded by Curtis).

Navicula campylogramma Ehr. = *Scoliopleura?* *campylogramma* (Ehr.) Rabh. (recorded by Briggs).

646

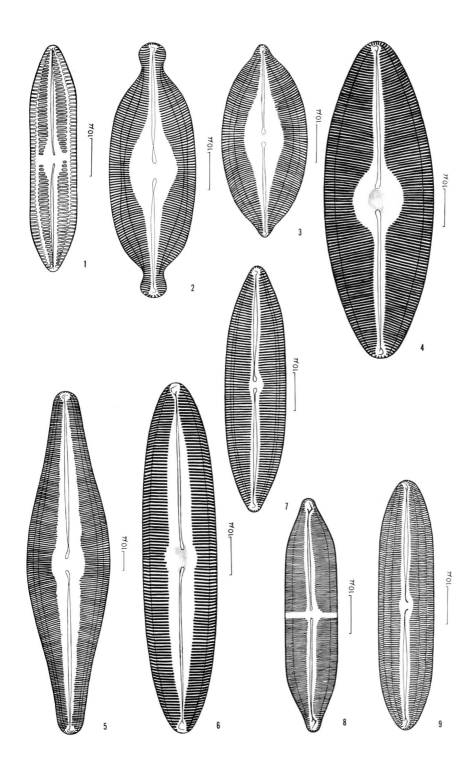

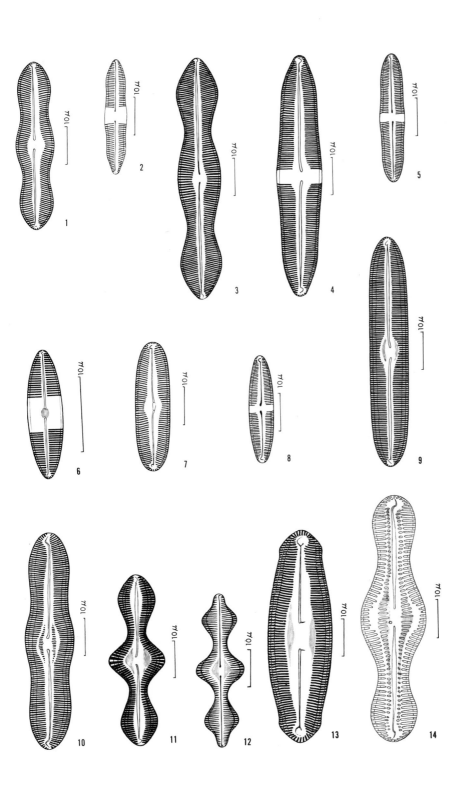

650

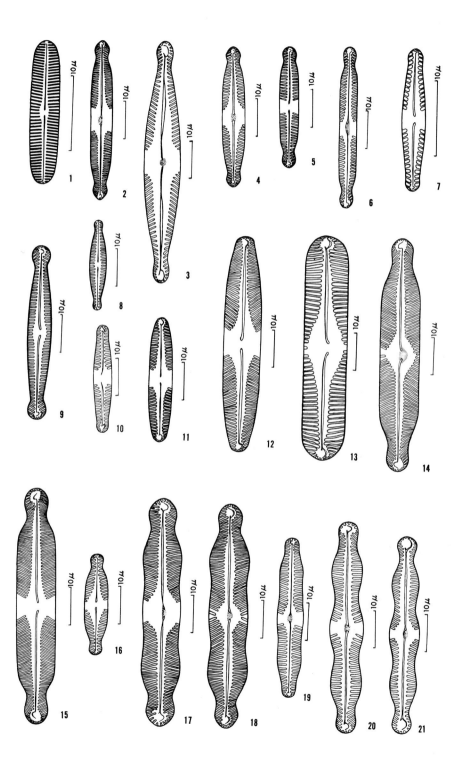

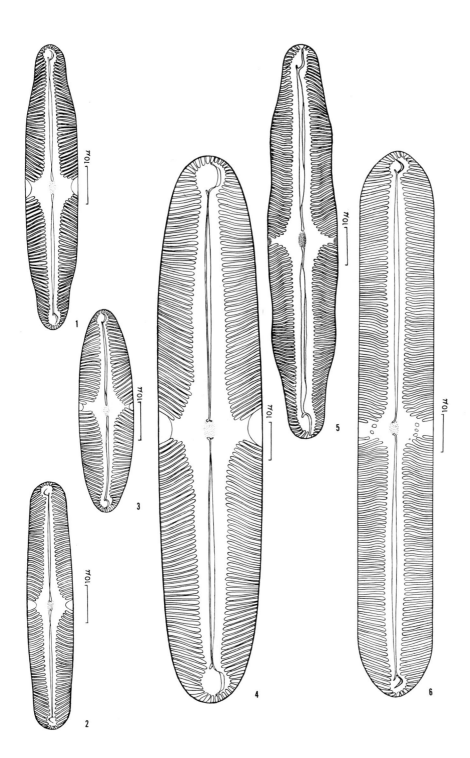

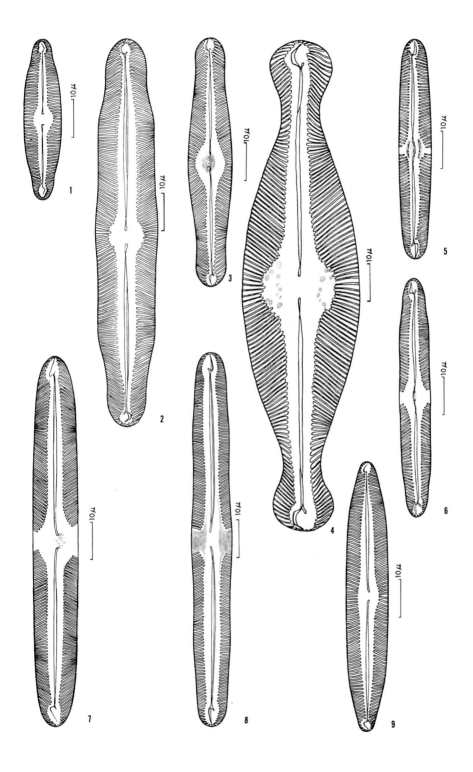

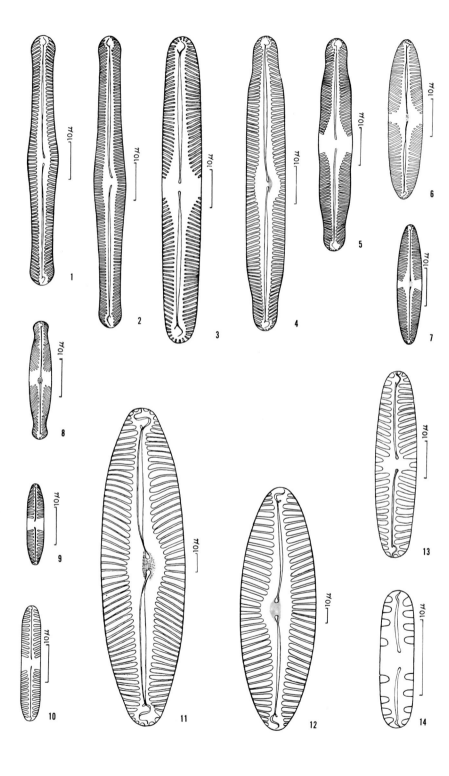

PLATE 59

Fig. 1. *Pinnularia lata* A-Boyer H-4-21, Maine.
Fig. 2. *Pinnularia lata* A-G.C. 10619, Rabh. Exsicc. No. 501, France, Falaise.
Fig. 3. *Pinnularia lata* var. *pachyptera* A-114, W.Sm. 167, England, Lancashire Co., Fell End.
Fig. 4. *Pinnularia acuminata* A-Cl. & Möll. 321, British Guiana, Demerara River.
Fig. 5. *Pinnularia acuminata* var. *bielawskii* comb. nov. Cal. Acad. Sci. H.T.-3465, Sov. 488-12, Oregon, Crater Lake National Park, Emerald Pool.
Fig. 6. *Pinnularia acuminata* var. *instabilis* comb. nov. A-T. & P. 172, Massachusetts, Boxford.
Fig. 7. *Pinnularia acuminata* var. *interrupta* comb. nov. A-Boyer K-1-5, Alabama, Montgomery Co.

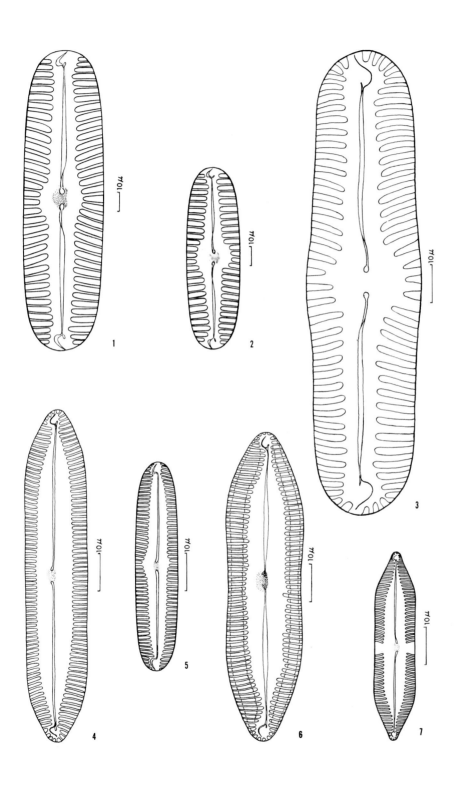

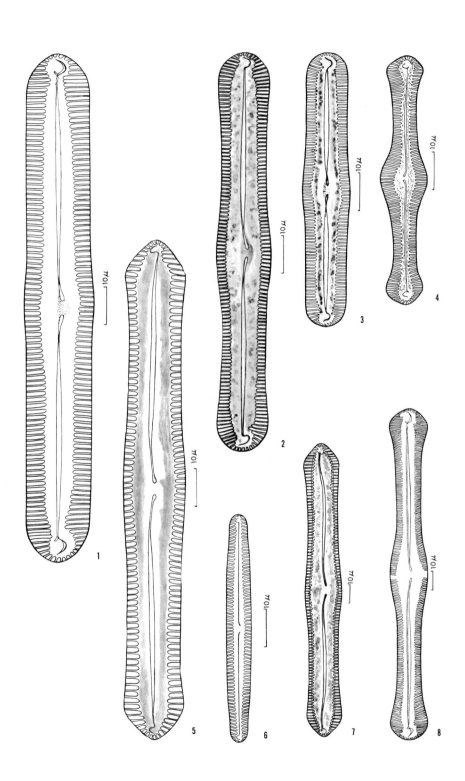

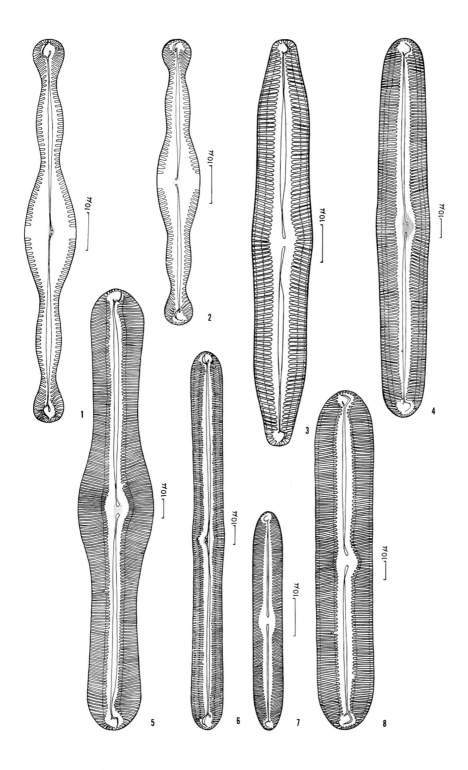

PLATE 62

Fig. 1. *Pinnularia latevittata* var. *domingensis* A-Boyer V-5-12, New Hampshire, Merrimac Co.

Fig. 2. *Pinnularia cardinaliculus* A-T. & P. 695, Connecticut, Winchester Township.

Fig. 3. *Pinnularia cardinaliculus* A-H.L.Sm. 523, Massachusetts, Middlesex Co.

Fig. 4. *Pinnularia dactylus* A-V.H. 51, Great Britain.

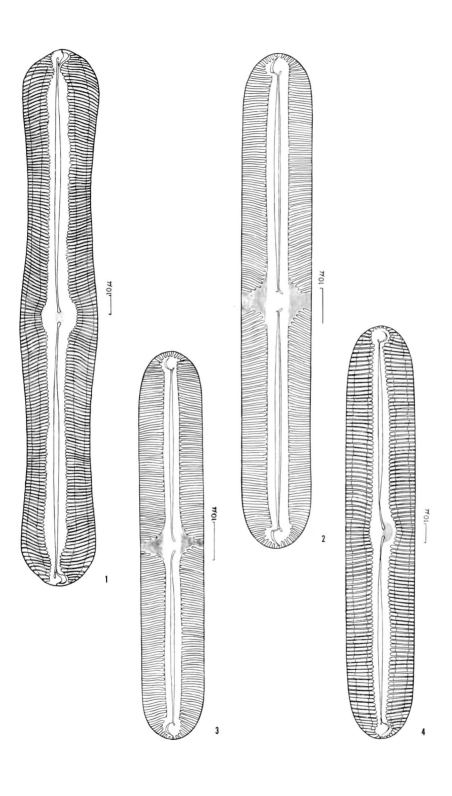

1 10 μ

2 10 μ

3 10 μ

4 10 μ

PLATE 63

Fig. 1. *Pinnularia dactylus* var. *dariana* A-Boyer E-2-18, Southwest British Columbia, Pitt River.
Fig. 2. *Pinnularia socialis* A-Boyer V-5-4, Pennsylvania, Delaware Co.
Fig. 3. *Pinnularia torta* comb. nov. A-Boyer 738, Connecticut, Fairfield Co.
Fig. 4. *Pinnularia bihastata* comb. nov. A-Boyer O-1-19, New Jersey, Camden Co.
Fig. 5. *Pinnularia aestuarii* A-Boyer E-2-20, Delaware, New Castle Co.
Fig. 6. *Pinnularia cardinalis* A-V.H. 60, Belgium, Brussels.
Fig. 7. *Pinnularia flexuosa* A-Boyer 738, Connecticut, Fairfield Co.

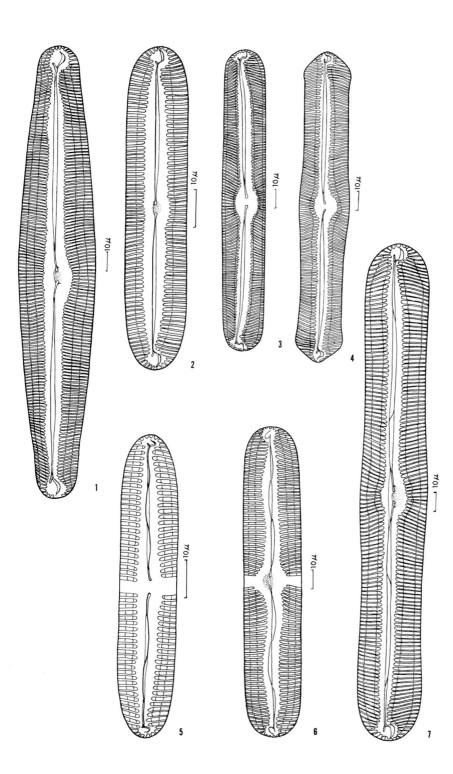

1

2

3

4

5

6

7

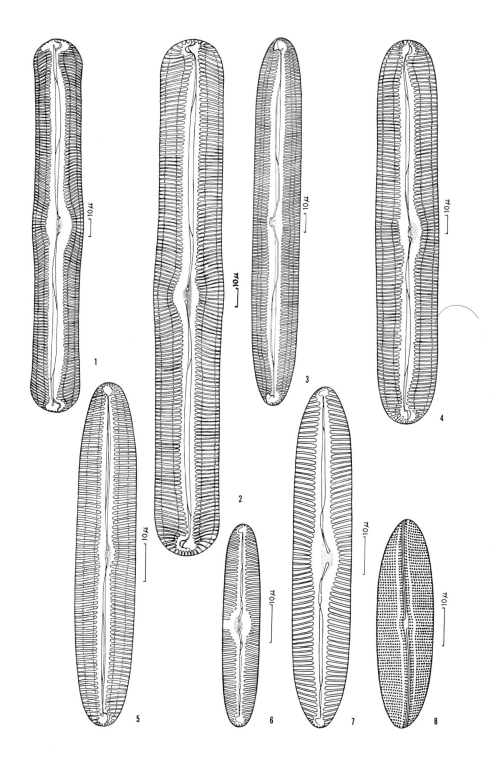

Appendix

ADDITIONAL TAXA RECORDED SINCE 1960

Achnanthes

Recorded by Hohn & Hellerman, 1963:

A. *acares* Hohn & Hellerm.
A. *grana* Hohn & Hellerm.
A. *lutheri* Hust.
A. *pseudotanensis* A. Cl.

Caloneis

Recorded by Hohn, 1961:

C. *schumanniana* var. *biconstricta* (Grun.) Reich. = C. *limosa*

Recorded by Hohn & Hellerman, 1963:

C. *trinodis* var. *inflata* Schultze = C. *lewisii*

Eunotia

Recorded by Hohn & Hellerman, 1963:

E. *aduncus* Hohn & Hellerm.
E. *cordillera* Hohn & Hellerm.
E. *flectuosa* (Bréb.) Grun.
E. *nivalis* Hohn & Hellerm.

Fragilaria

Recorded by Hohn, 1961:

F. *gnathastoma* Hohn
F. *harrisonii* var. *rhomboides* Grun.
F. *robusta* Hust.
F. *vaucheria* var. *distans* (Grun.) Boye P.

Recorded by Hohn & Hellerman, 1963:

F. *mutablis* (W. Sm.) Grun. = *Fragilaria pinnata*
F. *sublika* Hohn & Hellerm.
F. *virescens* var. *nipha* Hohn & Hellerm.

Navicula

Recorded by Hohn, 1961:

N. *bdesma* Hohn
N. *bievexa* Hohn
N. *birhis* Hohn
N. *bita* Hohn
N. *capsa* Hohn
N. *cerneutia* Hohn
N. *cincta* var. *minuta* Grun.
N. *cristula* Hohn
N. *dibola* Hohn
N. *eponka* Hohn
N. *karsia* Hohn
N. *muscerda* Hohn
N. *narinosa* Hohn
N. *ocallii* Hohn
N. *parodia* Hohn
N. *pletura* Hohn
N. *pupula* var. *major* O. Müll.
N. *scutula* Hohn
N. *skalenastriata* Hohn

Recorded by Hohn & Hellerman, 1963:

N. *admenda* Hohn & Hellerm.
N. *adumbrata* Hohn & Hellerm.
N. *algor* Hohn & Hellerm.
N. *americana* var. *alastos* Hohn & Hellerm.

N. *arenula* Hohn & Hellerm.

N. *buccella* Hohn & Hellerm.

N. *incomitatus* Hohn & Hellerm.

N. *indemnis* Hohn & Hellerm.

N. *kisber* Hohn & Hellerm.

N. *mediacomplexa* Hohn & Hellerm.

N. *paca* Hohn & Hellerm.

N. *rhodana* Hohn & Hellerm.

N. *sorella* Hohn & Hellerm.

N. *tracery* Hohn & Hellerm.

Pinnularia

Recorded by Hohn & Hellerman, 1963:

P. *absita* Hohn & Hellerm.

P. *aquilonaris* Hohn & Hellerm.

P. *castor* Hohn & Hellerm.

P. *doloma* Hohn & Hellerm.

P. *gibba* f. *constricta* Skv.

P. *interrupta* f. *bicapitata* (Lagerst.) Fritsch

P. *leptosoma* Grun.

Synedra

Recorded by Hohn, 1961:

S. *homostriata* Hohn

S. *netronoides* Hohn

S. *notha* Hohn & Hellerm.

S. *recava* Hohn

Recorded by Hohn & Hellerman, 1963:

S. *affinis* var. *faciculata* (Kütz.) Grun.

S. *stela* Hohn & Hellerm.

Register of Taxa in the Systematic Section[1]

ACHNANTHACEAE, 237
ACHNANTHALES, 237
Achnanthepyeq
  temperei, 278
Achnanthes, 245
  acares,° 671
  affinis
    var. affinis, 254
  americana,° 281
  arcus,° 256
  aretasii,° 260
  biasolettiana, 281
  binodis,° 278
  biporoma,° 281
  brevipes,° 246
  calcar,° 281
  chilensis
    var. subaequalis, 276
  chlidanos,° 281
  clevei
    var. clevei, 267
    var. rostrata, 267
  coarctata
    var. coarctata, 277
  conspicua,° 281
    var. brevistriata,° 281
  contracta
    var.,° 279
  curvirostrum
    var. curvirostrum, 279
  deflexa, 256
  delicatula,° 281
  detha,° 281
  didyma,° 281
  dispar,° 281
  elliptica,° 273
  exigua
    var. constricta, 258
    var. exigua, 257
    var. heterovalva, 258
    var. *heterovalvata,* 258
  exilis,° 281
  flexella
    var. flexella, 260
  gibberula
    var. angustior,° 263
    var. gibberula, 263
  grana,° 671
  grimmei
    var. grimmei, 274

Achnanthes (*cont'd*)
  harrisonii,° 277
  hauckiana
    var. *elliptica,* 268
    var. hauckiana, 267
    var. rostrata, 269
  haynaldii, 271
  hudsonis,° 281
  hungarica
    var. hungarica, 259
  hustedtii
    var. hustedtii, 264
  inflata
    var. elata, 280
    var. inflata, 279
  lanceolata
    var. apiculata, 270
    var. bimaculata,° 281
    var. *capitata,* 271
    var. dubia, 271
    var. elliptica,° 270
    var. haynaldii, 271
    var. lanceolata, 269
    var. lanceolatoides, 272
    var. oestrupii,° 276
    var. omissa, 272
    var. *rostrata,* 271
    var. *ventricosa,* 269
  lanceolatoides, 272
  lapponica,° 281
    var. ninkei, 259
  laterostrata,° 281
  lemmermanni
    var. lemmermanni, 265
  levanderi
    var. levanderi, 262
  lewisiana
    var. lewisiana, 266
  linearis
    f. curta, 252
    var. linearis, 251
    var. pusilla, 252
  longipes,° 246
  lutheri,° 671
  marginulata
    var. marginulata, 261
  microcephala
    var. microcephala, 250
  minutissima
    f. curta, 253

Achnanthes
  minutissima (*cont'd*)
    var. cryptocephala, 253
    var. macrocephala,° 281
    var. minutissima, 253
    var. robusta,° 281
  monela,° 281
  ninckei, 259
  nollii
    var. nollii, 253
  oestrupi,° 281
    var. *parvula,* 276
  pachypus,° 281
  parva,° 281
  peragalli
    var. fossilis, 275
    var. peragalli, 274
    var. parvula, 276
  pinnata, 266
  pseudotanensis,° 671
  ricula,° 281
  rupestoides,° 281
  saxonica
    var. saxonica, 265
  solea, 255
  stewartii
    var. stewartii, 264
  subatomus,° 281
  subhudsonis
    var. kraeuselii, 281
  sublaevis
    var. crassa, 262
  temperei
    var. temperei, 278
  trinodis,° 281
  ventricosa, 279
  wellsiae
    var. wellsiae, 255
Achnanthidium, 247
  brevipes,° 246
  coarctatum, 277
  delicatulum,° 246
  flexellum, 260
  hungaricum, 259
  lanceolatum, 269
    var. *inflata,* 269
  lineare, 251
  microcephalum, 250
  minutum,° 261
  rostrata, 271

[1] Taxa of the rank of genus or below appear in normal type if described in this manual; those whose names appear in the text but which are not considered are indicated by asterisks. Synonyms are given in italics.

673